Catalysis *by* Metals

Catalysis *by* Metals

G. C. BOND
Department of Chemistry
The University, Hull

1962

Academic Press
London and New York

ACADEMIC PRESS INC. (LONDON) LTD
Berkeley Square House
Berkeley Square
London, W.1

U.S. Edition published by
ACADEMIC PRESS INC.
111 Fifth Avenue
New York 3, New York

Library of Congress Catalog Number: 61–18780

PRINTED IN GREAT BRITAIN
BY W. S. COWELL LTD, AT THE BUTTER MARKET, IPSWICH

PREFACE

The opinion that "In the making of many books there is no end, and much reading is a weariness to the flesh" is one which commends itself to most scientists of today. It is therefore necessary to advance some cogent reasons for wishing to add to the already almost unmanageable body of scientific writing. My reasons are, I think, two-fold. First, the subject of catalysis by metals is one which, because it cuts across the conventional divisions of chemistry, has a diffuseness and incoherence which requires to be remedied. Second, this subject has reached a stage of advancement which makes an extensive review seem worthwhile. While it is commonly said that most scientific books are out-of-date before they are published, I nevertheless feel that much of the *factual* information presently available will stand the test of time.

Much however remains to be achieved in furthering our understanding of the proper interpretation of this information. The subject of heterogeneous catalysis has reached its present prominence largely as a result of its immense industrial significance, and even the mechanisms of the very simplest catalytic processes are not yet established beyond question. There are very many problems remaining for academic research to solve. I am reminded of the Irish managing director who, when told that his company would show a substantial profit on the year's working, remarked: "This is all very well in practice, but how is it going to work out in theory?" It is beyond all doubt that our theoretical knowledge is in far worse case than our experimental knowledge, and I have therefore tried wherever possible to separate "facts" from theories and to indicate the lines along which the resolution of disagreements on interpretation might be sought. I may have lost some friends in the process.

The subject matter to be covered is so vast and varied that a workable classification is essential. What happens in any catalytic system is a function both of the nature of the reactants and of the nature of the catalyst, and at first sight it might seem possible to classify the material according to either. However, it soon appears that the nature of the catalyst is not a suitable basis for a classification, since some reactions proceed on many different metals in very similar ways. Use of the nature of the reactants as the basis, although adopted here, is not without its drawbacks, because fundamental questions concerning the reasons for the particular behaviour shown by each metal and alloy system require some discussion in almost every chapter. This is inevitable, and in order to pull the loose ends together the concluding chapter summarizes the correlations which have been established or proposed between the various facets of the electronic structure of metals and alloys and their behaviour in chemisorption and catalysis. Part of the reason for the lack of rapid progress is the existence of many subtle variables which are hard to control or eliminate: particular attention must therefore be paid to those pieces of work in which these are minimized by the use of reproducible metal surfaces, but of equal interest is the establishing of those properties of metals which are independent of the precise form in which the metal is used.

I have tried to arrange my material in a logical sequence. After a short introductory chapter, I have considered in turn the physico-chemical properties of metals and alloys, and methods of forming them in a catalytically active state. There follow three chapters (Chapters 4 to 6) on chemisorption, in which I have stressed those aspects of the subject which have relevance to what follows. Chapter 7 treats the kinetics of surface reactions in general terms, and Chapters 8 to 10 concern isotopic exchange reactions, in which no net chemical reaction occurs. Catalytic hydrogenation is dealt with in Chapters 11 to 14, and these are followed by chapters on the Fischer–Tropsch synthesis, ammonia synthesis and decomposition, hydrogenolysis and dehydrogenation. The use of metals in the petroleum industry is considered in Chapter 19, and metals and alloys as oxidation catalysts in Chapter 20.

It will be evident that I have tried to cover most of the important applications of metals as catalysts. I have concentrated on what may be described as academic work, and have generally not discussed details of experimental or industrial procedures, since much of this information is irrelevant to the establishment of broad patterns and principles. Much wealth of detail is therefore inevitably missing, but my aim has been to try to see the subject as a whole, and to indicate its scope: in discussing catalysis it is more than usually easy to stress the trees at the expense of the wood. This book may therefore be of use to those who are engaged in research on catalysis and who wish to be informed of what is known outside their area of specialization; and if used judiciously it may be of some assistance to students, even if only to show them that the usual text-books do not tell quite all that is known about the subject.

Writing a book is a useful discipline: everyone should try it—once. One comes to see the measure of order which has been achieved in one's subject, and becomes painfully aware of the many gaps and inconsistencies which exist in it. These, however, suggest projects for future research, and as a result of having written this book, I am so provided for about the next fifteen years. Then I suppose I shall have to write another book.

I must end by thanking my former research students, John Newham and Peter Wells, for having read respectively part and the whole of the manuscript; they drew my attention to many infelicities of presentation, the removal of which has materially improved it. I also owe special debts of gratitude to Miss Joan Rooker for her skilful typing of my manuscript (including the algebra): and to my wife, who patiently spent many long evenings in silence while I was writing it.

GEOFFREY BOND

Hull
June, 1961.

ACKNOWLEDGEMENTS

The Author wishes to make the acknowledgements listed below for permissions to use certain diagrams.

Chapter 4, Figure 7: *Journal of the American Chemical Society*, The American Chemical Society, from the paper by E. L. Lee, J. A. Sabatka and P. W. Selwood (1957). Chapter 5, Figure 9: *Journal of the American Chemical Society*, The American Chemical Society, from the paper by P. H. Emmett and R. W. Harkness (1935). Chapter 5, Figure 10: *Bulletin*. Société chimique de Belgique, from the paper by W. M. H. Sachtler and G. J. H. Dorgelo (1958). Chapter 7, Figures 1 and 2: *Journal of the Institute of Petroleum*, Institute of Petroleum, from the paper by H. I. Waterman and A. B. R. Weber. Chapter 8, Figure 1: *Proceedings of The Royal Society*, The Royal Society, from the paper by B. M. W. Trapnell (1951). Chapter 11, Figures 11 and 12: *Quarterly Reviews of the Chemical Society*, The Chemical Society, from the paper by G. C. Bond (1954). Chapter 12, Figure 2: *Journal of the Chemical Society*, The Chemical Society, from the paper by G. C. Bond (1958).

ACKNOWLEDGEMENTS

The Author wishes to make the acknowledgements listed below for permissions to reproduce diagrams.

Chapter 4, Figure 1, *Journal of the American Chemical Society*, The American Chemical Society, from the paper by E. L. Lee, J. A. Sabatka and P. W. Selwood (1957); Chapter 5, Figure 9, *Journal of the American Chemical Society*, The American Chemical Society, from the paper by P. H. Emmett and E. W. Harkness (1935); Chapter 5, Figure 10, *Bulletin Société Chimique de Belgique*, from the paper by W. M. H. Sachtler and G. J. H. Dorgelo (1958); Chapter 7, Figures 7 and 8, *Journal of the Institute of Petroleum*, Institute of Petroleum, from the paper by H. I. Waterman and S. B. R. Walker; Chapter 8, Figure 4, *Proceedings of The Royal Society*, The Royal Society, from the paper by B. M. W. Trapnell (1953); Chapter 11, Figures 11 and 12, *Quarterly Reviews of the Chemical Society*, The Chemical Society, from the paper by G. C. Bond (1954); Chapter 13, Figure 2, *Journal of the Chemical Society*, The Chemical Society, from the paper by G. C. Bond (1958).

CONTENTS

CONTENTS

Chapter 1

An Introduction to Catalysis by Metals

1.1 Some Basic Definitions

Heterogeneous catalysts are solids which increase the rates of chemical reactions by virtue of the specific properties of their surfaces.

All catalytic processes possess certain common physico-chemical characteristics, and the definition of a catalyst as a substance which increases the rate at which a chemical system attains equilibrium without itself undergoing chemical change is broadly applicable. This definition carries the necessary rider that the equilibrium so attained must be the same as that which would have resulted if the catalyst had not been used: the catalyst therefore must increase both the rates of the forward and the backward reactions. This principle has been put to good use in the determination at or near room temperature of the heats of reaction of processes (especially hydrogenations) which in the absence of a catalyst proceed only with extreme slowness.

Thus it is apparent that a catalyst can only increase the rate of a process which is thermodynamically feasible, that is, one in which there is a decrease in free energy. However, for a given reactant there are sometimes several permissible reaction paths, and the type of catalyst used may determine which path is taken. The example most often quoted is that of ethanol, whose modes of decomposition are summarized as follows.

Decompositions over copper:

$$C_2H_5OH \rightarrow CH_3CHO + H_2$$

and

$$2C_2H_5OH \rightarrow CH_3COOC_2H_5 + H_2.$$

Decompositions over alumina:

$$C_2H_5OH \rightarrow C_2H_4 + H_2O$$

and

$$2C_2H_5OH \rightarrow C_2H_5OC_2H_5 + H_2O.$$

Catalytic materials are thus capable of directing the reaction path, or of exerting a specific directing influence: the catalyst plays not a passive but an active role in the reaction, and its chemical nature is all-important.

1.2 A Classification of Heterogeneous Catalysts

Heterogeneous catalysts may be classified according to the functions they best perform, and of great significance is the correlation between these and their electrical and thermal conductivity. The following Table illustrates this classification: less important functions are placed in parentheses.

TABLE I. *A Classification of Heterogeneous Catalysts According to their Principal Functions*

Class	*Metals*	*Metal oxides and sulphides*		*Salts and acids*
Conductivity type	conductors	semi-conductors	insulators	—
Functions	hydrogenation	oxidation	dehydration	polymerization
	dehydrogenation	reduction	isomerization	isomerization
	hydrogenolysis	dehydrogenation	(hydrogenation)	cracking
	(oxidation)	cyclization		alkylation
	(reduction)	(hydrogenation)		hydrogen transfer

The primary catalytic function of metals is hydrogenation and dehydrogenation. Metals catalyse these processes by virtue of their ability to adsorb the reactants or the products in an appropriate manner: thus in the example of ethanol decomposition above, copper effects the formation of acetaldehyde rather than ethylene or ether because of its ability to adsorb hydrogen rather than water. Whereas hydrogenation–dehydrogenation processes catalysed by metals occur at low or quite moderate temperatures, high temperatures are generally necessary for processes involving the addition to or the removal from reacting molecules of oxygen atoms. This is because the adsorption of oxygen in the necessary manner (i.e. as atoms) does not take place at low temperatures, and few metals, except the very "noble" ones such as platinum and silver, resist bulk oxidation to the oxide at the high temperatures required.

The same general principles hold when considering the primary catalytic functions of metal oxides. In those oxides which are of predominantly ionic character oxygen ions are fairly easily removed from, or sometimes added to, the lattice, and they are therefore capable of showing departure from stoichiometry and the phenomenon of semi-conduction. They therefore exercise their facility for effecting reactions involving oxygen-atom transfer through using lattice oxide ions. Although quite widely used for high temperature dehydrogenation and dehydrocyclization, they generally only effect hydrogenation at the necessarily low temperatures when extreme conditions of pressure are used.

Metal oxides having a predominantly covalent character are not capable of losing or gaining oxygen: they are therefore always stoichiometric, and are electrical insulators. Such oxides, of which alumina and silica are the most important, readily adsorb water, and hence are good dehydrating agents: the previously mentioned decomposition of ethanol is a case in point.

The chief catalytic role of solid acids and salts is to effect isomerization, polymerization and similar processes through the agency of carbonium ion intermediates.

1.3 Adsorption and Heterogeneous Catalysis

It has long been appreciated that the activity of a heterogeneous catalyst chiefly resides at the interface between the solid and the less dense phase, and that the reactant (or at least one of the reactants if there are more than one) must be adsorbed at this interface. Now an atom on the surface is joined by chemical forces to other atoms in the same plane and below it, but there are of course no atoms above it; there is therefore a net resultant force on each surface atom acting towards the bulk. The situation is represented diagrammatically in Fig. 1. If we suppose that a surface atom is capable of forming the same number of bonds as a bulk atom, such an atom must necessarily have one or more unused valencies directed outwards from the surface (see Fig. 1). The same conclusion is reached by considering the formation of a surface by fracture of a crystal. In this process, chemical bonds (whose nature depends on the kind of binding in the solid) are broken, and the free valencies thus created remain the property of the surface atoms. To a first approximation we may visualize a free valency at a metal surface as an unpaired electron associated with a particular atom.

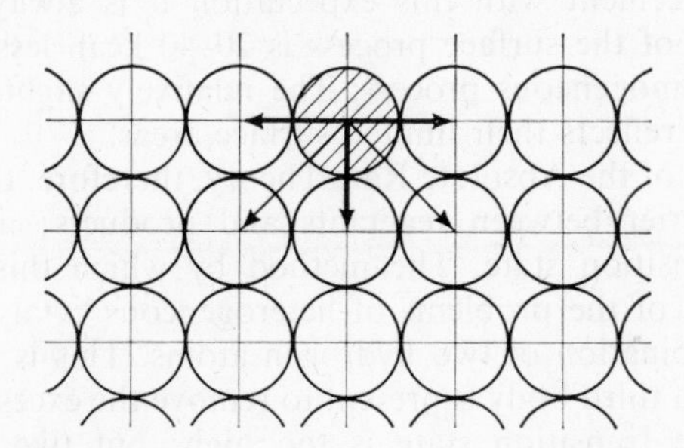

Fig. 1. Diagrammatic representation of the surface energy of a solid.

There is therefore a certain energy associated with the surfaces of solids, akin to the surface energy of liquids. Now in the adsorption process the unused valencies interact with the adsorbing molecules to an extent which depends on the nature of the adsorption: the adsorbing molecule loses entropy because its motion on the surface is more restricted than in the gas phase, and the free energy of the system also decreases as the surface valencies become saturated. Remembering that for an isothermal process

$$\Delta G = \Delta H - T\Delta S$$

we conclude that adsorption processes will always be exothermic.

For efficient catalysis, the strength of adsorption of the reactant(s) must lie within certain fairly wide limits. If a reactant is too strongly adsorbed it will be correspondingly difficult to remove, and it may then constitute a poison: if it is too weakly adsorbed, it will have little chance of remaining on the surface long enough to react. For a given reaction occurring on a series of related catalysts, we may therefore expect to find an inverse relationship between strengths of adsorption of reactants and the catalytic efficiency.

1.4 The Role of the Surface in Heterogeneous Catalysis

The Absolute Rate Theory shows that the ratio of the rate of a heterogeneous process to that of the corresponding homogeneous process should be $10^{-12\pm3}$ times $\exp(\Delta E/RT)$ where ΔE is the difference between the activation energies. Both rates are referred to 1 cm.^{3} of gas, and the heterogeneous rate of 1 cm.^{2} of surface. Thus if the activation energies were the same, the heterogeneous process would be very much slower than the homogeneous. If the heterogeneous process is to be made the faster, it must either have a much lower activation energy, or the surface area must be very large, or of course both. For unit surface area, ΔE would have to be 16.2 kcal. mole^{-1} at 300°K or 27.5 kcal. mole^{-1} at 500°K to produce identical rates.

Now although some porous solids have surface areas as large as 1000 m.^{2} g.$^{-1}$, values for metals rarely exceed 10 m.^{2} g.$^{-1}$ or 10^5 cm.^{2} g.$^{-1}$; the activation energy difference must therefore account for the remaining factor of $10^{-7\pm3}$. In agreement with this expectation it is always found that the activation energy of the surface process is 20–40 kcal. less than that of the corresponding homogeneous process. The relatively slight catalytic activity of liquid surfaces reflects their limited surface areas.

In the language of the Absolute Rate Theory, therefore, the catalyst lowers the potential barrier between reactants and products: in other words it stabilizes the transition state. The method by which this is achieved lies close to the heart of the problems of heterogeneous catalysis. Consider the process of recombination of two hydrogen atoms. This is impossible in the gas phase (unless a third body is present to remove the excess energy) because the energy of the transition state is too high: but two hydrogen atoms adsorbed at the surface of a metal recombine with an activation energy which is close to zero. The catalyst has clearly fulfilled the role of the third body, by acting as an energy sink, and a more stable transition state has thereby resulted.

While this role is doubtless sometimes an important one, as in the foregoing example, numerous other factors must operate, since the gas-phase analogues of many surface processes proceed readily, that is, the energy of the transition state is not prohibitively high. Nevertheless the activation energy, that is, the height of the largest potential barrier between reactants and products in the series of elementary steps, is always less when an active surface is present: but the rate-controlling step is not necessarily the same as in the gas-phase reaction.

A second important role which the surface plays is the "activation" of the reactants. Thus, for example, the slow rate of the homogeneous hydrogen–deuterium reaction at normal temperatures reflects the strengths of covalent bonds which have to be broken: in the catalysed reaction, the metal dissociates the molecules into atoms, a task which is performed in the homogeneous reaction by thermal or photolytic means. The same concept applies, *mutatis mutandis*, in for example the synthesis of ammonia from nitrogen.

In the catalytic hydrogenation of unsaturated hydrocarbons, the adsorbed hydrocarbon often assumes the configuration of the product: thus adsorbed ethylene is believed to have an ethane-like structure, so it only remains to break two carbon–metal bonds and to replace the metal atoms by hydrogen atoms. The most important and difficult part of the total operation is achieved in the adsorption step, and we may therefore expect to find a proportionality between heat of hydrogenation and heat of adsorption in a series of olefins and with a given catalyst: unfortunately, the data are at the moment too scanty to substantiate this generalization.

A third important way in which the surface can influence the reaction rate is by bringing the reactants together in a way which renders the formation of a transition state most probable. Whereas in gaseous reactions the first reactant must generally approach the second within a fairly small solid cone if the transition state is to be formed, the number of possible directions of approach in surface reactions is much restricted; to a first approximation one dimension has been rendered ineffective. These remarks apply necessarily only to bimolecular processes.

Such considerations lead us at once to an appreciation of the possible importance of the so-called geometric factor in catalysis. This is illustrated in a very formal way by the following diagram. Now the activation energy

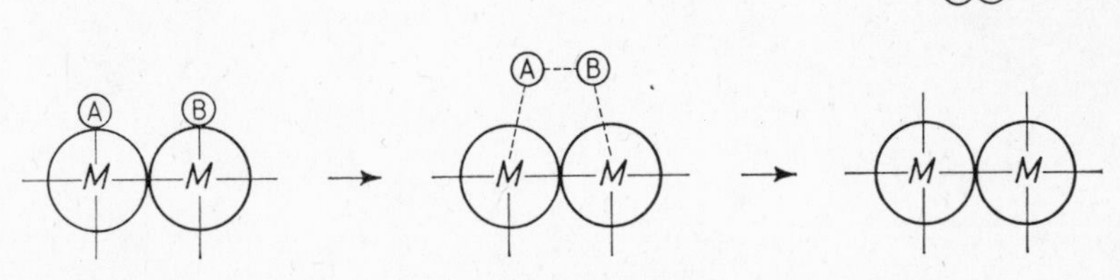

FIG. 2. Diagrammatic representation of the desorption of A and B to form gaseous AB, proceeding through a transition state.

will be a minimum when the energy of the transition state is also at a minimum, for which condition there will be an optimum value for the M—M distance: if this is larger or smaller than the optimum value, the transition state will be strained and not of minimum energy. However, the energy of the transition state will further be a function of the strength of binding of A and B to the metal atoms, viz. of their heats of adsorption, which in turn will depend on the electronic constitution of the metal. The precise manner in which the interrelated geometric and electronic effects determine the energy of the transition state will occupy our attention in subsequent chapters, but it is clearly of the greatest interest to have at our disposal a large and reliable body of information concerning the dependence of activation energies and pre-exponential factors on the nature of the metal.

It is commonly assumed that the behaviour of metal atoms at the surface parallels their behaviour in the bulk, and that the strengths of adsorption of species at the surface may be related to the strength of the metal–metal bonds in the bulk. With this in mind, we may now turn our attention to a reasonably detailed description and interpretation of the bulk properties of metals, to provide the raw material which will be needed later to understand the dependence of catalytic activity on the nature of the solid.

Chapter 2

The Physics and Chemistry of Metals

2.1 Characteristic Properties of Metals

On the basis of their physical and chemical properties the elements are broadly divisible into two categories, namely (i) metals and (ii) non-metals. There is, however, no sharp dividing line, but rather, at the borderline, a gradual change in character, so that between the two extremes there lie a number of elements which partake of the characteristics of both groups: these are referred to as metalloids or semi-metals.

The physical and chemical properties of the elements are most conveniently discussed in terms of the Periodic Classification, and the division into the three categories which will be adopted in this book is shown on a continuous form of the Periodic Table in Fig. 1. Free atoms of metals possess one or more loosely bound electrons, which may be in *s*-, *p*-, *d*- or *f*- states. The elements of Groups IA and IIA are therefore all quite definitely metallic, as are also the elements of Groups IIIA to VIII which form the Transition series, and those in Groups IB to IIIB which follow. In Groups IIIB to VIB there is a distinct increase in metallic character on passing down any one group. Thus in Group IIIB, boron is classified here as a semi-metal: in Group IVB, carbon is a non-metal, silicon and germanium are semi-metals, while tin and lead are metals, although tin shows the characteristic properties of metals and semi-metals in different allotropic modifications. In Group VB, only bismuth ranks as a metal; in Group VIB, polonium is tentatively classified as a semi-metal. About 75 per cent of the known elements are metals, 18 per cent non-metals and 7 per cent semi-metals.

Both chemical and physical properties are determined, partly by the size of the electron shell, but chiefly by the number and arrangement of the outermost electrons. The chemical properties which characterize metals are thus related to the characteristic physical properties through electronic structure. However, while the former largely depend on the electronic structures of the free atoms, the latter depend on the electronic constitutions of large aggregates of atoms: the parallelism between the two, while extensive, is by no means complete.

The chemical properties of metals reflect the fact that the free atoms have a marked tendency to lose electrons; they are therefore all in some degree

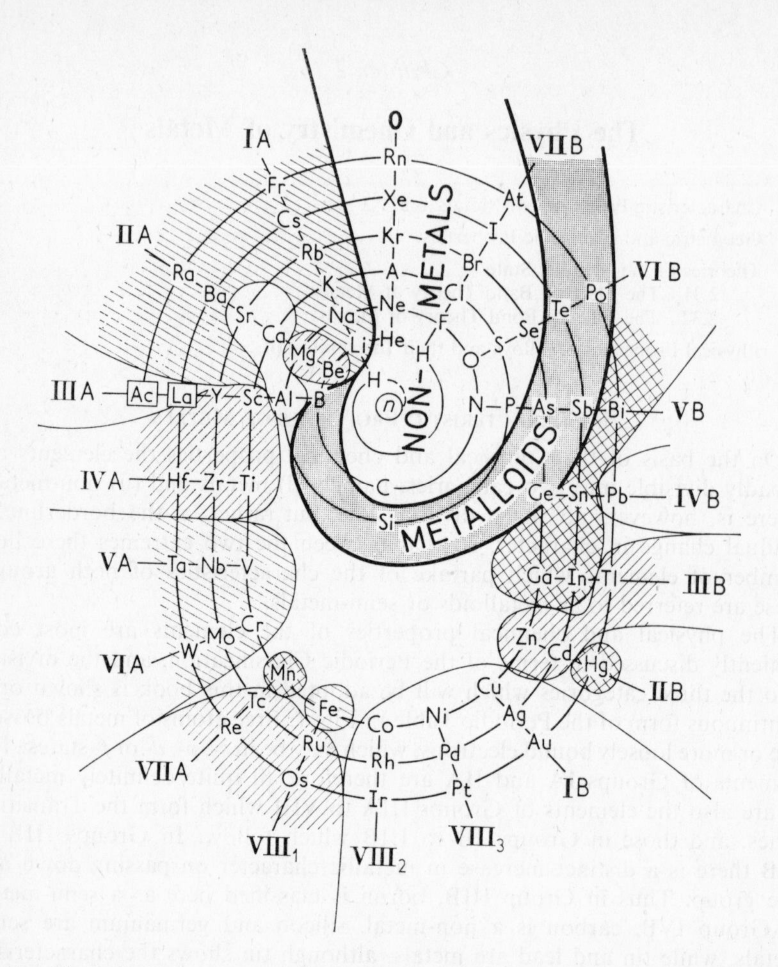

FIG. 1. The Periodic Classification of the elements, after S. I. Tompkieff, "A New Periodic Table of the Elements" (Chapman and Hall, London, 1954) and the normal crystal structures of metals.

Unshaded metals, face-centred cubic: ////, close-packed hexagonal; \\\\, body-centred cubic; #, other crystal structures.

electropositive, but curiously enough a classification of metals based on standard electrode potential (say less than +1.4 V. for metals) would include arsenic and antimony, in addition of course to hydrogen. Because of their high electropositivity, the inorganic chemistry of the metallic elements is largely the chemistry of their simple or complexed cations: the chief exceptions are the oxy-ions of elements in Groups VA to VIIA of the Transition series.

The chemical reactivity of the metallic elements varies widely and is determined by the degree of electropositivity. The most reactive elements, which are those in Groups IA and IIA, have electrode potentials between −2 and −3 V., and react vigorously with water and oxygen: at the other extreme, platinum and gold, having electrode potentials of about +1.3 V. are resistant to these reagents at all except the very highest temperatures.

The physical properties which characterize the metallic state are also associated with the existence of loosely bound valency electrons. The outstanding physical properties of metals are their high electrical and thermal conductivities, between which there exists a striking parallelism. A classification of elements into the three categories on the basis of electrical conductivity or resistance is possible. All elements having specific resistances near room temperature of less than 50 $\mu\Omega$–cm. are unmistakably metals, with the exceptions of arsenic and antimony (see also above): the only metals having resistances greater than this value are manganese, bismuth, mercury and gallium.

Of the elements whose thermal conductivity at room temperature is greater than 0.05 c.g.s. units, the majority are metals, but silicon is also in this group: antimony (0.045), zirconium (0.035 at 125°C), bismuth and mercury (each 0.020) fall below this dividing line. It therefore appears difficult to select any one physical property to provide a unique and satisfactory definition of the metallic state, since any classification based on such properties contains a number of anomalies. A classification based on the co-ordination number in the solid has been proposed: this number is high for metals (8 or 12) and low for semi-metals (not more than 4).

The important mechanical properties of metals are conditioned by physical form, typical properties only being shown by single crystals and polycrystalline materials. In the latter, mechanical strength is largely dictated by the forces acting across grain boundaries, while in the former it is limited only by the cohesive strength of the metal–metal bonds. Cohesive strength, like chemical reactivity, covers a very wide range, from mercury [boiling at 357°C: L_s, 14.5 kcal. (g. atom)$^{-1}$] to tungsten [boiling at about 6000°C; L_s, 202 kcal. (g. atom)$^{-1}$]. It is interesting to note that the most electropositive elements have low mechanical strengths (for example those in Group IA), and that the reverse is also true (for example platinum and gold).

A full description of the metallic state may be divided into descriptions of (i) the geometry of ideal arrays of positive nuclei; (ii) properties of the electron gas which holds the nuclei together; (iii) defects of arrangement in the bulk and (iv) properties of the surface. Item (iii) is of little relevance to catalysis while (iv) is the mainspring of the phenomenon.

The next section will consider the observable physical characteristics of metals which are pertinent to (i) and (ii). Consideration will henceforth be restricted to those elements which by the foregoing tests may be described as metals, and to certain of the semi-metals which have catalytic properties. Emphasis will be placed on the periodic variation of physical properties, and this will indicate the principal observations which theories of the metallic state must try to explain or interpret.

2.2 GEOMETRIC AND ELECTRONIC PROPERTIES OF METALS

Geometric properties of metals are those properties which refer to the arrangement of the positive nuclei in space and to the distances between them. Details of lattice structures and interatomic spacings of metals will be found in Appendix I (see also Figs. 1 and 2). Most metals crystallize in one or more of the forms shown in Table I. F.C.C. and c.p.h. structures are both forms of densest packing. Many metals, especially of the Transition series, have allotropic modifications which are stable in different regions of temperature and pressure: those quoted in Appendix I are those which are stable at room temperature and atmospheric pressure.

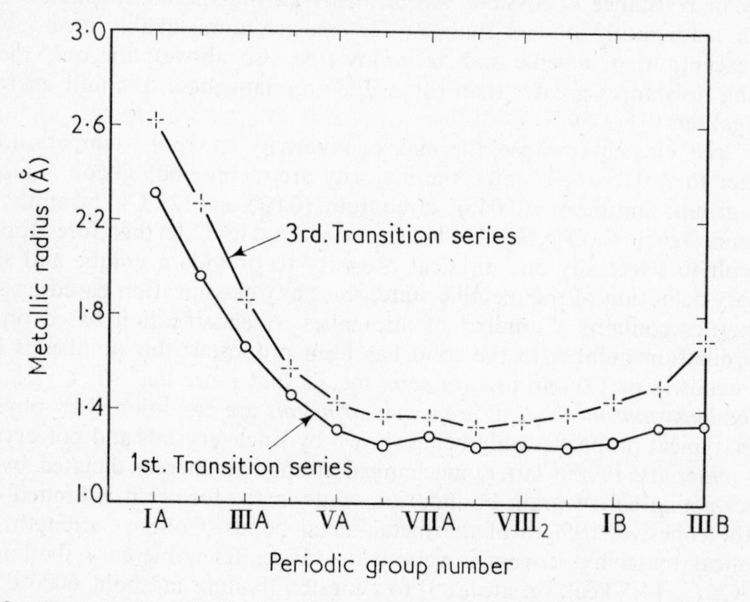

FIG. 2. The periodic variation of metallic radius in the first and third Transition series. The metallic radii in the second series are almost the same as in the third series.

TABLE I. *Lattice Structures of Metals*

Lattice structure	*Abbreviation*	*Other designations*	*Examples*
Face-centred cubic	f.c.c.	α : A1	many
Close-packed hexagonal	c.p.h.	β : A3	many
Body-centred cubic	b.c.c.	γ : A2	many
Rhombohedral (distorted f.c.c.)	—	A10	Hg, Bi
Body-centred tetragonal	—	A5	Sn
Face-centred tetragonal	—	A6	In
Orthorhombic (distorted c.p.h.)	—	A11	Ga, U

Within the Transition Series, the type of lattice which is stable under normal conditions is with few exceptions a periodic function of atomic number, as the following Table shows. The exceptions are manganese and mercury, which have somewhat complex structures, and iron which is b.c.c., not c.p.h.: attempts to interpret this regularity have only recently been made.

TABLE II. *Periodicity of Lattice Structures*

Groups	IIIA and IVA	VA and VIA	VIIA and VIII_1	VIII_2 to IB
Type	c.p.h.	b.c.c.	c.p.h.	f.c.c.

Interatomic distances or metallic radii also vary in a periodic manner (see Appendix I and Fig. 2). On passing from Group IA through to Group VIII in any of the long series there is a smooth decrease in radius (although manganese is slightly out of line): thereafter in the second and third series, radii begin to increase again, but in the first series the increase does not start until Group IB, since atoms of iron, cobalt and nickel have essentially the same size. Within any group, the metallic radius increases from the first to the second long series due to the effect of the size of the inner electron shells, but the differences between the second and third series are small because of the lanthanide contraction. Now metallic radius in any one series may be taken as a measure of cohesive strength, in the sense that the smaller the radius the greater must be the strength of binding. As electrons are added on passing across any series there is therefore a progressive increase in binding strength, followed ultimately by a decrease. This observation is of first importance to theories of the metallic state, and it is evident at once that geometric properties are determined by, or at least are closely related to, electronic constitution, and that any attempt to divorce the two effects will be both useless and misleading.

Many other physical properties show regular gradations indicating a progressive increase in binding strength followed by decrease on passing through the long series: these include density, melting-point, boiling-point and latent heat of sublimation (see Appendix I and Figs. 3–5). The question then arises as to which physical property most accurately reflects cohesive or binding strength, which may be defined as the work required to remove an atom from its position in the interior of the metal. Metallic radius, which is accurately measurable by X-ray diffraction, is certainly a bulk property, as are also density and melting- and boiling-points, but these last are not accurately known for the metals in which the cohesive strength is high.

It is necessary to treat latent heats of sublimation with some caution, since methods for their estimation invariably depend on the establishment of the solid–vapour equilibrium. Any method dependent on the establishment of this equilibrium must be affected by the presence of surface impurities which, in the case of metals strongly interacting with oxygen or nitrogen, must introduce some uncertainty into the result.[1]

Table III shows where maximum cohesive strength occurs according to the various physical properties (Figs. 2–5); it deserves some discussion.

TABLE III. *Maxima and Minima in Physical Properties of Transition Metals*

Property	*1st series*	*2nd series*	*3rd series*
Density (max) (g.cm.$^{-3}$)	Co, Ni, Cu (~8.9)	Rh (12.4)	Os, Ir (22.5)
Radius (min) (Å)	Cr, Fe, Co, Ni (1.24)	Ru (1.32)	Os (1.33)
M.P. (max) (°C)	V (1900)	Mo (2620)	W (3400)
L_s (max) (kcal. (g. atom)$^{-1}$)	V (121)	Nb (185)	W (202)

In each series there is reasonable agreement between the positions of maximum density and minimum radius; these occur at about Group VIII_1 or VIII_2, although the maxima and minima in the first series are both rather broad (Figs. 2 and 3). The positions of maxima in melting-point and L_s are in close agreement, but are at Group V or VI, several places to the left (Figs. 4 and 5). It must be concluded that electronic constitution affects different physical properties in different ways and that no single property is of unique value for assessing cohesive strength.

The plots of L_s and melting-point against group number show significant anomalies (Figs. 4 and 5). In the third series, L_s rises smoothly to tungsten, falls to mercury, and then rises again: in the second series the pattern is similar but there is a small dip where the maximum is expected (Groups VI

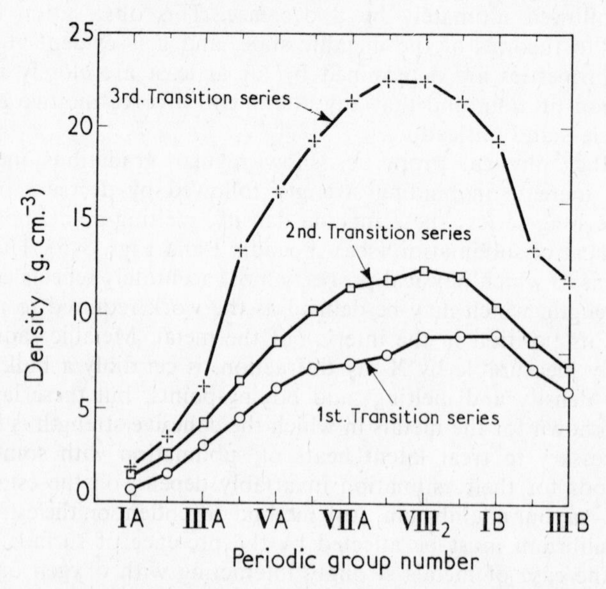

FIG. 3. The periodic variation of metallic density in the Transition series.

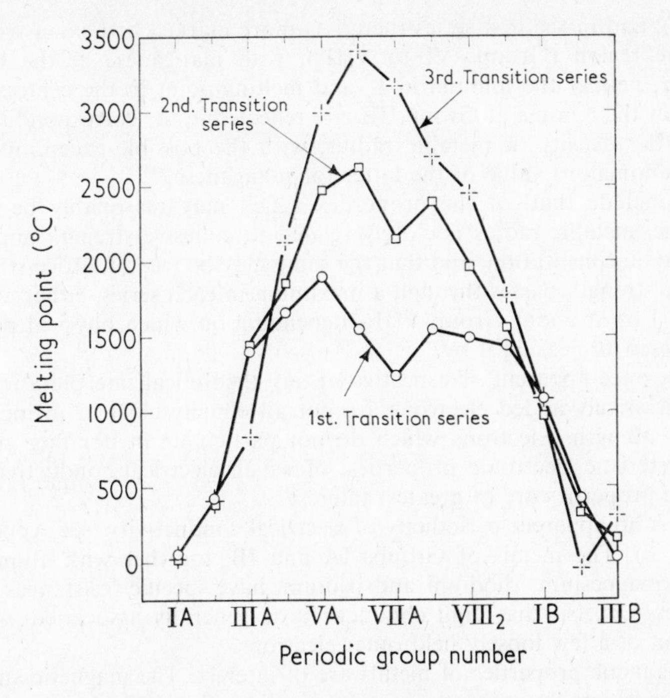

FIG. 4. The periodic variation of melting point in the Transition series.

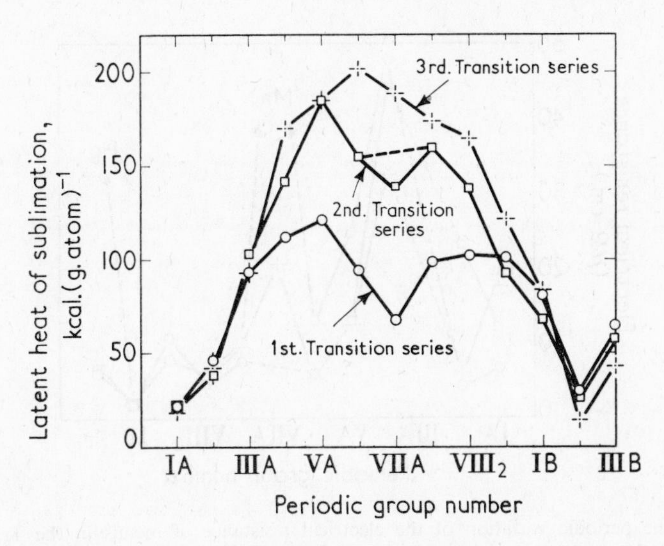

FIG. 5. The periodic variation of latent heat of sublimation in the Transition series.

and VII), and in the first series there is a more marked and extensive dip in the same region (Groups VI to VIII_2), with manganese at the bottom. However, neither the minima in L_s and melting-point in the centres of the series, nor the minima at Group IIB, are reflected in the corresponding plots using either density or metallic radius, with the possible exception of the slightly anomalous value of the latter for manganese.

We conclude that, of the properties which may reasonably be termed geometric, metallic radius is closely related to cohesive strength and hence to electronic constitution, and that the same may be true of lattice structure. Cohesive strength passes through a maximum in each series, either at about Group VI or at about Group VIII_2, depending on which physical property one chooses to measure it by.

It is at once apparent, irrespective of any theoretical interpretation, that the progressively added electrons are not all equally efficient in increasing cohesive strength. Electrons which do not participate in bonding give rise to characteristic electronic properties, of which electrical conductivity and magnetic properties are of greatest interest.

There is no apparent periodicity of electrical conductivity (see Appendix I and Fig. 6). The metals of Groups IA and IB, together with aluminium, calcium, magnesium, rhodium and iridium, have specific resistances of less than 5 $\mu\Omega$–cm., so that high conductivity is generally associated with the possession of a few loosely held outer electrons.

The magnetic properties of metals are of interest. The magnetic susceptibility κ represents the magnetizability of a solid and is defined as

$$I = \kappa H,$$

where I is the intensity of magnetization and H is the magnetic field strength.

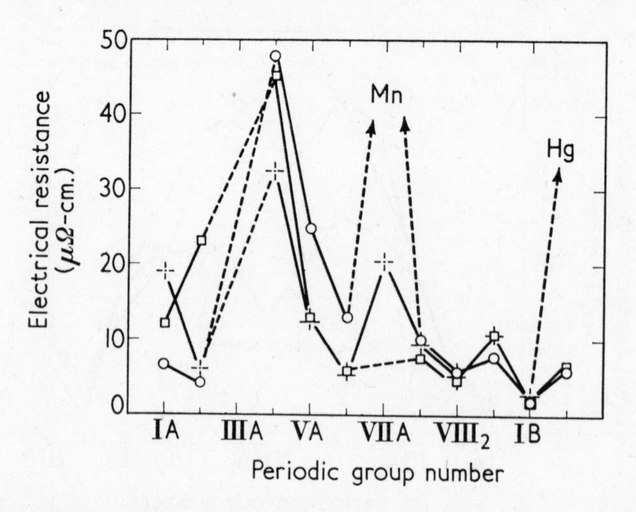

FIG. 6. The periodic variation of the electrical resistance of metals in the Transition series (symbols as in previous diagrams).

When κ is positive, the solid is said to be paramagnetic and when negative, diamagnetic. The magnetic susceptibility per unit mass, χ, is κ/ρ where ρ is the density; the gram-atomic susceptibility is χ times the atomic weight. A characteristic feature of many metals is their weak, temperature-independent paramagnetism. In the first long series (Fig. 7), the magnetic susceptibility rises, at first slowly and then very rapidly at V . . . Cr . . . Mn, the onset of strong paramagnetism denoting the existence of unpaired electrons. Iron, cobalt and nickel are of course ferromagnetic, that is, they can be permanently magnetized at temperatures below the ferromagnetic Curie point T_c; above this temperature, they exhibit a normal temperature-dependent paramagnetism. The saturation moment of magnetization μ_M, sometimes termed the atomic magnetic moment, when expressed in Bohr magnetons gives the average number of unpaired electrons per atom at 0°K. The numerical results are as follows: T_c (°C); Fe, 780; Co, 1075; Ni, 358: μ_M (Bohr magnetons); Fe, 2.22; Co, 1.71; Ni, 0.606.

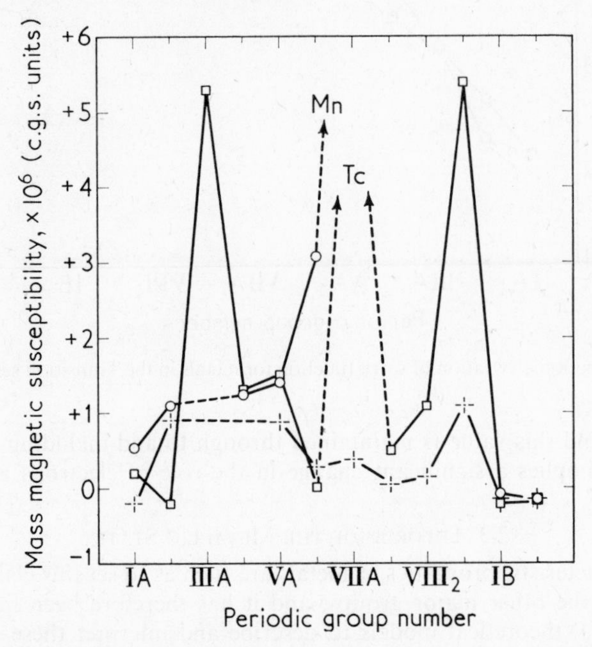

FIG. 7. The periodic variation of mass magnetic susceptibility of metals in the Transition series (symbols as in earlier diagrams).

In the second and third long series (Fig. 7), there is evidence of a fall in magnetic susceptibility at the point where in the first series it rises rapidly: in both the former series there is then a maximum in Group VIII_3, and in all series the metals of Group IB and its successors are diamagnetic.

A further important electronic property is the work function of a metal, defined as the energy required to remove an electron from the metal to infinity. Although basically a property of the bulk, the nature of the surface, especially its cleanliness and the lattice structure, has a marked influence. Because of the difficulty of producing absolutely clean surfaces, recorded values of the work function of certain metals vary widely. It is well established that the work function depends on the type of crystallographic plane through which the electron is withdrawn, showing once again the close connection between electronic and geometric properties. Appendix I gives the values of work functions which seem most reliable. Work functions in any group are much the same in each of the three long series (see Fig. 8): they rise almost linearly from about 2 eV. in Group IA to a maximum of about 4.5 eV. at

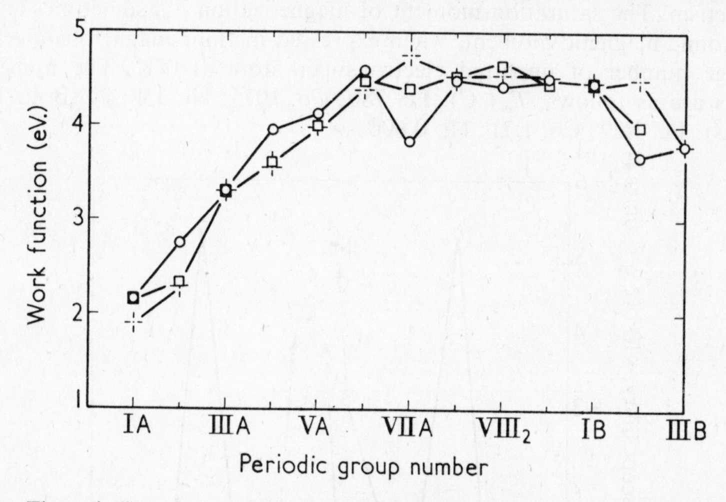

FIG. 8. The periodic variation of work function for metals in the Transition series (symbols as before).

Group VI and this value is maintained through to and including Group IB. This again implies a significant change in the role of electrons added after Group VI.

2.3 THEORIES OF THE METALLIC STATE

The characteristic properties of metals are such as to set this class of solids apart from the other major groups, and it has therefore been necessary to devise special theoretical models to describe and interpret these properties. The main object of theories has been to treat the behaviour of the valency electrons as manifested by the electronic properties of metals, which as we have just seen probably embrace all the observable properties. These indicate that the electrons progressively added through any of the long series do not have equivalent properties: cohesive strength reaches a maximum, perhaps near the centre of each series, and electrons added thereafter are not apparently bonding, but exist unpaired, giving rise to magnetic effects. The interpretation of these observations, together with the appearance of diamagnetism in Group IB, is the first target of all theories.

In Chapter 1 we saw how in principle the constitution of the solid may affect the efficiency of a catalytic process proceeding at its surface. Now theoretical approaches to the problems of the metallic state naturally concentrate on the properties of the bulk, but there has been no attack of similar vigour on the theoretical description of the surface. We therefore seek from the theories of the metallic state numerical values of quantities characteristic of the electronic constitution of the metal, more fundamental than any single physical property, to which we may hope to relate the parameters of adsorption and catalysis.

Two somewhat different approaches to a theoretical description of the metallic state have been essayed. The *Electron Band Theory* treats a metal crystal as an assembly of positive nuclei (together with the closed-shell electrons) through which the valency electrons roam more or less freely. With the appropriate application of quantum statistics, this model is used as a basis for deriving from first principles the cohesive strength and other electronic properties in terms of the number of valency electrons. A second, rather less fundamental, approach is termed the *Valence Bond Theory*: it considers the metal crystal as a giant covalent molecule in which each atom is bound to its neighbours by resonating covalent bonds. Cohesive strength and other properties are then described in terms of localized electron orbitals. The two approaches should not be regarded as mutually contradictory, but rather as alternative ways of regarding the same phenomena, each having its own particular merits for our purposes.

2.31 *The Electron Band Theory of Metals*[2, 3, 4, 5, 6]

Early attempts to treat the behaviour of the electron gas by classical Maxwell–Boltzmann statistics were unsuccessful. Significant advances were only possible when necessary quantum conditions were understood, and in particular the application of the Pauli Exclusion Principle (namely that not more than two electrons in a system could exist in the same energy state) revealed that the electron gas must be described by quantum or Fermi–Dirac statistics. In a free atom, as is well known, an electron may occupy an *s*-, *p*-, *d*- or *f*-orbital, and the ground electronic state of any atom may be uniquely defined, as for example:

Al: $1s^2\ 2s^2\ 2p^6\ 3s^2\ 3p^1$ or (neon core) $3s^2\ 3p^1$.
Ni: (argon core) $3d^8\ 4s^2$.
Cu: (argon core) $3d^{10}\ 4s^1$.
Zn: (argon core) $3d^{10}\ 4s^2$.

Each orbital in an atom corresponds to a definite energy level but when a number of atoms are assembled to form a crystal, each level is compelled by the Exclusion Principle to lose its identity and to be replaced by a corresponding energy band. The width of such an energy band is not significant for closed-shell electrons. The bands of valency electrons may overlap as shown in Fig. 9, so that electrons may be exchanged between two or more bands: nevertheless it is still customary to speak of, for example, 3*s*- or 3*p*-electrons in a metal, even although the true state of affairs is better represented as a "hybrid."

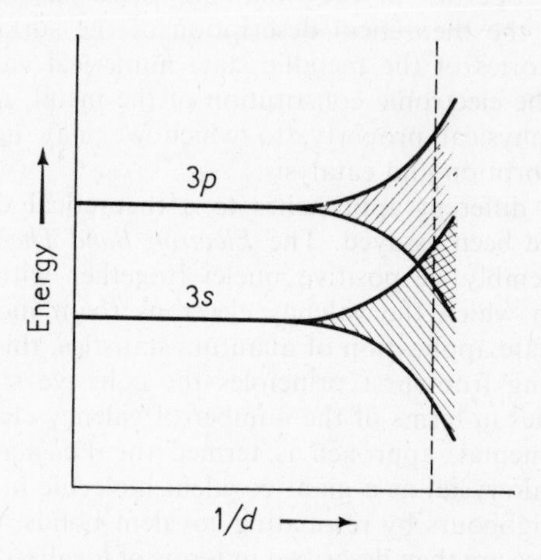

FIG. 9. A diagrammatic representation of the overlap of energy bands in for example aluminium: *d* is the internuclear distance and the dashed line corresponds to the internuclear distance obtaining in the metal.

It is now necessary to consider the probability of finding an electron at any energy within the permitted band. In the simplest form of the Electron Band Theory, the electron gas is considered to be confined within the crystal by a potential barrier (the work function) at the surface. Electrostatic repulsions between electrons are ignored, and the balancing positive charge is assumed to be distributed uniformly. Treatment of this model by Fermi-Dirac statistics shows that the maximum electron energy at 0°K, E_{max}, is given by

$$E_{max} = \frac{p^2_{max},}{2m}$$

where p_{max} is the momentum in the highest occupied state, and m is the electron mass. The mean energy per electron at 0°K (the mean Fermi energy) is $\frac{3}{5}$ E_{max}. The number of electrons $n(E)$ having energy within the narrow range E to $E + dE$ is termed the density of states or the electron level density at this energy, and $n(E)$ is found to vary as $E^{1/2}$ (see Fig. 10(a)). At 0°K an assembly of N electrons occupies the $N/2$ lowest states extending up to E_{max}. Electrons having the energy E_{max} are said to be at the *Fermi surface*: this is the surface of a sphere in momentum space which includes all the occupied states.

The first rise in temperature above 0°K can only affect those electrons in states near the Fermi surface, since it is necessary to have adjacent vacant states into which the electrons may be excited. The excitation energy for low energy electrons is prohibitive. The electron gas at 0°K is almost completely degenerate, and the relation between energy and temperature is

$$E = N\left\{\frac{3}{5}\,E_{\max} + \frac{\pi^2}{4}\cdot\frac{(kT)^2}{E_{\max}}\right\}.$$

At low temperatures (0–1000°K) the energy of the degenerate electron gas is therefore almost independent of temperature, and its specific heat is therefore almost zero. This electronic specific heat is in fact proportional to temperature, and can be separated from the contribution due to nuclear motion at low temperatures where the latter has become very small. At high temperatures the electron gas is expected to conform to classical statistics. The effect of increasing temperature on the $n(E)$ versus E distribution is shown in Fig. 10(b).

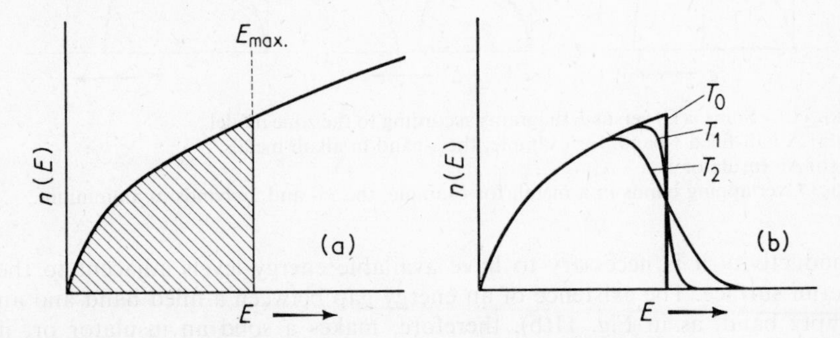

FIG. 10. (*a*) The distribution of electron level densities according to the free-electron model.
(b) The effect of the temperature, $T_2 > T_1 > T_0$.

This simple model is reasonably successful in accounting for the electronic properties of metals which have only one valency electron. It is generally inadequate for metals which possess more than one electron outside the closed shells. It does, however, lead to a satisfactory expression for the Wiedemann–Franz ratio; this is the ratio of the thermal to the electrical conductivity and according to the free-electron model is given by

$$\frac{\pi^2}{3}\left(\frac{k}{e}\right)^2 T.$$

This conforms to the Wiedemann–Franz Law which states that the ratio of the thermal to the electrical conductivities is constant for all metals and is proportional to absolute temperature. The calculated value is 2.45×10^{-8} V.^{2} deg.$^{-2}$, which is in good agreement with observation, particularly for the Group IB elements near room temperature.

The next stage in the refinement of the Electron Band Theory concerns the distribution of positive charge, previously but incorrectly assumed uniform. In fact the positive potential varies periodically, with the periodicity of the lattice. When this is taken into account it is found that the electron level density no longer increases continuously with increasing energy, but that instead there are zones of permitted energy, sometimes with energy gaps intervening. The distribution of level density within any band is also somewhat different, and some examples are shown in Fig. 11. For a solid to be able to show the typically metallic properties of thermal and electrical

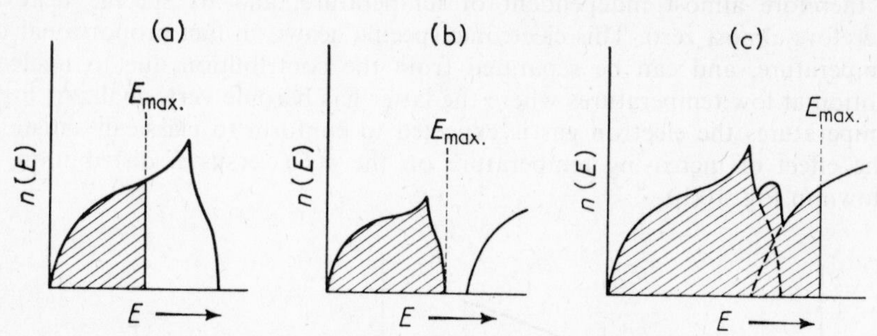

FIG. 11. Some $n(E)$ versus E diagrams according to the zone model.
(a) A half-filled *s*-band, for example, the *s*-band in alkali metals.
(b) An insulator.
(c) Overlapping bands in a metal, for example, the 3*s*- and 3*p*-bands in aluminium.

conductivity it is necessary to have available energy levels adjacent to the Fermi surface. The existence of an energy gap between a filled band and an empty band, as in Fig. 11(b), therefore, makes a solid an insulator or, if the gap is narrow, a semiconductor. Metals (except those in Groups IA and IIA) are characterized by having a system of overlapping incompletely-filled bands, as shown in Fig. 11(c).

Distributions of electron level densities in energy bands have been obtained experimentally by means of soft X-rays for some electronically simple metals, and the results are in good agreement with expectation. The cut-off at the high-energy end has been found to become less sharp with increasing temperature, also in harmony with expectation.

Because of their great importance in catalysis, much interest attaches to the band structure of the Transition metals.[7, 8, 9] The situation is unfortunately far from straightforward, but for various reasons it seems that the *s*-band is broad with a low maximum level density while the *d*-band is narrow with a much higher maximum level density (see Fig. 12). As electrons are progressively added in building up a long period, they first go into the *s*-band and this interprets the initial increase in cohesive strength. Thereafter they go into both bands and, perhaps because of repulsion between *s*-electrons, the cohesive strength diminishes. In the first long series, the 3*d*-band is half-full at about iron; at nickel it is almost filled, and at copper it is quite filled (Fig. 12). Paramagnetism is associated with unoccupied states in the *d*-band, and copper is therefore expected to be diamagnetic, as found. The number of unoccupied *d*-band states is therefore numerically equal to the

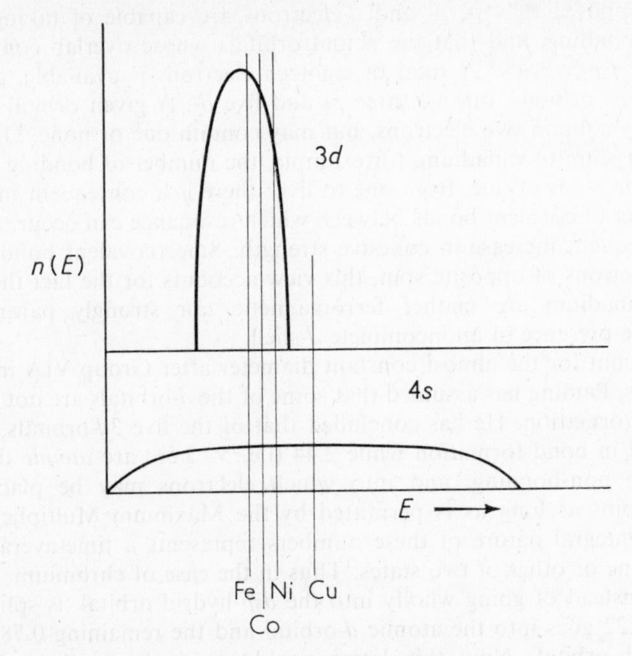

FIG. 12. Approximate representation of the band structure of iron, cobalt, nickel and copper, the vertical lines representing their Fermi energies.[2, 3]

saturation moment in Bohr magnetons, and solid nickel therefore has the electronic structure $3d^{9.4}\,4s^{0.6}$, with 0.6 "holes" in the *d*-band and therefore 0.6 *s*-electrons. The number of *s*-electrons in cobalt is hence 0.7 and in iron 0.2.

The Electron Band Theory thus gives a reasonably complete interpretation of the electronic structure of metals towards the end of each transition series, but because of the complex detailed structure of the *d*-band it can say little which is quantitative concerning the elements preceding Group VIII. An alternative approach, which is perhaps less fundamental, but of somewhat wider applicability, is therefore worth examining.

2.32 *The Valence Bond Theory of Metals*[2, 9, 10–15]

The Electron Band Theory is based on the concept of a free electron gas which obeys the appropriate statistical mechanical rules. The Valence Bond Theory, due to Pauling,[11] takes the opposite view, namely that the properties of metals are adequately described in terms of essentially covalent bonds between adjacent atoms: it tries to distinguish between those electrons which take part in cohesive binding and those which are non-bonding and responsible for magnetic properties. We will confine our attention to the application of this theory to the Transition metals.

It is supposed that *s*-, *p*- and *d*-electrons are capable of taking part in cohesive bonding, and that the actual orbitals whose overlap constitutes a bond are *dsp*-hybrids. A total of eighteen electrons is available, and these occupy nine orbitals, one *s*-, three *p*- and five *d*-. A given orbital does not necessarily contain two electrons, but may contain one or none. On passing from potassium to vanadium, for example, the number of bonding electrons increases in steps of one, from one to five: there is a consequent increase in the number of covalent bonds between which resonance can occur, and there is a consequent increase in cohesive strength. Since covalent bonds involve paired electrons of opposite spin, this view accounts for the fact that metals up to vanadium are neither ferromagnetic nor strongly paramagnetic, despite the presence of an incomplete *d*-shell.

To account for the almost constant diameter after Group VIA in the first long series, Pauling has assumed that some of the *d*-orbitals are not available for bond formation. He has concluded that of the five 3*d*-orbitals, 2.56 are concerned in bond formation while 2.44 (i.e. 5 – 2.56) are *atomic* d-*orbitals*, which are non-bonding, and into which electrons may be placed, with parallel spins as long as is permitted by the Maximum Multiplicity Rule. The non-integral nature of these numbers represents a time-average of an atom in one or other of two states. Thus in the case of chromium, the sixth electron instead of going wholly into the *dsp*-hydrid orbital, is split and on average 0.22 goes into the atomic *d*-orbital and the remaining 0.78 into the *dsp*-hybrid orbital. Now this latter could seemingly accommodate 6.56 orbitals, i.e. $1 + 3 + 2.56$ or $9 - 2.44$; but in actuality the maximum number is supposed to be 5.78, the remaining 0.78 being what Pauling terms *metallic orbitals*. These are characteristic of the metallic state and are required to effect the unrestricted synchronous resonance of the bonding orbitals.

Table IV gives the electronic structures of the metals chromium to nickel as deduced from the foregoing considerations. In this table, Σ is the total number of electrons in the atomic *d*-orbital, irrespective of the sign of their

TABLE IV. *Electronic Structures of some First Row Transition Metals According to the Valence Bond Theory*

Metal	*Total electrons*	*Electrons in* dsp-*hybrid orbital*	*Electrons in atomic* d-*orbital*		Σ	*Saturation moment*	
			spin +	*spin −*		*calc.*	*obs.*
Chromium	6	5.78	0.22	0	0.22	0.22	—
Manganese	7	5.78	1.22	0	1.22	1.22	—
Iron	8	5.78	2.22	0	2.22	2.22	2.22
Cobalt	9	5.78	2.44	0.78	3.22	1.66	1.61
Nickel	10	5.78	2.44	1.78	4.22	0.66	0.61

spin, so that this number added to the electrons in the *dsp*-orbital is in each case equal to the total number of electrons. The calculated saturation moment is the number of unpaired electrons in the atomic *d*-orbital. In chromium, manganese and iron the number of electrons in the *d*-orbital is less than the permitted maximum of 2.44, but in cobalt this number would be exceeded unless some pairing occurred. Further pairing occurs with nickel, and the calculated saturation moment is therefore a maximum at iron.

The reason behind the apparently arbitrary choice of numbers is now clear: the numbers were chosen to give optimum agreement with the observed saturation moments of the Group VIII metals, and to this extent the Valence Bond Theory is less fundamental than the Electron Band Theory. It is an interpretation rather than an explanation.

For the Transition metals, it is possible to compute the extent to which *d*-electrons participate in the *dsp*-binding-orbital.[11] The conclusion is expressed in terms of the percentage *d*-character of the metallic bond and this is given the symbol δ. The following Table gives the values of δ for the Transition metals. There is nothing very fundamental about these values, since they have been obtained from the observed properties of the metals, but we may note (i) the almost constant δ from chromium to nickel in the first series,

TABLE V. *Percentage* d-*Character in the Metallic Bond of Transition Elements*

Sc	Ti	V	Cr	Mn	Fe	Co	Ni	Cu
20	27	35	39	40.1	39.5	39.7	40	36
Y	Zr	Nb	Mo	Tc	Ru	Rh	Pd	Ag
19	31	39	43	46	50	50	46	36
La	Hf	Ta	W	Rh	Os	Ir	Pt	Au
19	29	39	43	46	49	49	44	—

(ii) the close correspondence between the values for any group in the second and third series, and (iii) the maximum value of δ (~50 per cent) in Groups VIII_1 and VIII_2 in these latter series. In each series, the rate of increase of δ per electron added falls, becoming zero and eventually negative in the second and third series. This is of course because of the introduction of electrons into the atomic *d*-orbitals, and δ has therefore been used as a measure of the degree of filling of these orbitals.

In the case of the Group VIII metals, the Valence Bond and Electron Band treatments are essentially equivalent: a partially filled *d*-band is equivalent to a partially filled atomic *d*-orbital. The advantage of the Valence Bond Theory is that it applies numbers to those elements whose band structure is too complex to be treated quantitatively by the Electron Band Theory.

An interesting attempt has recently been made to interpret the regular variations in lattice structure through the Transition series in terms of a slightly modified form of the Valence Bond Theory.[14, 16] The maximum percentage *d*-character of the metallic bond is now thought to occur at Group VA or VIA, that is, where the cohesive energy is also a maximum. The lattice structure may then be related to the weight of *d*-electrons per orbital. This quantity is about 0.7 in Groups IIIA, IVA, VIIA and VIII_1

where the structure is close-packed hexagonal; it is about 0.9 in Groups VA and VIA, where the structure is body-centred cubic, and about 0.5 in Groups IIA, VIII_2 and VIII_3 where the structure is generally face-centred cubic. The Electron Band Theory has not yet been able to explain this regular pattern of structure (see, however, Ref. 9).

2.4 Physical Properties of Alloys and their Interpretation[2, 17]

A characteristic property of metals is their ability to form alloys with other elements. We may firstly distinguish between (1) substitutional alloys, and (ii) interstitial alloys. *Substitutional alloys* are substances in which atoms of the second element replace atoms of the first. *Interstitial alloys* are substances in which atoms of the second element occupy interstices between atoms of the metal; the former must therefore be small compared with the latter, and such alloys are formed for example with palladium and hydrogen, and with many Transition metals and boron, nitrogen and carbon.

Substitutional alloys of two metals which are not too dissimilar in size and electronic structure may form a continuous series of solid solutions without change of phase if both metals have the same geometric structure: a partial list of face-centred cubic alloys is given in Table VI. In other systems, for example Pt–Ag and Ag–Cu, metal 1 will dissolve in metal 2, and vice versa (although generally not to equal extents), but a complete range of solid solutions is unattainable due to the limited compatibility of the two metals.

Of great interest in metallurgy, but of little interest heretofore in catalysis, are alloys between metals of different valency and structure. Alloys of Cu–Zn (brass) and Cu–Sn (bronze) are perhaps the most familiar examples. The phase diagrams of these systems are complex,[2] but the situation is rationalized by considering the average electron/atom ratio: the same structure often appears at the same electron/atom ratio in widely different systems. Thus for example b.c.c. or c.p.h. structures tend to be formed when this ratio is 3/2, the γ-brass structure at 21/13 and the c.p.h. structure again at 7/4. The effective valency of Group VIII metals in alloys of this type is apparently close to zero. These alloys have been termed *electron compounds*, since their structure is determined by the electron concentration. Alloys formed from a Group IB metal and any metal further to the right naturally have no *d*-band vacancies, and they are of little interest catalytically. In binary alloys formed from metals in Groups VA to VIII_3 there is also a regular gradation in structure with electron concentration:[16] many interesting alloys in this group have not yet been studied as catalysts.

Substitutional alloys are most satisfactorily prepared by melting together the separate metals, followed by annealing or quenching. Certain alloy compositions may be obtained in either an "ordered" or a "disordered" form. If "disordered," there is an entirely random distribution of the solute metal in the solvent metal; if "ordered", there is a regular geometrical arrangement of the solute molecules which constitutes a superlattice and this generally corresponds to a stoichiometric "compound" of the two metals, for example Cu_3Au.

TABLE VI. *Substitutional Alloys forming Complete Series of Solid Solutions having the Face-centred Cubic Structure (except where indicated)*

Cu – Ni, Pt, Pd, Au		
Ag – Pd, Au		
Au – Ni, Pd, Pt		
Co – Ir, Pd, Pt, Rh		
Co – Fe	.... f.c.c.	(0–25% Fe)
	.... b.c.c.	(100–15% Fe)
Ni – Pt, Pd, Co		
Ni – Fe	.... f.c.c.	(10–100% Ni)
	.... b.c.c.	(0–30% Ni)

Since it is possible to prepare alloys in a form more suitable for catalytic study than that which results by combining the molten metals, it is necessary to have at hand means of characterizing these more active preparations, to establish their composition and homogeneity. The electronic properties of metals vary only discontinuously, since each metal necessarily possesses one more electron than that which precedes it in the Periodic Table: however, by alloying pairs of adjacent metals, continuous variation of electronic structure may be achieved, sometimes over a considerable range, without change in lattice structure, as for example in the series Fe...Co...Ni... Cu (f.c.c. from 75 per cent Co in Fe onwards). The use of such alloys offers a valuable means of establishing the role of the electronic structure of the solid in catalytic activity, especially when, as in the Fe...Cu series, the range covers the filling of the *d*-band: the roles of the *s*-electrons (or *dsp*-hybrids) and of *d*-electrons may then be distinguished and separately assessed. The object of this section is therefore to review briefly the more important physical properties of substitutional alloys and their interpretation, chiefly according to the Electron Band Theory, with especial emphasis on those alloys which have found applications as catalysts.

Perhaps the most accurate method of characterizing an alloy is the determination of its lattice spacing (a_0) by the method of X-ray diffraction spectroscopy. Most alloys show deviations, either positive or negative, and sometimes very substantial, from Vegard's Law, obedience to which demands a linear relationship between lattice spacing and composition. Such deviations are probably associated with changes in compressibility. The accuracy attainable in the determination of lattice spacings is now very great (four or five significant figures), so that the magnitudes of the deviations are known precisely, and these provide valuable information for the detailed interpretation of the structure of alloys. The lattice spacing in an alloy almost invariably lies between the values of the two component metals (the Ag–Au system is one of the few exceptions), and the variation in spacing is therefore sometimes very small (e.g. 3.5240–3.5452 Å from nickel to cobalt). Figure 13 shows the variation in lattice spacing for the nickel–copper and the palladium–silver systems. A short bibliography of the relevant literature is given in Appendix II.

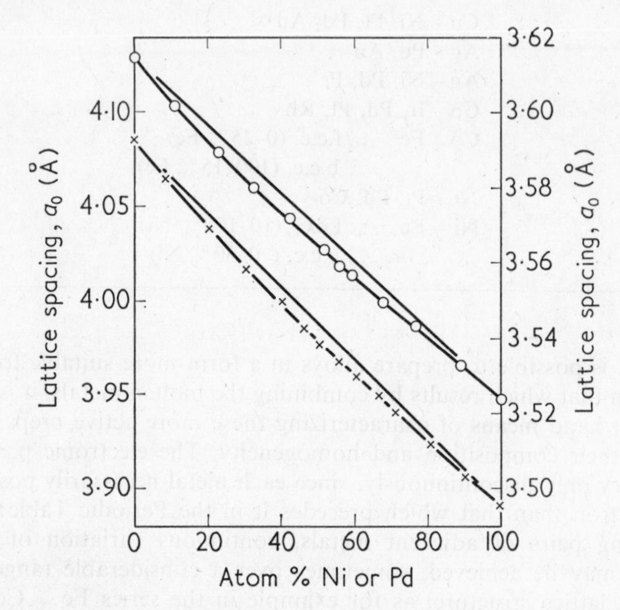

FIG. 13. The variation of lattice spacing (a_0) with composition for nickel–copper (○; right-hand scale) and palladium–silver (×; left-hand scale) alloys.[18]

The most readily accessible method of characterizing an alloy is perhaps the determination of its electrical conductivity, providing it is available in a suitable physical form: measured values do not, generally, however, lie between the values for the component metals, but pass through a distinct maximum. This is because the introduction of metal 1 into metal 2 or vice versa disturbs the ease with which the electron can migrate through the solid. Figure 14 shows the dependence of conductivity on composition in the palladium–gold system.

In alloys formed between metals of Groups VIII_3 and IB, there are important changes in magnetic properties associated with the filling of the *d*-band. According to the Electron Band Theory there are about 0.6 *d*-band vacancies per atom in nickel, so we should expect the additional electron possessed by copper to enter this band in nickel–copper alloys with a consequent progressive decrease in magnetic susceptibility to zero at a composition of about 60 per cent copper. Similar behaviour is to be expected in palladium–silver alloys.

The saturation moments and the Curie temperatures of nickel–copper alloys decrease linearly with increasing copper content, and recent measurements indicate that they become zero (i.e. the *d*-band is filled) at respectively

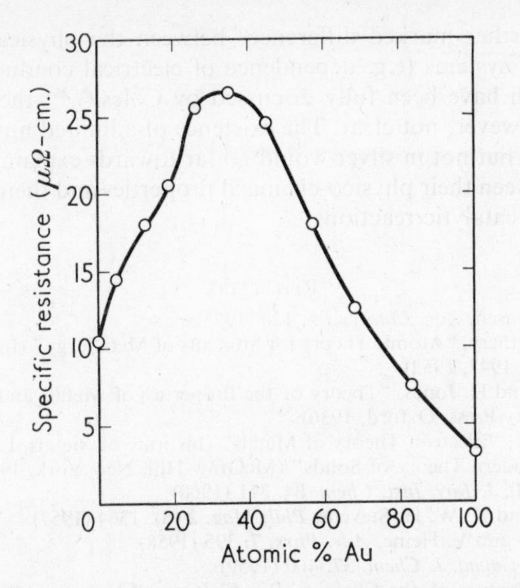

FIG. 14. The dependence of specific resistance on composition for palladium–gold alloys.[19]

52.5 and 57.0 per cent copper.[20, 21] There is, however, much other evidence to show that *d*-band vacancies persist to much higher copper contents, and possibly even in copper itself. (1) On the addition of nickel to copper, the atomic susceptibility at once rises, and the alloy containing 95 per cent copper is already paramagnetic.[22] (2) The high density of states in the unfilled *d*-band gives the transition metals a high electronic specific heat (γT) and the electronic specific heat coefficient γ gives information on the degree of filling of this band. The following table gives values of γ for some nickel-copper alloys.[23] The value of γ for the alloy containing 21.6 per cent nickel is greater

TABLE VII. *Low Temperature Electronic Specific Heat Coefficients for some Nickel–Copper alloys*[23]

% Ni	100	81.6	62.0	42.1	21.6	0
γ kcal. deg.$^{-1}$ (g. atom)$^{-1}$	1.74	1.58	1.52	1.66	0.46	0.18

than that for pure copper, showing that there are *d*-band vacancies in this alloy. (3) A recent direct determination[24] of the number of electrons in the *d*-band of copper is 9.8 ± 0.2.

Behaviour in the palladium–silver system appears to be more as expected. On the addition of palladium to silver, the atomic susceptibility is at first reduced to more negative values, that is, there is an increase in diamagnetism due to the reduction of the number of electrons in the 5*s*-band; it subsequently rises at about 40 per cent palladium, indicating that the *d*-band starts to empty at this point, as expected.

There are further marked differences between the physical properties of these two alloy systems (e.g. dependence of electrical conductivity on composition), which have been fully discussed by Coles[18, 25]: the detailed interpretation is, however, not clear. The existence of a limited number of *d*-band holes in copper but not in silver would go far towards explaining the marked differences between their physico-chemical properties and their behaviour in a wide variety of catalytic reactions.

References

1. E. A. Gulbransen, *Adv. Catalysis* **5,** 120 (1953).
2. W. Hume-Rothery, "Atomic Theory for Students of Metallurgy" (Institute of Metals, London, 1947, 1952).
3. N. F. Mott and H. Jones, "Theory of the Properties of Metals and Alloys" (Oxford University Press, Oxford, 1936).
4. G. V. Raynor, "Electron Theory of Metals" (Institute of Metals, London, 1953).
5. F. Seitz, "Modern Theory of Solids" (McGraw-Hill, New York, 1940).
6. J. A. Catterall, *J. Roy. Inst. Chem.* **84,** 311 (1960)
7. N. F. Mott and K. W. H. Stevens, *Phil. Mag.* **2** (8), 1364 (1957).
8. M. H. Cohen and V. Heine, *Adv. Phys.* **7,** 395 (1958)
9. W. R. Trost, *Canad. J. Chem.* **37,** 460 (1959).
10. L. Pauling, "Nature of the Chemical Bond" (Cornell University Press, Ithaca, N.Y., 1948).
11. L. Pauling, *J. Amer. Chem. Soc.* **69,** 542; (1947). *Proc. Roy. Soc.* **A196,** 343 (1949).
12. W. Hume-Rothery, *Ann. Reports* **46,** 42 (1949).
13. W. Hume-Rothery, H. M. Irving and R. J. P. Williams, *Proc. Roy. Soc.* **A208,** 431 (1951).
14. S. L. Altmann, C. A. Coulson and W. Hume-Rothery, *Proc. Roy. Soc.* **A240,** 145 (1957).
15. D. A. Robins, *J. Less-Common Metals* **1,** 396 (1960).
16. C. W. Haworth and W. Hume-Rothery, *Phil. Mag.* **3**(8), 1013 (1958).
17. W. B. Pearson, "Lattice Spacings and Structures of Metals and Alloys" (Pergamon Press, London, 1958).
18. B. R. Coles, *J. Inst. Metals* **84,** 346 (1956).
19. W. Geibel, *Z. anorg. Chem.* **69,** 38 (1911).
20. A. J. P. Meyer and C. Wolff, *Compt. rend.* **246,** 576 (1958).
21. S. A. Ahern, M. J. C. Martin and W. Sucksmith, *Proc. Roy. Soc.* **A248,** 145 (1958).
22. A. D. Kaufmann and C. Starr, *Phys. Rev.* **63,** 445 (1943).
23. W. H. Keesom and B. Kurrelmeyer, *Physica* **7,** 1003 (1940).
24. R. J. Weiss and J. J. de Marco, *Rev. Mod. Phys.* **30,** 59.
25. B. R. Coles, *Proc. Phys. Soc.* **65B,** 221.

Chapter 3

The Preparation and Study of Metal Surfaces

3.1 The Topographical Description of Metals and Metal Surfaces

Chapter 2 outlined the more important physico-chemical bulk properties of metals and alloys, and their interpretation, in the firm expectation that these properties and theories would be of value in interpreting catalytic behaviour. In Chapter 1 we saw that for efficient catalysis a high surface area is required. The present Chapter shows how metals and alloys may be prepared in a state suitable for effecting catalysis, and it describes briefly the physical methods which are available for the direct investigation of the surfaces of such catalysts.

Metals exist in a variety of physical forms, and those observable properties which have been already described refer chiefly to metals in a massive or macroscopic state: in this state a metal is either (i) polycrystalline, that is, it is composed of a very large number of compacted microcrystals or crystallites (whose size depends on the metallurgical history of the sample) separated from each other by grain boundaries; or (ii) it is monocrystalline, that is, a single crystal, with an almost perfect degree of order pervading the structure.

Metals in the massive state are near to their thermodynamic equilibrium state with respect to disorders in the bulk or on the surface: their surface areas are not greatly in excess of the apparent geometric area, that is, their roughness factor is low (generally <2), and they are correspondingly ineffective as catalysts. The description of the nature, size and disposition of the microcrystals in a polycrystalline material is the province of metallography, and is not within the scope of this book. Single crystals are quite readily prepared by slowly cooling the molten metal, and they naturally have certain mechanical properties not shared by polycrystalline forms. Single crystals have the advantage for adsorption and catalytic studies that they may be accurately machined to expose relatively large areas of well-defined crystallographic planes to the vapour phase.[1, 2] Filamentary metals ("metal whiskers") prepared by the gas-phase reduction of certain metal halides or sulphides consist of numerous small single crystals.

It is possible to prepare metals in a very high state of subdivision by a wide variety of methods. These we may refer to as *microscopic forms*, and they lack many of the characteristic physical properties of metals in the massive state, such as lustre, mechanical strength, and high electrical and thermal conductivity. Here the metal consists of innumerable microcrystals, generally smaller than those found in polycrystalline metal, but not compacted. The surface to volume ratio is therefore very much larger than for a metal in a massive state, and provided certain other necessary conditions are fulfilled, they make admirable catalysts. Metals in this state may be far removed from the state of thermodynamic equilibrium, that is, they may contain a high proportion of defects. They may be pyrophoric, and susceptible to sintering, which is loss of surface area due to growth of the elementary crystallites at high temperatures.

It is desirable to have the most accurate possible description of the average crystallite for the full understanding of its behaviour in adsorption and catalysis. This description may be subdivided into

(i) the description of the exposed crystallographic planes, i.e. of the geometry of the perfect arrays of nuclei presented to the gas phase, and
(ii) the description of the number and nature of surface disorders or defects, i.e. the departure from the ideal conditions presumed in (i).

It is generally supposed that the surface of any microcrystalline metal may be represented as the summation of a number of conventional crystallographic planes, in which the planes of low index (e.g. (100), (110), (111) for a f.c.c. structure) predominate. It is further supposed that the interatomic distances at the surface are the same as those within the bulk, but although there is evidence to the contrary in specific cases,[3, 4] the effects are probably not large. Figure 1 gives the arrangements of nuclei in some commonly encountered crystallographic planes.

The description of defects is more difficult. Defects within the bulk of the solid may be classified according to the number of dimensions in which they exist, as follows: (i) point defects, that is, lattice vacancies (Schottky defects) and interstitial atoms (Frenkel defects); (ii) line defects, that is, dislocations: and (iii) plane defects, that is, grain- and sub-grain boundaries and stacking-faults. Point defects may also occur at surfaces, as for example at the emergence of a dislocation, and one-dimensional defects result when plane defects within the bulk intersect the surface. Point defects may interact, and either cancel each other or form a larger defect: they may be treated statistically as if they were solute molecules in a dilute solution, and the kinetics of their interaction are being studied. The equilibrium concentration of point defects decreases exponentially with increasing temperature, becoming zero at the

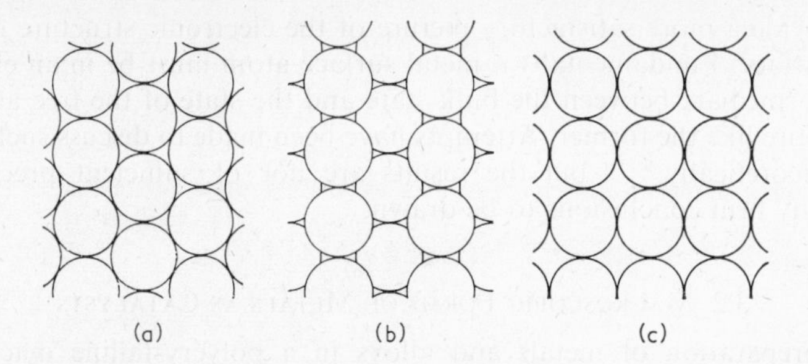

FIG. 1. The arrangement of atoms in some commonly encountered crystallographic planes.
(a) The (111) plane of a face-centred cubic crystal.
(b) The (110) plane of a face-centred cubic crystal.
(c) The (100) plane of a face-centred cubic crystal.

melting-point, but the non-equilibrium concentration actually obtaining is determined by the method and temperature of preparation and by the thermal history of the sample. Line and plane defects are non-equilibrium properties, since their concentrations also are governed by the history of the sample, and they cannot be treated by the methods of reversible thermodynamics.

The role of surface defects in adsorption and catalysis is hard to assess. They have been frequently invoked, and there is direct evidence that defects created by bombardment of surfaces by highly energetic particles can increase the rates of certain reactions.[5, 6, 7] On the whole, however, the part played by natural biographical defects is an inherent feature of the activity of surfaces. The demonstration of the existence of defects has been taken as direct evidence for the "active centre" hypothesis, although it now seems certain that experimental evidence which formerly supported this theory can be reinterpreted in alternative ways which are no less improbable and possibly more plausible and satisfying.

The essential difference between macroscopic and microscopic forms of metals lies in the proportion of the atoms which are at the surface. In the former case this proportion is very low. If, however, we consider a simple cubic array of atoms forming a cube having sides 15 Å long, it is readily computed that some two-thirds of the two hundred or so atoms present are at the surface. Particles of this kind of size have been prepared and used as catalysts.[8] No successful attempt has been made to demonstrate an inherent change in catalytic activity per atom or per unit weight with particle size, as might be expected if very small particles had properties significantly different from those of the massive metal. Such effects as have been observed are adequately interpreted in terms of the varying surface area.

The theoretical description of the electronic structure of surface atoms has not advanced far, and a thorough quantum mechanical treatment is urgently required. The Electron Band Theory is formulated for an infinite three-dimensional array of nuclei. For this reason, Pauling's Valence Bond Theory may provide a more satisfactory picture of the electronic structure of atoms at the surface. Fundamentally a metal surface atom must be in an electronic state intermediate between the bulk state and the state of the free atom, but rather more like the former. Attempts have been made to discuss such *surface states* theoretically,[9, 10] but the results are not of sufficient precision to enable any firm conclusions to be drawn.

3.2 Macroscopic Forms of Metals as Catalysts

The preparation of metals and alloys in a polycrystalline macroscopic state requires no description, since this is a metallurgical rather than a chemical matter: they are normally employed as wire (which may be knitted into gauze) or foil. Due to the high affinity which most metals except the very "noble" ones have for oxygen, metal surfaces which have been exposed to air are covered by either a layer of adsorbed oxygen or a thin layer of metal oxide, and these may render the surfaces ineffective as catalysts. Steps must therefore be taken to clean the surface of any material likely to interfere with its operation.

The nature of the cleaning process required depends on the use to which the material will subsequently be put. We may therefore distinguish between (i) the cleaning of surfaces to be used in fundamental studies of adsorption, and (ii) the cleaning of surfaces to be used as catalysts. In the first instance it is of the utmost importance to have a surface completely free from any adsorbed species whatever, and cleaning techniques must be directed to this end. In the second case, it is not normally necessary to have a surface free of *all* impurities, but only free of those adsorbed species which are likely to interfere with the reaction to be carried out. This means treating the oxidized surface by a reducing agent, generally hydrogen, in order to re-form the metal surface. The temperature required thoroughly to reduce the surface depends on the thermodynamic stability of the relevant oxide: it is low for platinum, palladium, etc. (room temperature), higher for nickel and cobalt ($>300°$) and higher still for iron ($>400°$). The metal surface so formed will be more disordered (i.e. rougher) than the original surface to an extent depending on the degree of penetration of the oxygen into the bulk, but it may of course be smoothed by sintering. The cycle of high temperature oxidation followed by low temperature reduction is sometimes purposely employed to create a roughened surface which has a large specific surface area and therefore a greater reactivity than the former surface.[11] The active metal surface is therefore properly regarded as being microscopic rather than macroscopic, but there is a continuous variation between the smooth surface of the macroscopic state and the very rough surface of the microscopic state, so that no clear distinction is possible. All reduced metal surfaces (except perhaps those not adsorbing oxygen) must therefore be in some degree rough, but it is conventional to regard them as characteristic of the macroscopic state unless they have definitely lost their metallic lustre. A surface formed by hydrogen reduction will necessarily be covered by adsorbed hydrogen at the finish, but this is no disadvantage if it is to be used to catalyse a hydrogenation reaction. Moreover, if a completely clean surface is required, hydrogen is more readily desorbed than oxygen. The surfaces of metallic foils and wires have also been efficiently cleaned by atomic hydrogen produced by a high-frequency (15 Mc/s) electrodeless discharge through hydrogen at 2 mm. pressure, followed by thermal desorption of the adsorbed hydrogen.[12]

The complete cleaning of pre-formed metal surfaces is an arduous task, and is only to be attempted when fundamental adsorption studies are in view. Two types of method have been used: (i) thermal desorption, and (ii) ion bombardment. In the first method, the temperature of the specimen is raised by external or resistance heating, under high or ultra-high vacuum (10^{-6} mm. or 10^{-9} mm.), until the adsorbed species have completely vacated the surface.[13, 14] The impurities may desorb from the surface or may migrate into the bulk; but the procedure commonly takes several days. Sensitive methods of determining the degree of coverage of the surface by the adsorbed species are required in order to know when the surface is sufficiently clean. In the second method, the surface to be cleaned is bombarded by fast-moving ions of the rare gases: these apparently simply knock adsorbed species off the surface into the gas phase, whence they are removed by pumping. This method is more rapid and perhaps more efficient than thermal desorption, but it has the disadvantages that additional surface defects may be created and that rare gas atoms may be left occluded within the bulk, unless a subsequent thermal treatment is employed.[5, 6, 7, 15]

3.3 Microscopic Forms of Metals as Catalysts: (i) Forms Containing no other Component

A microscopic form of a metal is the favoured form for practical catalysis because of the high surface area it possesses. A first subdivision of this class is into (i) metal preparations containing no other component, and (ii) metal preparations containing one or more other components besides the metal. Into category (i) come unsupported metal powders, colloidal metals and evaporated metal films; into category (ii) come a wide variety of supported and promoted metal catalysts. Microcrystalline metals are generally prepared either by the reduction of some compound of the metal or by some simple mechanical treatment of another physical form of the metal. Here the method of preparation is of direct concern to the behaviour of the product, and it is therefore necessary to summarize and comment upon the various available techniques.

The present class comprehends those preparations of metals and alloys having an uncompacted microcrystalline form, to which no non-metallic component has been purposely added. We may arbitrarily subdivide this class as follows.

(i) Metal preparations normally used in the liquid phase
  (a) colloidal metals
  (b) metallic sponges or "blacks"
  (c) skeletal metals

(ii) Metal preparations normally used in the gas phase
  (d) metal powders
  (e) evaporated metal films
  (f) electrodeposited films

3.31 *Colloidal Metals*

Colloidal metals are normally prepared by the reduction of a suitable salt in solution by one of a number of reducing agents; the following table gives a partial list of suitable reagents.

TABLE I. *Reducing Agents for the Preparation of Colloidal Metals*

Phosphorus (Faraday method)	Acetylene
Acetone	Carbon monoxide (Donau method)
Tannin	Citric acid
Oxalic acid	Sodium citrate
Hydroxylamine	Acetone dicarboxylic acid

The Bredig technique for the preparation of colloidal metals involves striking an arc between two wires of the metal under a very dilute solution of sodium hydroxide. Too little is known concerning the effects of the variables of the preparation on the shape, mean size and size distribution of the resulting particles, but a very thorough investigation of preparations of colloidal gold (unfortunately a metal of little interest catalytically) has been carried out with the aid of the electron microscope.[16] The most satisfactory reducing agent was found to be sodium citrate: the mean particle diameter, obtained by reducing at 100°C a chloroauric acid solution containing 0.005 per cent gold with a 1 per cent sodium citrate solution containing 50 mg. of the salt, was 200 Å and the size distribution was quite sharp. The particles were spherical. The mean size was a function of the temperature of the reduction, the concentration of the solutions and the ratio of the amounts of the reagents. Reduction of a solution of hexachloroplatinic acid with sodium citrate yields platinum particles about 15 Å in diameter.[8] Because of their small particle size and large specific surface area, suspensions of colloidal metals are sometimes very active catalysts, although the tendency to coagulate limits their useful life.

3.32 *Metallic Sponges*

Metallic sponges of the noble Group VIII metals are prepared by the reduction of a suitable salt by formaldehyde under alkaline conditions: they are the result of coagulating the initially formed colloid, and are therefore readily separated from the aqueous phase.

3.33 *Skeletal Metals*

These are prepared from binary alloys of the catalytic metal and a second metal easily soluble in suitable reagents. Raney nickel[17] is obtained by treating a 50 : 50 nickel–aluminium alloy with a concentrated solution of sodium hydroxide until most or all of the aluminium has dissolved. This form of nickel possesses a very open or skeletal structure and thus presents a high surface area. It is widely used in preparative organic chemistry, and its ease of preparation is attractive. The preparation and use of skeletal iron, cobalt[18] and copper[19] has been described, but they are generally less active than nickel.

3.34 Metal Powders

We turn now to methods of making unsupported metals in forms suitable for use as catalysts in gas-phase reactions. A very widely used method is the reduction of a suitable compound of the metal in a stream of reducing gas: of such gases, hydrogen is eminently the most successful, for it is readily purified and leaves no undesirable residues on the surface as do, for example, carbon monoxide and formic acid. The nature and source of the compound of the metal is important. It is customary with the noble metals of Group VIII to start with a chloride, since this is the form in which they are normally obtained: reduction, after an induction period in which the metallic nuclei are formed, may be possible at room temperature, but in any event the use of temperatures much over 200° is unwise by reason of the low sintering-temperature of these metals. With the metals between iron and copper a wider choice of starting materials is available. Most of the compounds of these metals (except the halides) if calcined in air or oxygen at 250° become converted to an oxide. Nitrates, hydroxides, carbonates and basic carbonates are frequently used, but in the latter cases the physical nature of the oxide depends on the conditions of the precipitation and dehydration or decomposition of the compounds. The nature of the metal ultimately formed in the reduction is determined by the physical state of the parent compound, but furthermore the conditions of the reduction affect the final product. Temperature certainly affects the surface area, while other possibly relevant variables are (i) the flow-rate and purity of the hydrogen, (ii) the rate at which the temperature is raised and (iii) the length of time the process is continued. If the metal has to be transferred to the reaction vessel, it is most desirable that the material be cooled to room temperature before exposure to air: but because of the pyrophoric tendency of such preparations it is better to reduce the oxide *in situ*. The following Table indicates the kind of surface areas which metal powders prepared in this way may have.

Metallic powders so prepared have been successfully freed from adsorbed hydrogen by prolonged thermal desorption.[14, 20]

An entirely different method of preparing metal powders is the thermal decomposition under vacuum of metal salts of organic acids; very often the formate is used. An interesting study of the cobalt formed in the decomposition of organic cobalt salts has recently been published.[25] It is the c.p.h. form of cobalt which is stable at room temperature, but the f.c.c. form into which it passes at about 420°C can exist metastably at lower temperatures;

TABLE II. *Surface Areas of Metal Powders prepared by the the Reduction of Oxides in Hydrogen*

Metal	*Oxide from:*	*Reduction temp.* (°C)	*Surface area* ($m.^2 g.^{-1}$)	*Reference*
Ni	Basic carbonate	500	0.41	21
Ni	Basic carbonate	500	0.15	22
Ni	Basic carbonate	350	0.82	23
Ni	Hydroxide	360 to 400	7	24
Cu	Basic carbonate	500	0.18	22
Cu	Basic carbonate	350	0.33	23

the f.c.c. to c.p.h. transition is apparently very sluggish. As the results in the following Table show, the proportion of the c.p.h. form produced in the decomposition of organic cobalt salts varies markedly but irregularly with the chain length of the organic anion; there is, however, a smooth relation between the proportion of the c.p.h. form and the surface area.

TABLE III. *Properties of Cobalt Powders produced by the Thermal Decomposition of Organic Salts of Cobalt*[25]

Salt	*% c.p.h. form*	*Surface area* ($m.^2 g.^{-1}$)
Formate	20	4
Acetate	70	8
Propionate	80	13
Butanoate	85	24
Pentanoate	50	6

The decomposition of nickel carbonyl yields nickel powder having a surface area of 1.48 $m.^2 g.^{-1}$, but its catalytic activity is limited by traces of adsorbed carbon monoxide which remain;[21] this process can also be made to yield a coherent film, which, however, appears to suffer similarly.[26]

Similar techniques have been successfully applied to the production of binary alloys in powder form. The chief advantage of such powders is that they may be used at temperatures very much lower than those necessary for alloys in a compacted polycrystalline form (foils, wires, etc.). The decomposition of mixed hydroxides,[24, 27] formates,[28] or basic carbonates[22, 23, 29] obtained by co-precipitation from solution yields homogeneous mixed oxides, and these on reduction in hydrogen yield homogeneous alloys. Alloys of Fe–Co, Fe–Ni, Ni–Co and Ni–Cu have been so prepared. Some of the criteria by which these alloys may be characterized have been mentioned in Chapter 2: magnetic[30] and X-ray crystallographic studies[29] have shown that alloys prepared in these ways have properties closely corresponding with those of the corresponding massive forms. Palladium–silver alloy powders have been prepared by the reduction in hydrogen at 100° of mixed oxides obtained by the calcination of the mechanically mixed nitrates.[24]

3.35 Evaporated Metal Films

Metals and alloys prepared in the foregoing ways are sometimes described as "dirty" since they inevitably retain traces of the parent compound unless extremely thoroughly reduced, together with traces of the hydrogen used in the reduction. Without very complete thermal desorption, which as previously remarked is tedious, such powders are not usable in basic adsorption studies. Very great interest therefore attaches to an alternative method of preparing metals in a state of high surface area and ultra-purity: this is the *evaporated film technique*.

Although films produced by the "sputtering" of metal wires were employed over twenty-five years ago,[31] the widespread use of evaporated metal films dates from the now classical work of Beeck and his associates, published in 1941.[32] The method is briefly as follows. A thin wire of the metal of which the film is to be formed is sealed into a Pyrex glass container; simultaneously there are applied external heating which causes the desorption of adsorbed species from the container walls and resistance heating of the wire which causes the removal of dissolved species (chiefly oxygen and nitrogen); the system is continuously pumped to remove these desorbed species. When the system is sufficiently purified, the external source of heat is removed and the temperature of the container walls brought to 0° or some lower temperature. The current through the wire is then increased until the temperature is a little below its melting point: atoms of the metal then evaporate from the wire and condense on the walls, the process being continued until a sufficient weight of metal has evaporated.

This technique is readily applied to metals which are available in wire form: other metals may be electroplated on to say a tungsten wire, or otherwise mechanically attached. It is difficult to de-gas metals which melt below about 1000° sufficiently to ensure complete purification, but substantially clean films of potassium, calcium and barium have been obtained.[33]

With evaporated nickel films, the surface area is proportional to the thickness of the film, showing that it must be very porous and have a large internal surface; in confirmation it has been shown that the electrical conductivity is about seven times less than for bulk nickel.[32] Surface areas attainable range from about 150 cm.^{2} up to several square metres. Films of all metals sinter to some degree when raised to temperatures above that at which they were deposited. Low-melting metals and those in Group IB sinter completely at temperatures above −80°; for metals melting between 1400 and 3000°, the specific surface area increases with melting point because of the corresponding disinclination to sinter at the deposition temperature.[34] Tungsten films are additionally sintered by the energy radiated during their evaporation.

It was originally claimed that when the evaporation of nickel was carried out in a vessel containing an inert gas (argon or nitrogen) at a pressure of about 1 mm., the film was preferentially oriented with the least dense plane, i.e. the (100) plane, parallel to the backing.[32] However, it now appears[20, 35] that the degree of orientation is chiefly determined by two other factors, namely (i) the temperature at which the film is deposited, and (ii) the thickness of the film. Oriented films are not obtained at temperatures below those at which the surface atoms of the film are mobile; the degree of orientation depends on film thickness, and is not increased by the presence of an inert gas. The difference between the two pieces of work may be due to the fact that the earlier work[32] was not carried out in a grease-free system. The greater activity claimed for the gas-deposited films over that of the vacuum-deposited films remains unexplained. Direct experimental evidence has been advanced to show that the (110) plane in oriented films is also exposed to the gas phase[36] but it is not substantiated by electron-diffraction measurements.[35]

Oriented films of other metals have been prepared, although oriented copper films cannot be made (see however Ref. 37); with iron, the (111) plane is parallel to the backing.[32]

The great advantage of the evaporation method is the cleanliness and reproducibility of the surfaces obtained, although these advantages are somewhat offset by the susceptibility of the films to sintering and to poisoning by mercury and tap grease.

Evaporated alloy films have been prepared by simultaneous[38a] and requential[38b] evaporation from two heated filaments.

3.36 Electro-deposited films

The electro-deposition of a metal from solution on to a foil of the same metal can under favourable conditions lead to the formation of a black metallic layer, having all the properties of a microcrystalline form. Such layers of suitable metals are active catalysts, but are readily poisoned by mercury and tap-grease.[8]

3.4 Microscopic Forms of Metals as Catalysts: (ii) Forms Containing one or more other Components

This category embraces the very large number of multicomponent "practical" catalysts on whose functions large sections of chemical industry rely. It is helpful to try to distinguish between (i) metals supported on carriers, (ii) promoted metals, and (iii) dual-function catalysts.

A *carrier* is a substance which has no catalytic activity of itself, but when a metal is supported on its surface the physical and mechanical properties of the resulting catalyst are superior to those of the unsupported metal. Here there is generally thought to be little or no chemical interaction between the carrier and the metal, the degree of improvement resulting from using the carrier being determined rather by its physical than by its chemical character; the manner in which the metal and the carrier are brought together is however very important. A supported metal usually contains more than 80 per cent by weight of carrier. A *promoter* may or may not have catalytic activity of itself, but a promoted metal will exhibit at some composition (generally less than 10 per cent by weight of promoter) an activity greater than that expected if both components were acting individually. There may be chemical interaction between a promoter and a metal, although the nature of the interaction is often hard to determine and to understand. Great care is necessary to distinguish satisfactorily between the tasks performed by carriers and by promoters: thus for example a promoter may also exercise the functions of a carrier. It is of course possible to prepare supported promoted metals: the cobalt–thoria–kieselguhr catalyst used in the Fischer–Tropsch synthesis is an example.

In comparing the catalytic activities of promoted, supported and unsupported metals, it is most desirable to refer the measurements to unit surface area of the metallic phase, but this is seldom easy. It is possible to suppose the area of the metal is the difference between the apparent area of the catalyst and the area of the carrier (or carrier + promoter) before the metal is introduced. Sometimes it is possible to remove the metal from the catalyst (for example, removal of nickel from nickel–silica by carbon monoxide) and to equate the resulting loss of area to the area of the metal[39]. Much more often, however, activities are compared on the basis of unit weight of metal, and this together with an assumption of equivalent activities per unit area of metal leads to an estimate of the metal's state of subdivision. Without measurements of area, however, it is not easy to be dogmatic about the method of functioning of promoters.

3.41 *Supported Metals*

There are three distinct techniques for the preparation of supported metals; these are (i) impregnation, (ii) co-precipitation, and (iii) deposition. In the impregnation method, the carrier is soaked in a solution of a metal salt and a deposit of the salt on the carrier is obtained: this material is dried, and then the salt is reduced to the metal by hydrogen at the appropriate temperature. In the co-precipitation method, the metal salt is placed in solution with another substance, and on the addition of a precipitating agent such as alkali, a homogeneous mixture of the metal hydroxide with the carrier is obtained. This material may then be dried and reduced in the normal way. Thus for example nickel–silica catalysts are obtained starting with nickel nitrate and sodium meta-silicate using sodium carbonate or potassium hydroxide as the precipitating agent.[39] In the deposition method, the preformed metal or one of its compounds is deposited from suspension onto a suspension of the carrier. This technique is capable of a great many modifications, and only a few examples will be quoted. (a) Colloidal platinum may be deposited on freshly precipitated alumina: the material is then filtered and dried.[8] (b) Hydrogen is passed through a solution of palladium nitrate in which activated charcoal is suspended; the reduced metal deposits on the charcoal. (c) Nickel hydroxide in suspension is deposited on silica also in suspension, and the material filtered, dried and reduced.[39]

It is clear that there will be substantial differences between catalysts prepared by these three methods. Those made by the impregnation and deposition methods will have the active component (after reduction where necessary) readily available at the surface of the carrier, while in a catalyst made by coprecipitation some of the active component may be embedded within the carrier and hence not accessible. Recent very thorough studies of the nature of nickel–silica catalysts (summarized in Ref. 39) have confirmed and amplified these expectations, and have shown that some revision of the role of carriers may be called for.

It has been shown that both in the impregnation of silica gel or kieselguhr with a nickel salt and the coprecipitation of silica with nickel hydroxide, one of two hydrosilicates having a layer structure is formed.[40, 41] Which of the two is actually formed depends chiefly on the Ni : Si ratio, and hardly at all on other conditions: when the Ni : Si ratio is 3 : 2, nickel antigorite is formed, and when the ratio is 3 : 4, nickel montmorillonite. In the impregnated material after reduction the nickel is widely spread on the very large silica surface: there is thus a great increase in the area of the accessible surface as compared with the accessible area of unsupported nickel. Nickel oxide so supported is more difficult to reduce than the bulk oxide, and this is a common feature of the preparation of supported catalysts: the difficulty of reduction increases with the dilution of the active components. The removal of the nickel by carbon monoxide from impregnation catalysts is quantitative, but this is far from being the case with co-precipitated catalysts, where much of the nickel is covered by a silica "skin" and is therefore inaccessible.

The high activity of these nickel catalysts is thus partly ascribable to the intermediate formation of a compound between nickel ions and the carrier, yielding on reduction small particles of metal widely dispersed on the support. The fact that the support is chemically involved in the process in no way contradicts the earlier statement that it is catalytically inert. It is at present uncertain how far these ideas are applicable to other systems, although it seems that the noble Group VIII metal ions do not enter into chemical liaison with carriers (see however Ref. 42). Three independent studies of the dispersion of the metal in platinum–alumina catalysts prepared by impregnation have recently been carried out: high-[43] and medium-area[44] α-Al_2O_3, and η-Al_2O_3,[45] were used as supports. The results are remarkably consistent. The chemisorption of hydrogen and X-ray line-broadening were used to estimate particle sizes, and it appeared that much of the platinum was so finely dispersed that almost every platinum atom was accessible: there was however also evidence for larger crystallites which grew in size as the catalyst was sintered.

Although as noted above it has been generally felt that there is no chemical interaction between the metal and the carrier in supported metals, there is nevertheless a growing body of evidence to show that this view may be naive. The distinction between carrier- and promoter-action is becoming progressively less clear and less helpful. Several groups of workers have shown that activity is dependent on the chemical nature of the support.[46, 47, 48, 49] This effect is particularly clear-cut in the case of nickel supported on nickel oxide and chromia to which altervalent oxides have been added to produce valency induction.[47] In another instance[48] an effect on the Fermi level of the metal electrons has been detected. Not only is the activity of the catalyst affected by changing the carrier, but sometimes also its specific directing influence. For example, the selectivity for nitric oxide production in ammonia oxidation by supported platinum increases with the size of the cation when the sulphates of magnesium, calcium, strontium and barium are used as carriers.[49]

The way in which these effects operate is by no means certain at the moment, and the question of the role played by the carrier remains one of the central problems in catalysis. There are two alternative views. (i) The chemical and catalytic properties of the metal are influenced by the chemical nature of the support in a subtle and hitherto-unsuspected way, and so the support is often also acting as a promoter. (ii) The presence of the metal on the carrier by some means activates the latter, so that it can participate in the catalysis. It is envisaged that adsorbed species may migrate from the metal to the carrier and there react in a manner naturally determined by the chemical nature of the carrier. Thus the activity and the specificity of the catalyst would vary from one carrier to another. This kind of process is known to occur during the operation of bifunctional catalysts (see Subsection 3.43), and it is possible that the phenomenon of bifunctionality is much more widespread than is generally thought.

A very large number of materials other than those specifically mentioned above have been used as carriers. A few of these are listed in Table IV, where they are classified according to their area and porosity.

TABLE IV. *Classification and Properties of Carriers*

Area	Porosity	Carriers
Low area (< 1 m.^{2}g.$^{-1}$)	Non-porous	Ground glass 'Alundum' (α-Al_2O_3) Silicon carbide
	Porous	Kieselguhr Pumice
High area (> 1 m.^{2}g.$^{-1}$)	Non-porous	Silica–alumina Carbon black Titania Zinc oxide
	porous (> 0.2 cm.^{3}g.$^{-1}$)	Natural clays Alumina Magnesia Activated carbon Silica Asbestos

The physical advantages resulting when a metal is supported on an inert carrier may now be summarized. The metal is well-dispersed and the accessible area of metal is larger than when unsupported; the dispersion inhibits crystal growth by sintering and the useful life of the catalyst is thereby prolonged. This effect is well shown in the copper–magnesia catalysts.[50] Other advantages of a more practical nature result from using granular catalysts or catalyst tablets: resistance to flow in the catalyst bed is smaller, and loss of metal is less, than when unsupported metal is used.

3.42 Promoted Metals

We return now to a consideration of *promoted metal catalysts*, and it is with reference to iron catalysts for ammonia synthesis and the Fischer–Tropsch reaction that the phenomenon of promotion is best understood. Early work of a largely empirical character showed that a singly promoted iron–alumina catalyst was more efficient than pure iron, while a doubly-promoted iron–alumina–potash catalyst was even better.[51] The work of Emmett and his associates on ammonia decomposition by such catalysts has greatly clarified the position;[52] some revealing results are shown in Table V. Values in the column headed "Activity" are the percentages of ammonia decomposed under standard experimental conditions using equal volumes of catalyst. The addition of 1 per cent alkali to essentially pure iron increases the activity but depresses the surface area, thus increasing the specific

TABLE V. *Activities of Singly and Doubly Promoted Iron Catalysts in Ammonia Decomposition*[52]

Catalyst number	% Al_2O_3	% K_2O	*Activity*	*Surface area* ($m.^2g.^{-1}$)	*Specific activity*
973	0.15	—	3.3%	1.03	3.2%
930	—	1.07	5.3%	0.40	13.2%
934	10.2	—	8.2%	7.98	1.03%
931	1.3	1.59	12.3%	2.06	5.97%

activity four-fold. Increasing the alumina content by about 100-fold increases the surface area and the activity, but the specific activity is less. The best catalyst (per unit volume) results when both alumina and alkali are present, the former overcompensating for the latter's depressing effect on the area: however, the specific activity is less than when alumina is absent.

Alumina increases the area and is therefore termed a *structural promoter*: it stabilizes the iron surface against sintering in a way which is not yet understood, but as regards the specific activity alumina is a poison. Alkali lowers the area but increases the specific activity, and is therefore termed an *electronic promoter*. However, in industrial use it is the activity per unit volume of catalyst which is important rather than the specific activity: therefore since both substances increase the rate per unit volume, both are to be regarded as promoters.

The proportions of the surface occupied by each of the three components have been measured by low temperature adsorption methods for a series of catalysts containing 0.42 per cent alumina and variable amounts of alkali;[53]

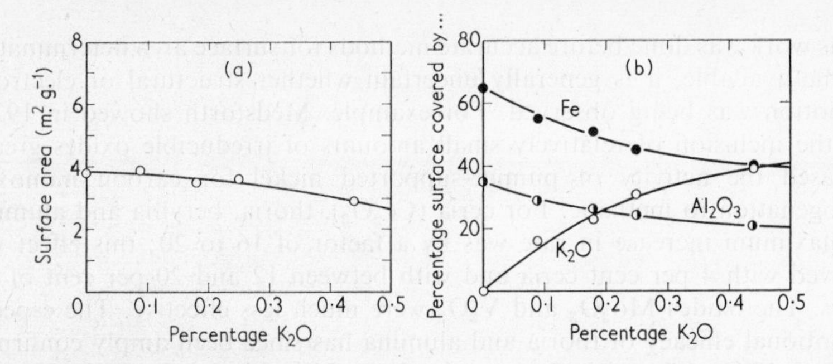

FIG. 2. Properties of doubly promoted iron catalysts (containing 0.42% Al_2O_3) as a function of alkali content.
(a) Total surface area.
(b) Proportions of the surface covered by the various constituents.

the results are shown in Fig. 2. The first thing to notice is that the concentration of the promoters at the surface is far greater than in the bulk; thus when alkali is present the 0.42 per cent alumina covers 35 per cent of the surface, and it is now clear why alumina is a poison in terms of specific activity. Progressive additions of alkali are accompanied by a less than corresponding increase in the fraction of surface covered by alkali: this presumably means that the alkali is entering into the metallic phase, changing its electronic character perhaps through an effect on the Fermi level of the iron, and hence acting as an electronic promoter.[54]

Similar studies have also been made on the complex promoted cobalt catalysts used in the Fischer–Tropsch synthesis.[55] The addition of 6 parts of thoria and 12 parts of magnesia to a supported cobalt catalyst (100 cobalt: 200 kieselguhr) increases the surface area from 6.9 to 41.9 m.^{2} g.$^{-1}$: one, or more probably both, of these oxides are therefore structural promoters, but they also serve to reduce the porosity. Surface areas of other promoted but unsupported catalysts are given in the following Table: the promotional

TABLE VI. *Surface Areas of Promoted Cobalt Catalysts*[55]

Composition (parts by weight)			*Surface area (m.²g.⁻¹)*
Co	ThO_2	MgO	
100	6	—	14.6
100	—	12	35.2
100	6	12	52.8

effects are approximately additive. Kieselguhr-supported catalysts have the advantage of not shrinking on reduction, while magnesia is claimed to reduce the tendency of the tableted catalyst to crumble by acting as a "binder."

The literature records many other examples of cases where small amounts of a promoter (almost invariably a metal oxide not reducible by hydrogen) have greatly increased the activity of the major component, but since much of this work was done before accurate methods for surface area determination became available, it is generally uncertain whether structural or electronic promotion was being observed. For example, Medsforth showed in 1923[56] that the inclusion of relatively small amounts of irreducible oxides greatly increased the activity of pumice-supported nickel for carbon monoxide hydrogenation to methane. For ceria (Ce_2O_3), thoria, beryllia and alumina, the maximum increase in rate was by a factor of 16 to 20; this effect was achieved with 4 per cent ceria and with between 12 and 20 per cent of the others. The oxides Mo_2O_3 and V_2O_3 were much less effective. The especial promotional efficacy of thoria and alumina has since been amply confirmed (see Ref. 57 for example). Once again the need is felt for determinations of the physical properties of promoted metals.

It is now clear that the differentiation between carriers and promoters is somewhat vague and arbitrary. The best one can say is that a substance having some beneficial effect on the metallic phase of the catalyst is to be called a carrier if it is present to more than 50 per cent by weight and a promoter if less than 50 per cent. A given substance (e.g. alumina) may thus be both a carrier and a promoter, in both cases serving to stabilize the active metal surface against sintering; as we have seen, a promoter may even be a poison.

3.43 *Bifunctional Catalysts*

In bifunctional catalysts, the metal is supported on a second component which plays an important role in the overall reaction. Several metals, but particularly platinum, when supported on an acidic oxide such as silica–alumina or halogen-promoted alumina are very selective for the isomerization, cyclization and dehydrogenation of straight-chain paraffins. The metal aids the adsorption and desorption of the hydrocarbon: in the intervening period the adsorbed radicals migrate to the acidic oxide where on conversion to carbonium ions they are enabled to isomerize and cyclize. These catalysts have come to occupy a position of great prominence in the petroleum industry (see Chapter 19).

3.5 Direct Methods for the Examination of Metal Surfaces

We conclude this Chapter with a short review of methods which may be applied to the direct examination of metal surfaces of various kinds; methods based on physical or chemical adsorption are excluded. The points to be covered are summarized in Table VII.

The methods of electron and X-ray diffraction require little description. Since electrons have little penetrating power, the information obtained from electron diffraction refers solely to the surface. Characteristic diffraction patterns are shown by the arrays of surface atoms, and from these the nature of the exposed crystallographic planes[32, 35, 58] and interatomic spacings may be found. Surface impurities, such as a complete or partial oxide layer, are similarly detected and the cleaning treatment is continued until the relevant diffraction pattern has disappeared.[5, 6]

TABLE VII. *Techniques for the Study of Metal Surfaces*

Form of Metal	*Problems*	*Methods*
Massive	Cleanliness of surface. Exposed faces.	Electron and X-ray diffraction.
Microscopic	Particle-size distribution.	Low-angle X-ray scattering. Magnetic measurements. Electron microscopy and diffraction.

With solid particles of less than a certain critical size, the diffraction rings are not sharp, but are diffuse to a degree determined by the state of subdivision: the method of low-angle X-ray scattering uses this principle to estimate the *mean* particle size. This technique supplies only limited information about particle size *distribution*, but it corroborates the results obtained by electron microscopy, by which method the breadth of the distribution can be obtained by direct observation.[59, 60] Electron microscopic studies[16, 60] reveal in addition intimate details of the morphology of individual particles: studies on supported metal catalysts have tended rather to confirm expectation than to reveal unsuspected phenomena.

A further method of determining particle size distributions is the magnetic method, but this is restricted to materials which are ferromagnetic.[39, 61, 62, 63] The thermomagnetic curves (showing the dependence of relative magnetization on absolute temperature) for supported nickel catalysts show no sharply-defined Curie temperature, but rather a slow progressive decrease of magnetization with rising temperature.[62] Sintered catalysts behave more like massive nickel, so it is reasonable to associate the anomalous behaviour with particle-size effects. For very small particles, thermal motion progressively breaks down the co-operation between electron spins, and the Curie temperature is therefore a function of particle-size. A relation is now derived between particle diameter and the mean co-ordination number of nickel atoms in the particle: this will be less than the normal value of twelve to an extent depending on the fraction of the atoms which are present at the surface.[63] It is assumed that for any nickel particle having a mean co-ordination number of $\bar{z}$ its Curie temperature T will be given by

$$T/T_c = \bar{z}/12$$

where T_c is 631°K, and it is then possible to assign a diameter to a particle if its Curie temperature is known. It is now supposed that the slope of the thermomagnetic curve at any temperature is proportional to the weight fraction of nickel present in particles having a Curie point at that temperature: it is then easily possible to convert the thermomagnetic curve into a particle size distribution. This technique leads to good agreement with measurements made by X-ray scattering in the range where comparison is possible, but the magnetic method is the only one which is useful for particles below about 50 Å diameter.

Related techniques have been described. Mean particle-sizes have been deduced through the dependence of magnetization on field-strength[39, 64] and size distributions through the measurement of the coercive force at very low temperatures.[61] Unsintered nickel–silica[63] and Raney nickel[61] have been shown to have many very small particles and a number of much larger ones, there being a minimum in between. The magnetic method has been employed to study the effect of preparation conditions, period of reduction and sintering in particle size distributions.[63]

New physical methods are continually being applied to the investigation of supported catalysts. Studies have recently been made of the X-ray *K*-absorption edges in cobalt supported on alumina and on silica,[65] and of the electron-spin resonance exhibited by charcoal-supported platinum.[66]

References

1. A. T. Gwathmey and R. E. Cunningham, *Adv. Cataylsis* **10,** 57 (1958).
2. A. J. Crocker and A. J. B. Robertson, *Trans. Faraday Soc.* **54,** 931 (1958).
3. F. W. C. Boswell, *Proc. Phys. Soc.* **A54,** 465 (1951).
4. E. A. Owen, Y. H. Liu and D. P. Morris, *Phil. Mag.* **39**(7), 831 (1948).
5. H. E. Farnsworth and R. F. Woodcock, *Ind. Eng. Chem.* **49,** 258; (1957). *Adv. Catalysis* **9,** 123 (1957).
6. R. E. Schlier and H. E. Farnsworth, *Adv. Catalysis* **9,** 434 (1957); H. E. Farnsworth, R. E. Schlier, T. H. George and R. M. Burger, *J. Appl. Phys.* **29,** 1150 (1958).
7. H. M. C. Sosnovsky, *J. Chem. Phys.* **23,** 1486 (1948); *J. Phys. and Chem. Solids* **10,** 304 (1959).
8. G. C. Bond, *Trans. Faraday Soc.* **52,** 1235 (1956).
9. E. T. Goodwin, *Proc. Cambridge Phil. Soc.* **35,** 221 (1939).
10. T. B. Grimley, In "Chemisorption", edited by W. E. Garner (Butterworths, London, 1957), p. 17.
11. W. E. Garner, T. J. Gray and F. S. Stone, *Proc. Roy. Soc.* **A197,** 294 (1949).
12. A. Couper and D. D. Eley, *Discuss. Faraday Soc.* **8,** 172 (1950); D. A. Dowden and P. W. Reynolds, *Discuss. Faraday Soc.* **8,** 184 (1950).
13. W. G. Frankenburg, *J. Amer. Chem. Soc.* **66,** 1827 (1944).
14. M. W. Roberts and K. W. Sykes, *Trans. Faraday Soc.* **54,** 548 (1958).
15. J. H. Leck, In "Chemisorption", edited by W. E. Garner (Butterworths, London, 1957), p. 162.
16. J. Turkevich, P. C. Stevenson and J. Hillier, *Discuss. Faraday Soc.* **11,** 55 (1951).
17. M. Raney, USP **1,** 628, 190 (1927); *Ind. Eng. Chem.* **32,** 1199 (1940); E. Leiber and F. L. Morritz, *Adv. Catalysis* **5,** 417 (1953); H. Littmann and D. Dew-Hughes *Ind. Eng. Chem.* **51,** 662 (1959); M. Pilkuhn and A. Winsel, *Z. Elektrochem.* **63,** 1056 (1959); R. J. Kokes and P. H. Emmett, *J. Amer. Chem. Soc.* **81,** 5032 (1959); **82,** 4497 (1960); P. Mars, J. J. F. Scholten and P. Zwietering. Proc. 2nd International Congress on Catalysis (Editions Technip., Paris, 1961) **1,** 1245.
18. B. V. Aller, *J. Appl. Chem.* **8,** 163, 492 (1958).
19. L. Fauconau, *Bull. Soc. chim. France* **4,** 58, 63 (1937); J. A. Stanfield and P. E. Robbins, Proc. 2nd International Congress on Catalysis (Editions Technip., Paris, 1961) **2,** 2579.
20. T. Kwan, *Adv. Catalysis* **6,** 67 (1954).
21. G. C. Bond and R. S. Mann, *J. Chem. Soc.*, 4738 (1958).
22. R. J. Best and W. W. Russell, *J. Amer. Chem. Soc.* **76,** 838 (1954).
23. W. K. Hall and P. H. Emmett, *J. Phys. Chem.* **62,** 816 (1958).

24. P. H. Emmett and N. Skau, *J. Amer. Chem. Soc.* **65,** 1029 (1943).
25. C. Moreau and G. Rodier, *Compt. rend.* **246,** 1861 (1958).
26. L. J. Baker and R. B. Bernstein, *J. Amer. Chem. Soc.* **73,** 4434 (1951).
27. J. H. Long, J. C. W. Frazer and E. Ott, *J. Amer. Chem. Soc.* **56,** 1101 (1934).
28. F. Lihl, H. Wagner and P. Zemsch, *Z. Elektrochem.* **56,** 612, 619 (1952).
29. G. C. Bond and R. S. Mann, *J. Chem. Soc.* 3566 (1959).
30. W. K. Hall and L. Alexander, *J. Phys. Chem.* **61,** 242 (1957).
31. G. I. Finch, *Proc. Roy. Soc.* **A141,** 414 (1933).
32. O. Beeck, A. E. Smith and A. Wheeler, *Proc. Roy. Soc.* **A177,** 62 (1941).
33. B. M. W. Trapnell, *Proc. Roy. Soc.* **A217,** 566 (1953); M. W. Roberts and F. C. Tompkins, *Proc. Roy. Soc.* **A251,** 369 (1959).
34. B. M. W. Trapnell, *Trans. Faraday Soc.* **51,** 368 (1955); D. F. Klemperer and F. S. Stone, *Proc. Roy. Soc.* **A243,** 375 (1957).
35. W. M. H. Sachtler, G. J. H. Dorgelo and W. van der Knapp, *J. Chim. phys.* **51,** 491 (1954).
36. O. Beeck and A. W. Ritchie, *Discuss. Faraday Soc.* **8,** 159 (1950).
37. R. Uyeda, *Proc. Phys. Math. Soc., Japan* **22,** 1023 (1940); **24,** 809 (1942); Y. Kainuma, *J. Phys. Soc. Japan* **6,** 135 (1951); S. Ogawa, D. Watanabe and F. E. Fujita, *Ibid.* **10,** 429 (1955).
38. (*a*) P. Michel, *Ann. Physique* **1**[13], 719 (1956); (*b*) M. K. Gharpurey and P. H. Emmett, *J. Phys. Chem.* **65,** 1182 (1961).
39. G. C. A. Schuit and L. L. van Reijen, *Adv. Catalysis* **10,** 243 (1958).
40. J. J. de Lange and G. H. Visser, *Ingenieur* (*Utrecht*) **58,** 24 (1946).
41. J. J. B. van Eijk van Voorthuysen and P. Franzen, *Rec. Trav. chim.* **70,** 793 (1951).
42. K. W. McHenry, R. J. Bertolacini, H. M. Brennan, J. L. Wilson and H. S. Seelig, Proc. 2nd International Congress on Catalysis (Editions Technip., Paris, 1961) **2,** 2295.
43. S. F. Adler and J. J. Kearney, *J. Phys. Chem.* **64,** 208 (1960).
44. G. A. Mills, S. Weller and E. B. Cornelius, Proc. 2nd International Congress on Catalysis (Editions Technip., Paris, 1961) **2,** 2221.
45. L. Spenadel and M. Boudart, *J. Phys. Chem.* **64,** 204 (1960).
46. E. B. Maxted and S. Akhtar, *J. Chem. Soc.*, 1995 (1960).
47. Z. G. Szabo, F. Solymosi and I. Batta, *Z. phys. Chem* (*Frankfurt*) **23,** 56 (1960); Proc. 2nd International Congress on Catalysis (Editions Technip., Paris, 1961) **2,** 1627.
48. G-M. Schwab, J. Block, W. Muller and D. Schultze, *Naturwiss.* **44,** 582 (1957).
49. I. E. Adadurov, I. I. Rivlin and N. M. Kovalev, *J. Phys. Chem.* (*U.S.S.R.*) **8,** 147 (1936).
50. R. H. Griffith, *Trans. Faraday Soc.* **33,** 412 (1937).
51. A. Mittasch, *Adv. Catalysis* **2,** 81 (1950).
52. P. H. Emmett and S. Brunauer, *J. Amer. Chem. Soc.* **62,** 1732 (1940).
53. P. H. Emmett and S. Brunauer, *J. Amer. Chem. Soc.* **59,** 1553 (1937).
54. W. G. Frankenburg and C. Bokhoven and C. van Heerden, R. Westrik and P. Zwietering, In "Catalysis" **3,** edited by P. H. Emmett (Reinhold, New York 1955, pp. 171, 265).
55. R. B. Anderson, W. K. Hall and L. J. E. Hofer, *J. Amer. Chem. Soc.* **70,** 2465 (1948).
56. S. Medsforth, *J. Chem. Soc.* **123,** 1452 (1923).
57. H. Bruckner and G. Jacobus, *Brennstoff-Chem.* **14,** 265 (1933).
58. R. L. Moss and I. Woodward, *Acta Cryst.* **12,** 255 (1959).
59. A. Guinier, *Discuss. Faraday Soc.* **8,** 344 (1950).
60. J. Turkevich, H. H. Hubbell and J. Hillier, *Discuss. Faraday Soc.* **8,** 348 (1950).
61. L. Weil, *J. Chim. phys.* **51,** 715 (1954).
62. P. W. Selwood, *Adv. Catalysis* **9,** 93 (1957).
63. P. W. Selwood, S. F. Adler and T. R. Phillips, *J. Amer. Chem. Soc.* **77,** 1462 (1955).
64. W. Henkelom, J. J. Broeder and L. L. van Reijen, *J. Chim. phys* **51,** 474 (1954).
65. R. O. Keeling, *J. Chem. Phys.* **31,** 279 (1959).
66. C. S. Nicholau, H. G. Thom and E. Pobitschka, *Trans. Faraday Soc.* **55,** 1430 (1959).

Chapter 4

Adsorption at Metal Surfaces: Introduction and Experimental Methods

4.1 Types of Adsorption[1, 2]

In Chapter 1 it was stated that the free valencies which exist at the surface of metals become saturated or partly saturated during the act of adsorption. It is now necessary to discuss the possible types of adsorption in detail.

The consensus of a very great deal of experimental work over the last four decades is that there are two quite distinct types of adsorption. In the first type, termed *physical adsorption* or van der Waals adsorption (or sometimes unfortunately physisorption) the adsorbed molecule is held to the surface by weak van der Waals or dispersion forces, of the type responsible for cohesion in liquids where there is no hydrogen bonding: in physical adsorption therefore free valencies are not satisfied and the surface energy is not reduced by as much as is possible. In the second type, termed chemical adsorption or *chemisorption*, there is a chemical reaction between the molecule being adsorbed and the metal surface, and this can ultimately lead to the complete satisfaction of the surface valencies. There is no doubt that of the two the latter is of vastly greater relevance to catalysis, and it will therefore occupy a correspondingly more prominent place in this chapter.

There is of course a third process which may occur between a metal and a gas, and this is *absorption* (or solution or occlusion): here molecules of the gas penetrate the surface and occupy positions in the interstices between metals atoms in the bulk, sometimes causing an expansion of the lattice. It is useful to have available criteria for distinguishing between absorption and the two types of adsorption.

The necessary criteria are best understood in terms of a diagram (Fig. 1) showing the variation of potential energy with distance from the surface (in either direction) for the interaction of a diatomic molecule A_2 with a metal M.

This type of diagram was first used by Lennard-Jones in 1932.[3] The chemisorption process can be formulated as

$$\begin{array}{c}A\text{—}A\\ |\qquad|\\ \text{—}M\text{—}M\text{—}\\ |\qquad|\end{array} \rightarrow \begin{array}{c}A\qquad A\\ |\qquad|\\ \text{—}M\text{—}M\text{—}\\ |\qquad|\end{array} \qquad \text{(a)}$$

The potential energy curve for physical adsorption (*P*) shows a broad and shallow minimum at a distance d_P from the surface: the distance between the zero of potential energy and the ground vibrational level, $-\Delta H_P$, is the heat of physical adsorption, and in consequence of the nature of the forces involved its value is usually found to be about the same as the heat of liquefaction of the gas concerned. The distance d_P is approximately the sum of the covalent radii of the metal and A plus the additional thicknesses of the two van der Waals envelopes: it is thus commonly between 3 and 4 Å. It will be noted that there is no potential barrier to physical adsorption which may therefore be expected to be observed at the lowest temperatures. Physical adsorption is impossible much above the critical temperature of the gas, and

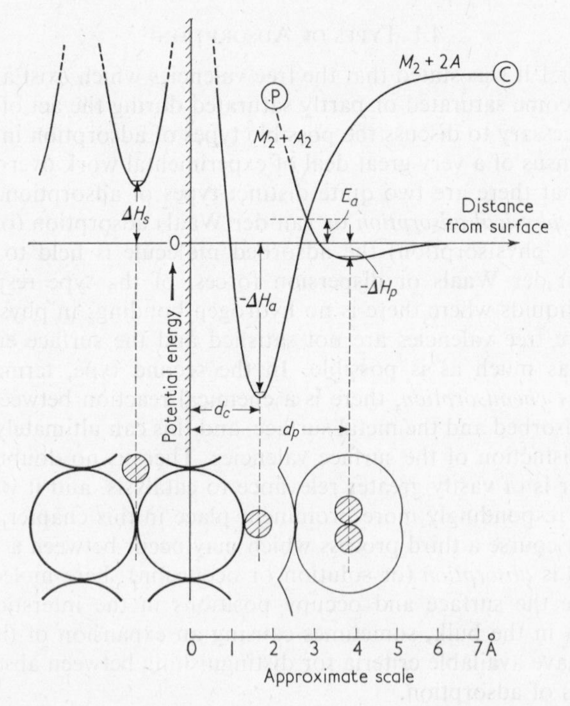

FIG. 1. Potential energy curves for the possible consequences of the interaction of a diatomic molecule A_2 with a metal surface: the lower part of the diagram gives an approximate physical picture of the processes.

is unlikely to be of significance at temperatures much above its boiling point. The kinetics of physical adsorption are virtually inaccessible.

Physical adsorption is non-specific, in the sense that a molecule or atom in this state is not bound to any particular surface metal atom. It occupies an area of the surface depending on its size, from which with a knowledge of the monolayer volume the surface area may be estimated by the well-known procedure of Brunauer, Emmett and Teller.[4] Physically adsorbed molecules and atoms possess a two-dimensional mobility somewhat less than their mobility in the liquid state at the same temperature.

The corresponding curve for chemisorption (C) is characterized by a deep and narrow minimum quite close to the surface, which has been defined here by the line through the centres of the nuclei of atoms in the surface layer. The depth of the trough to the ground vibrational state is a measure of $-\Delta H_a$, the heat of chemisorption, which in the case of a dissociating molecule is to be expressed per mole of the undissociated gas. If the atoms of A reside on surface metal atoms in the manner shown, the minimum is distant from the surface simply by the sum of the covalent radii which is typically between 1.5 and 3 Å. As the distance from the surface is increased, the curve becomes asymptotic to a line a distance D above the potential energy zero; D is the dissociation energy of the molecule A_2 into atoms.

The curves intersect a distance E_a above the energy zero; E_a represents a potential barrier to chemisorption and is thus the activation energy of chemisorption. It is the minimum energy which a physically adsorbed or gaseous molecule must acquire in order to be chemisorbed. It is readily seen that the magnitude of this activation energy is determined by the shape of the potential energy curves and especially by the relative distances of their minima from the surface[2] (Fig. 2); it may in principle have any value between zero and D.

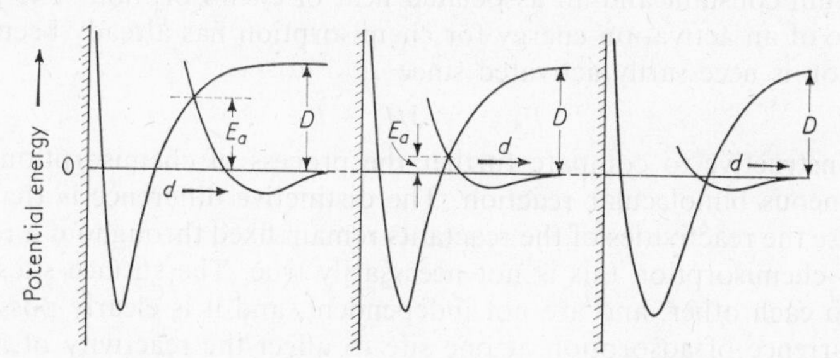

FIG. 2. The dependence of the activation energy for chemisorption on the shapes and positions of the relevant potential energy curves.

Little need be said concerning the interpretation of absorption on this basis, since its relevance to surface catalysis is probably limited. Within the bulk, potential energy minima will be found at intervals determined by the periodicity of the lattice, and these minima will be above the energy zero if the absorption is endothermic and vice versa. The process of diffusion within the bulk will be activated as will the initial transition from adsorption to absorption.[2]

Table I summarizes possible means of distinguishing between the two types of adsorption and absorption, from considerations largely based on Fig. 1. However, it should be stressed that neither any one criterion nor any combination of criteria is invariably satisfactory in practice.

TABLE I. *Criteria for Distinguishing between Physical Adsorption, Chemisorption and Absorption*

Criterion	*Chemisorption*	*Physical adsorption*	*Absorption*
Heat of reaction (kcal. mole^{-1})	Generally 10 to 150	2 to 5	Generally endothermic
Activation energy	Usually small	Zero	?
Temperature at which process occurs	Dependent on *E*, but usually low	Low	Generally high
Number of layers adsorbed	$\not> 1$	>1 Possible	—

The process of chemisorption is in many respects similar to a normal chemical reaction, although it possesses some features not shared by homogeneous reactions. It has been found possible to set up expressions for the rates of adsorption and desorption (see Chapter 6): since the rates of these opposing processes become equal at equilibrium, the system will have an equilibrium constant and an associated heat of chemisorption. The possible existence of an activation energy for chemisorption has already been noted; desorption is necessarily activated since

$$E_d = -\Delta H_a + E_a. \tag{1}$$

It is instructive to compare further the process of chemisorption with a homogeneous bimolecular reaction. The distinctive difference is that in the latter case the reactivities of the reactants remain fixed throughout a reaction, while in chemisorption this is not necessarily true. The surface sites are all linked to each other, and are not independent, and it is clearly possible for the occurrence of adsorption at one site to affect the reactivity of a neighbouring or even a distant site. Evidence in support of this view will be presented in due course: but it is well to be forewarned that there may be no unique value for any of the parameters describing a given adsorption process, and that their values may be a function of the extent to which the reaction has already proceeded.

An important consideration in discussing the reactions of adsorbed species is whether or not they are mobile at a given temperature.[1, 5] By this is meant, whether an atom or radical remains for the full period of its residence time on the site to which it first became attached on adsorption, or whether it is able to migrate from one site to another. In moving to another site, the adsorbed particle has to surmount a potential energy barrier: the height of this barrier is the activation energy for migration and is proportional to the strength of adsorption. This activation energy is normally less than the activation energy for desorption, since migration does not involve a *complete* breaking of the adsorption bond. The situation for a uniform surface is shown in Fig. 3. The question of mobility is simply determined by whether or not the adsorbed particle has sufficient energy to overcome successive barriers. We may therefore expect in general to find immobile layers at low temperatures, becoming mobile at some higher temperature depending on the intimate details of the system. Statistical calculation shows[6] that for a diatomic molecule dissociating into atoms occupying adjacent sites in an immobile layer, some 8 per cent of the sites will remain unoccupied at "complete" coverage; these exist as single sites, adjacent *pairs* only being able to act in adsorption. These single unoccupied sites, which would of course coalesce

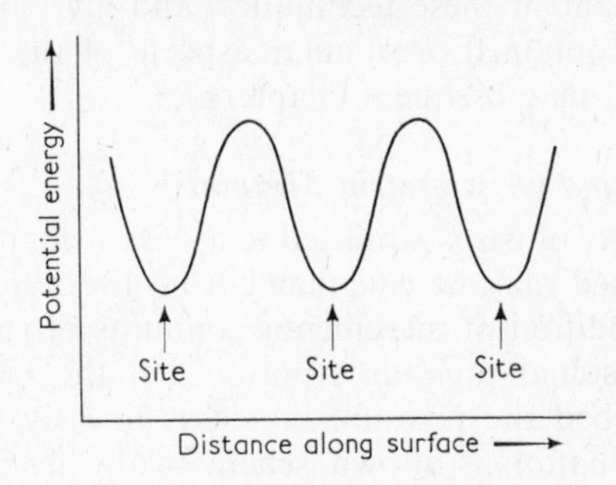

FIG. 3. Potential energy barriers which inhibit the migration of surface species.

if the layer were mobile, have been attributed a select role in certain catalytic processes. Species attached to the surface at two points would be expected to be less mobile than those adsorbed at only one point.

4.2 EXPERIMENTAL METHODS

4.21 The Information Required

Experimental studies of adsorption are directed towards providing information which will lead to as complete as possible a description of the process and of the adsorbed state. We may, therefore, now summarize the principal kinds of information needed, excluding for the moment any consideration of the rate at which equilibrium is set up.

(i) The first question is purely qualitative: does a given substance chemisorb on a given metal under standard conditions (say 20° and 10^{-2} mm. equilibrium pressure) or not?

(ii) What further criteria may be used to differentiate satisfactorily between chemisorption, physical adsorption and solution?

(iii) What is the stoichiometry of a chemisorption process, viz. with how many surface sites does one molecule react? Into what fragments (if any) does the molecule dissociate and how exactly are these located with reference to individual surface metal atoms? Are the molecules or their fragments mobile and what is the nature of the bond holding them to the surface?

(iv) What are the numerical values of the parameters describing the state of equilibrium in a particular system? How does the fraction of surface covered depend on pressure at constant temperature? What is the value of the equilibrium constant, and how does it vary with temperature? What therefore is the heat of adsorption, what the free energy of adsorption and are these independent of the fraction of surface covered?

(v) Is any given metal surface energetically homogeneous or not, viz. is the heat of adsorption the same at all points on the surface?

Although a wide variety of physical techniques has been applied to answering these questions, for few systems is the information now available nearly as complete as is desirable. We will now quickly review the principles of the more important of these techniques, and give some indication as to the kind of results obtained. Particular aspects of the results will then be more fully discussed in subsequent chapters.

4.22 Volumetric and Gravimetric Methods[1]

If a known quantity of gas is admitted to a system containing an adsorbent, the quantity adsorbed may be calculated from the residual gas pressure at equilibrium. The addition of incremental amounts of gas will result in progressively larger residual pressures, until when the maximum amount of gas has been adsorbed the pressure increases linearly with the amount of added gas. This situation is shown schematically in Fig. 4(a), where the quantities of gas are expressed as numbers of molecules; n_g is the number in

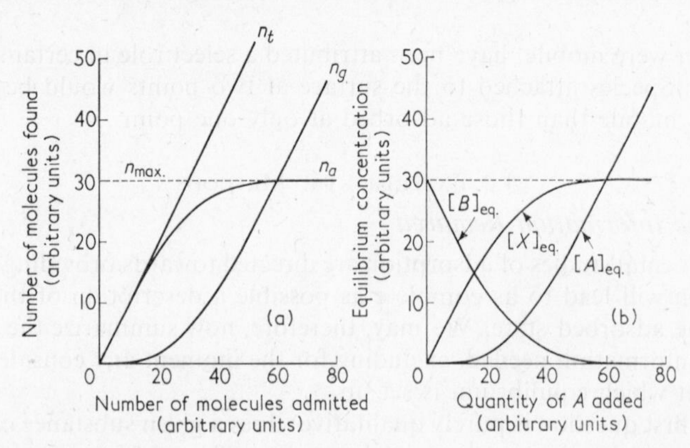

FIG. 4. (a) The dependence of n_t, n_g and n_a on the number of molecules admitted to an adsorption system.

(b) The variation of equilibrium concentrations on the quantity of A added to a homogeneous equilibrium.

the gas phase (estimated from the residual pressure and the free volume of the system), n_a the number adsorbed (equal to the total number admitted, n_t, less n_g) and n_{max} the total number of molecules which can be adsorbed. A formally analogous system is a homogeneous equilibrium

$$A + B \rightleftharpoons X, \qquad (b)$$

where the concentration of B (equivalent to the maximum number of adsorbed molecules) is kept constant, and the concentration of A (equivalent to the gas to be adsorbed) is varied: in this case the equilibrium concentration of X will vary with the quantity of A added to the system as shown in Fig. 4(b).

The relationship between the volume of gas adsorbed and the equilibrium gas pressure P at constant temperature is termed an *adsorption isotherm.* It may be derived from Fig. 4(a) by plotting n_a/n_{max} (which is θ, the fraction of surface covered) against n_g (Fig. 5): a chemisorption isotherm normally has this form, although other forms are possible for physical adsorption[1] where capillary condensation and multilayer formation may occur. The isotherm is

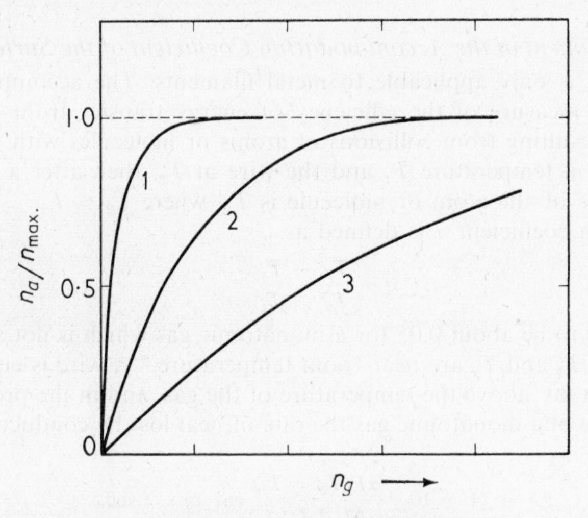

FIG. 5. Adsorption isotherms.

characterized by θ being proportional to P at low pressures and independent of P at high pressures. The "strength of adsorption" is a useful qualitative concept. The greater the strength of adsorption, the greater the degree of coverage at any pressure and the smaller the pressure required to effect complete coverage. The three isotherms in Fig. 5 qualitatively represent strong (1), medium (2) and weak (3) adsorption. Where the adsorption is non-activated, the equilibrium will shift towards the desorbed side with increasing temperature, since the process is exothermic. The adsorption will therefore weaken, so that the three isotherms in Fig. 5 might equally well represent qualitatively adsorption at low (1), medium (2) and high (3) temperatures. If the equilibrium constant for the adsorption is measured at a series of temperatures, application of the van't Hoff isochore yields a heat of adsorption: this point will be reverted to subsequently.

The experimental methods and difficulties are well-described elsewhere.[1] The technique employed depends on the magnitude of the quantity of gas likely to be adsorbed; this may be large for powders (up to 100 cm.^{3}), smaller for films ($\sim$0.1 cm.^{3}) and very small for filaments ($\sim 10^{-5}$ cm.^{3}). The volumetric procedure is fundamental to any adsorption study, and is frequently used in conjunction with other methods.

Equivalent information is obtained by gravimetric estimation of quantities of adsorbed gas;[1] it sometimes permits measurements to be made to higher pressures than are possible in volumetric work. The weights of gas involved are of course very small and sensitive methods are required. The simplest method is to measure the extension of a quartz spiral to which the sample of adsorbent is attached; buoyancy corrections must be applied. Suitably designed microbalances[7] are more sensitive, and buoyancy corrections may be eliminated.

4.23 *Measurement of the Accommodation Coefficient of the Surface* [1, 5, 8]

This method is only applicable to metal filaments. The accommodation coefficient is a measure of the efficiency of energy transfer from a heated wire to a gas resulting from collisions of atoms or molecules with the wire. If the gas is at a temperature T_1 and the wire at T_2, then after a collision the temperature of the atom or molecule is T_2' where $T_2 > T_2' > T_1$. The accommodation coefficient α is defined as

$$\alpha = \frac{T_2' - T_1}{T_2 - T_1} \tag{2}$$

and is expected to be about 0.05 for a monatomic gas which is not adsorbed by the metal if T_1 and T_2 are near room temperature.[9] A wire is electrically heated to about 20° above the temperature of the gas, and in the presence of a small pressure of a monatomic gas the rate of heat loss by conduction from the wire to the gas is

$$\dot{q} = 1.74 \times 10^{-4} \frac{\alpha P(T_2 - T_1)}{M^{1/2}\, T_1^{1/2}} \text{ cal. cm.}^{-2} \text{ sec.}^{-1}, \tag{3}$$

where P is the gas pressure and M its molecular weight: $\dot{q}$ is obtained from the energy required to maintain the wire at T_2 by electrical heating, and hence α may be calculated. Its value has been found to depend on the degree of coverage of the wire surface by adsorbed gas, and it may thus be used to determine the coverage. The method is limited to systems showing strong adsorption since an appreciable equilibrium pressure of a second gas would vitiate the results. It is particularly valuable for measuring the rates of fast irreversible adsorptions.

4.24 *The Calorimetric Determination of Heats of Adsorption*[1]

Heats of reactions may be determined calorimetrically using either isothermal or adiabatic procedures: the former is only suitable when sufficient heat is liberated to melt an appreciable quantity of the calorimetric fluid, and therefore its application is restricted to metal powders. Mercury, water, phenol and diphenyl ether have been used as the fluid. The adiabatic procedure is obligatory for films and filaments. Here the heat liberated is contained, and the resulting temperature rise is recorded; if the heat capacity of the system is known, the heat liberated can be estimated, and it is usual to try to keep the heat capacity as low as possible, to ensure a readily measurable temperature rise. Alternatively the system may be calibrated by means of electrical heating. The heat liberated by adsorption on a metal wire is readily measured by using the wire as a resistance thermometer.

It was discovered at an early stage and since repeated confirmed that the heat of adsorption usually decreases markedly with the fraction of the surface already covered by the gas. This decrease often follows one of the three basic forms shown in Fig. 6, although combinations of these basic forms are also encountered. Only occasionally is the heat independent of coverage over any considerable range. When the successive increments of gas added are

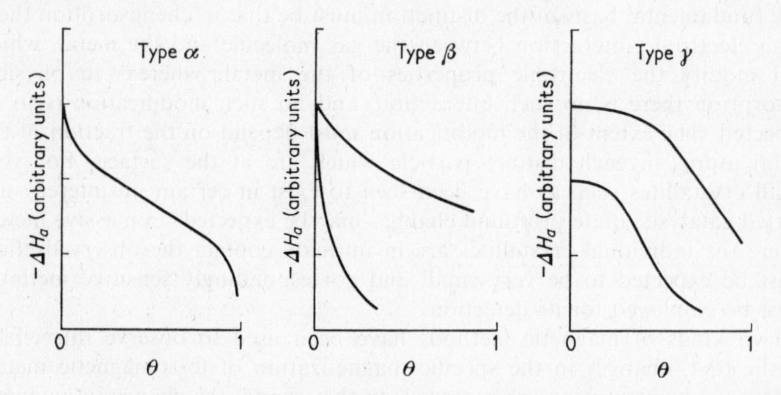

FIG. 6. Possible forms for the variation of heat of adsorption with surface coverage.

sufficiently small, the heat of adsorption within the narrow range $\theta \pm d\theta$ is termed a *differential* heat of adsorption. It is now necessary to consider the relationship between this heat, and that obtained by applying the van't Hoff isochore to the pressures required to give a fixed coverage at a series of temperatures. In this last case

$$\left(\frac{d \ln P}{dT}\right)_\theta = \frac{\Delta H_{a,i}}{RT^2}, \tag{4}$$

where $-\Delta H_{a,i}$ is termed the *isosteric* heat of adsorption. The *true differential* heat of adsorption is only obtained if no external work is done during the adsorption. The isosteric and true differential heats then differ by RT, viz.

$$-\Delta H_{a,i} = -\Delta H_{a,d} + RT, \tag{5}$$

RT being the maximum work done in adsorbing one mole of ideal gas. It is uncertain what fraction of the work done in adsorption is actually transferred to the calorimeter as heat, but the calorimetrically determined heat must lie between $-\Delta H_{a,i}$ and $-\Delta H_{a,d}$. However, since at room temperature RT is only about 600 cal. mole^{-1}, which is well within the uncertainty of the experimental measurements, it is usual to disregard any possible differences between the calorimetric and isosteric heats.

The possible causes of the decrease in heat of adsorption with coverage will be discussed later.

4.25 Magnetic Methods of Following Adsorption[5, 10]

We turn now to the first of a group of recently developed physical methods which have proved to be of great value in determining properties in the absorbed state. Of the experimental methods so far discussed, neither the volumetric–gravimetric nor the calorimetric method at once distinguishes between chemisorption and physical adsorption; the accommodation coefficient method was applicable only to cases of very strong adsorption. The fundamental basis of the distinction must be that in chemisorption there is an electronic interaction between the gas molecule and the metal, which will modify the electronic properties of the metal, whereas in physical adsorption there is no such interaction, and no such modification is to be expected. The extent of the modification must depend on the fraction of the metal atoms in each distinct particle which are at the surface. For very small crystallites such as have been seen to exist in certain unsintered supported catalysts, quite profound changes may be expected: in massive metals where the individual crystallites are in intimate contact the observed effect must be expected to be very small and correspondingly sensitive methods must be employed for its detection.

Two kinds of magnetic methods have been used to observe this effect. In the first, changes in the specific magnetization of ferromagnetic metals following chemisorption are recorded; in the second, the change in magnetic susceptibility of paramagnetic metals following chemisorption is observed. Of the two methods, the first is clearly limited in scope, but the apparatus required is relatively simple; the second has wider possibilities but the experimental technique is exacting.

It has been found that the adsorption of hydrogen on a nickel–silica catalyst leads to a loss of specific magnetization:[11, 12] simultaneous volumetric measurement of the amount of gas adsorbed shows the decrease to be linear with adsorbed volume. The interpretation of the results is complicated by the particle-size distribution. Very small nickel particles are not ferromagnetic at room temperature, and in for example co-precipitated nickel–silica some 10 per cent of the nickel is in non-ferromagnetic particles. These particles of course adsorb hydrogen, but no change in magnetization is detected: no correlation between adsorbed volume and magnetization change is possible unless the number of particles which are ferromagnetic at the temperature of measurement is known. The only valid method for obtaining the number of electrons gained by the nickel per hydrogen atom adsorbed is to find by extrapolation the saturation moments at 0°K in the presence and absence of the gas. This number has been estimated to be about 0.76.[13]

The rapid admission of hydrogen to a supported nickel catalyst gives rise to magnetization changes which vary with time as shown in Fig. 7; the subsequent increase following the initial rapid drop is a "thermal transient" caused by the heat of adsorption, and this observation forms the basis of a further method for obtaining heats of adsorption.[14, 15] In this way it has

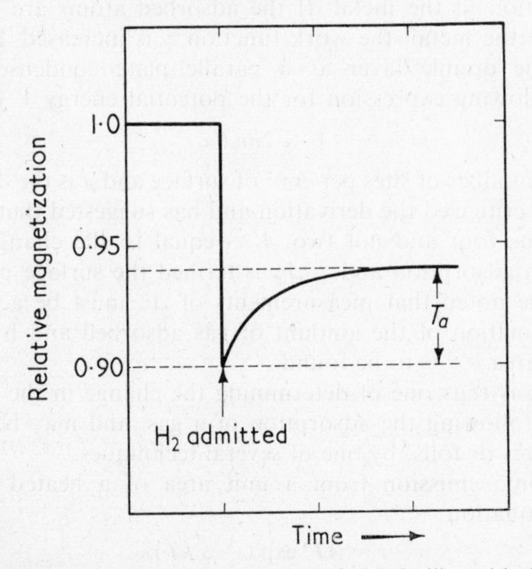

FIG. 7. The change in the relative magnetization of nickel–silica with time, following the adsorption of hydrogen: T_a is the "thermal transient".[14, 15]

been found that although chemisorption (as indicated by loss in magnetization) continues in the range 100–760 mm. and indeed even at superatmospheric pressures,[15] the heat of adsorption (as indicated by thermal transients) is very low above 100 mm.

The method has been extended to hydrocarbons [16, 17, 18] and it has enabled estimates to be made of the number of bonds formed between the adsorbed hydrocarbon and the metal under various conditions. Contradictory results have been obtained with oxygen.[11, 12]

Changes in magnetic susceptibility have also been observed following the adsorption of hydrogen and oxygen on platinum[19] and of dimethyl sulphide on palladium.[20]

4.26 Methods based on the Change in the Work Function of the Surface[1, 2, 5]

Adsorbed atoms will not normally have the same electronegativity as the atoms of the metal, and the bond joining the atoms to the surface will therefore be polarized in the appropriate sense. The moment of the dipole thus created will be small if the electronegativity difference is small, and the bond is then described as essentially covalent: if the electronegativity difference is large, the dipole moment will be correspondingly large and the bond is then essentially ionic. The determination of the dipole moment of a chemisorption bond can therefore establish its nature. An array of dipoles on a surface constitutes an electrical double layer which alters the potential barrier over which an electron leaving the metal must pass, that is, it alters the work function of the metal. If the adsorbed atoms are electronegative with respect to the metal, the work function φ is increased, and vice versa. By treating the double layer as a parallel-plate condenser, Langmuir[21] derived the following expression for the potential energy V of the layer:

$$V = 2\pi n_s \theta \mu, \qquad (6)$$

where n_s is the number of sites per cm.^{2} of surface and μ is the dipole moment. Mignolet[22] has criticized the derivation and has suggested that the numerical factor should be four and not two. V is equal to the change in the work function $\Delta\varphi$ on adsorption and $-\Delta\varphi$ is termed the surface potential of the layer. It will be noted that measurements of $\Delta\varphi$ must be accompanied by volumetric estimation of the amount of gas adsorbed and by a knowledge of the surface area if θ is to be found.

The problem is thus one of determining the change in the work function of the surface following the adsorption of a gas, and may be solved, using metal films, wires or foils, by one of several techniques.[1, 5, 23]

The thermionic emission from a unit area of a heated metal follows Richardson's equation:

$$i = AT^2 \exp(-\varphi/\boldsymbol{k}T), \qquad (7)$$

where i is the electron emission current, $\boldsymbol{k}$ Boltzmann's constant and A is a universal constant: φ is obtained from the variation of i with temperature. Unfortunately the temperatures required to obtain measurable emission with typical surfaces ($\varphi \simeq$ 4–5 eV.) are so large that the adsorbed layer is often destroyed; however, in the case of alkali metals adsorbed on tungsten the required temperatures are only ~150°, but this system has little relevance to catalytic problems.

More widely applicable is the photoelectric method.[24, 25] The electron emission current from a metal illuminated with radiation of suitable frequency obeys the relation

$$i = \kappa(\nu - \nu_0), \qquad (8)$$

where $h\nu_0$ is the work function (h being Planck's constant), ν the frequency of the radiation and κ a constant. No high temperatures which might destroy an adsorbed layer are necessary, but the method cannot be applied when $\varphi > 5$ eV. where the necessary radiation is in the far ultra-violet. The technique is suitable for measuring rates of adsorption and desorption, and gives good agreement with the thermionic method when the electron energy distribution in the metal is taken into account.

The contact potential method has also been widely applied. If two metals having different work functions are in contact at the same temperature, their electron emissivities as given by Richardson's equation will also differ, and the system can only attain equilibrium if there is a force driving electrons from one metal to the other at the point of contact: this force is the contact potential difference ΔV, and it is related to the work functions of the metals by the expression

$$\Delta V = \frac{\varphi_1 - \varphi_2}{e}, \tag{9}$$

where e is the electronic charge. If the change in the contact potential difference which results when one of the metals is covered by adsorbed gas (the other being maintained as the reference electrode) is $\delta\Delta V$, then

$$e\delta\Delta V = \Delta\varphi. \tag{10}$$

Several kinds of experimental technique for measuring $\delta\Delta V$ have been described,[1, 5, 23, 26–29] but the results obtained are sometimes discordant. However, this method is the only one with which measurements of the surface potentials of Group O gases physically adsorbed on metal surfaces have been determined.

An important application of changes in work function following adsorption is the field emission microscope.[1, 5, 30] If electrons emitted from a very sharp metallic point are allowed to impinge on a surrounding hemispherical fluorescent screen, the resulting pattern is a magnified image of the electron emission from the point, provided the electrons travel in straight lines. Now the work function of a metal varies from one crystallographic plane to another and is generally greatest for planes of highest density; since the intensity of fluorescence at the screen is proportional to the number of electrons arriving in unit time, planes of low work function are revealed as bright areas on the screen, and vice versa. By applying a potential of several thousand volts between the point and the screen, electron emission can be initiated at room temperature when the potential at the surface of the point v is large enough: v is equal to Vr_1/r_2 where V is the applied potential, and r_1 and r_2 are respectively the radii of the hemispherical screen and the point. Changes in the work functions of the various crystal faces when a gas is admitted can then be followed visually. Not only is it then possible to establish whether an electronegative or electropositive film is formed on any face, but also the relative rates of adsorption on different faces can be measured: rates of migration, and, on heating the metal point, rates of desorption can also be studied. The recently introduced ion emission microscope[31] has much greater resolution, enabling the electron emission from individual atoms to be observed.

4.27 Changes in Electrical Conductivity of the Metal[32]

We turn now to the last of the methods based on changes in the electrical properties of a metal due to chemisorption at its surface. Like the measurement of magnetic properties but unlike measurements of work function, the present method offers a certain criterion for distinguishing between chemisorption and physical adsorption. If on adsorption an electronegative layer is formed, electrons are withdrawn from the metal and the conductivity decreases, and vice versa. The method has been applied to films, wires and foils, and a determination of the change in electrical conductivity following adsorption of a gas therefore establishes the direction of the surface dipole. Some confusion has existed because contradictory results have been obtained, particularly for metal–hydrogen systems, which are usually found to exhibit a negative surface potential.[8, 26, 33, 34] However positive values have been found for hydrogen on platinum foil.[34, 35, 36] Hydrogen on aged nickel films causes a related increase in conductivity,[37] while fresh nickel films show the opposite effect.[38] The contradictions have been resolved[39, 40] and it appears that the initial cleanliness of the surface is critical. Negative surface potentials and conductivity decreases are found when nickel films are prepared under rigorous vacuum conditions, the adsorption proceeding instantaneously. Opposite effects result when "poor" (10^{-6} mm. Hg) vacuum conditions are employed and are to be attributed to initial contamination of the surface; under these conditions the rate of adsorption is measurable.

The conductivity method is more sensitive than volumetric measurements where the adsorption is marginal: thus the adsorption of hydrogen and carbon monoxide on bismuth films is detected by the former[41] but not by the latter[42] procedure.

4.28 The Infra-red Spectra of Chemisorbed Species[5, 43, 44]

The examination of chemisorbed gases by means of infra-red absorption spectroscopy offers a very direct means of obtaining information on the structure of the adsorbed species. Most of the experimental work to date has been carried out on supported metals: inert, non-porous forms of silica and alumina have been used as carriers, with particle sizes desirably in the range 150–200 Å to reduce radiation loss by scattering. Metal particles are preferably in the range 50–100 Å to minimize radiation loss by absorption. The supported metal is then laid on a fluorite plate and is surrounded by a small quartz furnace, the whole being contained in a cell having fluorite windows and connections for passing gas streams. High-temperature reduction with hydrogen is then possible, and after evacuation and the measurement of the background spectrum (caused by interatomic vibrations in the support), the gas under study is admitted, the non-adsorbed gas pumped off, and the spectrum redetermined. The method has been applied to the adsorption of various hydrocarbons,[45] and to carbon monoxide, nitric oxide and formic acid on several different metals.[46–52] Bands due to hydrogen and deuterium chemisorbed on supported platinum have also been detected.[53] The technique permits the investigation of surface species under reaction conditions, and thus gives information of direct value to mechanistic considerations.

Several methods for obtaining corresponding results with unsupported metals have been tried.[43] Dispersion of a metal "black" in an alkali halide, followed by compression into a disk, has been successfully used, as have also evaporated films. Attempts to study the infra-red spectra of adsorbed species in emission rather than absorption have had only limited success, but reflection spectra (including that of hydrogen on a rhodium film) have been obtained.[43, 54]

4.29 Other Methods

The technique of gas-solid chromatography has been applied to the study of chemisorption at metal surfaces. If the gas to be studied is driven through a column packed with a supported metal, the time the gas remains in the column will be determined by the equilibrium partial pressure in the gas phase, in the sense that the stronger the adsorption, the smaller the equilibrium partial pressure and the slower its rate of progress through the column.

The method has already yielded qualitative information of this type,[55, 56] and should be capable of providing integral heats of adsorption when the temperature-dependence of the retention time is measured.

The lifetime of adsorbed hydrogen has been measured by directing a molecular beam of hydrogen at a spinning nickel disk, the hydrogen evaporating from the surface at different times after deposition being collected and measured mass-spectrometrically.[57]

Electron diffraction was noted in Chapter 3 as one of the techniques which gives a quite direct indication of the state of cleanliness of metal surfaces,[58] but since the original experiments[59] (which have of course assumed a classic position in the history of physical science) were performed, little use has been made of the method for determining the arrangement and spacing of adsorbed species. Interest in this method has however recently revived, and it has been used to study the adsorption of oxygen on silicon and germanium,[60] and of oxygen, nitrogen and carbon monoxide on nickel.[61]

REFERENCES

1. B. M. W. Trapnell, "Chemisorption" (Butterworths, London, 1955).
2. J. H. de Boer, *Adv. Catalysis* **6,** 67 (1954).
3. J. E. Lennard-Jones, *Trans. Faraday Soc.* **28,** 333 (1932).
4. S. Brunauer, P. H. Emmett and E. Teller, *J. Amer. Chem. Soc.* **60,** 309 (1938).
5. P. M. Gundry and F. C. Tompkins, *Quart. Rev.* **14,** 257 (1960).
6. J. K. Roberts, *Proc. Cambridge Phil. Soc.* **34,** 388 (1938).
7. T. N. Rhodin, *Adv. Catalysis* **5,** 40 (1953).
8. J. K. Roberts, *Proc. Roy. Soc.* **A152,** 445 (1935).
9. J. M. Jackson, *Proc. Cambridge Phil. Soc.* **28,** 136 (1932).
10. P. W. Selwood, *Adv. Catalysis* **9,** 93 (1957).
11. P. W. Selwood, S. Adler and T. R. Phillips, *J. Amer. Chem. Soc.* **77,** 1462 (1955); R. J. Leak and P. W. Selwood, *J. Phys. Chem.* **64,** 1114 (1960).
12. J. J. Broeder, L. L. van Reijen and A. R. Korswagen, *J. Chim. phys.* **54,** 37 (1957).
13. L. E. Moore and P. W. Selwood, *J. Amer. Chem. Soc.* **78,** 697 (1956).
14. P. W. Selwood, *J. Amer. Chem. Soc.* **78,** 3893 (1956).
15. E. L. Lee, J. A. Sabatka and P. W. Selwood, *J. Amer. Chem. Soc.* **79,** 5391 (1957); P. W. Selwood and L. Vaski, *Ibid.* **80,** 1331 (1958).
16. P. W. Selwood, *J. Amer. Chem. Soc.* **79,** 3346 (1957).
17. P. W. Selwood, *J. Amer. Chem. Soc.* **79,** 4637 (1957).

18. P. W. Selwood, Proc. 2nd International Congress on Catalysis (Editions Technip., Paris, 1961) **2,** 1795.
19. T. J. Gray and C. C. McCain, 2nd International Conference of Surface Activity (Butterworths, London 1957), **2,** 260.
20. M. H. Dilke, E. B. Maxted and D. D. Eley, *Nature* **161,** 804 (1948).
21. I. Langmuir, *J. Amer. Chem. Soc.* **54,** 2798 (1932).
22. J. C. P. Mignolet, *Bull. Soc. chim. belges* **64,** 122 (1955).
23. R. V. Culver and F. C. Tompkins, *Adv. Catalysis* **11,** 67 (1959).
24. R. C. L. Bosworth, *Proc. Roy. Soc.* **A150,** 58 (1935).
25. W. M. H. Sachtler and G. J. H. Dorgelo, *J. Chim. phys.* **54,** 27 (1957).
26. R. C. L. Bosworth, *Proc. Cambridge Phil. Soc.* **33,** 394 (1937).
27. C. W. Oatley, *Proc. Phys. Soc.* **51,** 318 (1939).
28. J. C. P. Mignolet, *Discuss. Faraday Soc.* **8,** 326 (1950).
29. J. C. P. Mignolet, *Rec. Trav. Chim.* **74,** 685 (1955).
30. R. Gomer, *Adv. Catalysis* **7,** 93 (1955); J. A. Becker, *ibid.*, 136.
31. E. W. Müller, *J. Appl. Phys.* **27,** 474 (1956).
32. R. Suhrmann, *Adv. Catalysis* **7,** 303 (1955).
33. J. C. P. Mignolet, *Discuss. Faraday Soc.* **8,** 105 (1950).
34. W. M. H. Sachtler and G. J. H. Dorgelo, *Z. phys. Chem.* (*Frankfurt*) **25,** 69 (1960).
35. R. Suhrmann and W. M. H. Sachtler, *Z. Naturforsch.* **9a,** 14 (1954).
36. R. Suhrmann, G. Wedler and H. Gentsch, *Z. phys. Chem.* (*Frankfurt*) **17,** 35 (1958).
37. R. Suhrmann and K. Schulz, *Z. phys. Chem.* (*Frankfurt*) **1,** 69 (1954).
38. R. Suhrmann and K. Schulz, *Naturwiss.* **42,** 340 (1955).
39. W. M. H. Sachtler, *J. Chem. Phys.* **25,** 751 (1956).
40. R. Suhrmann, Y. Mizushima, A. Hermann and G. Wedler, *Z. phys. Chem.* (*Frankfurt*) **20,** 332 (1959).
41. R. Suhrmann, In "Chemisorption", edited by W. E. Garner (Butterworths, London, 1957), p. 106.
42. E. Greenhalgh and B. M. W. Trapnell, *Adv. Catalysis* **9,** 238 (1957).
43. R. P. Eischens and W. A. Pliskin, *Adv. Catalysis* **10,** 1 (1958).
44. V. A. Crawford, *Quart. Rev.* **14,** 378.
45. R. P. Eischens and W. A. Pliskin, *J. Chem. Phys.* **24,** 282 (1956); L. H. Little, N. Sheppard and D. J. C. Yates, *Proc. Roy. Soc.* **A259,** 242 (1960).
46. R. P. Eischens, W. A. Pliskin and S. A. Francis, *J. Chem. Phys.* **22,** 1786 (1954).
47. R. P. Eischens, W. A. Pliskin and S. A. Francis, *J. Phys. Chem.* **60,** 194 (1956).
48. A. C. Yang and C. W. Garland, *J. Phys. Chem.* **61,** 1504 (1957); C. W. Garland, *J. Phys. Chem.* **63,** 1423 (1960).
49. C. W. Garland, *J. Phys. Chem.* **63,** 1423 (1959).
50. R. A. Gardner and R. A. Petrucci, *J. Amer. Chem. Soc.* **82,** 5051 (1960).
51. A. Terenin and L. Roev, *Spectrochim. Acta.* **11,** 946 (1959); Proc. 2nd International Congress on Catalysis (Editions Technip., Paris, 1961) **2,** 2183.
52. K. Hirota, K. Kuwata and Y. Nakai, *Bull. Chem. Soc. Japan* **31,** 861 (1958); see Chapter 17 for other references.
53. W. A. Pliskin and R. P. Eischens, *Z. phys. Chem.* (*Frankfurt*) **24,** 11 (1960).
54. H. L. Pickering and H. C. Eckstrom, *J. Phys. Chem.* **63,** 512 (1959).
55. E. Cremer and L. Roselius, *Adv. Catalysis* **9,** 659 (1957); E. Cremer, *Z. analyt. Chem.* **170,** 219 (1959).
56. K. Tamaru, *Nature* **183,** 319 (1959).
57. J. Dewing and A. J. B. Robertson, *Proc. Roy. Soc.* **A240,** 423 (1957).
58. H. E. Farnsworth, R. E. Schlier, T. H. George and R. M. Burger, *J. Appl. Phys.* **29,** 1150 (1958).
59. C. J. Davisson and L. H. Germer, *Phys. Rev.* **30,** 705 (1927).
60. R. E. Schlier and H. E. Farnsworth, *J. Chem. Phys.* **30,** 917 (1959).
61. L. H. Germer, E. J. Scheibner and C. D. Hartman, *Phil. Mag.* **5,** 222 (1960); H. E. Farnsworth and J. Tuul, *J. Phys. and Chem. Solids* **9,** 48 (1959).

Chapter 5

The Chemistry and Energetics of Adsorption

5.1 The Chemistry of Adsorption

5.11 The Descriptive Chemistry of Adsorption[1]

It was seen in Section 4.21 that the first information required of adsorption studies is purely qualitative, namely, to ascertain how the ability to adsorb varies among the metals. We would then hope to relate this ability to the position of the metal in the Periodic Classification, and to interpret the observations in terms of the theoretical models described in Chapter 2.

The required information comes from three types of source. Firstly, there is the vast body of information pertaining to the catalytic efficiencies of metals in a wide variety of catalytic reactions; while in most of this work the metal surfaces have not been rigorously purified, nevertheless a significant general pattern of behaviour is revealed.[1, 2] Secondly, there is the considerable volume of work pertaining to the adsorption of gases on "dirty" surfaces, for example, metal powders. Thirdly, there is the smaller but growing body of information of the adsorption of gases at pure metal surfaces.

The observations from work of this last type may be classified as follows:

(i) In some cases adsorption at room temperature (and sometimes at much lower temperature) is immeasurably fast, leading initially to very small equilibrium pressures and ultimately to high coverages.

(ii) In other cases, adsorption proceeds in the neighbourhood of room temperature at measurable speeds which increase with temperature: such adsorptions are said to be activated, but genuine examples are few.

(iii) In yet other cases, there is no detectable adsorption at room temperature, although it is sometimes found at higher temperatures.

In the first case, the activation energy must be insignificant, while in the second case, values of between about 2 and 11 kcal. mole^{-1} have been reported. In the third case, there are two possible reasons why no adsorption is found: either the activation energy may be so high that the process cannot occur at a measurable rate at the temperature used, or the process may be endothermic. The former is probably the more general explanation.

The strength of adsorption in any system depends both on the gas and on the metal, and it is found possible to place a number of gases in a sequence such that any one is more strongly adsorbed by any metal than the ones succeeding it.[3] For the gases which have been most thoroughly studied the sequence is[4]

$$O_2 > C_2H_2 > C_2H_4 > CO > H_2 > CO_2 > N_2.$$

Metals and semi-metals can then be classified into groups depending on the number of gases adsorbed at room temperature, in the manner shown in Table I. This classification, due originally to Trapnell,[4] has been slightly

TABLE I. *Classification of Metals and Semi-metals Based on Adsorption Properties.* (A *indicates Adsorption*, NA *No Adsorption*)

Group	*Metals*	Gases						
		O_2	C_2H_2	C_2H_4	CO	H_2	CO_2	N_2
A	Ca, Sr, Ba, Ti, Zr, Hf, V, Nb, Ta, Cr, Mo, W, Fe†, (Re)	A	A	A	A	A	A	A
B_1	Ni, (Co)	A	A	A	A	A	A	NA
B_2	Rh, Pd, Pt, (Ir)	A	A	A	A	A	NA	NA
C	Al, Mn, Cu, Au‡	A	A	A	A	NA	NA	NA
D	K	A	A	NA	NA	NA	NA	NA
E	Mg, Ag†, Zn, Cd, In, Si, Ge, Sn, Pb, As, Sb, Bi	A	NA	NA	NA	NA	NA	NA
F	Se, Te	NA	NA	NA	NA	NA	NA	NA

† The adsorption of N_2 on Fe is activated, as is the adsorption of O_2 on Ag films sintered at 0°.

‡ Au does not adsorb O_2.

( ) Metal probably belongs to this group, but the behaviour of films is not known.

modified to incorporate more recent work. The results shown in this Table are taken mainly from Refs. 4, 5, 6 and 7, and while they refer specifically to evaporated films of the elements named, they largely confirm the consensus of experience obtained with metals in other forms. The chief difference is that chemically produced copper appears to adsorb hydrogen near room temperature, in line with its limited activity as a hydrogenation catalyst. Possible reasons for this difference are either that chemically produced copper retains some adsorbed oxygen atoms which act as activating centres or that the activation energy required is less for such preparations than for films, perhaps due to a difference in mean crystallite size in the two cases.[1]

Oxygen is readily adsorbed by all metals except gold, although the process on silver is sometimes activated. Metals having a filled *d*-band (except copper and gold) are unable to adsorb any other gas: the higher activity of copper and gold has been attributed to their fairly low promotional energies for excitation from *d*- to *s*-bands.[4, 8] Potassium, and also presumably other Group IA metals, probably adsorb acetylene ionically, i.e. as an acetylide. The high adsorptive activity of aluminium is unexpected, and it would clearly be of interest to have further information on other metals of the pure *sp*-type (e.g. magnesium). However, quite unmistakably the highest adsorption potential is shown by the *d*-metals. Metals in Groups VIII_2 and VIII_3 can chemisorb all gases except nitrogen, but due to its high valency more *d*-band vacancies are required to permit the chemisorption of nitrogen as atoms than are possessed by these metals. The reported adsorption of nitrogen on a copper surface cleaned by ion bombardment probably refers to an unusually activated surface.[9] The presence of calcium, strontium and barium in Group A requires some explanation, and it has been suggested[10] that there is some overlapping of the *s*-, *p*- and *d*-bands in these metals, giving them some of the characteristics of Transition metals. It is uncertain whether chemisorption of hydrogen and nitrogen by these metals is activated or not.[4, 6, 11]

Silicon and germanium have recently been much studied, and while it is generally agreed that these elements readily adsorb oxygen[12–15] and fail to adsorb carbon monoxide,[12, 16] discordant views on their ability to adsorb hydrogen have been presented. The early claim[16] that germanium chemisorbs molecular hydrogen but not carbon monoxide violates the sequence given earlier in this section and is therefore suspect. Germanium powder has been stated[12] not to chemisorb hydrogen at 25°, while adsorption on a germanium film prepared by decomposing germanium hydride is reported[17] to be activated and immobile, although only small coverages were achieved. It now appears[18–20] that both silicon and germanium very readily chemisorb hydrogen *atoms* to about complete coverage, and that the supposed adsorption of molecules[16] is to be attributed to the presence of adventitious atoms. For these reasons, silicon and germanium are put in Group E of Table I. Films of the metals of Group IB also chemisorb hydrogen atoms at low temperatures where adsorption of molecules is not found.[21]

Manganese films readily attain monolayer coverage by oxygen at low and room temperatures, but hydrogen adsorption is very weak and activated:[22] manganese therefore probably belongs to Group C (although its adsorption of other gases has not been studied) so that in this respect as in many others its behaviour is anomalous.

Saturated hydrocarbons are only adsorbed by Transition metals, and the process is activated.

5.12 Interpretation of the Descriptive Chemistry

The salient observation emerging from the last Section is that most Transition metals possess a capacity for chemisorption of a kind not possessed by *sp*-metals. This has encouraged the belief that in most cases the chemisorption bond is a covalence between electrons from the adsorbed species and the unpaired *d*-electrons of the metal. This belief is supported by the observed changes in saturation magnetization and in magnetic susceptibility following adsorption. This view has, however, come to be seriously questioned. The finding[21] that preformed hydrogen atoms can be chemisorbed by Group IB metals when molecular hydrogen cannot would seem to indicate that failure to achieve chemisorption is more generally due to the existence of a prohibitively high activation energy than to the absence of adsorption capability on the part of the metal. In harmony with this, it is known that Group IB metals can act as catalysts for hydrogen equilibration reactions at sufficiently elevated temperatures.[8]

It seems uncertain whether the Band Theory is capable of development to the extent of providing a sufficiently detailed picture of surface adsorption. For example, it cannot predict the number, nature nor the spatial distribution of the surface valencies, and the more recent attempts to interpret the specific adsorption capacities of metal surfaces have employed Pauling's Valence Bond Theory or some slight modification of it. According to this Theory (see Chapter 2) the metal to metal bonds in the solid result from the overlap of *dsp*-hybrid orbitals, and hence the free valencies possessed by surface atoms will presumably also be of this type, spatially directed in a manner determined by the structure of the bulk lattice. This must therefore be the chief kind of surface unsaturation to be satisfied by chemisorption. These hybrid orbitals will probably be directed towards positions where another metal atom would be expected to go if the metal surface were being built up.

However, there is no very sharp change in the nature of these orbitals (i.e. in the cohesive strength) on passing from Group VIII_2 to Group IB, and the potential energy curves for the chemisorption of, for example, hydrogen on palladium and on silver should be closely similar (see Fig. 1(a)). Now the observation is that there is a formidable activation energy required in the latter case, but not in the former. The difference between the metals lies in the fact that palladium possesses a partly vacant atomic *d*-orbital, while silver does not. It has been proposed[2] that this *d*-orbital is able to participate in a new type of chemisorption, termed *Type C Chemisorption*, with certain molecules. The kind of chemisorption referred to previously is now designated as Type A. The origin of these terms, and experimental evidence in support of an additional kind of chemisorption, are discussed in Section 5.8. If the potential energy curve appropriate to Type C chemisorption is of the form shown in Fig. 1(b), then the difference between the behaviour of palladium and of silver is elegantly interpreted. The transition from physical adsorption to *dsp*-chemisorption is greatly facilitated by the effective removal of the activation energy. Because of the zero (or at most small) activation energy

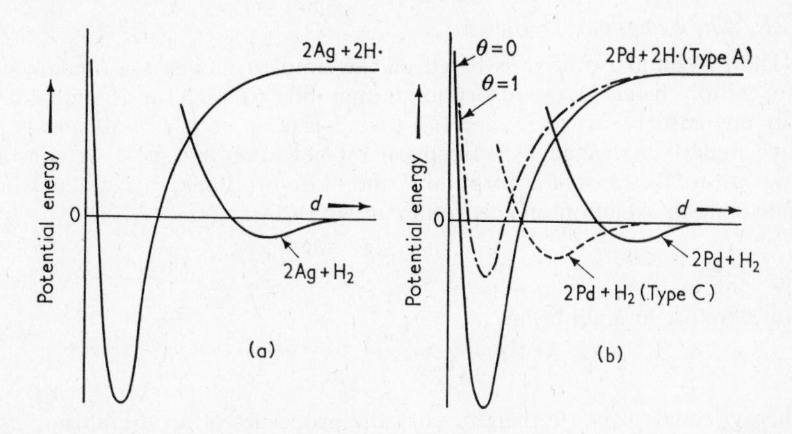

FIG. 1. Diagrammatic representation of the potential energy curves for the adsorption of hydrogen on (a) silver and (b) palladium.

required for the transition from physical to Type C adsorption, this latter form would be expected to be found at quite low temperatures. At small coverages, and at low temperatures, Type C adsorbed species will readily pass over to the *dsp*-adsorbed state, but because of the general tendency for heats of adsorption to decrease with surface coverage (see Section 4.23), an activation energy may appear at high coverages (see Fig. 1(b)). Type C adsorption may therefore be expected to have some stability at moderate temperatures in particular instances.

5.2 ADSORPTION ISOTHERMS[23]

We turn now to an examination of the quantitative aspects of adsorption systems. An introduction to the concept of adsorption isotherms has already been presented (Section 4.22). It is important to be able to derive theoretically isotherms based on various physical models, and to compare them with isotherms observed experimentally, in order to establish the particular model which is operative under the given experimental conditions. There are three possible methods for deriving theoretical isotherms.[23] (i) The kinetic method, where the equilibrium condition is determined by the equality of the rates of adsorption and desorption. (ii) The thermodynamic method, where the equilibrium condition is determined in the usual manner of thermodynamics.

(iii) The method of statistical thermodynamics, where the equilibrium condition involves a knowledge of the partition functions of the adsorbed and gas-phase molecules and the sites.

The three most important isotherms are those associated with the names of Langmuir, Freundlich and Temkin. Each is based on a different theoretical model, the principal difference being the way in which the heat of adsorption varies with surface coverage.

5.21 The Langmuir Isotherm

The Langmuir isotherm is based on the simplest model, the fundamental propositions being: (i) the adsorption is immobile, (ii) each site accommodates only one adsorbed particle, and (iii) the adsorption energy of all sites is the same and is unaffected by adsorption on neighbouring sites. At constant temperature the rates of adsorption r_a and of desorption r_d in a system where there is no dissociation on adsorption are given by:

$$r_a = k_a P(1 - \theta) \tag{1}$$

and

$$r_d = k_d \theta, \tag{2}$$

and therefore at equilibrium

$$\theta = \frac{bP}{1 + bP}, \tag{3}$$

where b equals k_a/k_d: b therefore has the properties of an equilibrium constant. The constant k_a is in fact equal to $\sigma/(2\pi m\boldsymbol{k}T)^{\frac{1}{2}}$, where σ is the chance that a collision of a gas molecule with a vacant site results in adsorption (the condensation coefficient), m the mass of the gas molecule and $\boldsymbol{k}$ Boltzmann's constant. Remembering that the adsorption may be activated and that the desorption certainly will be, the rates of adsorption and desorption at any temperature may be written as:

$$r_a = \frac{\sigma}{(2\pi m\boldsymbol{k}T)^{\frac{1}{2}}} \cdot P(1 - \theta) \exp\left(-\frac{E_a}{RT}\right) \tag{4}$$

and

$$r_d = k_d\, \theta \exp\left(-\frac{E_d}{RT}\right), \tag{5}$$

where $E_d - E_a = -\Delta H_a$, the heat of adsorption. The isotherm is now of the form

$$P = \frac{k_d}{\sigma}(2\pi m\boldsymbol{k}T)^{\frac{1}{2}}\left(\frac{\theta}{1-\theta}\right) \exp\left(\frac{+\Delta H_a}{RT}\right), \tag{6}$$

which reduces to the Langmuir expression if k_a, σ and $-\Delta H_a$ are independent of θ. The full expression for b at any temperature is therefore

$$\frac{1}{b} = \frac{k_d}{\sigma}(2\pi m\boldsymbol{k}T)^{\frac{1}{2}} \exp\left(\frac{+\Delta H_a}{RT}\right). \tag{7}$$

Statistical mechanical and thermodynamic derivations of the Langmuir isotherm have been given.[24, 25]

If the adsorption involves the dissociation of the adsorbing molecule into n fragments, the isotherm at constant temperature takes the form

$$\theta = \frac{bP^{1/n}}{1 + bP^{1/n}}. \qquad (8)$$

For the purpose of testing experimental results, the isotherm may be rewritten as

$$\frac{P}{\theta} = \frac{1}{a} + P. \qquad (9)$$

The plot of P/θ against P should therefore be a straight line of slope unity at all temperatures, and the intercept $(1/a)$ should increase approximately exponentially with temperature.

Although the first two propositions on the basis of which this isotherm is developed may sometimes be valid, it is doubtful whether the third is true except in rare cases. The Langmuir isotherm, despite its very wide application, therefore contains a fundamental weakness.

5.22 *The Freundlich Isotherm*

The Freundlich isotherm

$$\theta = kP^{1/n}$$

originated as an empirical relation between surface coverage and pressure: k and n are constants at a given temperature, both decreasing with increasing temperature, and n is always greater than unity. The isotherm has since been derived theoretically on the basis of an exponential decrease in heat of adsorption with coverage.[26] From the isotherm in the above form, it is to be expected that θ will increase continually with P, i.e. no saturation limit is predicted. However, from the theoretical derivation it appears that above a certain value of θ the heat of adsorption becomes negative and the adsorption then terminates. The theory indicates[26] that

$$n = -\Delta H_m/RT \qquad (10)$$

and

$$-\Delta H_a = +\Delta H_m \ln \theta, \qquad (11)$$

$-\Delta H_a$ being the heat of adsorption at coverage θ and $-\Delta H_m$ a constant. It is interesting to note that an exponential decrease in heat of adsorption cannot be interpreted in terms of lateral repulsion between adsorbed particles so that this explanation is ruled out when the isotherm holds: however, it may be taken to suggest an energetically heterogeneous surface.

5.23 *The Temkin Isotherm*

The Temkin isotherm[27] is based on the supposition that the heat of adsorption falls linearly with increasing surface coverage, viz.

$$-\Delta H_a = -\Delta H_0(1 - \alpha\theta), \qquad (12)$$

where $-\Delta H_0$ is the heat of adsorption when θ is zero and α is a constant.

On introducing this expression into the general form of the Langmuir isotherm, the result is obtained that

$$\theta = \frac{RT}{-\Delta H_0 \alpha} \ln(BP), \tag{13}$$

where B equals $b \exp(-\Delta H_0/RT)$, b being the adsorption coefficient defined previously. This expression is expected to hold only in the middle range of coverage (θ from 0.2 to 0.8) owing to the simplifying assumptions made in its derivation. The same result is obtained if the surface is taken to be energetically non-uniform. Although the Temkin isotherm does not apparently predict a saturation limit, this is merely because it does not apply at $\theta > 0.8$ by reason of the introduction of the assumptions referred to above.

5.24 *Tests of the Isotherms*

The Freundlich and Temkin relationships are more acceptable than that of Langmuir in that they make allowance for the generally observed dependence of heat of adsorption on coverage: of the two, the Temkin isotherm treats the most usually encountered case. Trapnell[23] has described the application of these isotherms to a wide variety of experimental results. Before it can be asserted that a particular isotherm accurately describes a given system, three conditions must be met. (i) The monolayer volume must be independent of temperature. Quite frequently the Langmuir isotherm is apparently obeyed, but this requirement is not fulfilled. (ii) The results must conform to the isotherm over the greater part of the range of coverages. (iii) It must be confirmed that the heat of adsorption varies with coverage in a manner consistent with that assumed in deriving the isotherm. Table II gives some examples of obedience to the various isotherms.

TABLE II. *Examples of Systems Obeying the Various Isotherms*

Freundlich			*Langmuir*			*Temkin*		
Gas	*Metal*	*Ref.*	*Gas*	*Metal*	*Ref.*	*Gas*	*Metal*	*Ref.*
H_2	evap. W films	28	H_2	Cu powder	31	H_2, N_2	Fe powder (promoted)	32
H_2	W powder	29				H_2	evap. Fe films	33
N_2	W powder	30						

It is interesting to note that for the adsorption of hydrogen on copper powder[31] it is the plot of P/θ against P which is linear, while the plot of P^2/θ against P^2 is not linear; this would indicate that the adsorption is molecular rather than atomic in nature.

5.25 *Simultaneous Adsorption of Two Species*

When two different kinds of molecules A and B are competing for adsorption on the same surface at a given temperature, it may be readily shown that

$$\theta_A = \frac{b_A P_A}{(1 + b_A P_A + b_B P_B)} \tag{14}$$

and

$$\theta_B = \frac{b_B P_B}{(1 + b_A P_A + b_B P_B)}, \tag{15}$$

so that the ratio of the coverages by A and B is simply given by

$$\theta_A/\theta_B = b_A P_A / b_B P_B. \tag{16}$$

Thus if equal pressures of A and B are taken, the ratio θ_A/θ_B is determined by the ratio of their adsorption coefficients. Making use of the previous expression for b (equation (7)), it appears that

$$\theta_A/\theta_B = k \exp\{-(\Delta H_{a,\,A} - \Delta H_{a,\,B})/RT\}, \tag{17}$$

where k is given by

$$\frac{k_{d,\,B}/\sigma_B}{k_{d,\,A}/\sigma_A}$$

if the masses of A and B are not too different. The result is that with increasing temperature the ratio θ_A/θ_B tends to unity, so that the relative coverage of the more weakly adsorbed component increases, and vice versa. Related expressions are readily obtained for the relative adsorptions of more than two components, or where any of the components dissociate on adsorption.

5.26 The Definition of Complete Coverage

Much interest has recently been attached to the values of the parameters of adsorption in the neighbourhood of complete surface coverage, and for this purpose it is necessary to have unequivocal criteria available for determining when complete coverage is attained. This point also bears on the use of chemisorption in estimating surface areas. It has been widely assumed (following Beeck[34]) that complete coverage is reached when the equilibrium pressure of hydrogen is 0.1 mm. This in turn assumes that the value of b when $\theta = 1$ is large, and therefore that the heat of adsorption is correspondingly large. In view of the finding[35] that heats of chemisorption as low as 3 kcal. mole^{-1} may be obtained (for hydrogen on tungsten films), this criterion must be suspect.[36, 37] Furthermore, it has been found that the volume of hydrogen rapidly chemisorbed by silica-supported nickel increases from about 14 cm.^{3} to about 17 cm.^{3} as the pressure is raised from atmospheric to 100 atm., the additionally adsorbed gas also causing a further decrease in magnetization.[38] There appears at the moment to be no uniquely satisfactory criterion for complete coverage, and indeed the occurrence of Type C chemisorption, which may be molecular in nature, may render the definition of complete coverage obscure or even meaningless.

5.3 Heats of Adsorption

Much work has been done over the last forty years on the measurements of heats of adsorption at metal surfaces. The results provide information of three types. (i) Initial heats of adsorption (i.e. extrapolated to $\theta = 0$) on a series of different metals in the same physical form indicate the relative adsorption potentials of the surfaces, and are the quantities which may be expected to be closely related to the electronic properties of the metals. (ii) Initial heats of adsorption for a given metal in a variety of physical forms throw light on the influence of physical form on reactivity. (iii) Measurements on the manner in which the heat depends on coverage may give information on surface heterogeneity and on the mobility of the adsorbed layer.

5.31 *Initial Heats of Adsorption on Various Metals*

Comparable measurements of heats of adsorption of various gases are available for evaporated films of various metals and for silica-supported metals (see Tables III–VIII). Despite the allegedly reproducible behaviour of evaporated films in adsorption, there are nevertheless sensible differences in heats of adsorption determined under closely similar conditions, and it is therefore necessary to enquire briefly into the causes of these differences. The values recorded in the Tables are those obtained calorimetrically (except as indicated) at temperatures close to ambient. The following factors appear to influence the heat of adsorption in the low coverage region ($\theta = 0$–~ 0.2).

(i) The temperature of the measurement.
(ii) The degree of sintering of the film.
(iii) The thickness of film.
(iv) The calorimeter design.

Differences are noted especially with regard to the dependence of heat of adsorption on coverage in the low-coverage range; Fig. 2 shows the $-\Delta H_a$—coverage plots obtained for the nickel–hydrogen and iron–hydrogen systems by various workers, and the above points may be discussed with reference to these systems. The differences between the measured heat curves over iron at about room temperature are trivial and require no discussion; however a series of results at $-183°$ give a heat of adsorption of about 27 kcal. mole^{-1} *independent of coverage*.[41]

More important differences are seen in the nickel–hydrogen system. The higher initial heat found by Klemperer and Stone[36] is attributed by them to the less sintered state of their films, resulting from the use of a larger vessel. Thus the design of the apparatus may affect the degree of sintering of the films through the difference in sintering induced by the hot wire (see also Ref. 48). The crystallites which compose the film are formed under conditions of very great supersaturation and they are likely to contain an abnormally large concentration of imperfections of various kinds. These will anneal out under the influence of the heat of adsorption, and the strain energy so released will contribute to the observed heat emission: for this reason, less sintered films may show higher heats of adsorption than more sintered films.[36]

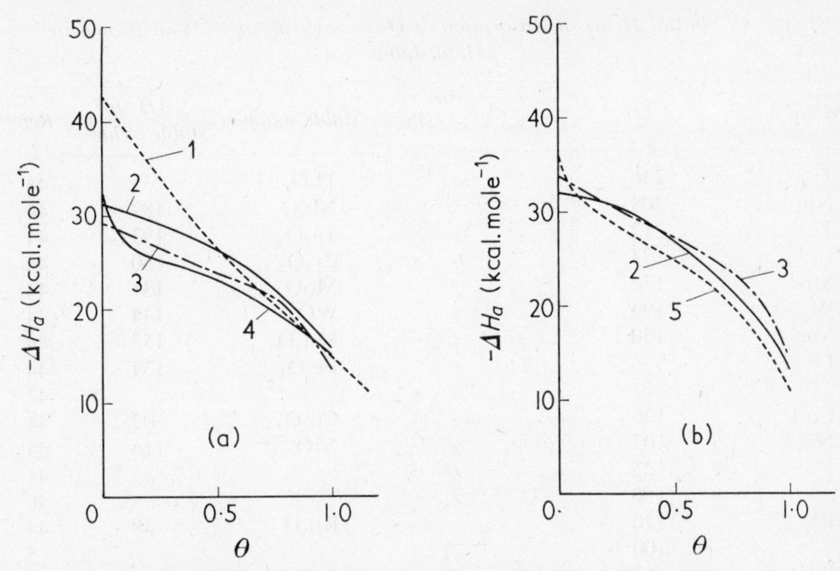

FIG. 2. The dependence of heat of adsorption of hydrogen on coverage for evaporated films of (a) nickel and (b) iron.

1, Klemperer and Stone;[36] 2, Beeck;[34] 3, Wahba and Kemball;[40] 4, Rideal and Sweett;[43] 5, Bagg and Tompkins.[42]

The results of Klemperer and Stone are therefore less typical of a normal (sintered) nickel surface than are those of other workers. In agreement with this view, a nickel film sintered at 150° shows lower heats of hydrogen adsorption over the range of coverage studied than do films sintered at room temperature, although the initial heats may be the same. The release of

TABLE III. *Heats of Adsorption of Hydrogen (kcal. mole⁻¹) on Evaporated Metal Films*

Metal	$-\Delta H_a, \theta = 0$	$-\Delta H_a, \theta = 0.2$	*Curve type*	*Ref.*
Ta	45	?	β	34
Cr	45	?	?	34
Mo	40	?	?	39
W	52 ± 5	39	α	40
	45 ± 2	38	α	41
Fe	34 ± 1	31	α	40
	36 ± 2	29	α	42
	32 ± 1	31	γ	41
Rh	26	25	*L*	34
Ni	29 ± 1	27	α	40
	31 ± 2	29	γ	41
	43 ± 2	34 ± 2	α	36
	32‡	26	α	43
Pd	27	?	?	34

TABLE IV. *Initial Heats of Adsorption of Oxygen* (*kcal. mole*$^{-1}$) *on Evaporated Metal Films*

Metal	$-\Delta H_a$	*Curve type*	*Stable oxide*	$-\Delta H_f$ *for stable oxide*	*Ref.*
Ti	236	γ	Ti_3O_5	235	44
Nb	208	γ	Nb_2O_5	182	44
Ta	212	γ	Ta_2O_5	193	44
Cr	174	γ	Cr_2O_3	180	44
Mo	172	γ	MoO_2	131	44
W	194	γ	WO_2	134	44
Mn	150	$\not\propto$	Mn_2O_3	153	44
Fe	136	γ	Fe_3O_4	134	44
	71	γ			42
Co	100	γ	Co_3O_4	102	44
Ni	107	γ	NiO	116	44
	125	$\not\propto$			41
	150	$\not\propto$			36
Rh	120		Rh_2O	48	44
	100	?			5
Pd	67*	?	PdO	42	44
Pt	64*	?	PtO	34	44
Al	~200*	?	Al_2O_3	266	44
Si	210	γ	SiO_2	210	44
Ge	132	γ	GeO_2	129	44

stored energy from unsintered films is likely to be achieved by the first few gas increments (up to $\theta \doteqdot 0.2$), and more reproducible values are expected (and indeed found) at coverages greater than this. For this reason, values for heats at $\theta = 0.2$ are given in Table IV as an example, and it is clear that the scatter of values for any one metal is less at this coverage than at zero coverage.

The adsorption of hydrogen on a nickel film at $-183°$ gives heats about the same as those found at room temperature, save that the values in the range of coverage from 0.7 to 1.0 are somewhat lower.[41] A very thick nickel film is found to give a higher initial heat than moderately thin ones.[36]

The initial isosteric heats of adsorption of hydrogen on several silica-supported metals (Table VIII) have been obtained from measurements of the temperature-dependence of the equilibrium gas pressure by a thermodynamic procedure which has been described in detail.[47, 49] Agreement with the values obtained with evaporated films (where cross-checking is possible) is satisfactory except in the case of nickel. This agreement lends weight to the view that the lower values recorded on evaporated films correspond to those for efficiently sintered surfaces.

Finally Tables IX to XI give a selection of the heats of adsorption of hydrogen, oxygen and other gases on other metallic forms, especially powders. As expected, the various values for any one system (where more than one is

TABLES V to VII. *Initial Heats of Adsorption of other Gases (kcal. mole⁻¹) on Evaporated Metal Films*

Gas	*Metal*	$-\Delta H_a$	*Curve type*	*Ref.*
Ethylene	Ta	138	*L*	34
	Cr	102	?	34
	W	102	?	34
	Fe	68	β	34
	Rh	50	*L*	34
	Ni	58	β	34
Carbon monoxide	Fe	32 ± 1	γ	42
	Ni	35	?	41
		35	?	36
	Cu	9‡	?	4
	Au	9‡	?	4
Ammonia	W	72 ± 2	γ	40
	Fe	45 ± 2	γ	40
	Ni	37 ± 1	α	40
Acetylene	Ni	67	⊄	36
	Cu	19‡	?	4
	Au	21‡	?	4
Nitrogen	Ta	140 ± 5	γ	45
	W	95	⊄	41
	Fe	70 ± 4	β	42
		40	?	41

TABLE VIII. *Initial Isoteric Heats of Adsorption of Hydrogen (kcal. mole⁻¹) on Silica-Supported Metals*[39, 46, 47]

Metal	$-\Delta H_a$	*Curve type*	*Metal*	$-\Delta H_a$	*Curve type*
Fe	32 ± 4	?*L*	Ru	26 ± 2	α
Co	24 ± 4	?	Rh	24 ± 2	β
Ni	26 ± 1	α	Ir	26 ± 2	?*L*
	25.5 ± 1†	γ	Pt	28 ± 1	α
Cu	28 ± 4	?			

† Calorimetric determination.

Explanatory notes to Tables III to VIII

L;	linear fall of heat with coverage:
⊄;	heat independent of coverage up to at least $\theta = 0.7$:
α, β, γ;	curve types (see Section 4.24):
?;	information lacking or uncertain:
‡;	isosteric heat:
*;	integral heat.

TABLE IX. *Initial Heats of Adsorption of Hydrogen (kcal. mole^{-1}) on Powders and Wires*

Metal	*Form*	$-\Delta H_a$	*Curve type*	*Comments*	*Ref.*
W	wire	~45	?*L*	†	50
	powder	~45	β	†	51
	point (F.E.M.)	64	?β	**	52
Fe	see Table XIX				
Co	powder	26	β	†	53
	powder	19	γ	‡	54
Ni	powder	21	*L*	†	55
	powder	27	*L*	‡	56
	powder	26	γ	‡	54
	powder	24	*L*	†	57
Pt	black	18	¢	‡	58
	black	16	¢	†	59
	black	32	β	†	60
	black	32	complex	†	61
Cu	powder	9	¢	†	62
	powder	35	?	‡	58
	powder	10	?	†	57

TABLE X. *Initial Heats of Adsorption of Oxygen (kcal. mole^{-1}) on other Forms of Metals*

Metal	*Form*	$-\Delta H_a$	*Curve type*	*Comments*	*Ref.*
W	wire	139	?	†	63
	wire	150	?	**	64
	wire	147 ± 3	?	**	65
Co	powder from formate	100 to 117	¢	†	53
	powder from nitrate	122	¢	†	66
Ni	powder from oxalate	100 ± 1	¢	†	67
	powder from nitrate	~97	¢	†	68
	powder from nitrate	111	?	*	69
Pd	black	50	?	*	70
Pt	black	53	?	*	69
	black	60	¢	†	71
Cu	powder by hydrazine reduction of Cu^{2+}	110	complex	†	72
	powder from nitrate	76	¢	†	68
	powder from oxide	~93	¢	†	73
	powder	120	complex	†	66
Ag	black	108	?	*	70

TABLE XI. *Initial Heats of Adsorption of other Gases (kcal. mole⁻¹) on Wires and Powders*

Metal	*Form*	$-\Delta H_a$	*Curve type*	*Comments*	*Ref.*
		(a) *Nitrogen*			
W	wire	28	?	**	64
	powder	75	⊄ to $\theta = 0.2$	‡	30
Fe	singly promoted	55	*L*	From $E_d - E_a$	74
	doubly promoted	50	*L*	‡	75
	doubly promoted	44	*L*	‡	76
		(b) *Carbon monoxide*			
Fe	pure powder	~20 at 0°	?	†	77
		9 to 12 at −183°	?	†	77
	doubly promoted	30 at 0°	α	†	77
		35 at −78°	α	†	77
		17 at −183°	β	†	77
Cu	powder	20	?	†	78
		(c) *Carbon dioxide*			
Fe	pure powder	~10 at −78°	γ	†	77
	doubly promoted	33 at −78°	?	†	77

Explanatory notes to Tables IX to XI:

† Calorimetric determination.
* Estimated using thermodynamics of water-dissociation equilibrium.
** Other methods.
Other symbols as in Tables III–VIII.

available) are somewhat discordant, although there is general qualitative agreement with values obtained with films on silica-supported preparations of the corresponding metal: however, the values for powders are usually lower.

5.32 *Correlation of Heats of Adsorption with Parameters of the Metals*

Although the information is less complete than is desirable, it is nevertheless worthwhile attempting empirical correlations between adsorption heats and parameters of the metals, in order to try to decide whether any single one of the latter quantitatively reflects the adsorption potential of metal surfaces. We may first note that the general order of heats of adsorption is

$$O_2 > N_2 \doteqdot C_2H_2 \doteqdot C_2H_4 > NH_3 > CO \doteqdot H_2,$$

which (except for the position of nitrogen) is in approximate agreement with that previously given and based simply on the adsorption powers of various metals. Following precedent, we may then plot heats of adsorption as a function of Group number; this is done in Figs. 3, 4, 5 and 6, and the following generalizations emerge. (i) Except for oxygen, heats are lowest and approximately constant in the second and third row Group VIII metals.

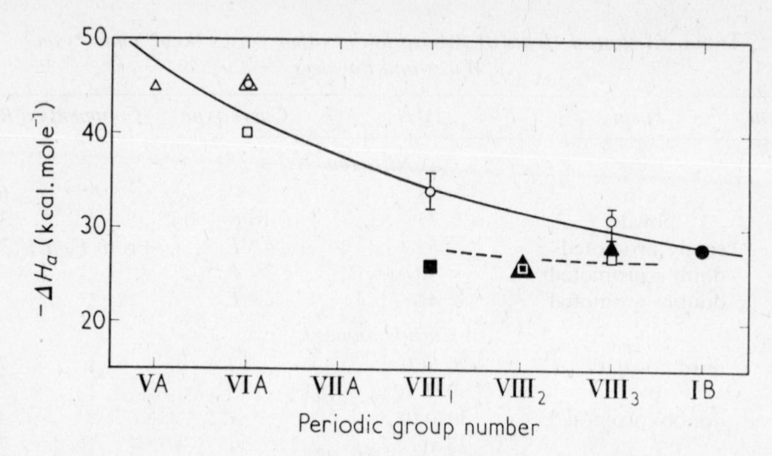

FIG. 3. Initial heats of adsorption of hydrogen on evaporated metal films (open points) and where helpful on silica-supported metals (hatched points): see Tables III and VIII. Circles, first row metals; squares, second row metals; triangles, third row metals.

(ii) They are a little higher and also almost constant in the iron triad. (iii) They increase progressively on passing from right to left through any series. Plotting heats versus Group number is of course equivalent to plotting them versus the electron/atom ratio or in terms of the Band Theory versus the energy of the Fermi surface,[2] but despite the constancy of heats in Group VIII it is clear that metallic valency is not the sole determining factor.

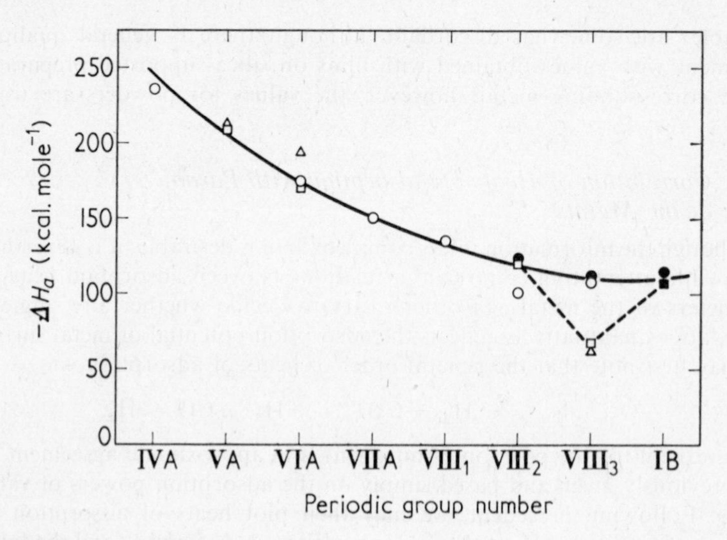

FIG. 4 Initial heats of adsorption of oxygen on evaporated metal films (open points) and where helpful on metal powders (filled points): see Tables IV and X. Legend otherwise as before.

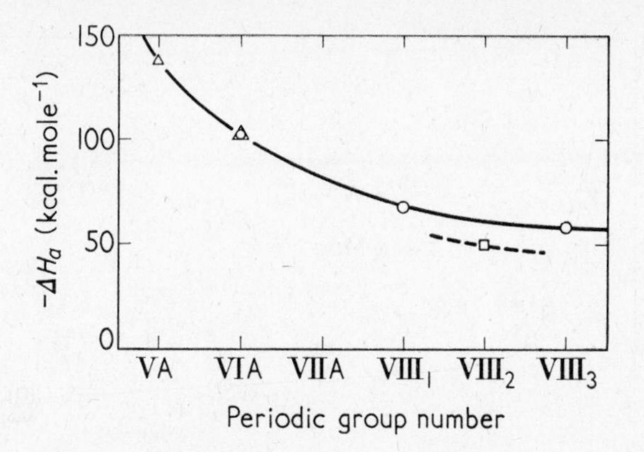

FIG. 5. Initial heats of adsorption of ethylene on evaporated metal films (see Table V): legend as before.

As the electron/atom ratio increases, so the nature of the hybridization of the metal–metal bonds also changes, and it is reasonable to look for a correlation between heats and say the percentage *d*-character of the metallic bonds (Chapter 2). Chronologically this was one of the first kinds of relationship to be tried:[34] its significance is however limited in two ways, as may be seen from Fig. 7 which shows the heats of hydrogen adsorption as a function of δ. First, the heats are relatively insensitive to values of δ in the range 0.4–0.5 and then rise very rapidly without corresponding changes in δ. Second, the values for tungsten and molybdenum lie away from the main curve, and any attempt to improve the situation involves postulates of an extremely *ad hoc*

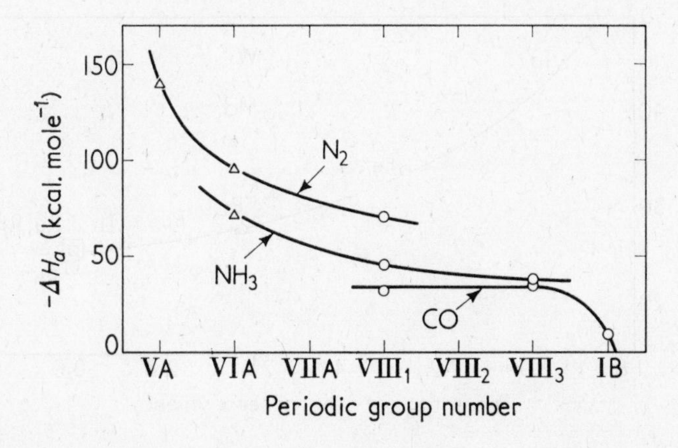

FIG. 6. Initial heats of adsorption of nitrogen, ammonia and carbon monoxide on evaporated metals films (see Tables VI and VII): legend as before.

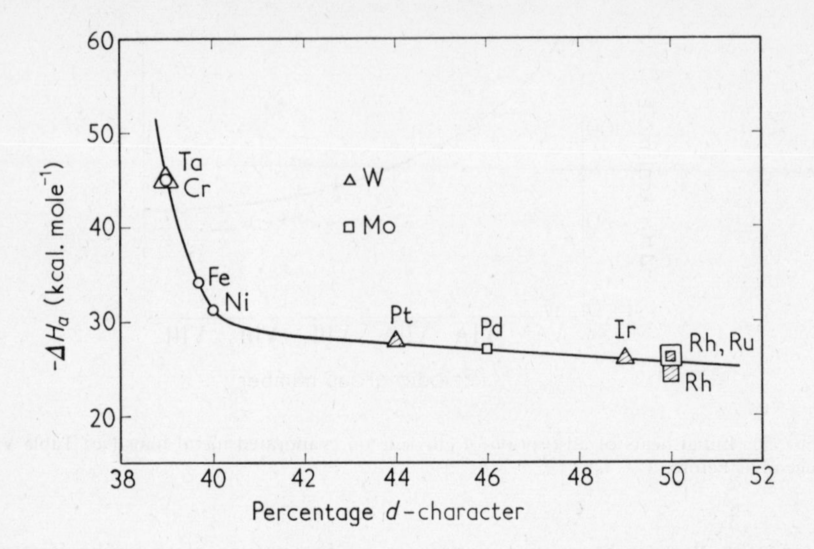

FIG. 7. Heats of adsorption of hydrogen as a function of percentage *d*-character: legend as before.

nature.[34] The picture is marginally different if the heats are plotted against the product of the metallic valency times δ (Fig. 8), although now chromium additionally lies away from the main curve. It is evident that any parameter which gives to any of the Group VI metals values between those for say nickel and palladium is going to prove of limited use in the correlation of adsorption properties.

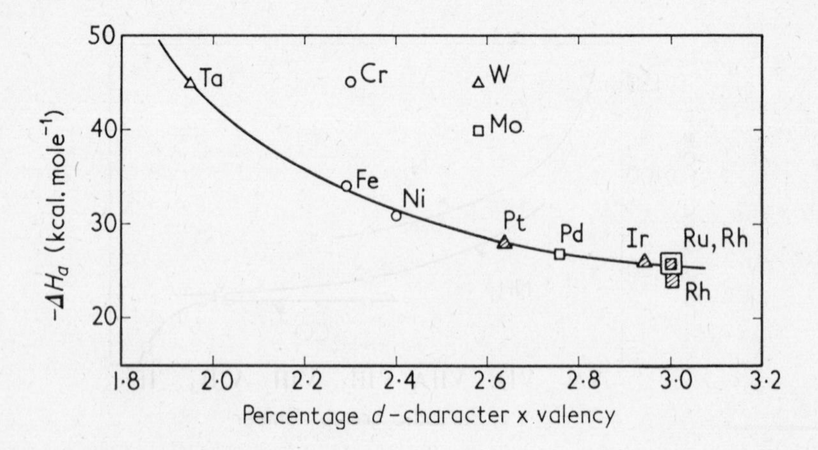

FIG. 8. Heats of adsorption of hydrogen as a function of percentage *d*-character times valency: legend as before.

5.33 The Calculation of Heats of Adsorption

An alternative approach lies in postulating a theoretical model for the chemisorption bond and then trying to calculate the bond energy or the heat of adsorption from first principles. The results of calculations of this type were first given by Eley[79, 80] and subsequently, with modifications, by other authors[23, 81, 82]. The model assumed is that of an essentially covalent but slightly polarized one-centre bond, and following Pauling the bond energy D_{MH} of a metal–hydrogen bond is given by

$$D_{MH} = \tfrac{1}{2}(D_{MM} + D_{HH}) + 23.06\,(x_M - x_H)^2, \tag{18}$$

and the heat of adsorption by

$$-\Delta H_a = 2D_{MH} - D_{HH}. \tag{19}$$

In these equations, D_{MM} is the energy of the metal–metal bond (taken to be 1/6th of the heat of sublimation), D_{HH} the dissociation energy of hydrogen (103.2 kcal. mole^{-1}) and x_M and x_H respectively the electronegativities of the metal and hydrogen atoms. The second term in the first equation therefore gives the contribution of the ionic character of the bond to the total energy. There are two methods of estimating the electronegativity difference. The first assumes that

$$x_M - x_H = \mu, \tag{20}$$

where μ is the dipole moment of the bond in Debye units. The moment at complete coverage μ_1 is related to the surface potential at complete coverage V_1 by

$$\mu_1 = \frac{V_1}{300\,(4\pi n_s)}, \tag{21}$$

n_s being the mean number of sites per cm.^{2}. For the purpose of the calculation, the moment at zero coverage μ_0 is required, and this is obtained from μ_1 by an equation due to Topping:

$$\mu_0 = \mu_1\left(1 + \frac{9\alpha}{a^3}\right), \tag{22}$$

where α is the longitudinal polarizability of the bond and a is the lattice constant for the surface (taken to be 3 Å). The electronegativity difference is therefore calculated from the surface potential V_1. Bond energies and heats of adsorption of hydrogen obtained in this way are shown in Table XII.

The second method for the electronegativity difference is based on Mulliken's association of the electronegativity of an atom with the mean of the first ionization potential and the electron affinity.[81] For a metal the relation

$$x_M = 0.355\,\varphi_M \tag{23}$$

has been deduced, φ_M being the work function in eV. Together with atom electronegativities tabulated by Pauling, a knowledge of the work function of the metal thus also gives a value for $(x_M - x_H)$, and the results of the two methods are in general agreement. Heats of adsorption of hydrogen calculated as before but employing this second method for $(x_M - x_H)$ are also

TABLE XII. *Comparison between Observed and Calculated Initial Heats of Chemisorption of Hydrogen, and of Strengths of Hydrogen–Metal Bonds*

	$-\Delta H_a$(*kcal. mole*$^{-1}$)						D_{MH}(*kcal. mole*$^{-1}$)	
	Observed	*Calculated from*					*Observed*	*Calculated from*
Metal		*Ref. 79*	*Ref. 80*	*Ref. 23*	*Ref. 81*	*Ref. 82*		*Ref. 81*
Cr	45	15.7	15	31.5	24.0	20.6	74.1	63.6
Fe	32 to 36	17	16	17.9	31.6	24.4	67.6 to 69.6	67.4
Co	24*	—	—	—	31.0	20.2	63.6*	67.1
Ni	29 to 32	17	17	18.2	28.9	16.2	66.1 to 67.6	66.0
Cu	28*	13.6	14	—	25.6	23.4	65.6	64.4
Mo	40	—	—	—	42.9	—	71.6	73.0
Ru	26*	—	—	—	38.1	—	64.6*	70.6
Rh	26	23	22	23.5	32.3	24.2	64.6	67.7
Pd	27	—	—	—	22.5	—	65.1	62.9
Ta	45	32	31	47.3	49.6	55.4	74.1	76.4
W	45 to 52	44	38	50.4	45.6	63.6	74.1 to 77.6	74.4
Ir	26*	—	—	—	38.1	—	64.6*	70.6
Pt	28*	—	—	36.9	22.6	30.8	65.6*	62.9

The observed values are for evaporated metal films where possible; those having an asterisk refer to silica-supported metals.

given in Table XII. These values correlate with the mean observed values rather better than do those calculated by the former method. The agreement in the cases of Fe, Co, Ni, Cu, Mo, Ta and W is gratifying: the value for Cr is very low, and those for Pd and Pt slightly low, while the values for Ru, Rh and Ir are too high. The results of a quantum-mechanical calculation[82] are also included in this Table. The subject is further discussed in Chapter 21.

The calculation of heats of adsorption of other gases has been performed in an analogous fashion[23, 79, 80] and has been used as a basis for discussing possible structures in the adsorbed state.[23, 79] The results are shown in Table XIII, and except in the case of carbon monoxide the results are somewhat disappointing, the calculated values being generally too low.

The partial failure of these calculations indicates the inadequacy of the assumed model, but it is not at the moment clear how it may be revised or modified. It may be significant that $(x_M - x_C)$ for ethylene is -0.9 from Pauling's electronegativities, while from surface potential measurements a positive value is obtained. This suggests[80] that the chemisorption bond may be π rather than σ in character. The assumption that the hydrogen–metal bond is a one-centre bond is also likely to be at fault.[83, 84] It may further be significant that the observed values of D_{MH} vary less than do the calculated values (Table XII): this may mean that no metal–metal bond is actually broken in the adsorption process, but rather that the adsorbing molecule interacts with already existing free valencies, after the manner outlined in Chapter 1, and that the energies of these half bonds are less dependent on the nature of the metal than are the energies of metal–metal bonds in the

TABLE XIII. *Comparison between Observed and Calculated Initial Heats of Adsorption of other Gases on Evaporated Films*

Ethylene

Process 1: $C_2H_4 + 2* \rightarrow \underset{*}{H_2C}-\underset{*}{CH_2}$.

Process 2: $C_2H_4 + 4* \rightarrow \underset{*}{HC}=\underset{*}{CH} + 2\underset{*}{H}$.

Metal	Ta	W	Cr	Fe	Ni	Rh
Heat, calc. for process 1 (Ref. 79)	51	64	34.7	36	36.2	42
Heat, calc. for process 1 (Ref. 80)	48	52	33	34	34	40
Heat, calc. for process 2 (Ref. 23)	72	73	40	26	27	38
Heat, observed	138	102	102	68	58	50

Oxygen

Process: $\frac{1}{2}O_2 + M \rightarrow M=O$.

Metal	W	Fe	Ni
Heat, calc. (Ref. 79)	95.6	—	—
Heat, calc. (Ref. 80)	133	—	—
Heat, calc. (Ref. 23)	95.6	60.8	60.2
Heat, observed	194	136	107

Nitrogen

Process: $\frac{1}{2}N_2 + M \rightarrow M\equiv N$.

Metal	Ta	W	Fe
Heat, calc. (Ref. 79)	109	118.5	—
Heat, calc. (Ref. 80)	158	167	—
Heat, calc. (Ref. 23)	109.1	117.3	65.3
Heat, observed	140	95	70

bulk. This observation therefore offers some support for the existence of surface states. The most that can be said of the results of the calculations is that they confirm in a general way the picture of the covalent chemisorption bond. Further refinements are, however, clearly demanded.

5.34 *Comparison between Heats of Adsorption on Films, Powders and Supported Metals*

Heats of adsorption recorded for metal powders and for silica-supported metals are usually lower than those for films. This is generally attributed to the former surfaces being incompletely free from adsorbed impurities, in spite of their being sometimes cleaned with the utmost care. It seems at least possible that the differences are attributable to genuine differences in the physical nature of the various surfaces: it may perhaps be that films sintered at room temperature contain more defects than for example powders which have been exposed to much higher temperatures. A further point is that heats derived isosterically result from measurements made at fairly high temperatures, where the equilibrium defect concentration is naturally lower than at room temperature. It would clearly be of interest to know how, if at all, the initial heats vary with sintering temperature over an extended range,[44] and how the degree of radiative sintering (varied by varying the geometry of the deposition vessel) affects the results.

5.4 Causes of the Decrease in Heat of Adsorption with Increasing Coverage

It remains now to discuss the possible causes for the fall in heats of chemisorption with increasing surface coverage and to show what theoretical models are consistent with the various observed types of curve (Section 4.24). Three distinct possible reasons for the decrease have been recognized: (i) *a priori* heterogeneity, (ii) mutual interaction of adsorbed species, (iii) induced heterogeneity or work function effect.

By *a priori* heterogeneity is meant that the surface is rough rather than smooth, and that adsorption on certain "active" sites is energetically more favoured than on other sites of lower adsorption potential. This concept may be generalized in the form of a continuous distribution for the energy of adsorption sites. Now the first addition of gas to such a surface will result in a preferential adsorption on the "active" sites either because the rate of adsorption on such sites is greater than on less "active" sites or if the adsorption is mobile because the adsorbed species will naturally migrate to sites of highest energy. Subsequent gas additions will be adsorbed on sites of progressively lower activity and the heat of adsorption will decrease. Historically this was the explanation first proposed, and is due to Taylor[85] and to Constable[86]. It is, however, necessary to re-examine this concept in the light of modern knowledge.

It is clear that the various kinds of defects and disorders now known to exist on metal surfaces could constitute "active" centres, and indeed it has already been suggested that they are responsible for unusually high initial heats of adsorption sometimes found with only slightly sintered evaporated films. Further, it now seems widely held that the rapid initial fall shown by Type α curves is due to such defects and that this effect has normally ceased at 20 per cent coverage.[36] A second way in which *a priori* heterogeneity may show up is through the exposure of a variety of crystallographic planes to the gas phase, each having a characteristic geometry, activity and work function. This kind of heterogeneity is inevitably present in all polycrystalline metals, but its role in causing the fall in adsorption heats has not been definitely established.[87]

No quantitative estimates of the kind of decrease in heat over the range zero to complete coverage attributable to these causes have been made. However, the types of distribution of site energy required to lead to linear and exponential (Type β) heat-coverage relations, and hence to the Temkin and Freundlich isotherms, have been calculated.[88]

A second possible cause of the fall in heats of adsorption with increasing coverage is the mutual interaction of the adsorbed species. This may be due to the interaction of dipoles, or possibly to the overlap of electron shells, although the latter effect is too small to be significant in the adsorption of hydrogen on metals. The statistical theory of dipole interactions has been presented by Trapnell[23] and the Table XIV embodies the conclusions. Although the predicted curves accord with some of those encountered experimentally, quantitative calculations show that the size of the heat decrease to be expected on the basis of dipole moments of the kind normally found is quite insufficient to fit the observations. This cause, while present in principle, makes in practice only a small contribution to the total heat decrease.

TABLE XIV. *Types of Heat-coverage Curves resulting from Dipole Interactions*

Mobility	*Number of sites occupied by one molecule when adsorbed*	*Nature of heat decrease*
Immobile	1	Linear
Immobile	2	Type γ: $\frac{d(-\Delta H)}{d\theta}$ decreasing continuously
Mobile	1 or 2	Type γ (sigmoid), or linear

The third possible cause has its origin in the progressive change in the work function of the surface as the coverage increases. The relevant theory was originally developed by de Boer to interpret the fall in the heat of adsorption of Group IA metal atoms on tungsten and molybdenum surfaces, but regardless of whether the dipole moment is assumed to be independent of coverage or not, the predicted curves are not of the required form.[89, 90] For example, if the moment is independent of coverage the change in work function (and hence in heat of adsorption) is proportional to coverage. From a review of the literature, Boudart[91] derived the empirical relation

$$\Delta(-\Delta H_a) = 0.5\, eV, \tag{24}$$

where e is the electronic charge and V the surface potential (i.e. $-\Delta\varphi$). Mignolet[92] has shown that Boudart's choice of data was inappropriate and that the factor of 0.5 is not required. Boudart's interpretation of his relation has been widely criticized.

This explanation of the decrease in adsorption heats is semi-quantitatively satisfactory for hydrogen–metal systems and it may be interpreted as follows.[93] If the electron contributed to the covalent chemisorption bond by the metal comes from the top of the conductivity band, then the energy of the Fermi surface will fall progressively as the adsorption proceeds, and hence the work function will increase. The greater the coverage, the greater the energy required to excite an electron from the conductivity band to the surface orbital and hence the smaller the heat of adsorption. It is to be noted that this model can only lead to a decrease of the heat of adsorption with coverage in the same manner in which the work function changes, and although this is normally assumed to change linearly, the situation may in reality be more complex.[94]

In summarizing the position with regard to the variation of heat of adsorption with coverage the following points may be made. (i) *A priori* and induced heterogeneity are more important than dipole repulsion, and will normally occur together. (ii) Surfaces of all polycrystalline metals will be heterogeneous in the sense of exposing a variety of crystal faces, and unsintered powders and films especially will contain defects of various kinds which will additionally contribute to the apparent heterogeneity. (iii) Quantitative calculations are generally unsuccessful because of the simultaneous operation of more than one factor. Type β curves can only be interpreted in terms of a predominant contribution from a *priori* heterogeneity, while a detailed interpretation of curves of Types α and γ is awaited.

5.5 Surface Potentials[95]

The nature of the normal chemisorption bond will be determined by the electronegativity of the adsorbed atom or by the electronegativity of the atom in the adsorbed molecule or radical through which the binding occurs. Table XV gives some of the available results on surface potentials of complete monolayers of *dsp*-chemisorbed species; less reliable older results are omitted.

Table XV. *Surface Potentials at Complete Coverage*

Metal	*Surface potential (V.)*	*Ref.*
	(a) *Hydrogen*	
Ta	−0.43†	96
	−0.44†	97
W	−0.48	98
	−1.12†	99
Fe	−0.43	21
	−0.47	100
	−0.19†	96
Co	−0.33	21
	−0.31	100
	−0.06†	96
Ni	−0.33	21
	−0.35	101
	~ −0.1†	96, 97, 102
Pt	−0.11	103
Cu	−0.35	9
	−0.325	104
Ag	−0.34	9
Au	−0.17	21

TABLE XV. *Surface Potentials at Complete Coverage*–continued.

Metal	*Surface Potential (V.)*	*Ref.*
	(b) *Carbon monoxide*	
Ta	−0.67†	96
Cr	−1.150	104
W	−0.86†	105
Fe	−1.68	21
	−1.33	104
	−1.15†	96
Co	−1.50	21
	−0.27†	96
Ni	−1.38	21
	∼ −1.3	104
Cu	+0.30	21
	+0.278	104
Ag	+0.32	21
Au	+0.93	21
Zn	+0.076	104
	(c) *Oxygen* (adsorbed atomically)	
W	−1.90	98
	−1.60 to −1.74	Various: see Ref. 98
Ni	−1.6	101
	−1.4	99
Pt	−1.19	105
	−1.1 to −1.2†	106
Pd	−0.9 to −1.25†	106
Ag	−0.2	107
Au	−0.9 to −1.2†	106
	(d) *Nitrogen* (adsorbed atomically)	
W	−0.50	98
	−0.54	108
Ta	−0.38†	97

Most of the recent results have been obtained with evaporated metal films although a few refer to wires. Values marked (†) were determined by a photoelectric technique at room temperature, while others were obtained using the vibrating condenser method or a thermionic method at low temperature (generally −196°). The values for hydrogen are all negative and in the range −0.1 to −0.5, indicating that the hydrogen–metal bonds are essentially covalent. There is no very marked change in passing from Group VIII_3 to Group IB (Ni to Cu and Pt to Au), although the values for the third row elements are considerably lower than those for first row elements.

Surfaces of Transition metals covered by carbon monoxide show more negative potentials and these are consistent with chemisorption at the carbon atom, the bond(s) being extensively polarized. The small positive values found for the post-Transition metals suggest that on these metals the molecule is held by charge-transfer bonds.[21]

Acetylene and ethylene adsorbed on an evaporated nickel film at 20° yield surface potentials of respectively +1.05 and +0.835 V.[101] The potentials due to the physical adsorption of the rare gases have been measured for a number of metals.[109]

Inspection of Table XV shows that while good agreement is obtained between repeated measurements on the same system using the same method and temperature, measurements made by the photoelectric method at room temperature are generally more positive than those obtained by other methods at low temperatures. It is uncertain whether it is the difference in temperature or in technique which is responsible.

The surface potential does not invariably (and indeed not even usually) change linarly with the fraction of surface covered:[21, 96] instead there is normally a progressive decrease in the rate of change which has been attributed to rehydridization of surface orbitals during the adsorption process. The effect may therefore be closely related to the change in heat of adsorption with coverage.

5.6 The Stoichiometry of some Chemisorption Processes

Important information on the structure of adsorbed species results if the mean number of sites occupied by the adsorbed molecule can be estimated. Together with a knowledge of the normal valencies of the elements concerned, it is then generally possible to determine for example whether the molecule has or has not dissociated on adsorption. With larger molecules it is, however, necessary to try to distinguish between those sites blocked by the adsorbed molecule and those to which it is chemically attached. The principle of the method is straightforward. The surface area is determined by non-specific physical adsorption and hence the number of sites per unit area (x) is known with fair precision. The monolayer volume per unit area of chemisorbed gas is then found and the number of molecules it contains (y) is derived. The stoichiometric equation then is

$$yA + xM \rightarrow M_xA_y. \tag{a}$$

Results are generally expressed in terms of the ratio y/x.

As is often the case, while the principle is simple, the practice is more complicated. The chief trouble lies in the accurate estimation of the monolayer volume. This is generally taken to be the volume of gas rapidly adsorbed up to an equilibrium pressure of 0.1 mm.; the unsatisfactory nature of this as a criterion for complete coverage (except perhaps at very low temperatures) has already been noted.

The fact that local oxidation of metal surfaces may result if the high heat of oxygen chemisorption is not dissipated sufficiently rapidly makes the interpretation of results for these systems especially difficult. It is, therefore, more instructive to examine the ratio of numbers of different molecules adsorbed under identical experimental conditions.

There is ample evidence to show that the stoichiometry of hydrogen chemisorption can usually be represented as[50, 110]

$$H_2 + 2M \rightarrow 2M\text{–}H. \qquad \text{(b)}$$

The stoichiometric equation for the atomic adsorption of oxygen is generally written as

$$O_2 + 2M \rightarrow 2M{=}O. \qquad \text{(c)}$$

This would imply an O_2/H_2 adsorption ratio of unity and values close to this have been obtained,[63, 111, 112] although reliable values of three[36] and four[113] have also been found. The disagreement would be partially resolved if the criterion of 0.1 mm. equilibrium pressure for complete coverage corresponded to a complete monolayer of oxygen but only a partial monolayer for hydrogen.

Using this arbitrary criterion for complete coverage, the ratio of volumes of carbon monoxide to hydrogen adsorbed has been found to vary from one metal to another: some values are shown in Table XVI. Since the adsorption

TABLE XVI. *Values of v_{CO}/v_{H_2} Adsorbed at Complete Coverage*

Metal	*Ratio v_{CO}/v_{H_2}*	*Average No. of sites covered by CO*	*Ref.*
Ta	1	2	111
W	1.40	1.6	111
Mo	1	2	111
Fe	1.47, 1.52	~1.5	42
	1.23	~1.8	111
Rh	1	2	111
Ni	1.6	1.4	113, 114
Pd, Pt	?2	?1	111

of hydrogen is dissociative, and hence involves two sites per molecule, if v_{CO}/v_{H_2} is found to be unity, carbon monoxide covers two sites; if the ratio is two, then each carbon monoxide molecule occupies one site, and so on. Possible structures for the adsorbed states are as follows:

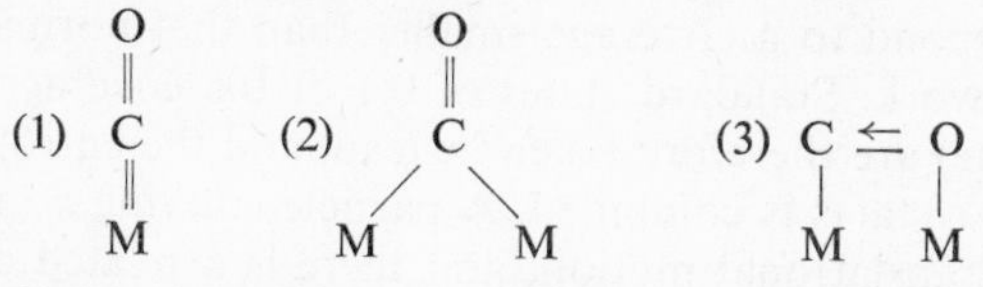

The probable existence of structures (1) and (2) has been inferred from infra-red spectroscopy of adsorbed carbon monoxide.[115–118]

Studies of the chemisorption of ethylene on evaporated metal films are complicated by reactions between the species formed initially, leading to the formation of ethane in the gas phase. Four sites are first required, but in the complete layer only two sites are occupied per ethylene molecule. Possible structures and reactions will be considered in greater detail when the mechanism of the catalytic hydrogenation of olefins is discussed (see Chapter 11).

5.7 Entropy of Adsorption and the Mobility of Adsorbed Layers[23, 119, 120]

An introduction to the concept of mobility in chemisorbed layers has already been given (see Chapter 4). It is now possible to add that if the heat of adsorption decreases with increasing coverage, the activation energy for migration will likewise decrease, and a transition from immobility to mobility may be experienced: this has been found for hydrogen on nickel films.[43]

The phenomenon of mobility is not readily accessible to direct investigation. Of the experimental methods surveyed in the last chapter, only Bosworth's photoelectric method of following work function changes and the field-emission microscope have been applied to this problem, and most of the work carried out by these methods has dealt with the adsorption of alkali or alkaline earth metals on tungsten. Only quite recently has the field-emission microscope been applied to systems of interest in catalysis.[120] A thorough study of the hydrogen–tungsten and hydrogen–nickel systems by this method has revealed a situation of great complexity;[52] at least two mechanisms of migration have been recognized, and their velocities and activation energies vary with coverage and the nature of the lattice plane.

Information on mobility may also be obtained by less direct methods. One such method involves the calculation of the entropy change accompanying adsorption, ΔS_a, defined as

$$\Delta S_a = -\left(\frac{\Delta G_a - \Delta H_a}{T}\right), \tag{25}$$

ΔG_a and $-\Delta H_a$ being respectively the free energy and the differential heat of adsorption. If the adsorption is reversible, ΔG_a may be calculated from the relation

$$-\Delta G_a = RT \ln(P_a/P_g), \tag{26}$$

P_g and P_a being respectively the equilibrium pressures in the gas phase and in the adsorbed layer. To calculate ΔG_a, it is usual to define a standard surface state where P_a is equal to one atmosphere, but in practice this is found to correspond to a coverage smaller than that normally accessible in chemisorption work. Standard states of 0.1 or 0.5 coverage (or some other convenient value) are therefore taken instead, and the entropy of adsorption into one of these states is computed. A particle entering a mobile layer loses one degree of translational motion, and there is a related entropy loss. On entering an immobile layer, the particle loses all three degrees of translational motion, but the greater entropy loss is partly compensated by the occurrence of a configurational entropy which arises because of the numbers of different ways in which the adsorbed particles may be distributed over the surface. The minimum entropy changes expected in each of these situations may be calculated from formulae quoted by Trapnell[23] and compared with experimental values.[4] This comparison leads to conclusions summarized in Table XVII.

TABLE XVII. *The Mobility of Adsorbed Layers as Deduced from Observed and Calculated Entropies of Adsorption*

System	*Temperature (°K)*	*Conclusion*
CO on Au and Cu films	200	mobile
C_2H_4 on Au and Cu films	280	immobile
N_2 on Fe	690	immobile

A second method of obtaining information on mobility is by the interpretation of the shape of heat of adsorption-coverage plots and in particular their temperature dependence. In certain systems the heat of adsorption is apparently constant over an extended range of coverage. This situation obtains either when the heat of adsorption is high (as with oxygen on many metals) or when the temperature of the measurement is sufficiently low (as with hydrogen on iron films at −183°). It is precisely under these conditions that the adsorbed species may be expected immobile. Now in the case of evaporated films, the surface is largely internal and the impinging gas will absorb first on the external surface. If the species are mobile, they will diffuse through the pore system and first cover the sites of highest energy, and the true initial differential heat will be recorded. If they are immobile, they will be unable to do so and will remain on the external surface on sites of differing energy: an integral heat will then result. If, however, the rate of adsorption is low (i.e. if the process is activated), the gas may have a chance to diffuse throughout the film and be adsorbed first by the most "active" sites, although the adsorbed species themselves are immobile. By these criteria, hydrogen on iron at −183° is immobile, but hydrogen on nickel at −196° is mobile (see however Ref. 43). Most surprising perhaps is the fact that ethlyene is apparently mobile at room temperature on all metals except copper and gold: acetylene however is not.

5.8 Type C Chemisorption

There is a very rapidly growing body of evidence that chemisorption is not a simple process, and that more than one kind of chemisorption is possible. It is not possible at this time to present a coherent and unified treatment; the object of this Section is therefore to present the unequivocal experimental evidence bearing on the complexity of chemisorption, and to review briefly the suggested interpretations.

5.81 Experimental Evidence

The complexity is well illustrated by reference to the adsorption isobar for hydrogen on a doubly promoted iron catalyst (Fig. 9).[121] There are three temperature regions where desorption occurs, and there must therefore be three distinct kinds of adsorption, denoted as A, B and C, as in Fig. 9. Now the type A is the normal, strong chemisorption, details of which have been given in the earlier Sections of this Chapter. Type B is a second kind of strong chemisorption peculiar to promoted iron, and there only observed above 100°. The third, Type C, is clearly weak, since desorption sets in at very low temperatures. It may be asked whether this is not physical adsorption. The answer is, however, a firm *no*: many determinations of heats of Type C adsorption (see Table XVIII) show beyond doubt that the heat liberated is much in excess of the maximum permitted by physical adsorption.

Since isobars do not provide definite evidence of the nature of the adsorbed

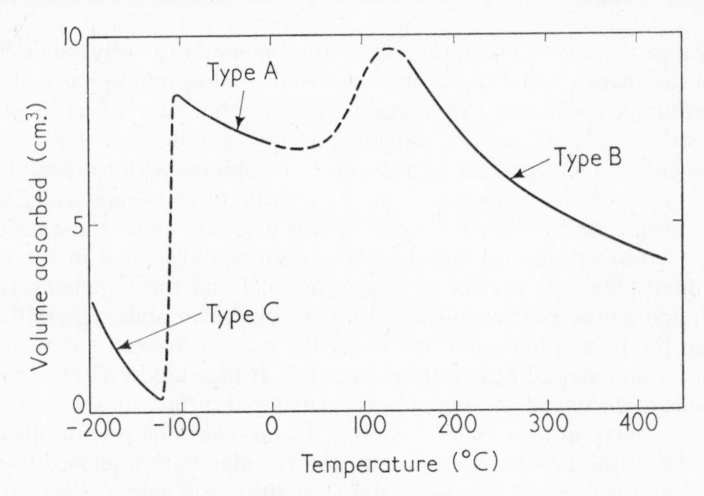

FIG. 9. The adsorption isobar of hydrogen at one atmosphere on doubly promoted iron, after Emmett and Harkness.[121]

state, there is little point in listing systems showing similar low temperature adsorptions, although in retrospect it now seems certain that physical adsorption and Type C adsorption have often been confused in the past. Much reinterpretation of the older work is probably called for, including the classic work of Benton and White,[122] whose study of hydrogen adsorption on nickel, so often referred to in textbooks, showed a low temperature adsorption usually described as physical adsorption, but which was undoubtedly due at least partly to Type C adsorption. If the potential energy curve which has been drawn for this form (Fig. 1) is anything like correct, we should indeed expect to observe the phenomenon either at low temperatures (as here) or, at more elevated temperatures, at high coverages (see Section 5.12).

Evidence for the existence of both strong and weak forms of adsorption now comes from a wide variety of quite direct methods. These include the measurement of surface potentials[103, 108, 123–126] and conductivity changes,[125–129] of changes in work function as seen by field-emission microscopy,[94, 130–132] and from observations on the rates and kinetics of adsorption and desorption as followed by what are now conventional techniques.[133–138] Some further discussion of these observations will be given in the following Chapter. The infra-red spectrum of hydrogen and deuterium chemisorbed on platinum–alumina also gives evidence for a weak state of binding.[84] Only the magnetic method fails to indicate multiple-type adsorption.[139]

Very direct evidence for the Type C state comes from Mignolet's work on surface potentials:[103, 123, 124] as the coverage of metal films by hydrogen increases, an electropositive component (i.e. showing a positive surface potential) appears, allowing ultimately of adsorption in excess of that expected on grounds of stoichiometry. These experiments support the view that in the Type C adsorbed state of hydrogen, electrons are partially withdrawn from hydrogen towards the metal. It is significant that there is no Type C chemisorption of hydrogen on copper.[104]

The same conclusion is reached from measurements of changes in electrical conductivity of nickel films following the slow admission of hydrogen at −78°.[127, 140] The resistance of the film changes with time in the manner shown in Fig. 10. The interpretation is that the first hydrogen molecules arriving at the surface dissociate and adsorb on the external surface of the film in the normal manner, increasing the resistance. When the external surface is completely covered (A), the heat of adsorption has fallen sufficiently low to permit Type C adsorption which then occurs with a decrease in resistance (AB). Hydrogen in the Type C state is mobile and diffuses to the internal surface where it becomes dissociatively adsorbed (Type A state) and for this reason the resistance again increases, but rather slowly (BC). The

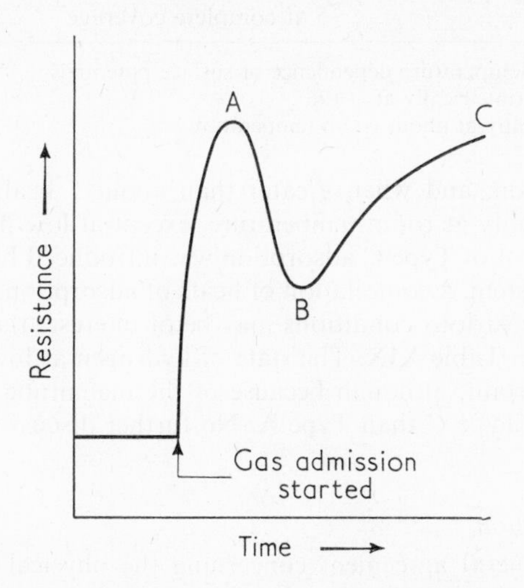

Fig. 10. The variation of the resistance of a nickel film with time during the slow admission of hydrogen at −78°.[127]

concentration of Type C hydrogen on the external surface is maintained constant by replenishment from the gas phase.

Type C chemisorption has now been recognized in the following systems: hydrogen on tungsten,[94, 130, 131, 137, 141] chromium,[135] iron,[135, 137, 142] nickel,[125, 127, 134, 135] palladium[126] and platinum;[61, 84, 135] nitrogen on tungsten[108, 134] and at low temperatures on iron,[143] cobalt[143] and nickel;[144] and carbon monoxide and oxygen on tungsten.[132, 134, 141] The list is rapidly extending. Type C nitrogen on tungsten is recognized to adsorb with a high condensation coefficient which is independent of coverage (unlike Type A); it has a low dipole moment and a low heat of adsorption.[108]

Table XVIII records the heats of Type C adsorption which have been determined to date: the values are all in excess of the expected heats of

TABLE XVIII. *Heats of Type C Adsorption*

Metal	*Form*	$-\Delta H_a$(*kcal. mole*$^{-1}$)	*Method*	*Ref.*
		(a) *Hydrogen*		
W	film	8	*	124
Fe	singly promoted	5.4 to 1.6 with increasing coverage	†	145
Fe	doubly promoted	5.3	†	77
Ni	film	9 to 5 with increasing coverage	‡	135
Pt	film	15	*	103
		(b) *Nitrogen*		
Fe, Ni	films	10 at zero coverage 5 at complete coverage	†	41

* Estimated from temperature dependence of surface potentials.
† Determined calorimetrically at −196°.
‡ Derived isosterically at about room temperature.

physical adsorption, and when greater than about 5 kcal. mole^{-1} imply a considerable stability at room temperature, except at low pressures.

Since the concept of Type C adsorption was introduced by reference to the iron–hydrogen system, a compilation of heats of adsorption, determined with this system under various conditions may be of interest: the observed initial values are given in Table XIX. The state of hydrogen at low temperature on the film is not certain, although because of the magnitude of the heat, it is more likely to be Type C than Type A. No further discussion of Table XIX is called for.

5.82 *Interpretation*

There is no general agreement concerning the physical state of Type C adsorbed hydrogen. It has been variously supposed that it is molecular[2, 147] or atomic[84, 138] in nature. For this reason the form of the potential energy

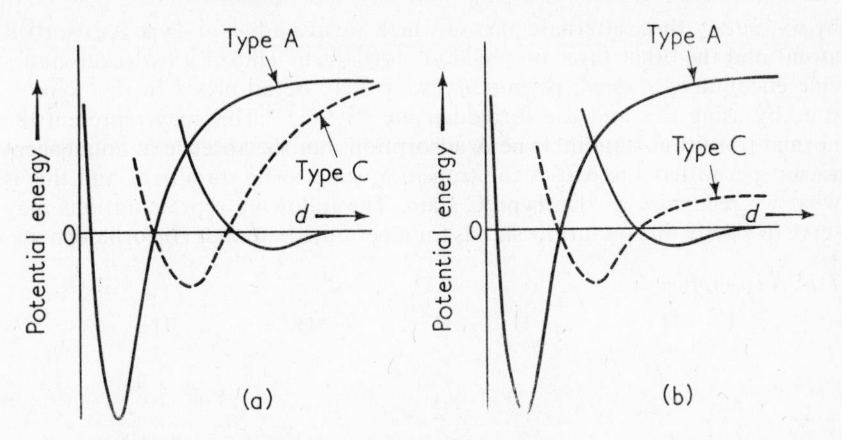

FIG. 11. Various forms of Type C potential energy curves.
(a) After Gundry and Tompkins.[138]
(b) After Dowden.[2]

TABLE XIX. *Heats of Adsorption of Hydrogen on Iron*

Type of iron	*Temp.* (°C)	*Type*	$-\Delta H_a$(*kcal. mole*$^{-1}$)	*Method*	*Curve type*	*Ref.*
Film	20	A	34 ± 2	†	α or γ	40–42
Film	−183	?A	28	†	α	41
Singly promoted	200	B	27 to 15 at $\theta = ?$	†	β	145
Singly promoted	0	A	16.5 to 8 at $\theta = ?$	†	β	145
Singly promoted	−196	C	5.4 to 1.6 at $\theta = ?$	†	?	145
Doubly promoted	−183	?C	5.3	†	?	77
Doubly promoted and pure powder	(high)	?B	19 to 5 at $\theta = 0.1$	†	β	146

curve has been variously drawn, the chief difference being in the "activation" required to prepare a molecule for this type of adsorption (Fig. 11). Gundry and Tompkins[138] have assumed the process to be dissociative (Fig. 11(a)), while Dowden[2] envisages that Type C hydrogen is a molecule partly ionized by donation of *s*-electrons to the vacant *d*-band of the metal: his potential energy curve (Fig. 11(b)) therefore requires little activation. In the absence of definite evidence, Fig. 1 assumes no "activation"; in fact the degree of "activation" is usually immaterial to arguments based on the behaviour of potential energy curves.

Further discussion concerning the state of Type C adsorption is therefore somewhat premature. However, it is now widely thought that hydrogen atoms in the Type A state reside in the interstices between the surface metal atoms,[83, 148] and on some lattice planes there is more than one such interstitial site per surface metal atom.[147, 148] This is the case for example on planes showing hexagonal symmetry, where each metal atom is surrounded by six "sites", three alternate ones of which are available for Type A adsorbed atoms and the other three of which are forbidden. Thus if a hydrogen molecule encounters a *single* permitted site, it may be adsorbed in the Type C state by using this and *one* forbidden site.[131, 147, 149] This may represent the normal transition state in Type A adsorption, but the absence of an adjacent vacant permitted site causes the transition state to be stabilized, and this is what we recognize as the Type C state. The following representations may serve to clarify this picture: * stands for a permitted site and (*) a forbidden site.

Type A adsorption

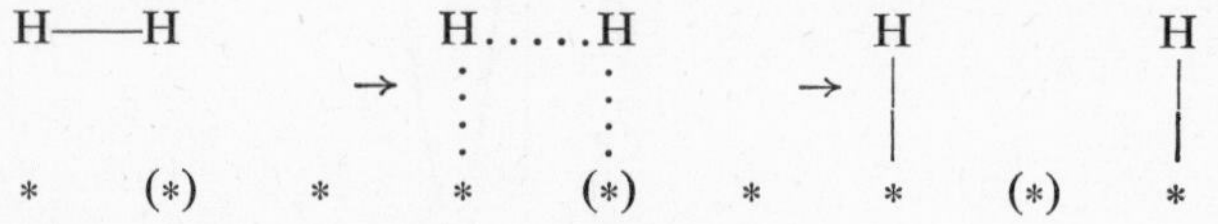

```
H——H              H.....H              H             H
           →      :     :        →     |             |
                  :     :              |             |
*     (*)    *    *    (*)    *        *     (*)     *
```

Type C adsorption

```
H——H        H     H.....H     H
            | →   :     :     |
            |     :     :     |
*     (*)   *     *    (*)    *
```

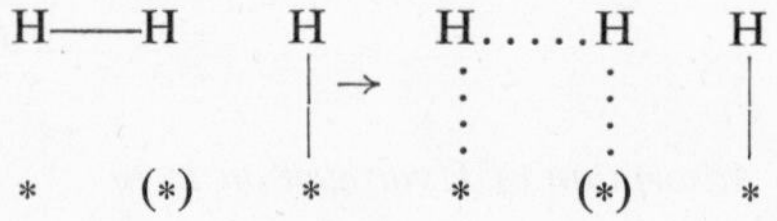

This picture also qualitatively accounts for the fact that the Type C state is detected most often at low temperatures or high coverages.

The situation with other diatomic molecules is similarly obscure. For nitrogen weakly adsorbed on iron films at low temperatures, the ratio of the monolayer volumes v_{N_2}/v_{H_2} is about unity,[41] and it is concluded therefore that Type C nitrogen occupies two sites per molecule, a possible structure being

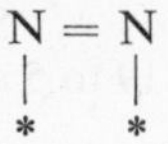

```
N = N
|   |
*   *
```

At room and higher temperatures, this form is replaced by activated atomic adsorption, with which it is impossible to achieve coverages greater than about 20 per cent ($\sim$50 per cent with tungsten). Nitrogen pre-adsorbed at 250° to 300° inhibits subsequent Type C adsorption on nickel powder,[144] and a similar phenomenon has been noted with carbon monoxide.[150]

Although direct evidence for Type C adsorption is presently confined to diatomic molecules, its possible application to other molecules has been discussed.[1] The fact that saturated hydrocarbons are not as readily chemisorbed as hydrogen may mean they are not capable of Type C chemisorption. The electrons constituting the C—H bond in for example methane may be sterically protected by the methyl group, and thus not able to interact with a vacant *d*-orbital of a metal atom. The fact that ethylene and acetylene are chemisorbed by Group IB metals indicates that here the Type C state is not a necessary intermediate: this may be because the potential energy curves for these molecules are such that there is no activation energy between the physically adsorbed and Type A adsorbed states (see Chapter 4).

5.9 Poisons

It is well known that a number of substances can effectively inhibit the catalytic activity of metal surfaces, sometimes even when present in very small amounts. Such substances are known as *catalyst poisons*, and the phenomenon of poisoning is caused by the fact that they are very strongly adsorbed at metal surfaces. A study of the chemical nature of poisons therefore sheds further light on the process of adsorption.

It has long been known that a catalyst poison reduces catalytic activity more than in proportion to the fraction of the surface it occupies;[151] this observation gave great weight to the concept of active centres,[85, 86] although it now appears that alternative interpretations are possible. In principle, the presence of any species more strongly adsorbed than the reactants will inhibit reaction. In practice, mercury, carbon monoxide and sulphur compounds are the most frequent sources of trouble. Atoms of mercury once deposited on a metal surface are essentially impossible to remove, and it is often necessary to protect sensitive metal surface from mercury (and tap grease) vapour by cold traps. Mercury displaces adsorbed hydrogen from metal surfaces and effectively prevents its readsorption:[152] it is, however, unable to displace a gas which is more strongly adsorbed, e.g. propylene.[153] Although according to Table I oxygen is always more strongly adsorbed than carbon monoxide, it is less objectionable in for example hydrogenation reactions because it is often quickly reduced to water, and at worst causes an induction period, whereas carbon monoxide is often not reducible under the same conditions, especially by the noble Group VIII metals.

A large body of empirical experience shows that poisoning power is shown by two broad classes of substance:[154] (i) certain compounds of the elements of Groups VB and VIB and (ii) certain metal ions. In class (i), poisoning power is largely determined by the oxidation state of the element, as is seen

Table XX. *Dependence of Poisoning Power on the Oxidation State of Group VB and VIB Elements*[154]

	Group VB			*Group VIB*	
Element	*Toxic compounds*	*Non-toxic compounds*	*Element*	*Toxic compounds*	*Non-toxic compounds*
N	NH_3, pyridine, piperidine, quinoline	NH_4^+, pyridinium$^+$ etc.	O	O_2	
P	PH_3	PO_4^{3-}	S	H_2S, RSH, R_2S, SO_3^{2-}, RSSR	SO_4^{2-}, RSO_3H, R_2SO_2
As	AsH_3	AsO_4^{3-}	Se	H_2Se, SeO_3^{2-}	SeO_4^{2-}
Sb	SbH_3	SbO_4^{3-}	Te	H_2Te, TeO_3^{2-}	TeO_4^{2-}

in Table XX: from the observation that in all the toxic compounds the central atom possesses at least one lone pair of electrons, it has been concluded that poisoning results from the formation of a strong dative bond between the toxic molecule and the metal. In the chemisorbed state, the lone pair electrons are thought to have entered the unfilled *d*-band of the metal, and as a result of the further pairing of the metal's *d*-electrons, the magnetic susceptibility falls.[155] Oxidation of the adsorbed toxic molecule renders the *in situ* revivification of poisoned catalysts possible.[154]

The heat of adsorption of diethylsulphide on platinum black at room temperature is 65–70 kcal. $mole^{-1}$, but the value for thiophen is lower (33 kcal. $mole^{-1}$) because of the loss of resonance energy on adsorption.[156]

The toxicity of metal ions in liquid phase catalysis has been investigated by Maxted (Ref. 154 and references therein), and certain regularities have emerged. Ions containing no *d*-electrons are not toxic, and neither are Cr^{2+} nor Cr^{3+}; ions possessing a filled *d*-shell are toxic, as are also Mn^{2+}, Fe^{2+}, Co^{2+}, Ni^{2+} and Cu^{2+}. It appears therefore that a minimum of five *d*-electrons are required by the ion to form a bond to the metal surface. This finding is interpreted if we suppose the toxic ion to be in a state of tetrahedral co-ordination at the metal surface, which induces only weak ligand-field splitting; four electrons are then accommodated in d_γ-orbitals, and the fifth (e.g. in Mn^{2+}) goes into a d_ε-orbital, which is able to take part in d_π-bonding with the surface metal atoms.

References

1. D. A. Dowden, *Bull. Soc. Chim. belges* **67**, 439 (1958).
2. D. A. Dowden, In "Chemisorption", edited by W. E. Garner (Butterworths, London, 1958), p. 3.
3. B. M. W. Trapnell, *Quart. Rev.* **8**, 404 (1954).
4. B. M. W. Trapnell, *Proc. Roy. Soc.* **A218**, 566 (1953).
5. E. Greenhalgh and B. M. W. Trapnell, *Adv. Catalysis* **9**, 238 (1957); A. C. Collins and B. M. W. Trapnell, *Trans. Faraday Soc.* **53**, 1476 (1957).
6. S. Wagener, *J. Phys. Chem.* **60**, 567 (1957); **61**, 267 (1957).
7. D. D. Eley and P. R. Wilkinson, *Proc. Roy. Soc.* **A254**, 327 (1960).
8. R. J. Mikovsky, M. Boudart and H. S. Taylor, *J. Amer. Chem. Soc.* **76**, 3814 (1954).
9. E. Schlier and H. E. Farnsworth, *Phys. Rev.* **78**, 316 (1950).
10. M. F. Manning and H. M. Krutter, *Phys. Rev.* **51**, 761 (1937).
11. Y. Sasaki, *J. Chem. Phys.* **27**, 281 (1957).
12. R. M. Dell, *J. Phys. Chem.* **61**, 1584 (1957).
13. J. Eisinger and J. T. Law, *J. Chem. Phys.* **30**, 410 (1959).
14. R. E. Schlier and H. E. Farnsworth, *J. Chem. Phys.* **30**, 917 (1959).
15. M. J. Bennett and F. C. Tompkins, *Proc. Roy. Soc.*, **A259**, 28 (1960).
16. J. T. Law, *J. Phys. Chem.* **59**, 543 (1955).
17. K. Tamaru, *J. Phys. Chem.* **61**, 647 (1957).
18. J. Eisinger, *J. Chem. Phys.* **30**, 927 (1959).
19. J. T. Law, *J. Chem. Phys.* **30**, 1568 (1959).
20. G. Heiland and P. Handler, *J. Appl. Phys.* **30**, 446 (1959).
21. R. V. Culver, J. Pritchard and F. C. Tompkins, *Z. Elektrochem.* **63**, 741 (1959); J. Pritchard and F. C. Tompkins, *Trans. Faraday Soc.* **56**, 540 (1960); R. V. Culver, J. Pritchard and F. C. Tompkins, Proc. 2nd International Conference on Surface Activity, (Butterworths, London 1957), **2**, 243.

22. E. Greenhalgh, D. O. Hayward and B. M. W. Trapnell, *J. Phys. Chem.* **61,** 1254 (1957).
23. B. M. W. Trapnell, "Chemisorption" (Butterworths, London, 1955).
24. I. Langmuir, *J. Amer. Chem. Soc.* **40,** 1361 (1918); R. H. Fowler, *Proc. Cambridge Phil. Soc.* **31,** 260 (1935).
25. G. Schay, *Acta. Chim. Acad. Sci. Hung.* **3,** 511 (1953).
26. G. Halsey and H. S. Taylor, *J. Chem. Phys.* **15,** 624 (1947); G. Halsey, *Adv. Catalysis* **4,** 259 (1952).
27. S. Brunauer, K. S. Love and R. G. Keenan, *J. Amer. Chem. Soc.* **64,** 751 (1942).
28. B. M. W. Trapnell, *Proc. Roy. Soc.* **A206,** 39 (1951).
29. W. G. Frankenburg, *J. Amer. Chem. Soc.* **66,** 1827 (1944).
30. R. T. Davies, *J. Amer. Chem. Soc.* **68,** 1395 (1946).
31. A. F. H. Ward, *Proc. Roy. Soc.* **A133,** 506 (1931).
32. P. H. Emmett and S. Brunauer, *J. Amer. Chem. Soc.* **56,** 35 (1934).
33. A. S. Porter and F. C. Tompkins, *Proc. Roy. Soc.* **A217,** 544 (1953).
34. O. Beeck, *Discuss. Faraday Soc.* **8,** 118 (1950).
35. E. K. Rideal and B. M. W. Trapnell, *Discuss. Faraday Soc.* **8,** 114 (1950).
36. D. F. Klemperer and F. S. Stone, *Proc. Roy. Soc.* **A243,** 375 (1957).
37. A. S. Porter and F. C. Tompkins, *Proc. Roy. Soc.* **A217,** 529 (1953).
38. P. W. Selwood and L. Vaski, *J. Amer. Chem. Soc.* **80,** 1331 (1958).
39. D. P. Stevenson, *J. Chem. Phys.* **23,** 203 (1955).
40. M, Wahba and C. Kemball, *Trans. Faraday Soc.* **49,** 1351 (1953).
41. O. Beeck, *Adv. Catalysis* **2,** 151 (1950).
42. J. Bagg and F. C. Tompkins, *Trans. Faraday Soc.* **51,** 1071 (1955).
43. E. K. Rideal and F. Sweett, *Proc. Roy. Soc.* **A257,** 291 (1960).
44. D. Brennan, D. O. Hayward and B. M. W. Trapnell, *Proc. Roy. Soc.* **A256,** 81 (1960)
45. O. Beeck, W. A. Cole and A. Wheeler, *Discuss. Faraday Soc.* **8,** 314 (1950).
46. G. C. A. Schuit, N. H. de Boer, G. J. H. Dorgelo and L. L. van Reijen, In "Chemisorption", edited by W. E. Garner (Butterworths, London, 1957), p. 39.
47. G. C. A. Schuit and L. L. van Reijen, *Adv. Catalysis* **10,** 242 (1958).
48. B. M. W. Trapnell, *Trans. Faraday Soc.* **51,** 368 (1955).
49. G. C. A. Schuit and N. H. de Boer, *Rec. Trav. chim.* **72,** 909 (1953).
50. J. K. Roberts, *Proc. Roy. Soc.* **A152,** 445 (1935); **A161,** 141 (1937).
51. W. G. Frankenburg, *J. Amer. Chem. Soc.* **66.** 1827 (1944).
52. R. Gomer, R. Wortmann and R. Lundy, *J. Chem. Phys.* **26,** 1147 (1957); **27,** 1099 (1957).
53. J. Rudham and F. S. Stone, *Trans. Faraday Soc.* **54,** 420 (1958).
54. T. Kwan, *J. Res. Inst. Catalysis, Hokkaido Univ.* **1,** 81 (1949).
55. A. Eucken, *Z. Elektrochem.* **53,** 285 (1949).
56. M. W. Roberts and K. W. Sykes, *Trans. Faraday Soc.* **54,** 548 (1958).
57. L. S. Shield and W. W. Russell, *J. Phys. Chem.* **64,** 1592 (1960).
58. T. Kwan, *Adv. Catalysis* **6,** 67 (1954).
59. E. B. Maxted and N. J. Hassid, *J. Chem. Soc.* 3313 (1931).
60. G. B. Taylor, G. B. Kistiakowsky and J. H. Perry, *J. Phys. Chem.* **34,** 799 (1930).
61. H. Chon, R. A. Fisher and J. G. Aston, *J. Amer. Chem. Soc.* **82,** 1055 (1960).
62. A. F. H. Ward, *Proc. Roy. Soc.* **A133,** 506 (1931).
63. J. K. Roberts, *Proc. Roy. Soc.* **A152,** 464 (1935).
64. R. C. L. Bosworth and E. K. Rideal, *Physica* **4,** 925 (1937).
65. M. C. Johnson and F. A. Vick, *Proc. Roy. Soc.* **A151,** 308 (1935).
66. J. J. Chessick, Y.-F. Yu and A. C. Zettlemoyer, Proc. 2nd International Conference on Surface Activity (Butterworths, London, 1957), **2,** 269.
67. R. M. Dell, D. F. Klemperer and F. S. Stone, *J. Phys. Chem.* **60,** 1586 (1956).
68. W. W. Russell and O. C. Bacon, *J. Amer. Chem. Soc.* **54,** 54 (1932).
69. O. D. Gonzalez and G. Parravano, *J. Amer. Chem. Soc.* **78,** 4533 (1956).
70. M. H. Bortner and G. Parravano, *Adv. Catalysis* **9,** 424 (1957).
71. E. B. Maxted and N. J. Hassid, *Trans. Faraday Soc.* **29,** 698 (1933).

72. R. M. Dell, F. S. Stone and P. F. Tiley, *Trans. Faraday Soc.* **49,** 195 (1953).
73. J. Rudham and F. S. Stone, *Trans. Faraday Soc.* **54,** 420 (1958).
74. J. J. F. Scholten and P. Zwietering, *Trans. Faraday Soc.* **53,** 1363 (1957).
75. T. Kwan, *J. Res. Inst. Catalysis, Hokkaido Univ.* **3,** 109 (1955).
76. P. H. Emmett and S. Brunauer, *J. Amer. Chem. Soc.* **56,** 35 (1934).
77. R. A. Beebe and N. P. Stevens, *J. Amer. Chem. Soc.* **62,** 2134 (1940).
78. R. A. Beebe and E. L. Wilder, *J. Amer. Chem. Soc.* **56,** 642 (1934).
79. D. D. Eley, *Discuss. Faraday. Soc.* **8,** 34 (1950).
80. D. D. Eley, "Catalysis and the Chemical Bond" (University of Notre Dame Press, Notre Dame, 1954).
81. D. P. Stevenson, *J. Chem. Phys.* **23,** 203 (1955).
82. I. Higuchi, T. Ree and H. Eyring, *J. Amer. Chem. Soc.* **79,** 1330 (1957).
83. T. Takaishi, *Z. phys. Chem. (Frankfurt)* **14,** 165 (1958).
84. W. A. Pliskin and R. P. Eischens, *Z. phys. Chem. (Frankfurt)* **24,** 11 (1960).
85. H. S. Taylor, *Proc. Roy. Soc.* **A108,** 105 (1925).
86. F. H. Constable, *Proc. Roy. Soc.* 355.
87. E. G. Brock, *Adv. Catalysis* **9,** 452 (1957).
88. R. J. Sips, *J. Chem. Phys.* **16,** 490 (1948); **18,** 1024 (1950).
89. J. H. de Boer, In "Chemisorption", edited by W. E. Garner (Butterworths, London, 1957), p. 27.
90. J. H. de Boer, *Adv. Catalysis* **8,** 18 (1956).
91. M. Boudart, *J. Amer. Chem. Soc.* **72,** 3556 (1952).
92. J. C. P. Mignolet, *J. Chem. Phys.* **23,** 753 (1955).
93. D. D. Eley, *J. Phys. Chem.* **55,** 1017 (1951).
94. J. A. Becker, 2nd International Congress on Catalysis (Editions Technip., Paris, 1961) **2,** 1777.
95. R. V. Culver and F. C. Tompkins, *Adv. Catalysis* **11,** 67 (1959).
96. G. I. Jenkins and E. K. Rideal, *Nature* **174,** 1185 (1954).
97. W. M. H. Sachtler and G. J. H. Dorgelo, *J. Chim. phys.* **54,** 27 (1957).
98. J. C. P. Mignolet, *Discuss. Faraday Soc.* **8,** 326 (1950).
99. R. C. L. Bosworth, *Trans. Faraday Soc.* **35,** 397 (1939).
100. J. C. P. Mignolet, *Bull. Soc. Chim. belges* **64,** 126 (1955).
101. J. C. P. Mignolet, *Discuss. Faraday Soc.* **8,** 105 (1950).
102. K. Azuma, *Shokubai* **10,** 1 (1954).
103. J. C. P. Mignolet, *J. Chim. phys.* **54,** 19 (1957).
104. J. C. P. Mignolet, *J. Chim. phys.* **54,** 53 (1957).
105. C. W. Oatley, *Proc. Phys. Soc.* **51,** 318 (1939).
106. J. Giner and E. Lange, *Naturwiss.* **40,** 506 (1953).
107. J. T. Kummer, *J. Phys. Chem.* **63,** 460 (1959).
108. P. L. Jones and B. A. Pethica, *Proc. Roy. Soc.* **A256,** 454 (1960).
109. J. C. P. Mignolet, In "Chemisorption", edited by W. E. Garner (Butterworths, London, 1957), p. 118.
110. O. Beeck and A. W. Ritchie, *Discuss. Faraday Soc.* **8,** 159 (1950).
111. M. A. H. Lanyon and B. M. W. Trapnell, *Proc. Roy. Soc.* **A227,** 387 (1955).
112. B. M. W. Trapnell, *Proc. Roy. Soc.* **A206,** 39 (1951).
113. O. Beeck, A. E. Smith and A. Wheeler, *Proc. Roy. Soc.* **A177,** 62 (1940).
114. B. M. W. Trapnell, In "Chemisorption", edited by W. E. Garner (Butterworths, London, 1957), p. 100.
115. R. P. Eischens and W. A. Pliskin, *Adv. Catalysis* **10,** 1 (1958).
116. R. A. Gardner and R. A. Petrucci, *J. Amer. Chem. Soc.* **82,** 5051 (1960).
117. V. A. Crawford, *Quart. Rev.* **14,** 378 (1960).
118. H. L. Pickering and H. C. Eckstrom, *J. Phys. Chem.* **63,** 512 (1959).
119. C. Kemball, *Adv. Catalysis* **2,** 233 (1950).
120. P. M. Gundry and F. C. Tompkins, *Quart. Rev.* **14,** 257 (1960).
121. P. H. Emmett and R. W. Harkness, *J. Amer. Chem. Soc.* **57,** 1631 (1935).
122. A. F. Benton and T. A. White, *J. Amer. Chem. Soc.* **50,** 2325 (1930).

123. J. C. P. Mignolet, *J. Chim. phys.* **47,** 172 (1950).
124. J. C. P. Mignolet, *Rec. Trav. Chim.* **74,** 701 (1955).
125. R. Suhrmann, Y. Mizushima, A. Hermann and G. Wedler, *Z. phys. Chem. (Frankfurt)* **20,** 332 (1959).
126. R. Suhrmann, G. Wedler and G. Schumicki, In "Structures and Properties of Thin Films", edited by Neugebauer, Newkirk and Vermilyea (Wiley, New York, 1959), p. 268.
127. W. M. H. Sachtler and G. J. H. Dorgelo, *Bull. Soc. chim. belges* **67,** 465 (1958); *Z. phys. Chem. (Frankfurt)* **25,** 69 (1960).
128. R. Suhrmann, G. Wedler and D. Schliephake, *Z. phys. Chem. (Frankfurt)* **12,** 128 (1957).
129. V. Ponec and Z. Knor, *Coll. Czech. Chem. Comm.* **25,** 2913 (1960); Proc. 2nd International Congress on Catalysis (Editions Technip., Paris, 1961) **1,** 195.
130. S. Z. Roginskii and I. I. Tretyakov, *Doklady Akad. Nauk. S.S.S.R.* **105,** 112 (1955).
131. W. M. H. Sachtler and G. J. H. Dorgelo, Proc. 4th International Conference on Electron Microscopy (Springer-Verlag, Berlin, 1958), **1,** 51.
132. J. A. Becker and R. G. Brandes, *J. Chem. Phys.* **23,** 1323 (1955).
133. G. Ehrlich, *J. Chem. Phys.* **23,** 1543 (1955).
134. A. G. Nasini, G. Saini and F. Ricca, Proc. 2nd International Congress on Catalysis (Editions Technip., Paris, 1961) **1,** 241.
135. N. N. Kavtaradze, *Zhur. fiz. Khim.* **32,** 1055 (1958).
136. N. N. Kavtaradze, *Zhur. fiz. Khim.* **32,** 1214 (1958).
137. T. W. Hickmott, *J. Chem. Phys.* **32,** 810 (1960).
138. P. M. Gundry and F. C. Tompkins, *Trans. Faraday Soc.* **52,** 1609 (1956).
139. P. W. Selwood, Proc. 2nd International Congress on Catalysis (Editions Technip., Paris, 1961) **2,** 1795.
140. J. H. Singleton, *J. Phys. Chem.* **60,** 1606 (1956).
141. T. W. Hickmott and G. Ehrlich, *J. Chem. Phys.* **24,** 1263 (1956).
142. P. Zwietering, H. L. T. Koks and C. van Heerden, *J. Phys. and Chem. Solids* **11,** 18 (1959).
143. R. J. Kokes, *J. Amer. Chem. Soc.* **82,** 3018 (1960).
144. R. J. Kokes and P. H. Emmett, *J. Amer. Chem. Soc.* **80,** 2082 (1958); **82,** 1037 (1960).
145. R. A. Beebe and E. R. Camplin, *J. Phys. Chem.* **63,** 480 (1959).
146. T. Kwan, *J. Res. Inst. Catalysis, Hokkaido Univ.* **1,** 100 (1949).
147. J. C. P. Mignolet, *Bull. Soc. Chim. belges.* **67,** 358 (1958).
148. C. J. Davisson and C. H. Germer, *Phys. Rev.* **43,** 292 (1933).
149. J. C. P. Mignolet, *Mem. Soc. roy. Sci. Liège*(5) **1** (1958).
150. M. V. C. Sastri, T. S. Viswanathan and T. S. Nagajunan, *J. Phys. Chem.* **63,** 518 (1959).
151. R. N. Pease and L. Stewart, *J. Amer. Chem. Soc.* **47,** 1235 (1925).
152. K. C. Campbell and S. J. Thomson, *Trans. Faraday Soc.* **55,** 306 (1959).
153. K. C. Campbell and S. J. Thomson, *Trans. Faraday Soc.* **55,** 985 (1959).
154. E. B. Maxted, *Adv. Catalysis* **3,** 129 (1951).
155. M. H. Dilke, E. B. Maxted and D. D. Eley, *Nature* **161,** 804 (1948).
156. E. B. Maxted and M. Josephs, *J. Chem. Soc.* 2635 (1956).

Chapter 6

The Kinetics of Adsorption and Desorption

6.1 The Formulation of Rates of Adsorption and Desorption

It may at first sight seem illogical to describe the results pertaining to the equilibrium state in adsorption systems before treating the factors affecting the rate at which the equilibrium is attained. There are, however, several reasons for giving rate phenomena lesser prominence. In the first place, rates of adsorption are often extremely rapid and their measurement is correspondingly difficult, and for this reason much more is known about the statics of adsorption than its dynamics. Secondly, because adsorption rates are generally rapid, they are not normally the rate-limiting step in surface reactions. Nevertheless in a few but important cases adsorption or desorption rates are the slowest step in the overall process, and for this reason it is necessary to offer some discussion of the factors affecting these rates.

A description of the available experimental techniques has already been given, and those methods particularly suited to studying rate phenomena have been noted (Chapter 4).

Rates of adsorption and desorption are to be expressed in terms of the change in the number of particles either in the gas phase or adsorbed, per unit time. For the process

$$A_2 + 2 * \rightarrow 2 \underset{*}{A}, \tag{a}$$

where $*$ represents a single adsorption site, the rate of adsorption will be given by

$$r_a = -\frac{dP_{A_2}}{dt} = [**]\, \sigma Z' \exp\left(\frac{-E_a}{RT}\right). \tag{1}$$

In this equation, P_{A_2} is the pressure of A_2 in the gas phase, $[*\,*]$ the concentration of pairs of empty sites, σ the chance that collision of a molecule of A_2 with a pair of empty sites will result in adsorption, Z' the number of collisions of A_2 molecules with the total surface per cm.^{2} per unit time, and E_a the activation energy for adsorption. Z', which may be designated the surface collision number, is given by

$$Z' = P_{A_2}(2\pi mkT)^{-1/2}, \tag{2}$$

m being the mass of the A_2 molecule and $\boldsymbol{k}$ the Boltzmann constant. A comparison of the combination of the last two equations with the full expression for a homogeneous bimolecular reaction shows that the condensation coefficient σ is the analogue of the steric factor.

For the desorption process

$$2\underset{*}{A} \rightarrow A_2 + 2*, \tag{b}$$

the rate expression may be formulated as

$$r_d = +\frac{dP_{A_2}}{dt} = k_d\,\theta^2 \exp\left(\frac{-E_d}{RT}\right), \tag{3}$$

where θ is the fraction of sites covered by atoms of A, E_d the activation energy for desorption and k_d a velocity constant.

The fact that rates of adsorption are often immeasurably fast, combined with the apparent lack of dependence of rate on temperature[1–3] leads to the conclusion that E_a in such systems is very small: values of about 0.5 kcal.

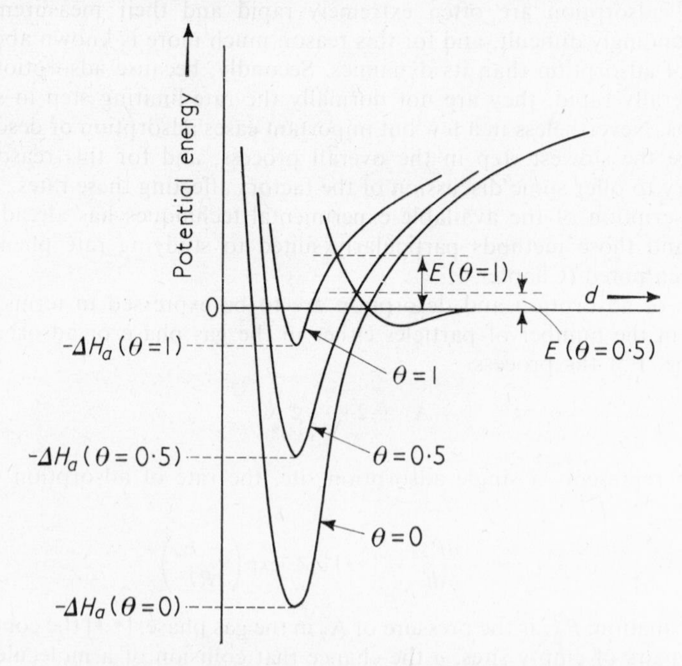

FIG. 1. Formal representation of the dependence of E_a on coverage.

mole^{-1} have been derived.[4, 5] In these cases the exponential term in the rate expression for chemisorption may be ignored. However, desorption is necessarily activated, and E_d is equal to $-\Delta H_a$ under the prevailing conditions if E_a is zero (see Chapter 4). Now we have already anticipated in Chapter 4 the factors which in principle may lead to a dependence of the parameters in the adsorption and desorption rate expressions on coverage, and we have in Chapter 5 presented and discussed the experimental findings which show that $-\Delta H_a$ often depends on coverage. The way in which the fall in $-\Delta H_a$ with coverage may affect the activation energies E_a and E_d is made clear in Fig. 1. The three curves A, B and C may be taken to correspond to coverages of zero, 0.5 and unity respectively, there being a corresponding fall in the heat of adsorption. The activation energy for chemisorption, initially zero, becomes positive and progressively larger as the coverage

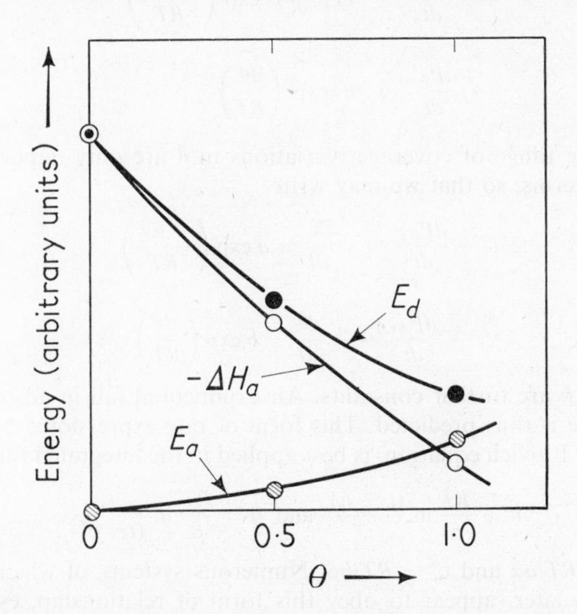

FIG. 2. The dependence of heat of adsorption and of activation energies of adsorption E_a and desorption E_d on coverage, as derived from Fig. 1.

increases. This diagram should be compared with Fig. 1 in Chapter 4 rather than with Fig. 1 in Chapter 5, since the possible existence of Type C chemisorption has been ignored in the present diagram. From Fig. 1 we may construct a further diagram (Fig. 2) to show the dependence of the heat of adsorption and of the activation energies on coverage. E_a can never of course exceed E_d, otherwise the adsorption would be endothermic.

We are now in a position to derive expressions for the variation in rates of adsorption and desorption with coverage. We may assume in the case of mobile adsorption that σ has a value close to unity and independent of coverage, for which there is considerable evidence.[6] Rates will then vary with coverage for two reasons: first, because θ and the concentration of vacant sites $(1-\theta)$ are of course varying, and second because of the dependence of E_a and E_d on θ. If the dependence is linear in each case, then

$$E_a = (E_a)_0 + \alpha\theta \tag{4}$$

and

$$E_d = (E_d)_0 - \beta\theta, \tag{5}$$

where $(E_a)_0$ and $(E_d)_0$ are respectively the activation energies for adsorption and desorption at zero coverage, and α and β are constants. Substituting into the rate expressions for adsorption and desorption (equations 1 and 2), and assuming σ and k_d to be independent of θ we obtain:

$$-\frac{dP_{A_2}}{dt} \propto (1-\theta)^2 \exp\left(\frac{-\alpha\theta}{RT}\right) \tag{6}$$

and

$$+\frac{dP_{A_2}}{dt} \propto \theta^2 \exp\left(\frac{\beta\theta}{RT}\right). \tag{7}$$

In the middle range of coverage, variations in θ are only important in the exponential terms, so that we may write

$$-\frac{dP_{A_2}}{dt} = +\frac{d\theta}{dt} = a \exp\left(\frac{-\alpha\theta}{RT}\right) \tag{8}$$

and

$$+\frac{dP_{A_2}}{dt} = -\frac{d\theta}{dt} = b \exp\left(\frac{\beta\theta}{RT}\right), \tag{9}$$

where a and b are further constants. An exponential fall in adsorption rate with coverage is thus predicted. This form of rate expression,[7, 8] commonly known as the Elovich equation, is best applied in the integrated forms

$$\theta = \frac{RT}{\alpha} \ln \frac{(t+t_0)}{t_0} \quad \text{and} \quad \theta = \frac{RT}{\beta} \ln \frac{t_0'}{(t+t_0')}, \tag{10, 11}$$

where $t_0 = RT/a\alpha$ and $t_0' = RT/b\beta$. Numerous systems, of which examples will be given later, appear to obey this form of relationship, especially in adsorption.[8]

We now turn to a brief review of experimental work on the rates and kinetics of adsorption and desorption processes.

6.2 Experimental Determinations of the Kinetics of Adsorption and Desorption

6.21 Fast Chemisorption

Because of the formidable technical difficulties, precise measurements on the rates and kinetics of fast chemisorption are very few. Wagener[9] has determined the rates of chemisorption of several gases on evaporated films of a number of metals by measuring the pressure differential across a fine

TABLE I. *Rates of Fast Chemisorptions on Evaporated Metal Films*[9]

Rate	*Gas*	*Metals*
~5 l. cm.$^{-2}$ sec.$^{-1}$	CO and CO_2	Ba, Sr, Ni
Initially > 2.5 l. cm.$^{-2}$ sec.$^{-1}$	CO	La, Ti, Zr, Nb, Ta, Cr, Mo, W, Mn, Fe
	N_2	La, Ti, Zr, Nb, Ta, Mo, W
~50 cm.^{3} cm.$^{-2}$ sec.$^{-1}$	H_2 and N_2	Ba, Sr, Ni

capillary through which the gas passes to the adsorption vessel. Some of his results are summarized in Table I. E_a for carbon monoxide and dioxide was estimated to be less than 0.2 kcal. mole^{-1}. The following activation energies for fast chemisorption processes have also been derived:

System	E_a*(kcal. mole*$^{-1}$*)*	*Ref.*
H_2/Ni wire	0.4	2
O_2/W wire	0.6	4
N_2/W wire	0.4	5

6.22 *Subsequent Slow Processes*

It is frequently found that initially rapid "non-activated" chemisorptions are followed by subsequent slower uptakes of gas whose rates are readily measured.[8] The distinction between the two is sometimes quite marked, and in other cases is less distinct.[10] The rates of these slow processes are often described by the Elovich equation.[8, 11] The relative extents of the fast and slow processes may be determined by an isobaric technique. The extent of fast chemisorption v_f is measured at low temperature (−196° or −183°); on warming to room temperature, the slow process rapidly comes to equilibrium which is maintained if the system is slowly cooled again to the low temperature. The additional uptake of gas v_s represents that adsorbed during the slow process (see Fig. 3).

Slow effects have been observed in a number of systems, some of which are recorded in Table II. Both films and powders show the effect, although Kwan[12] has claimed that it is absent with thoroughly reduced and degassed powders. The ratio v_s/v_{total} is usually larger for powders than for films. A variety of explanations for the phenomenon have been offered.[8] The slow chemisorption of oxygen on certain metals (especially nickel and iron) may be reasonably ascribed to diffusion of oxygen atoms from the surface to the interior, leading to the formation of the bulk oxide,[13, 14] but with other metals, such as tungsten, where the effect is small, the interpretation is less certain.

In the adsorption of hydrogen on evaporated nickel it was originally found[17] that v_s was independent of the degree of sintering, and therefore

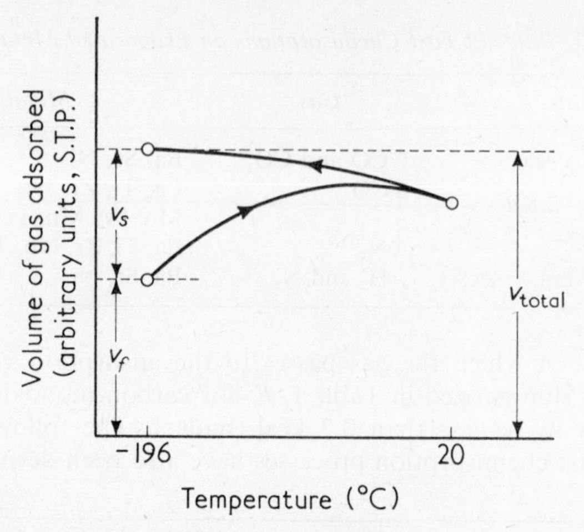

FIG. 3. Diagrammatic representation of the relative extents of fast and slow chemisorptions:
v_f = volume of gas adsorbed in fast process;
v_s = volume of gas adsorbed in slow process.

determined only by the weight or volume of the film: a similar result was obtained with hydrogen adsorption on tungsten films.[15] However, recent more thorough investigations show that in the adsorption of hydrogen and of carbon monoxide on iron and nickel films, the ratio of v_s/v_f is almost constant and independent of sintering temperature provided this does not exceed the critical values of 33° for nickel and 158° for iron.[16, 20]

TABLE II. *Systems Showing "Slow" Chemisorption*

Gas	*Metal*	*Refs.*
H_2	W films	15
	Fe films	16
	Ni films, powder and kieselguhr-supported	17–23
	Pd films	24
	Ru, Rh, Pd and Ir on Al_2O_3	25
	Cu powder	26
CO	W films	27
	Fe films	16
	Ni films	18, 20
	Pt and Pd films	28
N_2	Ta, W, Cr and Fe films	13, 29, 30
O_2	Most metals	10, 13, 14, 27, 31, 32

Recorded values of this ratio are: for hydrogen, 0.18 on iron and 0.19 on nickel, and for carbon monoxide on nickel, 0.16. The rates of the slow processes are proportional to the square root of the hydrogen pressure and the first power of the carbon monoxide pressure, showing that hydrogen atoms and carbon monoxide molecules are involved in the slow step. Activation energies increase linearly with the amount of gas adsorbed.

Slow chemisorptions on iron and nickel films are now established as surface phenomena below the critical temperatures mentioned above, for most of the slowly adsorbed gas is readily pumped off or displaced by mercury vapour. Above these critical temperatures, further gas uptakes are observed and are easily recognizable as absorptions.[20] Attempts to ascribe these slow processes to activated migration for "active" to "inactive" regions of the surface have proved unsuccessful,[16] and they are now elegantly interpreted in terms of an activated transition from an initial Type C adsorbed state to the final Type A state.[18, 33] The interpretation is as follows.

Figure 4 shows in a formal manner how an activation energy may appear

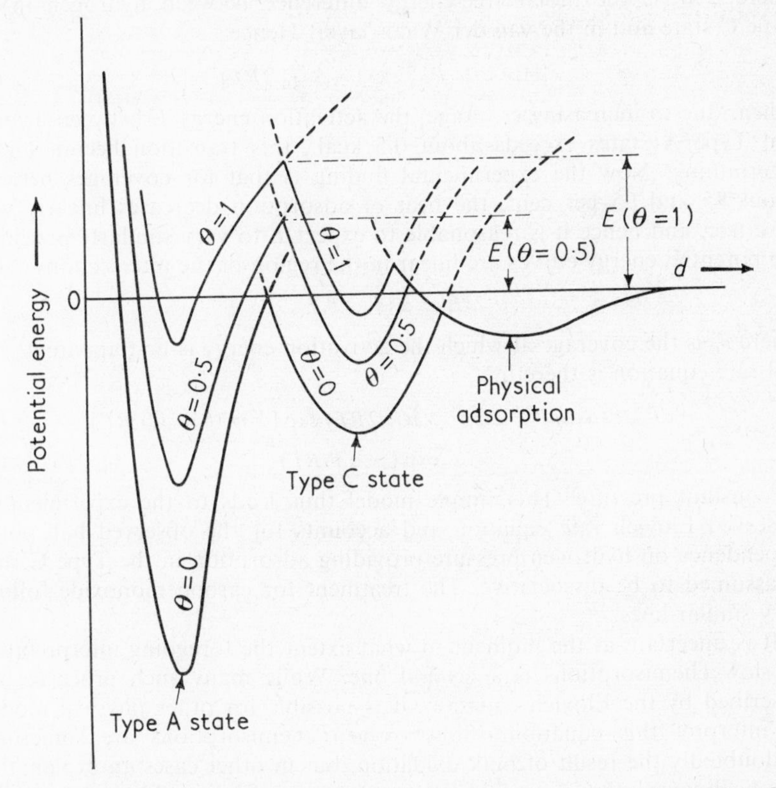

FIG. 4. A diagram indicating the appearance of an activation energy between Type C and Type A states at high coverage. Compare with Fig. 11 of Chapter 5 and Fig. 1 of this Chapter.

between the Type C state and the final state above a certain critical coverage. In constructing this diagram it has been assumed (following the original treatment[18]) that hydrogen in the Type C state is dissociated, and that the heat of adsorption in the Type C state decreases with coverage in the normal manner. The following argument is not, however, dependent on the validity of this last assumption.

For hydrogen, coverage in the physically adsorbed layer will always be small and proportional to the gas pressure, viz.

$$[H_2]_p = kP_{H_2}. \tag{12}$$

Assuming Type C hydrogen to be dissociated, we may define an equilibrium constant K_1 as

$$K_1 = [H]_C^2/[H_2]_p \tag{13}$$

and hence

$$K = kK_1 = [H]_C^2/P_{H_2} = a \exp(-\Delta G_C/RT), \tag{14}$$

where ΔG_C is the molar free-energy difference between hydrogen in the Type C state and in the van der Waals layer. Hence

$$[H]_C = a' P_{H_2}^{0\cdot5} \exp(-\Delta G_C/2RT). \tag{15}$$

When, due to increasing coverage, the activation energy E between Type C and Type A states exceeds about 0.5 kcal., this transition becomes rate-determining. Now the experimental finding is that for coverages between about 85 and 95 per cent, the heat of adsorption decreases linearly with coverage, and hence it is reasonable to expect E to vary similarly providing the potential energy curves are linear in the region of the intersections. Thus

$$E = \alpha'(\theta - \theta_0), \tag{16}$$

where θ_0 is the coverage at which the activation energy is first apparent. The full rate equation is therefore

$$-dP_{H_2}/dt = a'P_{H_2}^{0\cdot5} \exp(-\Delta G_C/2RT) \exp[-\alpha'(\theta - \theta_0)/RT] \tag{17}$$

$$= a'' \exp(-\alpha'\theta/RT) \tag{18}$$

at constant pressure. This simple model thus leads to the experimentally observed Elovich rate equation and accounts for the observed half-power dependence on hydrogen pressure providing adsorption in the Type C state is assumed to be dissociative. The treatment for carbon monoxide follows very similar lines.

It is uncertain at the moment to what extent the foregoing interpretation of slow chemisorptions is a general one. While many such processes are described by the Elovich equation, it is possible for other physical models to interpret this equation.[8] Slow oxygen chemisorptions are sometimes undoubtedly the result of bulk oxidation, but in other cases an explanation on the lines of the above model remains a possibility. The experimental evidence is still insufficient to render a firm decision possible. Slow chemisorptions of methane[34] and ethylene[35] on nickel have been shown to obey the Elovich equation,[11] but it has yet to be established whether either is capable of Type C chemisorption. The concept of Type C chemisorption has proved valuable in a problem well removed from that which it was originally devised to interpret, and this encourages the belief that it will be found to be important in yet further problems of chemisorption and catalysis.

6.23 *Activated Adsorption*

There are few systems in which there is a genuine activation energy for chemisorption at zero coverage. Many of the activated adsorptions which have been recorded are undoubtedly due to the surface not being initially in a clean state. Table III summarizes much of the available information on activated systems. Activation energies are mostly in the range 10–20 kcal. mole^{-1}; the adsorption of hydrogen is activated only in exceptional cases,[36–38]

TABLE III. *Systems Showing Activated Adsorption*

Gas	*Metal*	*Form*	E_a (*kcal. mole*$^{-1}$)	*Temp.* °C	*Comments*	*Ref.*
O_2	Ag	film	—	0	Only if film sintered above −78°	10
H_2	Ge	film	14.6*	190–280	—	36
H_2	Cu	powder	20.5	200–400	—	37
H_2	Fe	doubly promoted	10.4	−78–−96	—	38
N_2	W	powder	~8*	400–750	$E \doteqdot 25$ at saturation	39
N_2	Fe	doubly promoted	~10*	200–450	$E \doteqdot 21.4$ at saturation	40
N_2	Fe	singly promoted	17	?	—	41
N_2	Fe	singly promoted	~10*	300–500	†	42
N_2	Fe	singly promoted	~10*	200–250	†; $E = 27$ at $\theta = 0.25$	43, 44
N_2	Fe	singly promoted	5.2*	24–256	†; $E = 23$ at $\theta = 0.22$	45
CH_4	Ni	film	11	?	—	46

* : value at zero coverage.
† : E_a increases linarly with coverage.

while the adsorption of nitrogen is generally activated. In this process, tungsten and iron behave similarly: at zero coverage, the activation energy E_a is normally 8–10 kcal. mole^{-1} at $\theta \simeq 0.25$.

Especially careful studies[42–45] of nitrogen chemisorption on singly promoted iron have shown that the activation energy increases linearly with coverage, and hence the rates obey the Elovich equation. Very thorough reduction of an iron catalyst containing 0.85 per cent Al_2O_3 (estimated to cover 26 per cent of the surface) has enabled the adsorption to be detected at 0°, and measured between 24 and 256°. The equation relating the activation energy with coverage over the range 0.07 to 0.22 is:

$$E_a = 5.25 + 77.5\,\theta \text{ kcal. mole}^{-1},$$

the extrapolated initial activation energy being notably lower than for less thoroughly reduced catalysts. In the coverage range 0.25–0.7, the activation energy is constant at 23 kcal. mole^{-1}. The log A (frequency factor) term also rises linearly in the coverage range 0.07–0.25, but thereafter it decreases logarithmically with increasing coverage. It is concluded that nitrogen is chemisorbed as immobile atoms at low coverage and as mobile molecules ($\underset{*}{N}{=}\underset{*}{N}$) at high coverages.

The adsorption of the saturated hydrocarbons methane and ethane proceeds readily on all the Transition metals so far examined, with the exception of iron, cobalt and nickel.[46–48] On these last metals, the threshold temperatures for adsorption are high (CH_4–Ni, 140°; CH_4–Fe, 170°; C_2H_6–Fe, 70°), the activation energy in the methane–nickel system having been estimated as 11 kcal. mole^{-1}.[46] Even with the other Transition metals (e.g. tungsten), the adsorption process arrests itself before complete coverage is achieved. Study of these systems is complicated by the dissociation of the adsorbed radicals and the consequent liberation of hydrogen (see Chapter 9).

It would appear that there is no fundamental distinction between those systems which are activated over the entire range of coverage and those which, while initially non-activated, nevertheless develop an activation energy in the region near complete coverage. The determining factor is simply the relative positions of the potential energy curves of the states preceding and constituting adsorption. Linear increase of activation energy with coverage and consequent obedience to the Elovich equation does not depend on whether the process is activated at zero coverage or not. The nitrogen–iron system is the most thoroughly investigated, and seems most promising for further study. The rates on films are initially fast (although becoming activated at higher coverages) and are proportional to $P_{N_2}^{\frac{1}{2}}$,[30] but on promoted iron the process is activated even at the lowest coverages, and the rate is proportional to P_{N_2}.[44, 45] A possible interpretation is that the rate-controlling step on films is similar to that in the carbon monoxide–iron and –nickel systems, and that on promoted iron, where for some reason not yet understood there is no weak state, the slow step is the transition between physical adsorption and strong chemisorption. The fact that singly promoted iron shows weak chemisorption of hydrogen, but not of nitrogen, remains to be understood. A study of the kinetics of the adsorption of carbon monoxide and of hydrogen on promoted iron might prove rewarding.

6.24 *Desorption Kinetics*[49]

Relatively few measurements of the rates and activation energies of desorption are recorded. The rate expression for the desorption of oxygen at low coverage from tungsten is[50]

$$\text{rate} = 1.34 \times 10^{31} \exp(-162{,}000/RT) \text{ mol. cm.}^{-2} \text{ sec.}^{-1}$$

The activation energy for the desorption of nitrogen from singly promoted iron obeys the relationship

$$E_a = 64.5\text{–}20\,\theta \text{ kcal. mole}^{-1}$$

in the range of coverage between zero and 0.6.[44] More extensive measurements have been made[45] on a more thoroughly reduced singly promoted iron catalyst, from which the relation is

$$E_d = 55.0\text{–}29.2\,\theta \text{ kcal. mole}^{-1}$$

over the coverage range 0.10–0.84, and at temperatures between 280 and 445°. The frequency factor for desorption varies with coverage in the range 0.04–0.60 according to the equation

$$\log A_d = 14.68 + \log \theta^2 - 4.62\,\theta.$$

6.3 The Calculation of Rates of Adsorption and Desorption

The Absolute Rate Theory provides a means whereby the rates of adsorption and desorption may be calculated provided certain properties of the system are known. Since the *a priori* calculation of activation energies presents formidable difficulties, the Theory is generally applied in such a way that, when the observed activation energy is substituted into a theoretical expression, a rate is obtained which may be compared with that observed. The value of this approach lies in the test it provides for the validity of the assumed model, and while it is clear that the term "absolute rate" in this context must be liberally interpreted, the technique has very great potentialities, and must therefore receive attention.

A severe disadvantage of the method is that the derived rate expressions contain no parameter characteristic of the surface, except in so far as it influences the experimental activation energy. Thus for fast chemisorptions proceeding at low temperatures with apparently zero activation energy, the Absolute Rate Theory predicts a limiting rate only slightly dependent on the adsorbing molecule and independent of the surface. The most fruitful application of the Theory will clearly be to those systems showing readily measurable activation energies. Before proceeding to describe these applications, however, it will be well to summarize the basic tenets of the Theory.

6.31 *The Theory of Absolute Reaction Rates*

According to the Collision Theory, the rate constant of a chemical reaction is given by

$$k = PZ \exp(-E/RT), \tag{19}$$

where P is a "steric factor", Z the collision number and E the activation energy. Furthermore the equilibrium constant is given by

$$K = \frac{k_1}{k_2} = \frac{P_1 Z_1}{P_2 Z_2} \exp\left[\frac{-(E_1 - E_2)}{RT}\right], \tag{20}$$

where the subscripts 1 and 2 refer respectively to the forward and reverse reactions. Now $-(E_1 - E_2)$ is the heat of reaction, $-\Delta H$; and while it is reasonable to assume that Z_1 equals Z_2, the same cannot be necessarily said for the steric factors. We must therefore write

$$K = (P_1/P_2) \exp(-\Delta H/RT). \tag{21}$$

But the proper definition of the equilibrium constant is

$$K = \exp(-\Delta G^0/RT), \tag{22}$$

where $-\Delta G^0$ is the standard free energy change; and since

$$\Delta G^0 = \Delta H^0 - T\Delta S^0 \tag{23}$$

for an isothermal change, it follows that

$$K = \exp(\Delta S^0/R) \exp(-\Delta H^0/RT). \tag{24}$$

The ratio of the steric factors is thus equal to $\exp(\Delta S^0/R)$. Now it is reasonable to suppose that the standard free energy change for the reaction is the difference between the free energies of activation for the forward and reverse reactions, viz.

$$-\Delta G^0 = \Delta G_1^{\ddagger} - \Delta G_2^{\ddagger}. \tag{25}$$

Hence we may write the rate constant of any reaction as

$$k = Y \exp(-\Delta G^{\ddagger}/RT) \tag{26}$$

$$= Y \exp(\Delta S^{\ddagger}/R) \exp(-\Delta H^{\ddagger}/RT), \tag{27}$$

where $\Delta S^{\ddagger}$ and $-\Delta H^{\ddagger}$ are respectively the entropy of activation and the heat of activation, the latter equalling approximately the activation energy. The object of the Absolute Rate Theory is to evaluate the constant Y and to provide a means of estimating the entropy and heat terms.

The transition from reactants to products must involve a continuous change in the position and energy co-ordinates of the system, but there must be some critical intermediate configuration which if achieved must lead to the formation of products. Such a state, which is situated at the top of the energy barrier on the most favourable path, is termed the *transition state* or *activated complex*. The quantities $\Delta G^{\ddagger}$, $\Delta S^{\ddagger}$ and $\Delta H^{\ddagger}$ above represent the differences between the free energy, entropy and heat content of the reactants and the transition state. Now the rate of reaction, r, will be given by the product of the concentration of transition states and the frequency with which they cross the top of the barrier, viz.

$$r = [T^{\ddagger}]\nu. \tag{28}$$

Furthermore, according to the methods of statistical mechanics, the equilibrium constant of the process

$$aA + bB \rightleftharpoons xX \tag{c}$$

is given by

$$K = \frac{F_X^x}{F_A^a \; F_B^b} \exp\left(\frac{-E_0}{RT}\right), \tag{29}$$

where F_A is the partition function per unit volume of A, etc. and E_0 the zero point energy change. It is now supposed that the transition state may be regarded as being in equilibrium with the reactants, and hence an equilibrium constant K^{+} for the reaction

$$A + B \rightleftharpoons T^{+} \tag{d}$$

may be written as

$$K^{+} = \frac{[T^{+}]}{[A]\,[B]} = \frac{F^{+}}{F_A\, F_B} \exp\left(\frac{-E_0}{RT}\right), \tag{30}$$

where F^{+} is the partition function of the transition state T^{+} and E_0 the activation energy at the absolute zero.

The partition functions may be factorized into separate terms corresponding to translational, rotational, vibrational and electronic energy. It is assumed that the transition state behaves as a normal molecule except for the fact that one of the vibrational modes has a very low frequency, and that dissociation according to this mode leads to products. For this particular degree of freedom, therefore, it is permissible to use in place of the usual factor

$$\{1 - \exp(-h\nu/kT)\}^{-1}$$

its limiting value as ν tends to zero: this term is simply $kT/h\nu$. We may therefore write

$$\frac{[T^{+}]}{[A]\,[B]} = \frac{kT}{h\nu} \cdot \frac{F_{+}}{F_A\, F_B} \exp\left(\frac{-E_0}{RT}\right), \tag{31}$$

where F_{+} is now the partition function of the transition state from which the energy of the vibrational mode for dissociation has been subtracted. On rearranging this expression we obtain

$$[T^{+}]\nu = r = [A]\,[B] \frac{kT}{h} \cdot \frac{F_{+}}{F_A\, F_B} \exp\left(\frac{-E_0}{RT}\right) \tag{32}$$

and, since $r = k\,[A]\,[B]$,

$$k = \frac{kT}{h} \cdot \frac{F_{+}}{F_A\, F_B} \exp\left(\frac{-E_0}{RT}\right). \tag{33}$$

Finally we may define a further equilibrium constant K_{+} as

$$K_{+} = \frac{F_{+}}{F_A\, F_B} \exp\left(\frac{-E_0}{RT}\right) \tag{34}$$

$$= \exp\left(\frac{-\Delta G_{+}}{RT}\right). \tag{35}$$

The new equilibrium constant differs from that formerly used in lacking a term corresponding to the vibrational mode of dissociation and since this involves the entropy and not the heat, we may write

$$K_{\ddagger} = \exp(\Delta S_{\ddagger}/R) \exp(-\Delta H^{\ddagger}/RT) \quad (36)$$

$$= \exp(\Delta S_{\ddagger}/R) \exp(-E_0/RT). \quad (37)$$

We therefore obtain an alternative expression for the rate constant, viz.

$$k = (\boldsymbol{k}T/h) \exp(\Delta S_{\ddagger}/R) \exp(-E_0/RT). \quad (38)$$

The constant Y in equations (26) and (27) is thus approximately equal to the basic frequency $\boldsymbol{k}T/h$, which has a value of about 10^{13} sec.$^{-1}$ at room temperature.

Attempts to estimate absolute rates hinge on the evaluation of the partition function ratio. F_A and F_B are known if the structure and normal vibration frequencies of the molecules are known; it then remains to hazard a guess at $F_{\ddagger}$. Alternatively the basic equation may be used as a means of acquiring information about the nature of the transition state.

6.32 *Application to Rates of Adsorption*[51]

The above rate expressions may be readily applied to the adsorption process

$$A + * \rightarrow \underset{*}{A^{\ddagger}} \rightarrow \underset{*}{A} \quad (e)$$

and if A is immobile when adsorbed the rate r_a will be given by

$$r_a = [A]\,[*]\,\frac{\boldsymbol{k}T}{h} \cdot \frac{F_{\ddagger}}{F_A\, F_*} \exp\left(\frac{-E_a}{RT}\right). \quad (39)$$

In this equation, the partition functions $F_{\ddagger}$ and F_* refer to unit area of surface, and F_A to unit volume of gas. Both $F_{\ddagger}$ and F_* may then be equated to unity since neither contains translational nor rotational terms, and only high-frequency vibrational terms. Substitution of the appropriate expression for F_A enables a value for the condensation coefficient σ to be obtained.[6] It appears to be about 10^{-5} for an immobile layer and about unity for a mobile layer. The first conclusion from the theory therefore is that adsorption will be much faster if the resulting layer is mobile than if it were immobile.

The equation requires only slight modification for adsorption processes involving dissociation. Table IV embodies a number of observed and calculated adsorption rates, the latter being obtained from the appropriate theoretical rate equations. For the first five entries in this Table, the agreement is as good as may be hoped for. Of itself, however, this only proves that the theoretical rate expressions describe the rate processes acceptably, and little is added to our knowledge of the details of those processes. More significant are the last two entries where the disagreement is acute (by a factor of $\sim 10^6$): it is further significant that these are both non-activated processes. Possible explanations for the discrepancies are (i) that only about 10^{-4} of the sites participate (unlikely); (ii) that there is in fact an activation energy of 1.5

TABLE IV. *A Comparison of Observed and Calculated Rates of Adsorption*

Metal	*Gas*	*Temp.* (°C)	E_a(*kcal. mole*$^{-1}$)	r_a(*obs.*)*	r_a(*calc.*)*	*Ref.*
Fe (doubly prom.)	H_2	−78	10.4	9.0×10^{11}	2.8×10^{11}	38
Fe (doubly prom.)	N_2	271	14.4	8.7×10^{10}	9.2×10^{11}	40
Fe (singly prom.)	N_2	212	23.0	2.0×10^{18}	1.5×10^{19}	45
W powder	N_2	100	10	8.5×10^{8}	7.1×10^{9}	39
Cu powder	H_2	400	20.5	9.0×10^{10}	4.8×10^{10}	42
W powder	H_2	−195	~0	5.9×10^{12}	9.8×10^{17}	1
Ni wire	H_2	−183	~0	1.0×10^{13}	1.0×10^{18}	2

* : r_a in molecules sec.$^{-1}$.

kcal. mole^{-1} (barely possible); (iii) that the measured rate is not that of the actual adsorption, but of a slower process such as diffusion of gas to the surface (most probably). The chief value of calculating rates is therefore a negative one, in that more is revealed (or suggested) by disagreement than by agreement. Our earlier anticipation that the method would prove most reliable when applied to activated processes is amply confirmed.

6.33 *Application to Rates of Desorption*[51]

For the process

$$\underset{*}{\mathrm{A}} \rightarrow \underset{*}{\mathrm{A}^{\ddagger}} \rightarrow \mathrm{A} + * \tag{f}$$

the rate equation takes the form

$$r_d = \left[\begin{matrix}\mathrm{A} \\ *\end{matrix}\right] \frac{kT}{h} \frac{F_{\ddagger}}{F_a} \exp\left(\frac{-E_d}{RT}\right), \tag{40}$$

where F_a is the total partition function of adsorbed A per unit surface area. For the recombinative process

$$2\,\underset{*}{\mathrm{A}} \rightarrow \underset{**}{\mathrm{A}_2^{\ddagger}} \rightarrow \mathrm{A}_2 + 2* \tag{g}$$

the corresponding equation is

$$r_d = \left[\begin{matrix}\mathrm{A} \\ *\end{matrix}\right]^2 \frac{kT}{h} \frac{F_{\ddagger}}{F_a^2} \exp\left(\frac{-E_d}{RT}\right). \tag{41}$$

In the former case, the usual rate expression is

$$r_d = k_d\,\theta_{\mathrm{A}} \exp\left(-E_d/RT\right). \tag{42}$$

Now $[\underset{*}{\mathrm{A}}]$ is equal to $[*]\,\theta_{\mathrm{A}}$ if $[*]$ is the number of sites per cm.^{2}, and hence

$$k_d = [*] \frac{kT}{h} \frac{F_{\ddagger}}{F_a} \cdot \tag{43}$$

If the adsorbed species and the transition state have identical degrees of freedom, then $F_{\ddagger}$ equals F_a and so

$$k_d = [*]\frac{kT}{h} = 10^{15} \times 6 \times 10^{12} = 6 \times 10^{27} \text{ cm.}^{-2} \text{ sec.}^{-1}$$

at room temperature. This is a minimum value, which may be exceeded if the transition state is more mobile than the adsorbed species.

For process (9), the same result follows if both the adsorbed species and the transition state are immobile. The possible effects of mobility of the adsorbed species and/or the transition state are more difficult to assess in this case[6] (see, however, Ref. 52).

Observed[6] values of k_d are greater than about 10^{28} cm.$^{-2}$ sec.$^{-1}$ and the only conclusion that can safely be drawn is that the transition state is more mobile (i.e. has a greater number of degrees of freedom) than the adsorbed species from which it is formed.

REFERENCES

1. J. K. Roberts, *Proc. Roy. Soc.* **A152,** 445 (1935).
2. A. Matsuda, *J. Res. Inst. Catalysis, Hokkaido Univ.* **5,** 71 (1957).
3. A. G. Nasini, G. Saini and F. Ricca, Proc. 2nd International Congress on Catalysis (Editions Technip, Paris, 1961), **1,** 241.
4. J. L. Morrison and J. K. Roberts, *Proc. Roy. Soc.* **A173,** 1 (1939).
5. J. A. Becker and C. D. Hartman, *J. Phys. Chem.* **57,** 153 (1953).
6. B. M. W. Trapnell, "Chemisorption" (Butterworths, London, 1957).
7. S. Yu. Elovich and G. M. Zhabrova, *Zhur. fiz. Khim.* **13,** 1761, 1775 (1939); see also Ya. Zeldovich, *Acta Physiochim. U.R.S.S.* **1,** 449 (1934).
8. M. J. D. Low, *Chem. Rev.* **60, 267** (1960).
9. S. Wagener, *J. Phys. Chem.* **60,** 567 (1956); **61,** 267 (1957).
10. B. M. W. Trapnell, *Proc. Roy. Soc.* **A218,** 566 (1953).
11. N. Thon and H. A. Taylor, *J. Amer. Chem. Soc.* **74,** 4169 (1952).
12. T. Kwan, *Adv. Catalysis* **6,** 67 (1954).
13. O. Beeck, *Adv. Catalysis* **2,** 151 (1950).
14. Z. Oda, *Bull. Chem. Soc. Japan* **27,** 465 (1954); *Chem. Abs.* **49,** 15357 (1955).
15. B. M. W. Trapnell, *Proc. Roy. Soc.* **A206,** 39 (1951).
16. A. S. Porter and F. C. Tompkins, *Proc. Roy. Soc.* **A217,** 529, 544 (1953).
17. O. Beeck, A. W. Ritchie and A. Wheeler, *J. Colloid Sci.* **3,** 505 (1948).
18. P. M. Gundry and F. C. Tompkins, *Trans. Faraday Soc.* **52,** 1609 (1956).
19. M. McD. Baker, G. I. Jenkins and E. K. Rideal, *Trans. Faraday Soc.* **51,** 1592 (1955).
20. P. M. Gundry and F. C. Tompkins, *Trans. Faraday Soc.* **53,** 218 (1957).
21. J. H. Singleton, *J. Phys. Chem.* **60,** 1606 (1956).
22. A. F. Benton and T. A. White, *J. Amer. Chem. Soc.* **52,** 2325 (1930).
23. L. Leibowitz, M. J. D. Low and H. A. Taylor, *J. Phys. Chem.* **62,** 471 (1958).
24. A. Matsuda and T. Nakata, *J. Res. Inst. Catalysis, Hokkaido Univ.* **6,** 88 (1958).
25. M. J. D. Low and H. A. Taylor, *Canad. J. Chem.* **37,** 544 (1959); **38,** 588 (1960); *J. Electrochem. Soc.* **106,** 138 (1959).
26. A. F. H. Ward, *Proc. Roy. Soc.* **A133,** 506 (1931).
27. E. K. Rideal and B. M. W. Trapnell, *Proc. Roy. Soc.* **A205,** 409 (1951).
28. M. A. H. Lanyon and B. M. W. Trapnell, *Proc. Roy. Soc.* **A227,** 387 (1955).
29. B. M. W. Trapnell, *Trans. Faraday Soc.* **48,** 160 (1952).
30. E. Greenhalgh, N. Slack and B. M. W. Trapnell, *Trans. Faraday Soc.* **52,** 865 (1956).
31. M. J. Bennett and F. C. Tompkins, *Proc. Roy. Soc.* **A259,** 28 (1960).

32. R. Kh. Burshtein, L. A. Larin and G. F. Vorinina, *Doklady Akad. Nauk S.S.S.R.* **130,** 801 (1960).
33. P. L. Jones and B. A. Pethica, *Proc. Roy. Soc.* **A256,** 454 (1960).
34. M. Kubokawa, *Rev. Phys. Chem., Japan* **12,** 157 (1938).
35. S. Yu. Elovich and G. M. Zhabrova, *Zhur. fiz. Khim.* **13,** 1761, 1775 (1939).
36. K. Tamaru, *J. Phys. Chem* **61,** 647 (1957)
37. T. Kwan, *J. Res. Inst. Catalysis, Hokkaido Univ.* **1,** 95 (1949).
38. P. H. Emmett and R. W. Harkness, *J. Amer. Chem. Soc.* **57,** 1631 (1935).
39. R. T. Davis, *J. Amer. Chem. Soc.* **68,** 1395 (1946).
40. P. H. Emmett and S. Brunauer, *J. Amer. Chem. Soc.* **56,** 35 (1934); S. Brunauer, K. S. Love and R. G. Keenan, *Ibid.* **64,** 751 (1942).
41. S. S. Gaukhman and W. A. Royter, *Zhur. fiz. Khim.* **13,** 593 (1939).
42. T. Kwan, *J. Res. Inst. Catalysis, Hokkaido Univ.* **3,** 16, 109 (1953); T. Kwan and M. Kujirai, *J. Chem. Phys.* **19,** 798 (1951).
43. P. Zwietering and J. J. Roukens, *Trans. Faraday Soc.* **50,** 178.
44. J. J. F. Scholten and P. Zwietering, *Trans. Faraday Soc.* **53,** 1363 (1957).
45. J. J. F. Scholten, P. Zwietering, J. A. Konvalinka and J. H. de Boer, *Trans. Faraday Soc.* **55,** 2166 (1959).
46. C. Kemball, *Proc. Roy. Soc.* **A207,** 539 (1951).
47. B. M. W. Trapnell, *Trans. Faraday Soc.* **52,** 1618 (1956).
48. P. G. Wright, P. G. Ashmore and C. Kemball, *Trans. Faraday Soc.* **54,** 1692 (1958).
49. P. M. Gundry and F. C. Tompkins, *Quart. Rev.* **14,** 257 (1960).
50. I. Langmuir and D. S. Villars, *J. Amer. Chem. Soc.* **53,** 486 (1931).
51. K. J. Laidler, In "Catalysis", edited by P. H. Emmett (Reinhold, New York, 1954), **1,** 75, 195.
52. D. Brennan and P. C. Fletcher, *Proc. Roy. Soc.* **A250,** 389 (1959).

Chapter 7

The Kinetics of Surface Reactions

7.1 A Comparison Between the Kinetics of Homogeneous and Heterogeneous Reactions

Reactions proceeding at the surfaces of solids differ from those proceeding homogeneously in several obvious ways. First, in the former case, the reactants and intermediates are confined to a thin layer over the surface, the volume of which is typically about 10^{-6} of the total. There are a few exceptions to this rule, where the surface remits to the gas or liquid phase an intermediate which initiates a homogeneous reaction. Second, the kinetics of surface reactions are less accessible than those of homogeneous reactions in that the rates of the former are determined by the concentrations of the reactants *in the reactive layer*, and these are only indirectly related (through the appropriate isotherms) to the gas pressures. Third, the kinetics of surface reactions are less reproducible than those of homogeneous reactions since the nature of the surface and its method of preparation have profound effects.

Both kinds of reactions may be studied in either static or dynamic systems, but the former have many advantages. Results obtained with dynamic systems are less readily interpreted, and the derivation of reactions orders and rate constants is no straightforward matter; this is especially so if the reaction leads to a change in the total number of molecules present, when there will be a pressure gradient as well as the inevitable concentration gradient through the catalyst bed. Most fundamental work has been carried out in static systems, and no attempt will be made here to describe the derivation of rate expressions for dynamic systems, particularly since satisfactory treatments have appeared elsewhere.[1–3]

While in homogeneous reactions the partial pressures of the species participating in the rate-controlling step are often directly observable quantities, the same is not true of surface processes where the reactant (or at least one reactant if there are more than one) has to be adsorbed. The concentrations of adsorbed species are not *directly* observable, unless the appropriate measurements can be made by a suitable direct method.[4] The full rate expression for, for example, a bimolecular surface reaction where both species have to be adsorbed therefore comprises (i) a relation between the rate and the concentrations of adsorbed species, and (ii) a relation between the latter and the directly observable partial pressures in the gas phase, based on the appropriate (usually Langmuir) isotherms. The first relation presupposes a knowledge of the reaction mechanism and the second an accurate means of describing the isotherm through a fairly wide range of partial pressures and hence coverages.

In contrast to homogeneous reactions, the observed orders of heterogeneous reactions are frequently found to be sensitive to temperature, as indeed they must be. If for example A is considerably more strongly adsorbed than B at a certain temperature, the observed rate expression will be

$$-\frac{dP_A}{dt} = kP_A^0 P_B. \tag{1}$$

At any higher temperature, the difference between their strength of adsorption will not be so great since

$$\frac{\theta_B}{\theta_A} = \frac{b_B P_B}{b_A P_A} = \frac{P_B}{P_A} \exp\left(\frac{-\delta\Delta G_a}{RT}\right) \tag{2}$$

where $\delta\Delta G_a$ is the difference between the free energies of adsorption of the two reactants. Hence ultimately both will be equally strongly adsorbed and the rate expression will then be

$$-\frac{dP_A}{dt} = kP_A P_B\,. \tag{3}$$

Because of this effect, orders of reaction determined over the same pressure interval become more positive with increasing temperature, unless of course the adsorption is strongly activated. The complete rate expression for a heterogeneous reaction therefore describes not only the temperature variation of the rate constant (and hence the parameters of the Arrhenius equation) but also the temperature variation of the orders of reaction or of the adsorption coefficients. It is thus necessary to state at what temperature any rate expression has been found to be valid, and over what range of partial pressures.

In homogeneous systems the reacting centres are uniformly distributed, but as already noted in heterogeneous systems the reaction is confined to a thin layer on the surface. For this reason, transport of the reactants to, or of products from, this layer may be the rate-limiting step. Since the rate of molecular diffusion is not very sensitive to temperature, and since transport limitation of the rate is most probable when the rate is fast, the phenomenon is usually revealed as a fairly sharp fall in the apparent activation energy above a certain critical temperature. Transport-limited rates are naturally sensitive to agitation of the system, and various simple methods are available for overcoming this limitation and of extending the temperature range over which valid measurements may be made. For gas–solid systems the most important are thermal syphoning and forced circulation.

For these reasons, valid kinetics are hard to derive for solid–liquid–gas systems. Rates are usually limited by the diffusion of the gas through the liquid to the surface of the catalyst, unless extremely efficient agitation is provided. For systems where one component is in the liquid phase or in solution, the most useful information comes from a study of the nature of the products and their dependence on the variables of the system.

The rates of heterogeneous reactions generally conform, at least approximately, to the Arrhenius equation. However, examples are known where under certain conditions the activation energy changes quite rapidly with temperature, sometimes even becoming negative: explanations for this will be advanced as examples are met.

If the situation were not already sufficiently complex, it is further complicated by the observation[5] that for many surface processes the orders determined by the initial rate method are not in agreement with those derived by following the change in rate as a function of time through a given reaction. Relatively little attention has been given to this matter (see e.g. Ref. 1) for which there is not likely to be a single and unique interpretation. It is, however, desirable to state by what method orders of reaction are determined, and thus whether they constitute an initial rate law or a "course" rate law.

Finally the definition of a number of terms to be encountered later is in order.

The *activity* of a catalyst for a particular reaction is the rate or rate constant of that reaction which results under specified conditions of temperature and partial pressures, per unit weight of catalyst. The term *specific activity* is reserved for those cases where the surface area of the catalyst is known, and where the rate or rate constant may therefore be referred to unit surface area: the subscript s denotes specific quantities. While the activation energy is of course unaffected by the units in which the rates are expressed, rate constants and pre-exponential factors for surface reactions must (in addition to possessing such units of concentration and time as are appropriate to the order of reaction) refer to either unit weight or area of catalyst.

7.2 The Formulation of Rate Expressions for Surface Reactions[1,6]

7.21 *Unimolecular Reactions*

It is convenient to classify surface reactions according to the number of species taking part in the reaction; this is generally one or two, and rarely greater than two. Unimolecular reactions are formally simple: the adsorption of the species by the surface is a necessity, and provided only measurements of initial rates are performed, qualitative information is at once available on the strength of adsorption of the reactant. If on the other hand the rate is measured as a function of time throughout a reaction in a static system, attention must then be given to the influence of the adsorption of the products on the rate. The various possible cases are presented below.

The generalized formulations of rate expressions which are to be discussed in this Section are based on the assumed validity of the Langmuir isotherm, and they are therefore liable to suffer from its limitations. The rate of unimolecular decomposition of a reactant A is governed at constant temperature by θ_A, the fraction of the surface it occupies, and this is related to the pressure of A in the gas phase P_A by the Langmuir isotherm, viz.

$$-\frac{dP_A}{dt} = k\theta_A = \frac{kb_A P_A}{1 + b_A P_A}. \tag{4}$$

The reaction is therefore first order at low pressures, zero order above the pressure at which θ_A attains its limiting value, and apparently of some fractional positive order in A in the intermediate range. The lowest pressure at which the order becomes zero depends firstly on the value of the adsorption coefficient b_A and secondly on the temperature.

Since b_A is an equilibrium constant,

$$b_A = \exp(-\Delta G_{a,A}/RT) = \exp(+\Delta S_{a,A}/R)\exp(-\Delta H_{a,A}/RT), \tag{5}$$

where the thermodynamic functions are those for the adsorption of A. When the reaction is first order the rate is given by

$$-\frac{dP_A}{dt} = kb_A P_A \tag{6}$$

and the first-order rate-constant k_1 equals kb_A. Hence

$$k_1 = A_y \exp(-E_y/RT) = kb_A = A_z \exp(\Delta S_{a,A}/R)\exp(-E_z/RT) \exp(-\Delta H_{a,A}/RT), \tag{7}$$

where A_y and A_z are frequency factors, and E_y and E_z respectively the apparent and true activation energies. Therefore

$$E_y = E_z + \Delta H_{a,A}. \tag{8}$$

The apparent activation energy is thus lower than the true one by the heat of adsorption. If conditions are chosen such that θ_A is about unity throughout the temperature range studied, there is no desorption to allow for and hence the apparent activation energy is the true one. An additional complication, however, is that the heat of adsorption is generally a function of coverage (see Chapters 4 and 5), so that temperature variation at constant pressure affects not only coverage but also by extension the heat of adsorption. The apparent activation energy should therefore be temperature-dependent; this effect, which has not apparently been detected experimentally, would be corrected if a rate expression based on an alternative form of isotherm were employed.

In a static system the rate will naturally decline as the reactant is consumed, but moreover the order will also change from zero (if θ_A is initially about unity) through a fractional value, to first order. The usual tests can be applied to follow such changes.

We must now briefly consider how the rate expression may be affected if the product (or one of the products) is adsorbed. If the product X is adsorbed, then θ_X will increase throughout the reaction, and only that fraction of the surface not covered by X, viz. $(1-\theta_X)$, will be available to adsorb the reactant. Then

$$-\frac{dP_A}{dt} = k\theta_A = \frac{kb_A P_A}{1 + b_A P_A + b_X P_X}. \tag{9}$$

If $b_X > b_A$ (and/or if $P_X > P_A$), then the term $b_A P_A$ may be neglected in comparison with $(1 + b_X P_X)$: the differential and integrated forms of the resulting equation are given below for two different cases. P_X will be proportional to the amount of A reacted if all the inhibitor X is formed from A.

Case I: $b_X > b_A$.

$$-\frac{dP_A}{dt} = kb_A \frac{(P_A)_t}{1 + j\{(P_A)_0 - (P_A)_t\}} \tag{10}$$

$$(kb_A)t = [1 + j(P_A)_0] \ln \frac{(P_A)_0}{(P_A)_t} - \frac{j[(P_A)_0 - (P_A)_t]}{t}. \tag{11}$$

Case II: $b_X \gg b_A$.

$$-\frac{dP_A}{dt} = kb_A \frac{(P_A)_t}{(P_A)_0 - (P_A)_t}, \tag{12}$$

$$(kb_A)t = (P_A)_0 \ln \frac{(P_A)_0}{(P_A)_t} - \frac{(P_A)_0 - (P_A)_t}{t}, \tag{13}$$

In these equations, $(P_A)_0$ and $(P_A)_t$ are respectively the pressures of A initially and after time t, and j equals b_X modified by a factor dependent on the stoichiometry of the reaction.[1]

A rate law obtained by measurements of initial rates will naturally not cover the possibility of products inhibiting. On the other hand, the application of the integrated forms of the rate expressions is somewhat tedious and the interpretation may be uncertain. Where poisoning by a product is suspected, complementary information is obtained by adding various pressures of the product to the reactant, and determining the resulting initial rate law. It is always advisable to determine whether or not the products of a reaction are inhibiting.

Considerations similar to those applied before show that the apparent activation energy of a reaction whose progress is inhibited by a strongly adsorbed product is given by

$$E_y = E_z + (\Delta H_{a,A} - \Delta H_{a,X}). \tag{14}$$

7.22 Mechanisms of Bimolecular Reactions

There has been and continues to be much disputation concerning the mechanisms of bimolecular reactions. According to the original hypothesis of Langmuir, adopted by Hinshelwood and Bonhoeffer, such reactions proceed through the adsorption of the two species on adjacent sites, followed by their interaction and the desorption of the product(s). Such a mechanism may be treated in terms of adsorption isotherms of the reactants, and of the products if they are adsorbed. There are well authenticated instances of such mechanisms. An alternative formulation, due originally to Rideal and adopted by Eley and others, supposes that it is only necessary for one of the two species to be adsorbed, and that reaction occurs on collision of the second species, coming from the gas phase, with the surface. There are several variants of this notion, and it is not easy to distinguish between them and the "adjacent adsorption" mechanism on the basis of kinetic measurements alone.

The variants of the Rideal–Eley mechanism may be summarized as follows.

(i) Reactant A strongly adsorbed but mobile, no vacant surface sites: reactant B physically adsorbed. The plausibility of this depends on the mean residence time t of B, and t is a function both of the heat of physical adsorption $-\Delta H_p$ and of the absolute temperature T. The relation is

$$t = t_0 \exp(-\Delta H_p/RT), \tag{15}$$

where t_0 is effectively the time of one vibration in the adsorbed state. It has been calculated[7] that for hydrogen at 0°C, t will correspond to only about fifteen vibrations if $-\Delta H_p$ is 1.5 kcal. mole^{-1}, and that this process cannot obtain significantly above this temperature where reactant B is hydrogen. The mechanism merits consideration however when B has a higher boiling point and a higher heat of physical adsorption than hydrogen. The rate expression will be equation (1) since the concentration in second layer must inevitably be low.

(ii) Reactant A strongly adsorbed but mobile: reactant B colliding from gas phase. A process conforming to this mechanism must inevitably also yield expression (1), both from initial rate measurements and from determinations of the time-dependence of the rate in any reaction, at least until P_A is no longer adequate to maintain complete coverage.

(iii) Reactant A strongly adsorbed and immobile: reactant B adsorbed over gaps in the first layer. This is the situation originally envisaged by Rideal: if reactant A in the adsorbed state occupies two adjacent sites, and is immobile, there will be about 8 per cent *single* sites in a "complete" layer, and reactant B (supposed in the absence of A to require two adjacent sites) may then adsorb, perhaps "end-on" over such sites. It must be emphasized that this situation cannot arise unless adsorbed A is immobile; and this process is therefore perhaps more plausible when A is say an unsaturated hydrocarbon than when both A and B are differing forms of hydrogen. If A is a molecule in which the adsorbing function is sterically protected (e.g.

*iso*butene), single and even dual gaps may exist in the primary layer even if the adsorbed state of A were mobile. The chief virtue of this mechanism is to provide a means of bringing B into intimate contact with the surface under circumstances where (e.g. if A were very much more strongly adsorbed than B) B could not chemisorb in competition with A sufficiently to bring about efficient reaction. The heat of adsorption over such vacant single sites could be considerably greater than the normal heat of physical adsorption, and the objection referred to above is thereby obviated. However, the degree of coverage of these sites might well still be low, and the usual rate expression could result, but some falling-off in rate at very high pressures of B might be expected.

When it is recalled that a rate expression, zero order in A and first in B, results from the "adjacent adsorption" mechanism when A is much more strongly adsorbed than B, it is evident that any attempt to establish the mechanism on the basis of kinetic measurements alone is bound to fail.

We turn now to a consideration of the formulation of rate expressions for bimolecular reactions based on the Langmuir isotherm.

7.23 *Rate Expressions for Bimolecular Reactions*

As has been seen previously (Chapter 5), the fractions of surface covered by the gases A and B are

$$\theta_A = \frac{b_A P_A}{1 + b_A P_A + b_B P_B} \quad \text{and} \quad \theta_B = \frac{b_B P_B}{1 + b_A P_A + b_B P_B}. \qquad (16, 17)$$

If the rate of reaction is determined by the number of pairs of unlike species on adjacent sites, then the rate will be proportional to the product $\theta_A \theta_B$ or

$$-\frac{dP_A}{dt} = k\theta_A\theta_B = \frac{kb_A b_B P_A P_B}{(1 + b_A P_A + b_B P_B)^2}. \qquad (18)$$

If either P_A or P_B is held constant, and the other varied, the rate in each case will pass through a maximum when $b_A P_A$ equals $b_B P_B$; the approximate ratio of the adsorption coefficients may be found in this way. If both A and B are only weakly adsorbed, the denominator of the rate expression will approximate to unity, and the rate will be proportional to both P_A and P_B, and therefore of overall second order:

$$-\frac{dP_A}{dt} = kb_A b_B P_A P_B = k' P_A P_B. \qquad (19)$$

When A is only weakly adsorbed, the rate expression reduces to

$$-\frac{dP_A}{dt} = \frac{kb_A b_B P_A P_B}{(1 + b_B P_B)^2} \qquad (20)$$

and the rate is thus proportional to P_A, but a maximum will be observed as P_B is varied. If B is sufficiently strongly adsorbed that $b_B P_B$ is greater than unity, then

$$-\frac{dP_A}{dt} = \frac{kb_A P_A}{b_B P_B}. \tag{21}$$

An infinite variety of intermediate cases is of course possible.

If one of the products inhibits the reaction, or if an inhibitor is initially present, an additional term $b_X P_X$ is introduced within the brackets of the denominator of equation (18). Thus for example, the rate equation for the case where both reactants are only weakly adsorbed becomes

$$-\frac{dP_A}{dt} = \frac{kb_A b_B P_A P_B}{(1 + b_X P_X)^2} \tag{22}$$

and, if the inhibitor is very strongly adsorbed ($b_X P_X \gg 1$),

$$-\frac{dP_A}{dt} = \frac{kb_A b_B P_A P_B}{(b_X P_X)^2}. \tag{23}$$

Apparent activation energies must be corrected for the heats of adsorption of reactants and inhibitors, as shown in Table I.

TABLE I. *Apparent Activation Energies for Bimolecular Reactions*[1]

Reactant A	*Reactant B*	*Inhibitor X*	E_y
Weakly ads.	Weakly ads.	—	$E_z + (\Delta H_{a,A} + \Delta H_{a,B})$
Weakly ads.	Strongly ads.	—	$E_z + (\Delta H_{a,A} - \Delta H_{a,B})$
Weakly ads.	Weakly ads.	V. strongly ads.	$E_z + (\Delta H_{a,A} + \Delta H_{a,B} - 2\Delta H_{a,X})$

Rate expressions for the Rideal–Eley mechanism may be formulated as follows. Where B is not adsorbed at all,

$$-\frac{dP_A}{dt} = \frac{kb_A P_A P_B}{1 + b_A P_A}, \tag{24}$$

which becomes zero order in A and first in B when $b_A P_A \gg 1$ and first order in both when $b_A P_A \ll 1$. This expression differs from that derived on the basis of the adsorption of both reactants, in that the rate can only attain a limiting value and cannot pass through a maximum. The apparent activation energy has to be corrected for the heat of adsorption of A in the usual manner, unless A is strongly adsorbed. Certain atom- and radical-recombination processes definitely conform to this mechanism.

The applicability of equation (18) may in principle be tested as follows. Writing $-dP_A/dt$ as r_A, the equation may be written as

$$\sqrt{\frac{P_A}{r_A}} = \frac{1 + b_B P_B}{\sqrt{(kb_A b_B P_B)}} + P_A \sqrt{\frac{b_A}{kb_B P_B}}. \tag{25}$$

For series of experiments performed at constant P_B, a plot of $(P_A/r_A)^{\frac{1}{2}}$ against P_A should afford a straight line if the expression is obeyed. A similar expression to (25) should apply for experiments performed at constant P_A, and from the slopes and intercepts it is possible to derive values for b_A and b_B. Experience shows, however, that while linear plots may be obtained, the intercepts are so small as to defy accurate estimation, and only very approximate values of the adsorption coefficients may be found in this manner.

7.24 *Selectivity in Heterogeneous Reactions*

The concept of the specific directing influence possessed by catalyst surfaces has been introduced in Chapter 1. Most catalytic surfaces have the ability to assist a variety of reactions, and certain catalysts will commend themselves in practical application by their ability to act selectively on only one of the reactants present, and in so acting to form the desired product to the exclusion of others. It is of interest therefore to enquire into the factors affecting selective behaviour and to attempt their mathematical formulation.

There are three distinguishable kinds of selectivity. If two different reactants A and C are initially present, we may set down the kinetic scheme as

$$\begin{aligned} A &\xrightarrow{k_1} B \\ C &\xrightarrow{k_2} D \end{aligned} \qquad \text{(I)}$$

and depending on the relative strengths of adsorption of the reactants, and other factors to be described, either of the products may be obtained in preponderance. We follow Wheeler[8] in describing this as Type I selectivity. The treatment employed in this and the following paragraphs assumes that each reactant disappears according to first-order kinetics and that the rate constants refer to unit surface area, including the internal surfaces of pores. The ratio k_1/k_2 is termed the selectivity factor, σ, and a high value of this ratio denotes the preponderant formation of B. By integration of the expression for the relative rates of reactant removal, the following equation is obtained:[8, 9]

$$\alpha_A = 1 - (1 - \alpha_C)^\sigma. \qquad (26)$$

Here α_A and α_C are respectively the fractions of A and C reacted. The dependence of the relative amounts of A and C on time is shown in Fig. 1 for various values of σ. Wheeler[8] has shown how the above equation would be modified if the reaction were proceeding within the pores of a porous catalyst: for very small pores, the selectivity factor would be approximately the square root of the value obtaining if the reaction were proceeding on a plane surface. The reason for this is that a larger fraction of the internal surface is available to the slower reaction than the faster reaction, which is thus retarded to a larger extent.

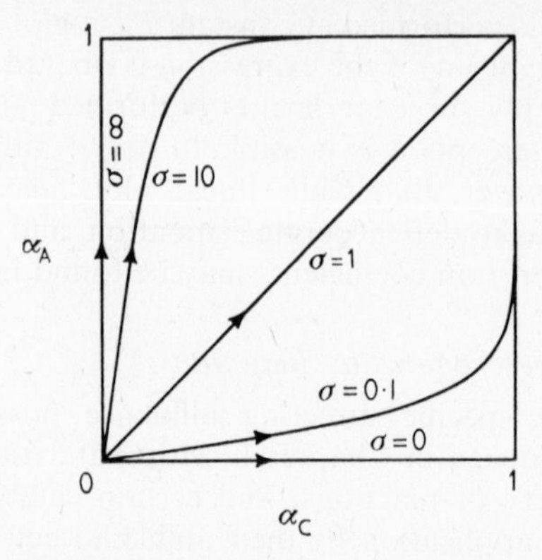

FIG. 1. The fractions of A and C converted to products as a function of time for various selectivity factors (Type I selectivity). The arrows denote the direction of increasing time.

Type II selectivity concerns the simultaneous reactions of a single reactant, and the kinetic scheme is

$$A \begin{cases} \xrightarrow{k_1} B \\ \xrightarrow{k_2} C \end{cases} \tag{II}$$

This is the simplest of the three cases. Defining the selectivity factor σ as before, we have

$$\alpha_B = \sigma\alpha_C \tag{27}$$

and, for simultaneous reactions of the same order, the pore size is without effect on the selectivity.

Type III selectivity concerns the further reaction of the desired product B to an undesired product C, viz.

$$A \xrightarrow{k_1} B \xrightarrow{k_2} C \tag{III}$$

This kind of behaviour, which is the most common and important selectivity phenomenon, is in principle readily distinguished from Type II, since here the yield of B will decrease markedly with increasing conversion of A, whereas in the Type II case it will be constant throughout the reaction. In practice, however, both Type II and Type III phenomena often occur together. The relative rates of change of the concentrations of A and B are given by the relation

$$-\frac{d[B]}{d[A]} = 1 - \frac{1}{\sigma} \cdot \frac{[B]}{[A]}, \tag{28}$$

integration of which yields

$$\alpha_B = \frac{\sigma}{\sigma - 1}(1 - \alpha_B)[(1 - \alpha_A)^{\frac{1-\sigma}{\sigma}} - 1], \tag{29}$$

where α_A is the fraction of A reacted, α_B the fraction converted to B and σ is the selectivity factor defined in the usual manner. The variation of α_B and α_C (the fraction of A converted to C) with time is shown in Fig. 2 for several

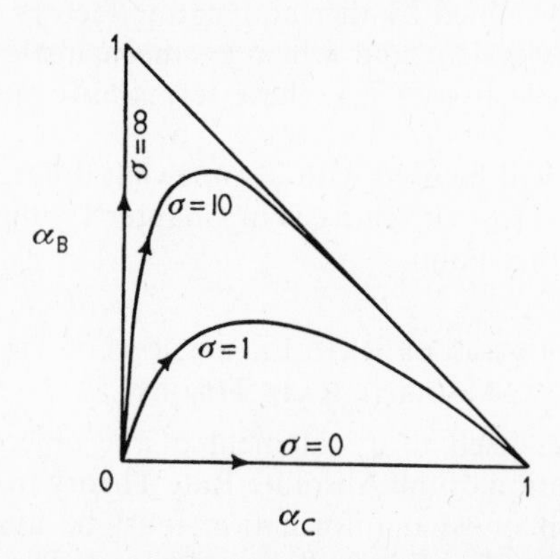

FIG. 2. The fraction of A converted to B and C as a function of time for various selectivity factors (Type III selectivity). The arrows denote the direction of increasing time.

selectivities. The maximum attainable yield of B at any selectivity is reduced by a factor of about two if the reaction is proceeding in very fine pores instead of on a plane surface.

Waterman and his collaborators[9] have extended the mathematical analysis of this problem and its application to practical situations. The equation describing the curves in Fig. 2 is that of a hyperbola. The application of the method to the hydroisomerization of paraffin wax has been described in detail, and the value of one result, properly interpreted, has been stressed.

The foregoing remarks have as their basis the experimental observations concerning the changing concentrations of reactants and products with time. Now high Type I selectivity clearly demands the preferential adsorption of A and in fact

$$\frac{d[\mathrm{B}]}{d[\mathrm{D}]} = \frac{k_1}{k_2} \cdot \frac{\theta_A}{\theta_C} \tag{30}$$

$$= \frac{k_1}{k_2} \cdot \frac{P_A}{P_C} \cdot \exp\left(\frac{-\delta \Delta G_a}{RT}\right). \tag{31}$$

This effect has been referred to as the *thermodynamic factor* in selectivity.[10] This factor is also important in Type III selectivity, where the highly selective formation of B, while any A remains, hinges on (i) the ability of B to desorb rapidly, or to be displaced by A, before it suffers further reaction and (ii) the inability of B, once desorbed, to readsorb while any A remains. In the case of simultaneous reactions on the other hand, these considerations do not apply and highly selective formation of the desired product depends on the specific properties of the catalyst, and has therefore been termed *mechanistic* in origin.[10]

Because the selectivity factor σ may vary between the limits of zero and infinity, it has been found convenient to redefine selectivity as $\sigma/(1 + \sigma)$; this expression is given the symbol S and varies only between zero and unity. When selectivity is determined by thermodynamic factors we shall speak of thermodynamic selectivity (S_t) and when by mechanistic factors we shall speak of mechanistic selectivity (S_m): these terms have special relevance to Chapter 12.

The term selectivity will be used with a somewhat different meaning when we discuss the Fischer–Tropsch synthesis in Chapter 15, but its new meaning will be made clear at that point.

7.3 The Formulation of Rate Expressions in Terms of the Absolute Rate Theory

This Section confines itself to a statement of the objects expected to be achieved by the application of the Absolute Rate Theory to surface reactions, and to a consideration of what information must be available, and what conditions fulfilled, before fruitful results are obtained. The results of calculations based on this Theory for particular systems will be given later under the appropriate Sections. A short introduction to Absolute Rate Theory has already been given (Section 6.31).

7.31 Unimolecular Reactions

Laidler[1] describes the formulation of the rate expression for unimolecular reactions in terms of a rate-controlling process very similar to that involved in the adsorption process, viz.

$$\mathrm{A} + * \rightleftharpoons \underset{*}{\mathrm{A}^{\ddagger}} \rightarrow \mathrm{X}, \tag{a}$$

the only difference being that here the decomposition of the transition state leads to the product rather than the adsorbed reactant. Then as before for a one-site mechanism

$$r = [\mathrm{A}]\,[*]\,\frac{kT}{h}\,\frac{f_{\ddagger}}{F_{\mathrm{A}} f_{*}} \exp\left(-\frac{E_0}{RT}\right) \tag{32}$$

and for a two-site mechanism

$$r = [\mathrm{A}]\,[**]\,\frac{kT}{h}\,\frac{f_{\ddagger}}{F_{\mathrm{A}} f_{**}} \exp\left(-\frac{E_0}{RT}\right). \tag{33}$$

Also as before $f_{\ddagger}$ may be taken as unity if the transition state is immobile.

When A is only weakly adsorbed, the concentration of single or pairs of empty sites is essentially constant. The rates are then simply proportional to [A], in agreement with the earlier finding. The full rate expression is obtained by substituting the appropriate form of F_{A}: thus when A is a diatomic molecule

$$r = [\mathrm{A}]\,[**]\,\frac{kT}{h}\,\frac{\sigma_{\mathrm{A}}}{\sigma^{\ddagger}}\,\frac{h^4}{8\pi^2 I(2\pi mkT)^{1/2}} \exp\left(-\frac{E_0}{RT}\right), \tag{34}$$

where σ_A and σ^{+} are respectively the symmetry numbers of A and of the transition state, and I and m are respectively the moment of inertia and mass of A. More complex expressions result with larger molecules.[1]

When A is strongly adsorbed on a single site, the concentration of empty sites varies inversely as the concentration of A, and thus the isotherm may be written

$$\frac{[\overset{\text{A}}{*}]}{[*]} = [\text{A}] \frac{f_{a,\text{A}}}{F_\text{A} f_*} \exp(-\epsilon/RT). \tag{35}$$

Combining this with equation (32) above, we get

$$r = [\overset{\text{A}}{*}] \frac{kT}{h} \frac{f_{\neq}}{f_{a,\text{A}}} \exp\left(-\frac{E_0 - \epsilon}{RT}\right). \tag{36}$$

Both $f_{\neq}$ and $f_{a,\text{A}}$ may be taken as unity, and the rate expression is then delightfully simple:

$$r = [\overset{\text{A}}{*}] \frac{kT}{h} \exp\left(-\frac{E}{RT}\right). \tag{37}$$

Rates calculated from this last expression are in very satisfactory agreement with those observed in for example ammonia decomposition over tungsten and molybdenum, in the zero-order range. The agreement in the case of several reactions showing first-order kinetics is generally poorer, for which there are several possible explanations. (i) If the roughness factor is greater than unity, the number of sites will be greater than the assumed value of 10^{15} cm.$^{-2}$ and the calculated rates will be too low. (ii) If not all the surface is active, the calculated rates will be too high. (iii) If the transition state possesses translational, vibrational or rotational energy, the calculated rates will be too low. A comparison between observed and estimated rates therefore throws some light on these factors.

7.32 *Bimolecular Reactions*

Absolute Rate Theory expressions for bimolecular reactions proceeding by an adjacent adsorption mechanism are formulated in the following manner. If the process is

$$\text{A} + \text{B} + ** \rightleftharpoons (\underset{**}{\text{AB}})^{+} \rightarrow \text{X}, \tag{b}$$

the rate is given by

$$r = [\text{A}][\text{B}][**] \frac{kT}{h} \frac{f_{\neq}}{F_\text{A} F_\text{B} f_{**}} \exp\left(-\frac{E_0}{RT}\right). \tag{38}$$

Now $[**]$ equals $\frac{1}{2}s[*]^2/n_s$, where s is the number of sites adjacent to any chosen site and n_s is the *total* number of sites per cm.^{2}, so that

$$r = [\text{A}][\text{B}] \frac{\frac{1}{2}s[*]^2}{n_s} \frac{kT}{h} \frac{f_{\neq}}{F_\text{A} F_\text{B} f_{**}} \exp\left(-\frac{E_0}{RT}\right). \tag{39}$$

The adsorbed concentrations of A and B, and the free site concentration [*], are interrelated through the adsorption coefficients b_A and b_B, whence

$$[*] = \frac{n_s}{1 + b_A[A] + b_B[B]} \cdot \tag{40}$$

The rate then becomes

$$r = \frac{\frac{1}{2}sn_s[A][B]}{(1 + b_A[A] + b_B[B])^2} \frac{kT}{h} \frac{f_{\neq}}{F_A F_B f_{**}} \left(\exp - \frac{E_0}{RT}\right). \tag{41}$$

This is the general formulation of the rate of a bimolecular process on the Absolute Rate Theory: it is convenient now to consider limiting cases due to various strengths of adsorption of A and B, in the usual manner

Case I: $b_A \doteqdot b_B \ll 1$.

In this case

$$r = \tfrac{1}{2}sn_s[A][B] \frac{kT}{h} \frac{f_{\neq}}{F_A F_B f_{**}} \exp\left(-\frac{E_0}{RT}\right). \tag{42}$$

The reaction will be of the second order.

Case II: $b_A \gg 1 \gg b_B$.

$$r = \tfrac{1}{2}sn_s \frac{[B]}{b_A^2[A]} \frac{kT}{h} \frac{f_{\neq}}{F_A F_B f_{**}} \exp\left(-\frac{E_0}{RT}\right). \tag{43}$$

When b_A is expressed in terms of partition functions, and the substitution made,

$$r = \tfrac{1}{2}sn_s \frac{[B]}{[A]} \frac{kT}{h} \frac{F_A f_{\neq} f_{**}}{F_B f_{a,A}^2} \exp\left(-\frac{E_0 - 2\epsilon}{RT}\right). \tag{44}$$

These rate expresions can be applied and can be expected to yield the same type of information as that provided by unimolecular rate expressions.

Corresponding rate equations based on the collision of a gas-phase molecule with an adsorbed molecule (the Rideal–Eley mechanism) are readily formulated, but they are very similar to those presented above which were derived on the basis of the "adjacent adsorption" mechanism. It is therefore not possible to distinguish between likely mechanisms by the criterion of agreement or otherwise with rates calculated by the Absolute Rate Theory.

Absolute Rate expressions for bimolecular reactions in which there is inhibition by products have been devised and tested.[1] Attempts to derive rate expressions for energetically inhomogeneous surfaces on the basis of this Theory have not so far been successful, and Laidler admits that "progress in this important field must probably await further knowledge of the structure of solid surfaces and of its relationship to catalytic activity." There is still a place for the experimental chemist.

7.4 The Application of the Power Rate Law to Surface Reactions

It can hardly be claimed that the Absolute Rate Theory has added significantly to our knowledge of the mechanism of catalytic action. Where agreement is obtained between observed and calculated rates, the Theory justifies itself: where disagreement results, possible explanations may be advanced, and on the whole the failures of the Theory are more significant than its successes. It is therefore of interest to examine an alternative approach which although rather more empirical, nevertheless permits of a somewhat deeper insight into the thermodynamics of catalytic systems. This second approach is termed the Power Rate Law, and is due to Schuit and van Reijen.[11, 12] The argument is developed along the following lines.

If for any reaction the rate constant k is the proportionality constant equating the rate to the pressures of reactants (in atmospheres) raised to the appropriate powers, then we may define a *specific* rate constant k_s as

$$k_s = \frac{N_g^0}{n_s} \cdot k, \tag{45}$$

where N_g^0 is the total number of molecules which there would be in the reaction vessel at the relevant temperature and one atmosphere pressure, and n_s is the total number of sites: k_s therefore has the units of molecules per site per second.

Now in the previous Section the Absolute Rate Theory was applied to surface reactions by substituting into the basic rate equation the proper form of the adsorption isotherm, so that the rate could be directly correlated with gas pressures. The Power Rate Law supposes that it is simply sufficient to express the rate constant as

$$k = k^0 P_A^m P_B^n \exp(-E/RT) = A \exp(-E/RT), \tag{46}$$

where k^0 is the frequency factor at unit pressure and m and n are the experimentally-found orders of reaction and A and B respectively, generally *not* equal to the number of molecules of A and B participating in the stoichiometric equation. The Power Rate Law is an attempt to relate k^0, E, m and n to the thermodynamic properties of the reactants and of the normal and activated intermediates.

For the stoichiometric equation

$$a\text{A} + b\text{B} \rightarrow \text{X} \tag{c}$$

the transition state of the slowest step is supposed to have the composition $(\text{A}_a\text{B}_b)^{\ddagger}$ and to occupy τ_T surface sites. The reactants A and B respectively occupy fractions θ_A and θ_B of the surface, the adsorbed molecules covering respectively τ_A and τ_B sites. A fraction θ_f of the surface is left vacant, and

$$\theta_f = 1 - \theta_A - \theta_B. \tag{47}$$

Now according to the Absolute Rate Theory, the rate is given by

$$r = \frac{kT}{h}\left[P_A \exp\left(\frac{\varphi_A^0}{R}\right)\right]^a \left[P_B \exp\left(\frac{\varphi_B^0}{R}\right)\right]^b \exp\left(-\frac{\varphi_A^0}{R}\right)\theta_f^{\tau_T} \exp\left(-\frac{E}{RT}\right). \tag{48}$$

In this equation the free energy function, φ^0, given by

$$\varphi^0 = \frac{G_T^0 - H_0^0}{T} \tag{49}$$

for the gas at one atmosphere pressure, has replaced its partition function, since

$$P_A \exp(\varphi_A^0/R) = [A]F_A^{-1}. \tag{50}$$

Then, for an ideal gas, the specific heat is independent of temperature, so that

$$\varphi_A^0 = C_p - S_A^0, \tag{51}$$

where S_A^0 is the standard molar entropy of A. In the application of the above equation, φ_T^0 is neglected: this corresponds to assuming $F_{\ddagger}$ to be unity. The Power Rate Law then seeks to express the frequency factor and the orders m and n in terms of the above equation, without making assumptions concerning the reaction mechanism.

If all the adsorbed species are in equilibrium with the gas phase, a calculation of θ_f may be made with the appropriate Langmuir isotherms, as for example

$$(\theta_A/\tau_A)/\theta_f^{\tau_A} = P_A \exp(\Delta\varphi_A^0/R) \exp(-\Delta H_{a,A}^0/RT), \tag{52}$$

where $-\Delta H_{a,A}^0$ is the standard heat of adsorption of A at 0°K, that is, the difference between the standard enthalpies of A in the gas phase and in the adsorbed state. Similarly $\Delta\varphi_A^0$ is the difference between the standard free energy functions of A in these states, but since $\varphi_{a,A}^0$ is normally low, $\Delta\varphi_A^0$ may be equated to φ_A^0. θ_f can now be expressed to a good approximation by the Power Rate Law:

$$\theta_f \simeq [P_A \exp(\varphi_A^0/R) \exp(-\Delta H^0_{,A}/RT)]^{-\theta_A/\tau_A}[P_B \exp(\varphi_B^0/R) \exp(-\Delta H_{a,B}^0/RT)]^{-\theta_B/\tau_B}. \tag{53}$$

If the approximations are made that the contributions to the activation energy due to the temperature dependence of kT/h, $\varphi_{A,B}^0$, $-\Delta H_{a,A,B}^0$ and $\theta_{A,B}$ are negligible, substitution of this equation into the rate expression yields the following value for the frequency factor:

$$A = \frac{kT}{h}[P_A \exp(\varphi_A^0/R)]^m[P_B \exp(\varphi_B^0/R)]^n \tag{54}$$

$$= \frac{kT}{h} \exp[(m\Delta S_{a,A}^0 + n\Delta S_{a,B}^0)/R], \tag{55}$$

where m equals $(a - \theta_A\tau_T/\tau_A)$, n equals $(b - \theta_B\tau_T/\tau_B)$ and ΔS_a^0 is the standard entropy of adsorption of the species indicated by the subscript.

An alternative approach which gives information on the significance of the experimental activation energy E involves consideration of the stoichiometry of the formation of the transition state. Of the τ_T sites required for the transition state, an average of $\theta_A\tau_T$ are occupied by adsorbed A, $\theta_B\tau_T$ by adsorbed B, and $\theta_f\tau_T$ are empty. Therefore at the τ_T sites being considered,

$\theta_A\tau_T/\tau_A$ molecules of adsorbed A are available (and similarly for B), the remainder having necessarily come from the gas phase. Thus the stoichiometric equation for the formation of the transition state, whose composition is represented by T, is

$$T \rightleftharpoons \left(a - \frac{\theta_A\tau_T}{\tau_A}\right) P_A + \left(b - \frac{\theta_B\tau_T}{\tau_B}\right) P_B + \frac{\theta_A\tau_T}{\tau_A} A_a + \frac{\theta_B\tau_T}{\tau_B} B_a, \quad (56)$$

where the symbols A_a and B_a respectively denote adsorbed A and B. This equation can be employed to express T in terms of P_A and P_B by (i) applying the thermodynamic condition of equilibrium, and (ii) inserting the Langmuir formulae for the configurational entropy of the adsorbed species: but all these cancel to a satisfactory approximation apart from the term $RT \ln\theta_T$ for the transition state. We then have

$$\left(a - \frac{\theta_A\tau_T}{\tau_A}\right)\left(G_A^0 + RT \ln P_A\right) + \left(b - \frac{\theta_B\tau_T}{\tau_B}\right)\left(G_B^0 + RT \ln P_B\right)$$

$$+ \frac{\theta_A\tau_T}{\tau_A} G_{a,A}^0 + \frac{\theta_B\tau_T}{\tau_B} G_{a,B}^0 = G_T^0 + RT \ln \theta_T. \quad (57)$$

Now θ_T can be transformed, by the methods of Absolute Rate Theory, into a reaction rate, with a result which is identical with that given before: in addition, however, the activation energy is given by

$$E = (H_T^0 - aH_{a,A}^0 - bH_{a,B}^0) + m\Delta H_{a,A}^0 + n\Delta H_{a,B}^0, \quad (58)$$

where H_T^0 is the standard heat content of the transition state. These treatments have been applied[11] to large number of simple catalytic processes, with the result that the mean values of $A/(kT/h)$ obtained by calculation and by experiment are generally in good agreement. The exceptions are reactions over tungsten where calculated rates are 10^6–10^{12} times greater than the observed; this has been interpreted as implying that only a very small fraction of the surface of tungsten is catalytically active.

Thus the main achievement of this application of Absolute Rate Theory, as of the more familiar one, is that it enables one to decide whether almost all the surface is active, or whether activity is confined to a small fraction of the sites. The Power Rate Law is in the unfortunate position of having of necessity to apply a treatment based on a surface assumed to be homogeneous to systems where heterogeneity is reasonably certain. In this respect it is no advance on the usual form of the Absolute Rate Theory, where attempts to modify the treatment to cover heterogeneous surfaces have, as already noted, had no success.

7.5 Kinetic Parameters and Catalyst Structure: the Compensation Effect

7.51 Kinetic Parameters and Catalyst Structure

A number of reactions have been widely employed to assess the influence of electronic constitution and geometry of metal catalysts in the same physical state on their catalytic efficiency. Most of this work has been done using hydrogenation or dehydrogenation reactions, and will be described in some detail in the succeeding chapters; little has been done to assess the importance of these variables in oxidation reactions. Interest has generally centred on the variation of the kinetic parameters of the sole reaction path, and there has only been slight interest in the relationship between catalyst structure and catalytic specificity.

Activity variations shown by a series of related catalysts, such as a series of different metals, or a given metal treated in a variety of ways, or an alloy series, may be the result of variations in the activation energy E or in the pre-exponential factor A, or in both simultaneously. It is important to the attainment of the maximum information concerning a given system that these quantities be determined in addition to the activity. The activity is of course defined by the rate constant k, or less satisfactorily by the rate under constant conditions of partial pressures. Uncertainty arises if rates rather than rate constants are employed, since any change in the orders of reaction with temperature will destroy the proportionality. It is unfortunate that while many studies have been made concerning variations in *rate* over a series of catalysts, few have given evidence on concomitant changes in reaction orders. If varying amounts of catalysts are used, it is well to establish the proportionality between the amount and the rate: there are subtle reasons why the proportionality may sometimes fail.

7.52 Phenomenological Description of the Compensation Effect

Of great significance is the frequently observed relationship between the activation energy E and the pre-exponential factor A for a given reaction over a series of related catalysts. It is usually of the form

$$\log A = mE + c \tag{59}$$

and is referred to as a compensation effect or the Theta Rule. The former name is meaningful, since an increase in $\log A$ at constant E implies a higher rate, while an increase in E at constant $\log A$ implies a lower rate: simultaneous increases or decreases in E and $\log A$ therefore tend to compensate from the standpoint of the rate. When such a compensation operates, it is possible for striking variations in E and $\log A$ through a catalyst series to yield only relatively small changes in activity; alternatively when the effect does not operate (that is, when either E or $\log A$ alone changes) striking variations in activity result. Such cases, although rare, are of particular significance. It is clearly of importance to the proper understanding of the mechanisms of catalytic action to know how the basic kinetic parameters, as well as the rate, respond to changes in catalyst structure.

It may be readily shown that if a compensation effect described by the above equation is operating, there must be some characteristic temperature T_s at which all the rates are equal. Consider the situation formally represented

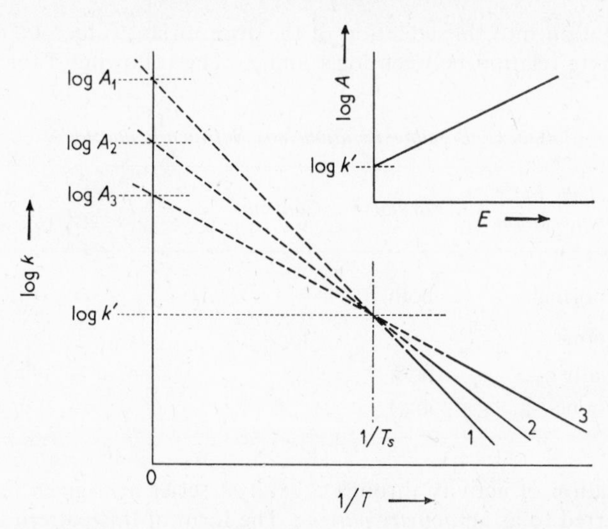

FIG. 3. Diagrammatic representations of a simple compensation effect (Case I).

in Fig. 3: in this diagram $\log k'$ must be the value of $\log A$ when the activation energy is zero, so that

$$\log A = mE + \log k'. \tag{60}$$

Now the value of the slope of any line is given by

(i) $\dfrac{-E_i}{2.303R}$, and also by (ii) $-\dfrac{(\log A_i - \log k')}{1/T_s}$. Hence

$$(\log A_i - \log k') = mE_i = \frac{E_i}{2.303RT_s} \tag{61}$$

and hence

$$m = (2.303RT_s)^{-1}. \tag{62}$$

An equation of the desired form therefore follows if there is a temperature T_s at which all the rates become equal; the converse must therefore be true. T_s is of course easily estimated from the experimental results.

Three other cases must be considered (Figs. 4–6). Cases II and IV (Figs. 4 and 6) are situations where there is no compensation, since in Case II $\log A$ is constant and E varies, while in Case IV E is constant and $\log A$ varies. In the former case, $1/T_s$ is zero and T_s is infinity: in the latter case $1/T_s$ is plus or minus infinity, so that T_s is zero or imaginary. In Case III (Fig. 5), which is designated an "anti-compensation" effect, $1/T_s$ is negative and T_s is imaginary, and it is easily shown that here

$$\log A_i = -(2.303RT_s)^{-1}E_i + \log k'. \tag{63}$$

The general form of the relation between E and $\log A$ which covers all the cases is

$$\log A_i = \pm \frac{E_i}{2.303RT_s} + \log k' \tag{64}$$

and substitution into this equation of the appropriate value of T_s yields the corresponding relation between $\log A$ and E. The following Table acts as a summary.

TABLE II. *Possible Relationships Between* E *and log*A

Case	*Type of compensation*	*Variable*	*Constant*	$1/T_s$	T_s
I	normal	both	—	$0 < \frac{1}{T_s} < \infty$	$0 < T_s < \infty$
II	none	E	$\log A$	0	∞
III	anti-	both	—	negative	imaginary
IV	none	$\log A$	E	$\pm\infty$	0 or imaginary

The variation of activity through a catalyst series at a given temperature will be referred to as an *activity pattern*. The form of this pattern is clearly a function of temperature: from Fig. 3, the order of catalyst activity at all temperatures greater than T_s is $1 > 2 > 3$, whereas at all temperatures below T_s the order is the exact reverse. This raises the important question of how to describe relative activities. It is commonly done in one of two ways: either (i) by comparing the temperatures required to effect a certain rate or conversion, or (ii) by comparing the rates at some representative temperatures. The drawbacks of the first method are (a) that the activity order is not unique but depends on the arbitrarily chosen rate and (b) it is only qualitative. The statement that "catalyst 1 is 50° more active than catalyst 2 at 10 per cent conversion" may have some practical value, but is useless in a fundamental investigation. Where only this type of information is recorded in the literature and where further computation is impossible, it has been assumed that relative activities are proportional to the reciprocal of the absolute temperature required to effect the chosen conversion. Method (ii) is therefore much to be preferred, in that it places relative activities on a readily understandable and quantitative footing, and it enables the temperature-dependence of the activity order to be assessed.

7.53 *Interpretations of the Compensation Effect*

Of the various interpretations of the compensation effect which have been offered, three are worth serious consideration. Chronologically the first is the treatment initially due to Constable,[13] since developed by others.[14] It assumes an energetically heterogeneous surface. The argument in its simplest form takes the following lines.[1]

If the number of sites of the ith type is n_i and if the activation energy on these sites is E_i, the total rate is given by

$$r = k \sum_i n_i \exp(-E_i/RT). \tag{65}$$

If further the number n_i is related to E_i by an equation of the form

$$n_i = a \exp (E_i/b), \tag{66}$$

where a and b are constants, then the total rate takes the form

$$r = ka \sum_i \exp (gE), \tag{67}$$

where

$$g = \frac{1}{b} - \frac{1}{RT}. \tag{68}$$

This rate expression may be integrated between the limits E_1 and E_2 if the distribution of site energy is assumed to be continuous between these limits, whereupon we obtain

$$r = \frac{ka}{g} [\exp (-gE_1) - \exp (-gE_2)]. \tag{69}$$

It is found experimentally that the magnitudes of g, E_1 and E_2 are such as to permit the neglecting of the second exponential term, and hence

$$r = \frac{ka}{g} \exp (-gE_1) \tag{70}$$

$$= \frac{ka \exp (E_1/b)}{g} \exp (-E_1/RT). \tag{71}$$

The final result shows that the reaction must be proceeding almost exclusively on the most active sites where the activation energy is a minimum: but furthermore the activation energy has appeared in an exponential term in the "pre-exponential" factor, with, however, a positive and not a negative sign. If, therefore, on another catalyst the activation energy is greater, the A factor will also be greater, and a partial compensation will result.

Cremer and Schwab[14] have supposed that in the case of a metal formed by reduction of a precursor at a temperature θ, the energy of the surface sites attains an equilibrium distribution, and that the value of the constant b under such conditions is given by $R\theta$. In agreement with this view, b is sometimes found to have the same value for a given reaction over a series of different catalysts, but especially for preformed metals the derived value of θ is often ridiculously different from the temperature at which they had been treated. It is incidentally to Cremer and Schwab that the name Theta Rule is due.

It is therefore clear that the foregoing interpretation cannot be a perfectly general one, particularly since it is developed from the questionable standpoint of a heterogeneous surface. A second interpretation is as follows.[15] If the true activation energy and pre-exponential factor are dependent on temperature, then it may be readily shown that the apparent activation energy is given by

$$E_y = RT \ln A_y + (E_{z,T} - RT \ln A_{z,T}), \tag{72}$$

where A_y is the apparent pre-exponential factor, $A_{z,T}$ the value of the true pre-exponential factor at the temperature T and $E_{z,T}$ the value of the true activation energy at that temperature. Now the term within the brackets may be expressed as $-RT \ln k_T$, and so the equation may be rewritten as

$$\ln A_y = \frac{E_y}{RT} + \ln k_T, \tag{73}$$

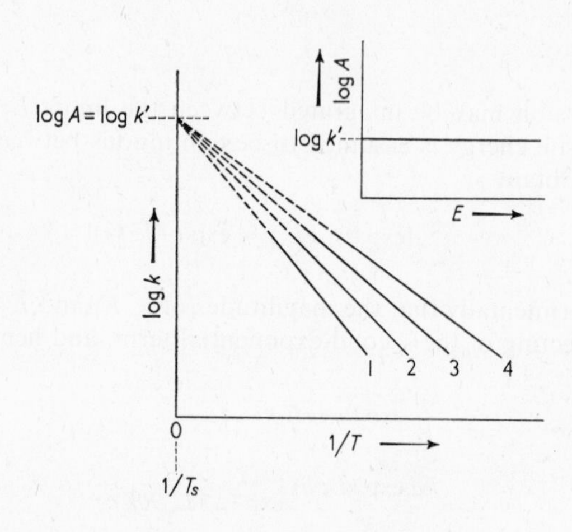

FIG. 4. Diagrammatic representations of a "no-compensation" effect; E variable, $\log A$ constant (Case II).

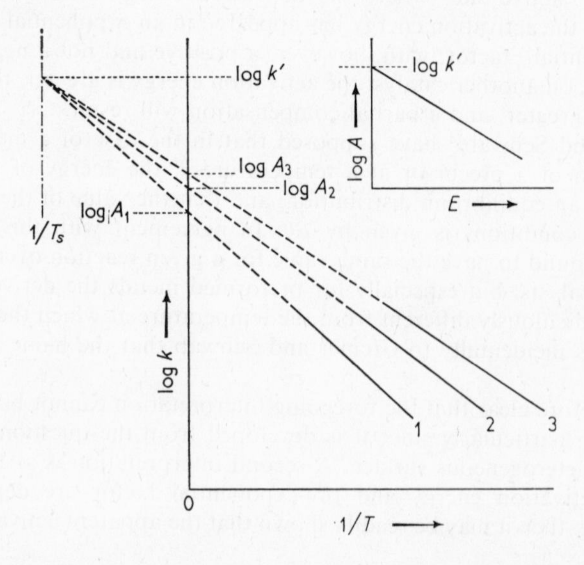

FIG. 5. Diagrammatic representations of an "anti-compensation" effect (Case III).

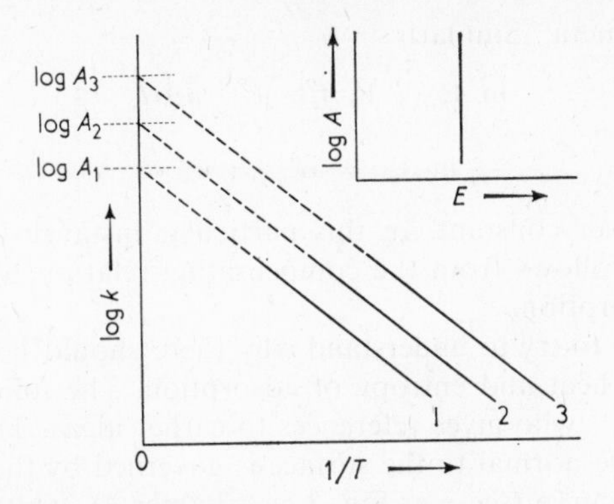

FIG. 6. Diagrammatic representation of a further "no compensation" effect; E constant, $\log A$ variable (Case IV).

which is similar to the general equation for the compensation effect deduced in the last Section. There is, however, no physical picture to account for a temperature-dependence of true parameters of the rate equation.

There remains the third interpretation, which has been suggested in slightly differing forms by several authors.[15, 16] The basis of this interpretation is that there is a relationship between the heat and entropy of adsorption, and that this leads to a connection between activation energy and entropy of activation (and hence pre-exponential factor). The following argument is due to Kemball.[16]

The gas A is adsorbed without dissociation on single sites according to the Langmuir isotherm: the adsorption coefficient b_A may be expressed as

$$b_A = \exp(\Delta S_a/R)\exp(-\Delta H_a/RT) \tag{74}$$

and, if the gas is strongly adsorbed,

$$1-\theta_A \doteqdot (b_A P_A)^{-1} = \exp(-\Delta S_a/R)\exp(\Delta H_a/RT)P_A^{-1}. \tag{75}$$

The activation energy of any reaction involving a vacant site will therefore be increased by $-\Delta H_a$ and the frequency factor by $\exp(-\Delta S_a/R)$. Now there is considerable evidence from studies of physical adsorption[17] that heats and entropies of adsorption are often related as

$$\frac{\Delta S_{a,i}}{R} = u\Delta H_{a,i} - v, \tag{76}$$

where u and v are constants and the subscript i denotes any relevant adsorption system. The evidence for the existence of a relation of this type in chemisorption systems is at present slight. However, supposing its validity, we would write for a process requiring a vacant site

$$E_{y,i} = E_z - \Delta H_{a,i} \tag{77}$$

i indicating any metal. Similarly

$$\ln A_{y,i} = \ln A_z + v - u\Delta H_{a,i} \tag{78}$$

and hence

$$\ln A_{y,i} = uE_{y,i} + w, \tag{79}$$

where w is another constant. In this particular instance therefore, a compensation effect follows from the compensating relation between heats and entropies of adsorption.

It remains now to try to understand why there should be a compensation relation between heat and entropy of adsorption. The following suggestion is due to Everett,[17] who gives references to earlier ideas. The motion of any adsorbed molecule normal to the surface is governed by the familiar type of potential energy curve (see e.g. Fig. 1 in Chapter 4), while motion parallel to the surface is determined by the system of potential energy curves shown in Fig. 3 of Chapter 4. Now the vibrational entropy of the molecule arising from either of these translational motions depends on the curvature at the potential minima, and this will be greater the greater the depth of the minima. Similarly entropy contributions arising from rotation of the adsorbed molecule are likely to be more restricted the greater the strength of adsorption. A proportionality between heat and entropy of adsorption is therefore to be expected.

Finally a few comments of a general nature are in order. It was shown in the last Section that compensation between the activation energy and the pre-exponential factor of a reaction on a series of catalysts necessarily implies the existence of a temperature T_s at which the rates over all the catalysts are equal. The equation of the compensation effect is then

$$\ln A_i = \frac{E_i}{RT_s} + \ln k', \tag{80}$$

which is simply the Arrhenius equation relating the rate parameters at T_s. Remembering that

$$\ln A_i = \ln\left(\frac{kT}{h}\right) + \frac{\Delta S_i^{\ddagger}}{R} \tag{81}$$

and

$$E_i \doteqdot \Delta H_i^{\ddagger}, \tag{82}$$

it follows that

$$-\frac{\Delta G_i^{\ddagger}}{RT} = -\ln\left(\frac{kT}{h}\right) + \ln k'. \tag{83}$$

This relation could of course have been obtained directly from the expression

$$k' = \frac{kT}{h}\exp\left(-\frac{\Delta G_i^{\ddagger}}{RT},\right) \tag{84}$$

and so it appears that the equation for the compensation effect is merely a means of expressing the fact that $-\Delta G^{\ddagger}$ has the same value for all catalysts at T_s. Complete compensation is therefore only possible at this temperature, and the difference between the logs of the rates over any two catalysts at any other temperature T_i will be proportional to (i) the difference between the reciprocal temperatures, viz. $(1/T_i) - (1/T_s)$, and (ii) the difference between the free energies of activation at the temperature T_i.

It is also interesting to note how the cases (II and IV) where no compensation occurs may be interpreted. If the heat of adsorption of the reactant varies from one catalyst to another in the series considered, the apparent activation energy will change, but if there is no variation in the entropy of adsorption, or if such variation is immaterial, we obtain the situation of Case II. On the other hand, if the variation in the entropy of adsorption is relevant and the variation in the heat of adsorption irrelevant (as for example at full surface coverage) then we obtain the situation of Case IV.

A number of other discussions of the compensation effect have been given.[18–21]

References

1. K. J. Laidler, In "Catalysis", edited by P. H. Emmett (Reinhold, New York, 1954), **1,** 119, 195.
2. K. J. Laidler, *Canad. J. Chem.* **36,** 1081 (1958).
3. O. A. Hougen and K. M. Watson, "Chemical Process Principles" (Wiley, New York, 1948).
4. K. Tamaru, *Trans. Faraday Soc.* **55,** 824 (1959).
5. N. Thon and H. A. Taylor, *J. Amer. Chem. Soc.* **75,** 2747 (1953).
6. J. C. Jungers and J. C. Balacéanu, *Rev. Inst. franç. Pétrole* **10,** 30 (1955).
7. J. R. Anderson, *Rev. Pure Appl. Chem. (Australia)* **7,** 165 (1957).
8. A. Wheeler, *Adv. Catalysis* **4,** 250 (1951).
9. H. I. Waterman and A. B. R. Weber, *J. Inst. Petroleum* **43,** 315 (1957); H. Breimer, H. I. Waterman and A. B. R. Weber, *ibid,* **43,** 299; H. I. Waterman, C. Boelhouwer and J. Cornelissen, *Analyt. Chim. Acta* **18,** 497 (1958). See also J. H. de Boer and R. J. A. M. van der Borg, Proc. 2nd International Congress on Catalysis (Editions Technip, Paris, 1961), **1,** 919.
10. G. C. Bond, D. A. Dowden and N. Mackenzie, *Trans. Faraday Soc.* **54,** 1537 (1958).
11. G. C. A. Schuit and L. L. van Reijen, *Adv. Catalysis* **10,** 243 (1958).
12. G. C. A. Schuit and L. L. van Reijen, *Bull. Soc. chim. belges* **67,** 489 (1958).
13. F. H. Constable, *Proc. Roy. Soc.* **A108,** 355 (1925).
14. E. Cremer and G.-M. Schwab, *Z. phys. Chem. (Leipzig)* **A144,** 243 (1929); G.-M. Schwab, *Z. phys. Chem. (Leipzig)* **B5,** 406 (1929).
15. E. Cremer, *Adv. Catalysis* **7,** 75 (1955).
16. C. Kemball, *Proc. Roy. Soc.* **A217,** 376 (1953).
17. D. H. Everett, *Trans. Faraday Soc.* **46,** 957 (1950).
18. A. Couper and D. D. Eley, *Proc. Roy. Soc.* **A211,** 544 (1952).
19. T. Kwan, *J. Phys. Chem.* **59,** 285 (1955).
20. P. Zwietering and J. J. Roukens, *Trans. Faraday Soc.* **50,** 178 (1954).
21. P. Rüetschi, *Z. phys. Chem. (Frankfurt)* **14,** 19 (1958).

Chapter 8

The Reactions of Hydrogen at Metal Surfaces

8.1 Introduction

8.11 A General Review

The object of this chapter is to give an account of the processes in which hydrogen atoms and their isotopic equivalents are formed, or interact, or are destroyed at metal surfaces. The term "hydrogen" will be used generically, except when the isotopic nature of the species in question is relevant.

At low and moderate temperatures, hydrogen atoms formed in the gas phase recombine at metal surfaces to form molecular hydrogen. At temperatures between −200 and 400° (depending on the catalytic efficiency of the metal), molecular hydrogen dissociates at metal surfaces to form hydrogen atoms, which subsequently recombine: this sequence allows the occurrence of hydrogen equilibration reactions. Finally at high temperatures adsorbed hydrogen atoms may vacate the surface, resulting in the appearance of gas-phase atoms.

The first and third of these processes have not been widely investigated. Hydrogen equilibration reactions have on the other hand been very intensively studied over the past thirty years. The reactions are attractive by reason of their simplicity: since reactant and product are chemically identical, the formulation of rate expressions is straightforward and the observed kinetics generally uncomplicated. The result is therefore a much deeper insight into detailed mechanism than is yet possible for any other catalytic system. This is not, however, to say that a state of perfect understanding has yet been reached, but the mechanistic controversy which has existed for many years now appears about to be settled.

8.12 Forms of Hydrogen

The diatomic molecule formed from atoms of the element carrying a nuclear charge of one is capable of existing in a number of distinguishable forms. There are three isotopes of this element:

(i) hydrogen (sometimes called protium); symbol, H; mass 1;
(ii) deuterium; symbol, D; mass 2;
(iii) tritium; symbol, T; mass 3.

The latter is a weak β-emitter with a half-life of 12.5 yr.; deuterium is not radioactive. The following isotopic variants of the molecule are therefore possible: H_2, D_2, T_2, HD, HT and DT. Analysis of species containing tritium is achieved with highest accuracy using radioactive counting methods. Species containing deuterium may be analysed mass-spectrometrically or by measurements of thermal conductivity. Alternatively if the sample is sufficiently large, the "hydrogen" may be burnt to water, the deuterium content of which can be determined by micropyknometry.

Furthermore, diatomic molecules composed of two isotopically identical atoms may exist in either of two forms which differ in the relative orientation of the spins of the nuclei. The form having parallel spins is referred to as *ortho* (*o*-), and the form with antiparallel spins as *para* (*p*-). The forms are known for hydrogen and deuterium, but little is known about the *ortho*- and *para*-spin isomers of tritium. The equilibrium between *ortho*- and *para*-hydrogen lies entirely on the side of the *para*-form at the absolute zero, but the equilibrium proportion of *para* falls with rising temperature to a limiting value of 25 per cent, achieved at room temperature and above. It is the *ortho*-form of deuterium which is favoured at low temperature, its proportion falling to the limiting value of 67 per cent with rising temperature. The physical properties of the pure spin isomers differ only insignificantly from those of the equilibrium mixtures, except that the thermal conductivities are sufficiently different to enable them to be used as the basis of an analytical method.

Equilibration between the two forms may be brought about, without dissociation of the molecule, by strongly paramagnetic substances such as charcoal, oxygen, rare earth ions, or indeed anything containing a high concentration of unpaired electrons. Very nearly pure *para*-hydrogen and *ortho*-deuterium may therefore be prepared by exposing the gases to active charcoal at low temperature. Equilibration by this "paramagnetic" mechanism also sometimes occurs at metal surfaces, but under these conditions the equilibration of hydrogen isotopes will not take place. This is because the equilibration of a hydrogen–deuterium mixture necessarily involves the dissociation of the molecules into atoms, followed by their recombination. This "chemical" mechanism is also available for *para*-hydrogen equilibration, and so the occurrence of a reaction between hydrogen and deuterium is the only unequivocal way of demonstrating the existence of atoms as intermediates.

Experimental methods for the preparation and analysis of the hydrogen forms are well described in the literature.[1, 2]

8.13 Positions of Equilibria in Hydrogen Systems

The temperature-dependence of the equilibrium proportions of spin isomers has been obtained both theoretically and experimentally.[1] Table I presents a small selection of the calculated values.

TABLE I. *Equilibrium Proportion of* Para-*Hydrogen and* Ortho-*Deuterium as a Function of Temperature*

Temperature (°K)	*% para-hydrogen*	*Temperature (°K)*	*% ortho-deuterium*
20	99.82	20	97.97
30	96.98	30	92.07
55	70.96	50	79.19
65	60.33	70	71.78
77	50.41	100	67.82
95	40.48	220	66.66
130	31.03	∞	66.66
273	25.13		
∞	25.00		

Sufficient information is available to calculate the equilibrium constant for the system

$$H_2 + D_2 \rightleftharpoons 2HD$$

by the methods of statistical mechanics. It differs from the statistically-expected value of four since (i) the partition functions do not cancel and (ii) the heat of reaction is not precisely zero. Calculated values, which have been confirmed experimentally, vary with temperature according to the equation

$$-\log K = \frac{155}{4.57T} - 0.6276.$$

Selected values of K are 2.265 at 100°K, 3.268 at 298.1°K and 3.800 at 800°K. Thus for example at room temperature the equilibrium composition of a mixture containing 50 atom per cent of deuterium is:

$$[H_2] = [D_2] = 26.2\%; [HD] = 47.6\%.$$

8.2 PARA-HYDROGEN CONVERSION AND HYDROGEN–DEUTERIUM EQUILIBRATION REACTIONS: KINETICS AND MECHANISMS

The catalysis of these reactions by Transition metals is remarkably efficient. Depending on the state of dispersion of the metal, they may be conveniently studied in the temperature range from room temperature to about $-200°$; indeed, to study them above room temperature requires the use of very small amounts of metal or of metal forms having very low specific areas. On the other hand, the *sp*-metals are notably less efficient and in general temperatures in excess of 100° are needed. This observation is of course in perfect harmony with the known reluctance of the *sp*-metals to chemisorb hydrogen (see Chapter 5), except at temperatures where electron promotion from *d*- to *s*-levels becomes possible.

Progress in this field of catalysis has been especially stimulated by fundamental disagreements concerning the reaction mechanism. Much of the experimental work of the last two decades has had as its aim the resolution of this disagreement: the instructive story of this effort is briefly related in Section 8.21. It is not until very recently that it has become apparent that neither of the proposed mechanisms is entirely correct, but rather that the truth is probably a compromise between them.

One of the techniques particularly used in these attempts to establish mechanisms is that whereby adsorbed atoms of one isotope are caused to react with another isotope, initially entirely in the gas phase. If the isotope in the gas phase is present in large excess we may represent the process as for example

$$\underset{*}{H} + D_2 \rightarrow \underset{*}{D} + HD \tag{a}$$

Processes of this sort will henceforth be described as *exchange reactions*: the term *equilibration reaction* will be reserved for those processes in which *both* isotopes or forms of hydrogen are initially present in the gas phase. The kinetics of equilibration reactions at constant pressure are always simple. The course rate expression is invariably first order in the concentration of *para*-hydrogen or of hydrogen or deuterium in excess of the equilibrium concentration; the kinetics may then be discussed in terms of the pressure and temperature dependence of the first-order rate constant k_e. The relevant information is presented in Sections 8.22 and 8.23. The kinetics of exchange reactions are on the contrary quite complex; these will be discussed in Section 8.24. Finally in Section 8.25 an attempt will be made to arrive at a self-consistent model for all these processes.

8.21 Historical Development of Mechanistic Theories

The rates and kinetics of the three most studied equilibration reactions are very similar for any given catalyst. Thus, over nickel rates[3] and kinetics[4] of *para*-hydrogen conversion and of H_2–D_2 equilibration are almost identical. Table II provides further information. The rate of *ortho*-deuterium conversion is expected to be somewhat slower than that of the *para*-hydrogen conversion because of isotopic effects.

The foregoing results make it certain that both equilibration reactions can under certain circumstances proceed by the same mechanism, necessarily involving the dissociation of the molecules. The earliest views on this

TABLE II. *Comparison of Rates and Activation Energies of Equilibration Reactions*

Metal	*Form*	$r(H_2–D_2)$	$r(\text{p-}H_2)$	$r(\text{o-}D_2)$	$T(°C)$	$E(H_2–D_2)$	$E(\text{p-}H_2)$	$E(\text{o-}D_2)$	*Ref.*
Pt	platinized foil	1.0	1.5	0.7	26	—	—	—	5
Fe	evap. film	1.0	5.0	2.0	20	9.0	8.1	8.4	6
W	wire	1.0	~1.0	—	−78 to −155	3.07	3.07	—	7

The rates are expressed relative to that of the $H_2–D_2$ reaction at the temperature shown in col. 6.

mechanism were those of Bonhoeffer and Farkas[8] who suggested the following steps.

$$\left.\begin{array}{ll}\text{Para-hydrogen conversion:} & p\text{-}H_2 + 2* \rightleftarrows 2\underset{*}{H} \rightarrow o\text{-}H_2 + 2* \\ H_2\text{–}D_2 \text{ reaction:} & H_2 + D_2 + 4* \rightleftarrows 2\underset{*}{H} + 2\underset{*}{D} \rightarrow 2HD + 4*\end{array}\right\} \quad \text{(b)}$$

In each case, the hydrogen molecules will evaporate from the surface with their various forms in the equilibrium concentrations appropriate to the temperature of the experiment.

Certain drawbacks to this mechanism soon, however, became evident. The work of Benton and White[9] showed that the desorption of chemisorbed hydrogen from the surface of nickel powder only occurred above −100°, although the $H_2–D_2$ reaction proceeded measurably on nickel at about −190°.[10] Further, though the *para*-hydrogen conversion on tungsten wire took place at −110°,[8] tungsten powder only started to *chemisorb* hydrogen at 150°.[11] The careful work of Roberts (see Chapters 4 and 5) showed however that, while rapid chemisorption of hydrogen on *cleaned* tungsten wires occurred at −190°, desorption only started to be appreciable at about 400°. Equilibration reactions therefore can take place under conditions where the adsorbed hydrogen is apparently very strongly adsorbed. Objections to the Bonhoeffer–Farkas mechanism seemed to be well-founded.

An alternative mechanism was therefore proposed by Rideal.[12] Statistical calculations had shown[13] that in an immobile layer of hydrogen atoms there would be about 8 per cent vacant single sites, and Rideal suggested the following process employing such sites.

$$\left.\begin{array}{l}\begin{array}{ccccccccc} & D & & & & D & & & D \\ & & \diagdown & & \cdot\cdot & & \cdot\cdot & & \diagup \\ & & D & & & & & H & \\ H & & & \rightleftarrows & H & & D & \rightleftarrows & & D \\ * & & * & & * & & * & & * & * \end{array} \\ \text{or} \quad \begin{array}{ccccccccc} & p\text{-}H_2 & & & & H & & & o\text{-}H_2 \\ & & & \rightleftarrows & \cdot\cdot & & \cdot\cdot & \rightleftarrows & \\ H & & & & H & & H & & & H \\ * & & * & & * & & * & & * & * \end{array}\end{array}\right\} \quad \text{(c)}$$

A general description of this and similar processes has already been given (Chapter 7). Objections to this mechanism were, however, also forthcoming. It was evident that equilibration reactions may take place under conditions where adsorbed hydrogen is known to be mobile, and where therefore no vacant sites can exist. Further, as is clear from the above reaction schemes, the occurrence of the reactions as formulated implies a migration of the vacant sites, so that they must of necessity eventually coalesce and permit the adsorption of further molecules of hydrogen; the concentration of vacant sites should therefore diminish to zero. The original form of this type of mechanism thus contains the seeds of its own destruction.

Couper and Eley[14] have modified this mechanism so that vacant sites are no longer a necessary requirement. The intermediate state is now a triatomic complex, and the process may be represented as

$$\underset{*}{H} + D_2 \rightleftarrows H \overset{D}{\underset{*}{\diamond}} D \rightleftarrows HD + \underset{*}{D}. \qquad (d)$$

We may pause at this stage to consider the possible means of distinguishing between the Bonhoeffer–Farkas mechanism and the Rideal–Eley mechanisms. One possible means is through a study of the pressure-dependence of the rate. For the Bonhoeffer–Farkas mechanism, the reaction order should vary from first at low coverages to zero at high coverages, the latter condition being that most commonly encountered. For the Rideal–Eley mechanisms, the order should be first, providing the atomic layer is complete and the molecular species only weakly adsorbed, or not at all. A second possible means of distinguishing between these mechanisms is by application of Absolute Rate Theory or the Power Rate Law. The conclusions drawn from these considerations will be discussed in Section 8.25 when some experimental results have been presented.

In the third phase of this story, new experimental work and a critical examination of some of the older work have shown that the original objections to the Bonhoeffer–Farkas mechanism were ill-founded. Thus for example it now appears that the values for the heat of adsorption of hydrogen on tungsten recorded by Roberts and by Beeck for allegedly complete coverage in fact refer to coverages appreciably less than unity. In the case of Roberts, it seems that his experimental techniques were insufficiently sensitive to detect incremental adsorption occurring at equilibrium pressures if greater than 3×10^{-4} mm.: in the case of Beeck, his adoption of an arbitrary criterion for complete coverage (viz. an equilibrium pressure of 0.1 mm.) has proved misleading (see Chapter 5).

Frankenburg's work[15] on hydrogen adsorption on tungsten powder indicated that above 10^{-4} mm. (where he estimated the coverage to be only 21 per cent) there was a region of weak, reversible chemisorption of low heat, extending to complete coverage. In spite of the rigorous procedures employed, the purity of Frankenburg's surfaces has been questioned; however, results

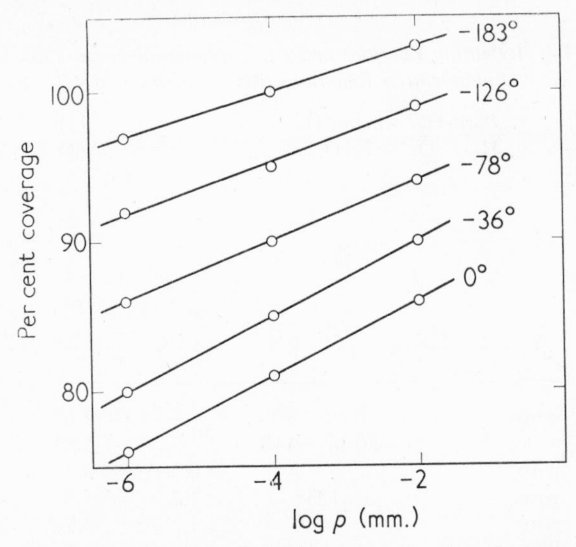

FIG. 1. The coverage of tungsten films by hydrogen as a function of pressure and temperature.[16]

of a similar nature have been obtained with evaporated tungsten films.[16] Adsorption isotherms were obtained at a series of temperatures between 0 and $-183°$, and at each temperature a certain proportion of the adsorbed gas was removable by pumping at 0°C. Heats of adsorption, obtained isosterically, were shown to decrease from 15 kcal. mole^{-1} at $\theta = 0.81$ to 2.4 kcal. mole^{-1} at $\theta = 1$. The dependence of coverage on temperature and pressure is shown in Fig. 1. Much of the low temperature, reversible adsorption must therefore be chemisorption, since the heat of physical adsorption of hydrogen does not exceed 2 kcal. mole^{-1}. Other recent work on different metals showing very low heats at complete coverage has already been mentioned (Chapter 5). The discovery of weak, reversible chemisorption at room temperature and below has largely removed the earlier objections to the Bonhoeffer–Farkas mechanism.

TABLE III. *Orders of Reaction for the Para-Hydrogen Conversion on Transition Metals*

Metal	*Form*	*Temp.* (°C)	*Pressure range* (*mm.*)	*Order*	*Ref.*
W	wire	−100	25 to 400	0.3	8
W	wire	−113	0.1 to 6	~0.2*	17
W	wire	−123	~1 to 10	0	18
W	wire	~−140	0.01 to 16	0.1 to 0.6	7
Co	wire	−43	~1 to 10	~0.5	18
Ni	tube	12	0.004 to 4.5	0.6	8
Ni	film	20	0.005 to 0.026	0.65	19

* Langmuir isotherm accurately obeyed.

TABLE IV. *Activation Energies and Pre-exponential Factors for Hydrogen Equilibration Reactions over Transition Metals*

Para-H_2 → *ortho*-H_2 . . . . (1)
$H_2 + D_2 \rightarrow 2HD$ . . . . (2)

Reaction	*Metal*	*Form*	*Temp. range (°C)*	*Pressure (mm.)*	*E(kcal. mole⁻¹)*	*log A*	*Ref.*
1	W	wire	0 to −80	50	2.65	—	8
			−80 to −110		5.75	—	
1	W	wire	?	0.5	3.8	23.32	20
1	W	wire	−123*	1.2	3.7	23.75	18
1	Fe	wire	−43*	1.2	3.9	20.81	18
1	Fe	film	85 to 160	18	8.1	—	21
2	Fe	filings	?	65	8.1	15.22	22
1	Co	wire	−43*	1.2	4.5	21.93	18
2	Co	sponge	?	65	7.9	16.43	22
1	Ni	film	∼−78	?	1.4	—	23
2	Ni	film	104 to 165	37	7.5	—	24
1	Ni	wire	−43*	1.2	2.6	19.93	18
1	Ni	foil	?	?	5.0	—	25
1	Ni	plate[a]	152 to 225	?	9.3	—	26
1	Ni	rolled foil[b]	?	?	9.6	—	26
1	Ni	powder[b]	?	?	10.6	—	26
2	Ni	Raney and powder	?	65	8.0	17.57	22
1	Pd	plate	?	?	2.3, 5.8	—	27
1	Pd[c]	plate	?	?	5.4, 9.6		27
1	Pd	wire	−103 to 57	1.2	3.68*	20.81*	14
1	Pd[c]	wire	17 to 127	1.2	∼11	24.3	14
1	Pd	foil	?	?	5.3	—	25
1	Pt	foil	132 to 232	?	8.65	—	28
1	Pt	wire	−123*	1.2	2.7	21.32	18
1	Pt	wire	?	6.4		—	29
2	Pt	wire, sponge, black	0 to 330	65	7.5	—	22
			−196 to −70	65	0.5	—	
2	Pt	on SiO_2	−70 to 100	65	3.0	—	22
			−183 to −70	65	0.5	—	

Notes. *A* is in molecules cm.$^{-2}$ sec.$^{-1}$: *; mean value: a; heat treated at 225°: b; outgassed at 300°: c; hydrogen-saturated.

8.22 *The Kinetics of Hydrogen Equilibration Reactions on Transition Metals*

This Section summarizes, without comment on the mechanistic implications, some of the principal experimental observations on the kinetics of hydrogen equilibration reactions over various forms of Transition metals. Most of this work has employed the *para*-hydrogen conversion, and most of the investigations have used unsupported metals, because of the greater ease of estimating surface areas. The results are shown in Tables III and IV.

In view of the significance of the order of the reaction in discussions of mechanisms, it is somewhat surprising that so few observations have actually been made. Precise measurements are confined to nickel and tungsten: over tungsten wire[17] at 160°K, the rate dependence on pressure is in the form of a Langmuir isotherm, viz.

$$k_e p = \frac{bp}{1 + bp}\cdot$$

Unpublished work on platinum wire is reported[30, 31] to show the same behaviour, and further that measurements at different temperatures lead to a heat of adsorption of the relevant form of hydrogen of 2.3 kcal. mole^{-1}. There is, however, scope for much more work on the order of hydrogen equilibration reactions, and its dependence on temperature.

Much more information is available on the temperature dependence of the rate of equilibration reactions (Table IV). However, there is little agreement between values for the activation energy when the same metal is studied in a variety of forms: the most extreme case is nickel, where values of 1.4 to 10.6 kcal. mole^{-1} are reported. Several investigations have pointed to the extreme susceptibility of the kinetics of the *para*-hydrogen conversion to the treatment the catalytic surface has received. Couper and Eley[32] have obtained activation energies between 1.8 and 5 kcal. mole^{-1} and frequency factors between 10^5 and 10^{10} cm. min.$^{-1}$ for tungsten wires treated in various ways. The results show a good compensation effect represented by the relation:

$$E = -1 + 0.6 \log A.$$

Calculation shows that the variation in the rate at 200°K within the range covered is only about a factor of ten. Cremer and Kerber[26] have shown that when nickel plate is pretreated at a series of temperatures, the activation energy rises slightly and the frequency factor *falls* steeply as the pre-treatment temperature is increased. The results are shown in Figs. 2 and 3: they are of interest since they show an apparent "anti-compensation" effect (Fig. 2). Closer examination shows however that this effect may be spurious, first, since the range of values of the activation energy is barely greater than allowable experimental error (say $\pm$ 0.2 kcal. mole^{-1}), and second, the activation energy is an accurately linear function of the mean temperature of measurement.

While these experiments demonstrate the relevance of the treatment given to one form of a metal to the kinetic parameters it exhibits, they offer no

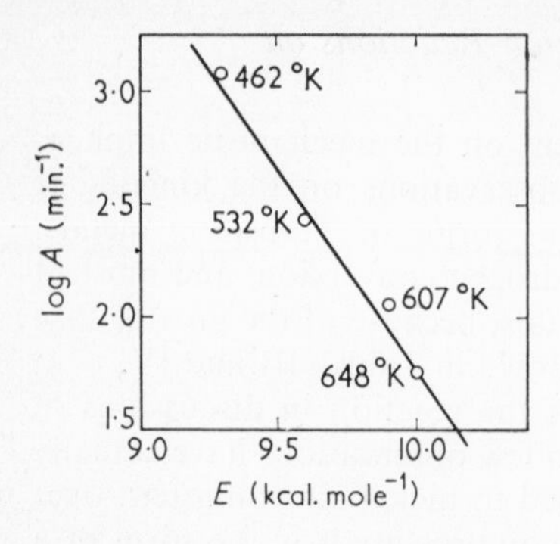

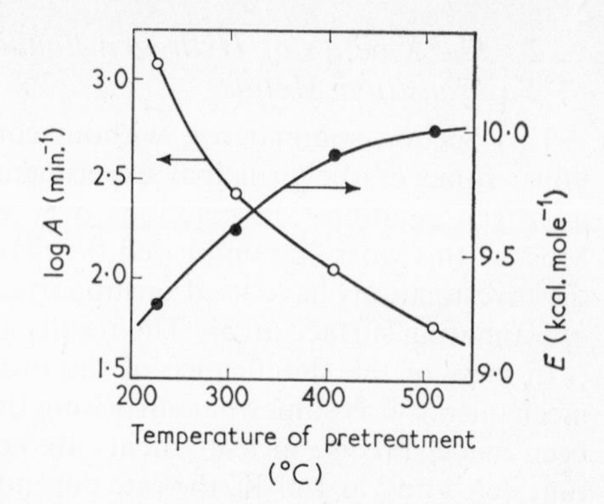

FIG. 2. (Left) Compensation effect in *para*-hydrogen conversion over nickel plate pretreated at various temperatures.[26] The mean temperature of measurement is shown against each point.

FIG. 3. (Right) Dependence of activation energy and frequency factor for *para*-hydrogen conversion on temperature of pretreatment of nickel plate.[26]

aid in the correlation of these parameters for different metal forms. It is however worth noting that the various forms of iron, nickel and platinum show consistently higher activation energies in the higher temperature ranges (Table IV). The same effect has been reported[22, 23] for a number of silica-supported metals: for nickel–silica[33] the rate above $-130°$ is controlled by diffusion with catalyst pores, the activation energy being about 3 kcal. mole^{-1} above this temperature and zero below. This is, however, unlikely to be the general explanation, since activation energies much in excess of those expected for diffusion-limited reactions are often encountered, and it seems possible that a change in the activation energy may denote a change in the nature of the chemical mechanism.

It seems best to try to assess the relative efficiencies of metals for hydrogen equilibration reactions in terms of their activity (preferably specific) at a chosen temperature. The presently available information is contained in Table V: tungsten and platinum appear to be the most active metals, while in the iron triad, iron itself by common consent is the least active. Some further discussion of the possible significance of these activity patterns will be given later (see Chapter 21).

Some interesting experimental work points to the important part which may be played by dissolved hydrogen. Two pieces of work[14, 27] (Table III) show that hydrogen dissolved in palladium leads to a decreased activity for *para*-hydrogen conversion through an increased activation energy which is not sufficiently compensated by a change in the frequency factor. The removal of dissolved hydrogen from Raney nickel[35] leads first to a *drop* in activity and then finally as the last traces are removed, to a rapid increase in activity. We may suspect this is due to two separate effects: (i) an electronic effect, as with palladium, and (ii) at higher concentrations of dissolved hydrogen,

TABLE V. *The Relative Efficiencies of Metals for Hydrogen Equilibration Reactions*

A: log$k$ (sec.$^{-1}$) at 250°K for silica-supported metals.[33]
B: logk_s (mol. cm.$^{-2}$ sec.$^{-1}$) at 300°K for metal wires.[18]
C: logk_s (mol. cm.$^{-2}$ sec.$^{-1}$) at 293°K for evap. metal films.[34]
D: logk_s (mol. cm.$^{-2}$ sec.$^{-1}$) at 373°K for various forms.[22]

Metal	*A*	*B*	*C*	*D*
Ti	—	—	16.3	—
V	—	—	16.1	—
Cr	—	—	16.1	—
W	—	21.07	—	—
Mn	—	—	15.1	—
Fe	−0.8	17.98	16.1	13.52
Co	1.2	18.67	16.2	14.78
Ni	0.6	18.07	16.3	15.92
Pd	—	18.15	—	—
Pt	3.1	19.36	—	—

the internal hydrogen atoms may catalyse the overall process, as is sometimes suggested.

The treatment of tungsten wires and films by oxygen, nitrogen, carbon-monoxide and ethylene poisons these catalysts for *para*-hydrogen conversion.[7, 32, 36] Table VI contains the kinetic parameters found after tungsten wires have been exposed to the poisoning gas and the excess pumped off. Thus for example the effect of ethylene is to decrease the rate calculated for 200°K by a factor of about 10^3 over that for the unpoisoned wire showing an activation energy of 1.8 kcal. mole^{-1}. These results show an approximate compensation effect, expressible as

$$E = -2 + 0.87 \log A.$$

Trapnell[36] has shown that oxygen and ethylene completely inhibit the conversion over tungsten films by virtue of their covering the surface entirely and thus forbidding the adsorption of hydrogen. On the other hand, a tungsten film covered to 50 per cent the theoretical capacity by irreversibly-held nitrogen still permitted the adsorption of hydrogen, although the

TABLE VI. *Kinetic Parameters for* Para-*hydrogen Conversion on Poisoned Tungsten Wires*

Poison	*E(kcal. mole^{-1})*	*log A* (*cm. min.$^{-1}$*)	*log k at 200°K*
N_2	6.1	7.82	1.17
CO	10.8	10.0	−1.75
C_2H_4	4.0	5.18	0.80

ensuing conversion rate was slower by a factor of 340 as compared with an unpoisoned surface. It was concluded that the poison reduced the condensation coefficient of the hydrogen, perhaps due to the relatively large nitrogen atoms shielding vacant sites.

8.23 The Kinetics of Hydrogen Equilibration Reactions on Non-Transition Metals

As already noted, the *sp*-metals are notably less efficient for hydrogen equilibration reactions than the *d*-metals due to their smaller ability to interact with hydrogen. As a result, kinetic measurements below room temperature are rarely reported. Once again, there is a surprising dearth of information on the order of reaction: it is reported to be about unity for *para*-hydrogen conversion on copper, silver and gold wires at about 60°,[18] and for gold wire at 525°.[14] More precise work[37] has shown that the rate depends on pressure in the form of the Langmuir isotherm over silver foil and copper films, and in the latter case variation of the temperature (108 to 148°) has led to estimations of the heat and entropy of adsorption of hydrogen. Taking the standard states to be $P_{H_2} = 1$ mm. and $\theta = 0.5$, $-\Delta H_a$ is 8.0 kcal. mole^{-1} and ΔS_a -26 e.u. It is surprising to say the least that the value of 8.0 kcal. mole^{-1} for copper is considerably larger than the value of 2.3 kcal. mole^{-1} found for platinum.

Table VII reveals once again a wide diversity of activation energies for a

TABLE VII. *Activation Energies for Hydrogen Equilibration Reactions on Non-transition Metals*

Para-H_2 → *ortho*-H_2 . . . . (1)
$H_2 + D_2 \rightarrow 2HD$ . . . . (2)

Reaction	*Metal*	*Form*	*Temp. range (°C)*	*E(kcal. mole^{-1})*	*Ref.*
1	Cu	foil	?	12.1, 12.8	28
1	Cu	foil	?	10.5, 11.8	25
2	Cu	foil	310 to 350	23.1	38
1	Cu	powder	?	15	39
2	Cu	powder	?	16	22
2	Ag	foil	400 to 460	16.5	38
2	Ag	granular	130 to 230 230 to 300	6.0 10.8	38
2	Ag	filings	−196 to 80 130 to 260	0.5 5.0	22
2	Ag	powder	−183 to 30 80 to 180	0.3 2.0	22
2	Ag	1% on MgO	70 to 100	18.3	38
2	Au	foil	330 to 400	13.9	38
1	Au	wire	225 to 525	17.5	14
2	Au	wire	?	7.0	22
1	Al	film	225 to 525	9.9	18

given metal. Eley and Rossington[37] have demonstrated that activation energies and frequency factors for *para*-hydrogen conversion vary considerably for a given form of a metal, but unlike the case of tungsten without apparent reason. The values obtained with a given form (wire, foil or film) of copper, silver and gold conform to the same compensation effect relation, as is seen by the example shown in Fig. 4. The equations are as follows:

wires . . . $E = -1.25 + 1.8 \log A$;
films . . . $E = 5.0 + 1.1 \log A$;
foils . . . $E = 7.5 + 1.2 \log A$.

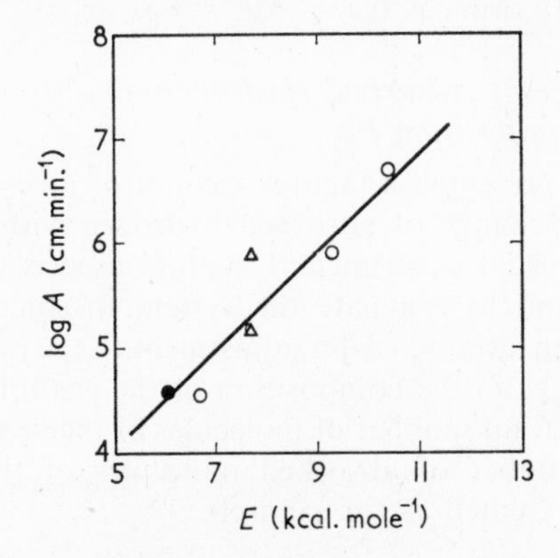

FIG. 4. Compensation effect for *para*-hydrogen conversion on metal wires.[37] ⊙ Copper; △ silver; ● gold.

In these equations, A is the apparent frequency factor corrected for the volume of the reaction vessel and the area of the catalyst, and has the units of cm. min.$^{-1}$ From the rates on the copper film examined between 1 and 10 mm. from 108 to 148°, it was possible to derive a true activation energy and frequency factor: the values are respectively 13 kcal. mole^{-1} and 5.6 $\times 10^6$ sec.$^{-1}$, whence the entropy of activation is deduced to be 29 e.u. The results of Rienäcker and his associates for copper foils[25, 28] also conform to the appropriate equation.

From the above equations, it is possible to calculate the approximate range of activities for each metal form: the results are summarized in Table VIII. Thus the order of the specific activities of the various forms is wire

TABLE VIII. *Range of Activities at 350°K for Various Forms of Copper, Silver and Gold in* Para-*hydrogen Conversion*

	logk at 350°K		
	Wire	*Film*	*Foil*
$E =$ 10 kcal. mole^{-1}	0.35	−1.45	−4.05
$E =$ 5 kcal. mole^{-1}	0.68	−2.82	−4.92

> film > foil, and in agreement with this, foils were generally studied at higher temperatures than films, and wires at the lowest temperatures. For each form, values of the activation energy and frequency factor fall in the sequence Cu > Ag > Au. The activity order for films and foils is also Cu > Ag > Au, but for wires the activities are all comparable.

Much higher activation energies have been found with foils of these metals for the hydrogen–deuterium equilibration:[38] they were, however, determined in higher temperature ranges than those used by Eley, and this may be the origin, but not of course the explanation, of the discrepancies. The observed activity order is Cu > Au > Ag.

8.24 *The Exchange of Adsorbed Hydrogen, and its Role as a Poison in Equilibration Processes*

In this Section is presented a factual account of investigations of the rate and extent of the exchange of adsorbed hydrogen with another isotope in the gas phase. The usual experimental method used is to cover the surface with one isotope, and to evacuate the system to some low pressure; the second isotope is then admitted after adjustment to the required temperature, and the rate of change in the composition of the gas followed by a suitable method. Then if the total number of molecules of the second isotope is much greater than the number of absorbed molecules of the first, the overall process may be represented as for example

$$\underset{*}{2D} + H_2 \rightarrow \underset{*}{2H} + D_2. \qquad \text{(e)}$$

There is, furthermore, some evidence that the manner of adsorbing the hydrogen has, in certain systems, an influence on the rate of subsequent equilibration reactions. Because of the relevance of these observations to discussions of mechanisms, some account of them is given in this Section.

With regard to the exchange of adsorbed hydrogen, there are two points at issue. The first is whether or not the rate of the exchange is identical or closely similar to the rate of an equilibration process, that is to say, whether or not the times taken for the two systems to come to equilibrium are about equal. If indeed they are, then this is good evidence that the same kind of adsorbed hydrogen is involved in both processes, and therefore by inference that the equilibration proceeds by a Rideal–Eley mechanism. It was to put this point to the test that Eley carried out the earliest work on the exchange process.[40] The second point at issue is whether or not all the adsorbed hydrogen is readily exchangeable, even at very low temperatures.

Eley succeeded in showing that, at 20°, −80° and −196° over evaporated tungsten films, the exchange equilibrium was rapidly set up.[40] His deduction that this finding precluded the operation of the Bonhoeffer–Farkas mechanism has, however, been criticized by Trapnell[41] in whose view the addition of the second gas may lead to further chemisorption and hence to the operation of this mechanism utilizing the least strongly adsorbed species. Similar experiments have been performed with films of other metals:[19] measurements on very thin nickel films at 20° confirmed Eley's findings, but the surprising result was found that over palladium and platinum films the *para*-hydrogen conversion was more rapid than the exchange by factors of respectively about fifteen and five. This pointed to the possibility of the two processes occurring through different mechanisms. With nickel–silica catalysts, the rates of exchange and equilibration are in fair agreement above 140°K, but below this temperature the latter is much the faster[33] (see also Ref. 42). We conclude that the results depend on the nature of the system and on the temperature, and that the two processes do not invariably involve the same mechanism.

We turn now to information bearing on the completeness of the exchange. Eley[40] noted that there was no apparent exchange between adsorbed hydrogen and gaseous deuterium over a tungsten film at −196°, and that the reverse process occurred less completely than expected from observations at higher temperatures. This could not be completely understood on the basis of a preferential adsorption of deuterium, and he concluded that only some 20 to 40 per cent of the adsorbed deuterium was exchangeable with hydrogen at −196° in the time of the experiment. Similar results have been found by Kummer and Emmett[43] using a singly promoted iron catalyst: after cooling from 500° to −196° in hydrogen or deuterium, there was no detectable exchange with the other isotope in periods of 40 to 60 min., although the catalyst was extremely active for the hydrogen–deuterium equilibration at this temperature. However, tritiated hydrogen adsorbed at −196°, the catalyst having been cooled from the reduction temperature in helium, was readily exchangeable.

Three quite detailed accounts of this phenomenon have been published,[33, 42, 44] and the agreement between them is reassuring. On the basis of this work it is possible to recognize three distinct kinds of adsorbed "hydrogen": (i) that which is very rapidly exchanged when contacted with another isotopic form in the gas phase (in less than $\sim$5 min.); (ii) that which is slowly exchangeable (complete in generally not more than 2 hr.); and (iii) that which is not exchangeable. Nickel films and nickel–silica catalysts show similar results,[33, 44] as is seen in Fig. 5: type (i) "hydrogen" increases rapidly between 100 and 200°K, while type (ii) "hydrogen" is a maximum between 150 and 170°K. Tungsten films and powder show analogous results (see also Fig. 5). Essentially similar results are found regardless of which isotope is first absorbed. The order of the strengths of adsorption has, however, been assessed as $T > D > H$ on platinum films,[42] and the heat of adsorption of deuterium on nickel is 0.6 kcal. mole^{-1} greater than for hydrogen.[44] The gas leaving the surface appears always to be in thermodynamic equilibrium.[33,44]

The kinetics of these exchanges have been examined over sintered platinum films.[42] It is claimed that the exchange of type (ii) hydrogen follows a first-order rate law, but the results are not in close accord with this view, and a higher order seems probable. The activation energy measured between 78 and 90°K is about 5 kcal. mole^{-1} at the start of the slow exchange. The rate of exchange of adsorbed tritium is independent of the pressure of

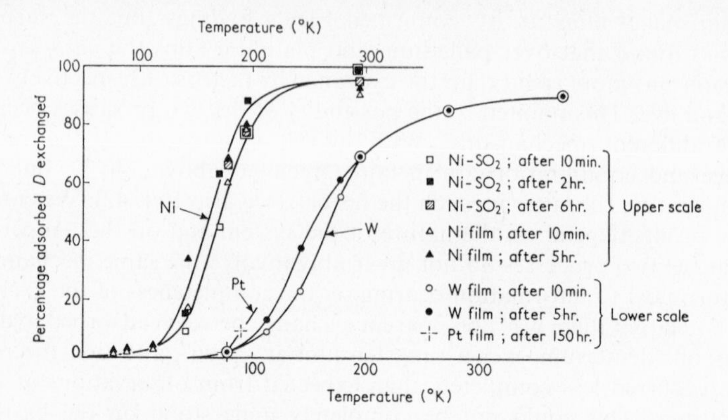

FIG. 5. The temperature-dependence of completeness of exchange of adsorbed deuterium with gaseous hydrogen.

$Ni\text{-}SiO_2$:	after 10 min.	Upper scale
$Ni\text{-}SiO_2$:	after 2 hr.	
$Ni\text{-}SiO_2$:	after 6 hr.	
Ni film:	after 10 min.	
Ni film:	after 5 hr.	
W film:	after 10 min.	Lower scale
W film:	after 5 hr.	
Pt film:	after 150 hr.	

gaseous hydrogen and indeed of the isotopic nature of the gas-phase partner; but the rate of removal of adsorbed deuterium by hydrogen is some seven times faster than the removal of adsorbed tritium by hydrogen, as might be expected from the above sequence of strengths of adsorption. The significance of these results will be discussed in the next Section.

Finally in this Section it is necessary to consider the evidence which points to the ability of strongly chemisorbed hydrogen to act as a poison for hydrogen equilibrations. The phenomenon is best understood for the various promoted iron catalysts, and combined with a knowledge of the way in which hydrogen is chemisorbed by these materials, it offers valuable suggestions concerning reaction mechanisms. It was remarked some twenty-five years ago[45] that doubly promoted iron was some ten to twenty times more active for *para*-hydrogen conversion at $-190°$ if cooled from the reduction temperatures of 450° in helium than if cooled in hydrogen. Further experiments showed that hydrogen adsorbed at 100° (Type B) was about four times more active a poison than hydrogen adsorbed at $-78°$. Continued operation at $-190°$ however led to no loss of activity.

A later investigation[43] placed these observations on a more quantitative footing, and the relevant results are shown in Table IX. In contrast to the above findings, singly promoted iron is *not* poisoned by hydrogen adsorbed at high temperatures: the effect on doubly promoted iron was confirmed. The much lower activity of both materials for hydrogen–deuterium equilibration shows that *para*-hydrogen conversion must be largely proceeding through

TABLE IX. *Values for the Time of Half-reaction for Hydrogen Equilibrations over Iron Catalysts at* $-195°$

Conditions	*Reaction*	*Singly promoted Fe*	*Doubly promoted Fe*
Cooled in He	pH_2 conv.	0.06 sec.	0.4 sec.
Cooled in H_2	pH_2 conv.	0.06 sec.	8.0 sec.
Cooled in He	$H_2 + D_2$	3–10 sec.	6000 sec.

the paramagnetic mechanism, and in view of this ever-present possibility it is regrettable that so much work has been done with the latter reaction and so little with the former. Be this as it may, the difference between the activities of the two catalysts for hydrogen–deuterium equilibration is significant, and it becomes the more so when correlated with the hydrogen adsorption isotherms of the catalysts at $-195°$. Singly promoted iron showed a weak activated adsorption at this temperature, and it was not inhibited by hydrogen adsorbed at 100°: on the other hand, doubly promoted iron showed essentially no chemisorption at $-195°$. High activity for equilibrations at low temperatures thus for the first time becomes directly linked with Type C chemisorption.

Other metals show related phenomena. Nickel powder slowly loses activity for *para*-hydrogen conversion at $-190°$.[45] Table X shows how the activity declines with time when nickel powder cooled in helium from the reduction temperature is used in a flow-system. Exposure to hydrogen for 32 minutes

TABLE X. *Change of Activity of a Nickel Powder for* Para-*hydrogen Conversion at* $-190°$ *with Time*

t min.	0	12	40	125	150
k min.$^{-1}$	30.4	28.5	24.6	22.4	21.9

at $-78°$ reduces the value of k at $-190°$ to 0.91 min.$^{-1}$. Evaporated nickel films[23] and platinized asbestos[45] show similar behaviour. The interpretation must be that under these conditions Type A adsorption is occurring more or less rapidly, and that this reduces the ability of the surface to accommodate Type C adsorbed hydrogen and hence a loss of activity for equilibration processes results.

8.25 *Mechanisms of Equilibration and Exchange Processes*

The historical development of the ideas on the mechanism of equilibration reactions was presented in Section 8.21. It was stated there that the possible grounds for distinguishing between the rival mechanisms were (i) kinetic measurements and (ii) theoretical calculations. We have seen that accurate measurements of orders of reaction are disappointingly few: obedience of the kinetics to a Langmuir isotherm supports the modified Rideal–Eley mechanism, but is not necessarily evidence against the Bonhoeffer–Farkas mechanism, particularly in view of the revised concepts of the dependence of coverage on pressure. We therefore conclude that an unequivocal decision cannot be arrived at from kinetic considerations alone.

It is instructive to see what contribution to the problem has been made by application of theoretical methods. The rate of *para*-hydrogen conversion on tungsten wire at $-100°$ and a pressure of 1 mm. is 2.1×10^{18} mol. cm.$^{-2}$ sec.$^{-1}$. The rate may now be calculated using the appropriate Absolute Rate equation containing the gas pressure to the first power: taking $\theta = 0.90$, $f_{\ddagger}$ unity and $f_{p\text{-}H_2} = 3.4 \times 10^{23}$, the calculated rate is found to be 3.1×10^{18} $\exp(-E/RT)$ mol. cm.$^{-2}$ sec.$^{-1}$. Although this calculation claims to support the Bonhoeffer–Farkas mechanism, the value of E required to secure the agreement is less than that observed experimentally. The rate calculated for the Rideal–Eley mechanism is $10^{20} \exp(-E/RT)$ when the value of E required for agreement is 1.5 kcal. mole^{-1}. Straightforward application of the Absolute Rate Theory does not therefore distinguish between the possibilities.

An alternative approach[16, 41] is based on the application of the Peierls equation for the rate of adsorption: this is

$$r_a = \frac{\sigma P}{(2\pi mkT)^{1/2}} \cdot \frac{1-\theta}{1+\epsilon}, \tag{1}$$

where $(1+\epsilon)^{-1}$ is the probability that a site adjacent to an unoccupied site is itself unoccupied. The other symbols have their usual significance. If there is a repulsion energy V between adjacent adsorbed atoms, vacant sites will tend to separate, and this is expressed by the relation

$$\frac{\theta}{1-\theta} = \frac{\epsilon[1 + \epsilon \exp(-V/RT)]}{1+\epsilon}. \tag{2}$$

The rate of *para*-hydrogen conversion under non-equilibrium conditions is given by

$$r = \frac{\sigma(P - P_e)}{(2\pi mkT)^{1/2}} \cdot \frac{1-\theta}{1+\epsilon}, \tag{3}$$

where P and P_e are respectively the instantaneous and equilibrium pressures of *para*-hydrogen. Thus the rate may be calculated if σ and ϵ (or V) are known. A theoretical treatment[46] suggests that σ for tungsten is 0.3, independent of temperature, and there are good grounds for believing that V lies between zero and 0.4 kcal. The kinetics of the conversion may then be calculated from the adsorption isotherms for these two extreme values of V; they are compared with the observations in Table XI. The choice of this range of values of V has been criticized by Couper and Eley,[17] who prefer a value of 4.8 kcal. derived from measured adsorption isotherms on tungsten *films*:[16] kinetics based on this value of V are also shown in Table XI. Since the calculated rate is too low by a factor of 10^6, Couper and Eley reject the Bonhoeffer–Farkas mechanism. The last word has not yet, however, been said. Trapnell[41] and Laidler[47] criticize the use of the high value of V,

TABLE XI. *Comparison of Observed Kinetics for* Para-*hydrogen Conversion on Tungsten Wire (T, −100°; P, 1 mm.) with those Calculated for the Bonhoeffer-Farkas Mechanism*

	E_y (*kcal. mole*$^{-1}$)	*Order of reaction*	*Rate* (*mol. cm.*$^{-2}$ *sec.*$^{-1}$)
Observed	1.95	0.1–0.5	2.1×10^{18}
Calculated, $V = 0$ kcal.	1.65	0.6	2.2×10^{17}
Calculated, $V = 0.4$ kcal.	2.15	0.6	7.8×10^{16}
Calculated, $V = 4.8$ kcal.	8.3	—	2.6×10^{12}

the latter stating that it is correct to ignore repulsive interactions since they affect both the number and the partition function of the pairs of vacant sites to equal and opposite extents. Laidler is not above criticism[48] for his simultaneous use of results obtained from both wires and films. However, it appears that the Bonhoeffer–Farkas mechanism reasonably interprets the results on tungsten if a small repulsion energy and the applicability of the Peierls equation are assumed.

Rate calculations can be made to prove almost anything. Halsey[49] favours the Rideal–Eley mechanism, but his treatment has been condemned.[41] Eley and his associates have calculated values of the frequency factor on the basis of this model and have obtained good agreement with the experimental findings.[7, 14, 50] Application of the Power Rate Law to the problem is equally unhelpful.[33] The modified Rideal–Eley mechanism is the most satisfactory in describing the hydrogen-deuterium equilibration on nickel–silica catalysts, but since the Bonhoeffer–Farkas mechanism appears to interpret the exchange reaction it is not clear why it does not also participate in equilibration processes (see also Ref. 42). The contradictory conclusions recorded in the foregoing paragraphs must shake one's faith in the validity of this kind of approach.

It is now time to pose some fundamental questions, and to clear up some misconceptions. It is evident that the Bonhoeffer–Farkas mechanism must occur whenever the adsorption is sufficiently readily reversible. The first question is, therefore, is this mechanism always a *sufficient* explanation? It has been visualized by some enlightened authors that both the rival mechanisms may occur, under differing conditions, or possibly even simultaneously. When such massive bodies of experimental and theoretical work are advanced in support of opposing views, we are entitled to wonder whether both views are not partly right and partly wrong. The idea that a compromise mechanism is possible has been suggested.[51] It further seems likely that the discordant results of the theoretical work arise in part from their being based on too simple a model of the reaction, and specifically no attempt has been made until recently to examine the possible influence of the detailed surface geometry.[51] Neither has any thorough attempt been made to consider simultaneously the mechanisms of equilibration, exchange and hydrogen poisoning. Furthermore, evidence showing the existence of various states of adsorbed hydrogen has until recently been ignored. Thus for example the experiments showing the dependence of the degree of exchange of adsorbed deuterium or tritium with gaseous hydrogen on temperature have been interpreted[33, 42, 44] in terms of *energetically* heterogeneous surface, whereas they more probably show that *the adsorbed hydrogen is heterogeneous* and the surface possibly homogeneous. The time is perhaps not ripe for a complete resolution of this very confused situation, but nevertheless in the following paragraphs an attempt will be made to indicate the lines along which such a clarification must ultimately be sought.

We will start with the hypothesis that Type C chemisorbed hydrogen plays an important role in equilibration reactions at low temperatures. The work described in Chapter 5 indicated that this state may in certain cases be quite stable at about −190° even on an otherwise bare surface, because of the intervention of a small activation energy between Type C and Type A states: but if the activation energy is insufficient to isolate the Type C state, the two states may coexist. The Type C state may even have some stability at room temperature. These observations overcome the difficulty, seen by Eley[18] and Trapnell,[41] that the modified Rideal–Eley mechanism requires a complete "second-layer" coverage at −160° and 1 to 10 mm. pressure on tungsten. Obedience of the rate to the Langmuir isotherm in this pressure range[17] is then reasonable, since the concentration of Type C hydrogen is expected to increase with pressure as dictated by this isotherm.

We now have to try to decide whether equilibration at low temperatures involves *only* the Type C state or whether the Type A state is also involved. The observations on the extent of the exchange reaction and the poisoning of the equilibration are clearly very relevant. Now it is clear that at low temperatures the equilibration goes very much faster than the exchange on a variety of surfaces:[19, 33, 42, 43, 44, 50] the activation energy for the equilibration is here very low and sometimes even zero.[33] We conclude that *equilibration must be able to proceed solely through the Type C state*, and (at least at 90°K or below) without significant involvement of Type A adsorbed "hydrogen." This implies either that the Type C state is atomic or that the atoms are so loosely joined that interchange between neighbouring "molecules" readily occurs.

We turn now to examine the mechanism of exchange. It seems reasonable to say that the exchange of Type A "hydrogen" proceeds as either

$$\underset{*}{D}_{(A)} + H_{2(C)} \rightarrow \underset{*}{DH_2^{+}} \rightarrow \underset{*}{H}_{(A)} + HD_{(C)} \qquad (f)$$

or

$$\underset{*}{D}_{(A)} + 2H_{(C)} \rightarrow \underset{*}{DH_2^{+}} \rightarrow \underset{*}{H}_{(A)} + H_{(C)} + D_{(C)}, \qquad (g)$$

depending on one's view of the Type C state. The parenthetical subscripts denote the type of adsorbed state. These mechanisms also commend themselves for the equilibration at higher temperatures, where the rates of equilibration and exchange are more nearly equal. Mechanism (f) is essentially a one-site Rideal–Eley mechanism, and this hypothesis accommodates the generally held feeling that it is not operative on any metal above about room temperature (where the Type C state is insufficiently stable) or on *sp*-metals (where the Type C state cannot exist).

Now the activation energy for equilibration above about 150°K is typically near 5 kcal. mole^{-1}, and if this is the value appropriate to mechanisms (g) or (f) it may be sufficient to render the exchange at or below 90°K extremely slow. We might then expect that the rate of exchange would become progressively faster with rising temperature, but while this is true[42] it is not the whole story, for the exchange appears to cease before completion, except with nickel at about room temperature. We may tentatively interpret the time-course of the exchange as follows. It is known (see Chapter 5) that an activation energy may appear between the Types C and A states when the coverage of the former is high. The initial rapid exchange therefore occurs at once, before the Type C concentration and hence the activation energy have risen to their maximum values. In the second stage the rate is measurable because of this activation energy. The process does not generally go to completion because the adsorbed hydrogen is heterogeneous, probably because it is adsorbed on different crystallographic planes. It is also known that Type C "hydrogen" does not favour all planes equally (see Chapter 5) and so the variation with temperature of the final amount of exchange is a function of the number of planes on which the Type C state is stable at that temperature. If this hypothesis is true, then the total amount of exchange should vary discontinuously with temperature. It appears from the fact that the exchange of deuterium adsorbed on tungsten is incomplete even at 100°[44] that the Type C state cannot exist on certain faces of this metal.

Nickel powder at −190° slowly loses activity for *para*-hydrogen conversion[45] presumably because of a slow activated formation of the Type A state which then reduces the ability of the surface to hold the Type C state.[23] Doubly promoted iron has little or no ability to form Type C hydrogen,[43] while on singly promoted iron (which has) Type B hydrogen does not retard the low-temperature conversion, nor does continued use at low temperatures lead to a decrease in the rate. Hence the activation energy for the Type C to Type A transition must be higher here than on nickel.

Further detailed studies on the temperature-dependence of the extents and rates of exchange, together with measurements of rates of equilibration and of isotherms, are much needed. Additional metals require investigation, particularly manganese (where the situation may be simpler): and the use of single-crystal faces might also simplify matters.

To summarize briefly the situation as it appears at the moment, it is accepted that the Bonhoeffer–Farkas mechanism probably operates in equilibration reactions on *sp*-metals at all temperatures, and on Transition metals above room temperature. It may also make a contribution on Transition metals below room temperature, but here a Rideal–Eley mechanism involving Type C hydrogen is also possible. Further attempts to assess the relative importance of the rival mechanisms *in their original forms* under these conditions must be regarded as misdirected.

8.3 The Electronic Factor in Hydrogen Equilibration Reactions

The foregoing discussion of reaction mechanisms stems from observations made only on pure metals, and it is convenient to consider separately the measurements made on alloys. These measurements were designed to bring out the importance of the electronic constitution of the catalyst in determining activities and the Arrhenius parameters, and hence indirectly to indicate how the strength of binding of the hydrogen to the surface affects these quantities. Thus in this way additional evidence on the kind of mechanisms operating may be obtained. It is unfortunate that these correlations remain to the present time indirect, and that no extensive measurements of heats of adsorption of hydrogen on alloys have yet been reported: there are, however, severe practical difficulties.

To record the experimental observations in the most economic way, the practice will be adopted of showing graphically the variation of activity with composition, and the compensation effect. Hydrogen equilibration reactions have been studied on series of palladium–gold wires,[14] platinum–gold wires and filings,[22] on platinum–copper[28] and palladium–copper foils,[25] and on nickel–copper foils[25] and powders.[39] Some of the results are shown in Figs. 6–9.

Two points are noteworthy in the palladium–gold series.[14] Firstly, the activity passes through a maximum at about 30 per cent gold (a fact not explicitly remarked on by the authors), the alloy of this composition being some five to ten times more active than pure palladium (Fig. 6(a)). Second, there appears to be an anti-compensation effect, and not a normal one (Fig. 6(b)). The form of activity pattern is not dependent on temperature.

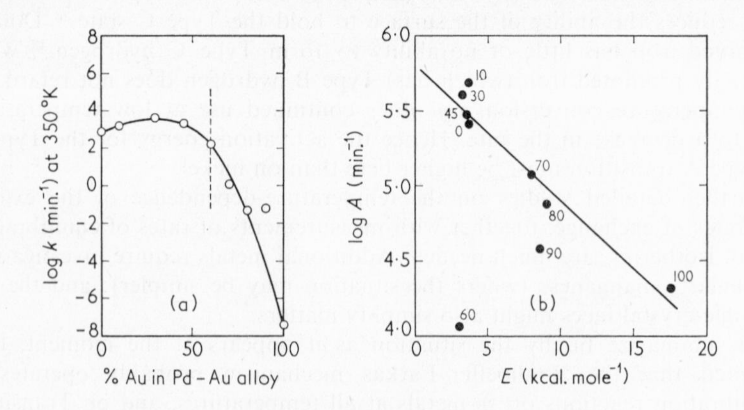

FIG. 6. *Para*-hydrogen conversion on palladium–gold alloy wires.[14]
(a) Dependence of activity on composition.
(b) Compensation effect: the composition (% Au) to which each point refers is indicated.

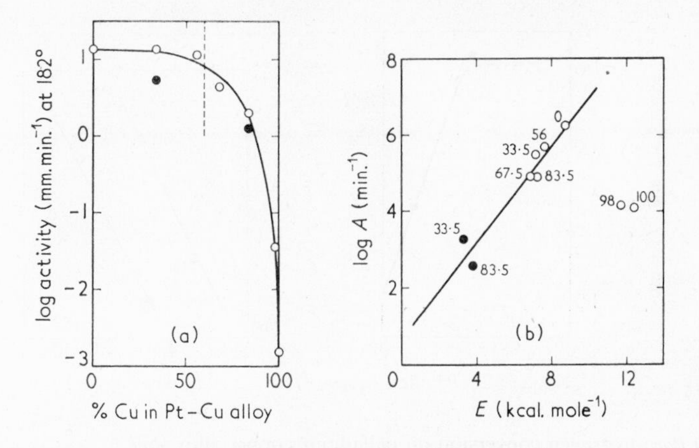

FIG. 7. *Para*-hydrogen conversion on platinum–copper alloy foils.[28]
(a) Activity as a function of composition.
(b) Compensation effect; the composition (%Cu) to which each point corresponds is indicated.
○, Disordered alloys; ●, ordered alloys.

The first fact suggests that as the *d*-band is filled, the strength of binding decreases and the activity increases, although the maximum is attained before the band is filled. Other effects may be present, however: for example, as the strength of binding decreases, so will the coverage and hence the rate, and so these opposing effects may lead to a maximum. Some confirmation stems from the finding that the 60 per cent gold alloy shows first-order kinetics at 350°K. The activation energy is constant at 3 to 4 kcal. mole^{-1}

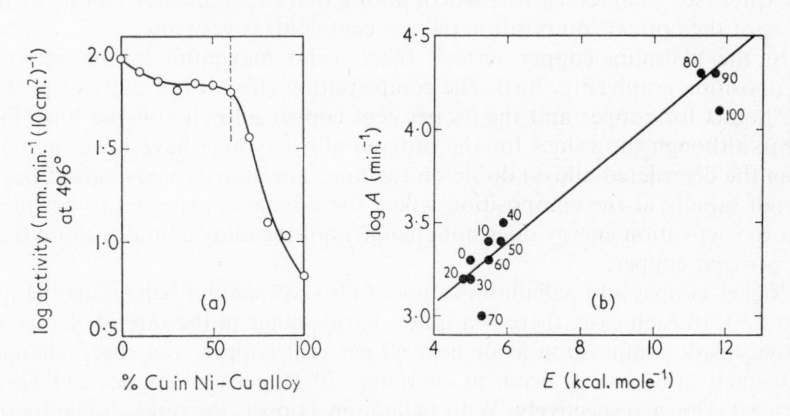

FIG. 8. *Para*-hydrogen conversion on copper–nickel alloy foils.[25]
(a) Activity as a function of composition.
(b) Compensation effect: the composition (%Cu) to which each point corresponds is indicated.

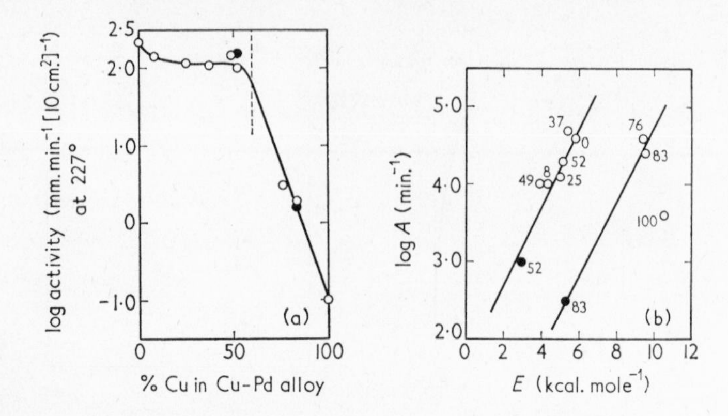

FIG. 9. *Para*-hydrogen conversion on palladium–copper alloy foils.[25]
(a) Activity as a function of composition.
(b) Compensation effect: the composition (%Cu) to which each point corresponds is indicated.
○, Disordered alloys; ●, ordered alloys.

in the region of zero to 60 per cent gold, whereupon it rises rapidly to about 8 kcal. mole^{-1}. Since the rates on the alloys containing less than 60 per cent gold were largely measured at less than 330°K, and those for alloys containing more than 60 per cent gold at more than 330°K, it may be wondered whether the sudden change in activation energy does not represent a change in mechanism. This is unlikely to be so, however, since there is sometimes an overlap of the temperature ranges, and no sign of a temperature-dependent activation energy is reported. The anti-compensation effect is difficult to interpret (see Chapter 7). It is worth noting that the frequency factor for the alloy of the critical composition (60 per cent gold) is very low.

In the platinum–copper series[28] there is no maximum in the activity-composition graph (Fig. 7(a)). The compensation effect is normal, except that the points for copper and the 98 per cent copper alloy lie off the line (Fig. 7(b)), although the values for the ordered alloys (which have lower activity than the disordered alloys) do lie on the line. The activity does indeed begin to fall rapidly at the composition where the *d*-band is expected to be filled, but the activation energy does not change until the alloy contains more than 84 per cent copper.

Nickel–copper and palladium–copper foils show similar behaviour[25] (Figs. 8 and 9). In each case, there is a quite sharp change in the rate of change of activity with composition at or near 60 per cent copper, and sharp changes in the activation energy occur in the ranges 70–80 per cent copper and 52–76 per cent copper respectively. With palladium–copper, the rates shown by the ordered and disordered alloys of the same composition are almost identical, although their Arrhenius parameters differ widely. Two compensation effect lines (as shown in Fig. 9(b)) must therefore exist, and this could also conceivably be the case in the copper–nickel system: thus one would seem to apply before the *d*-band is filled, and the second after it is filled.

The activity of nickel–copper alloy powders for *para*-hydrogen conversion has been investigated at −196° and at −20° using both samples cooled *in vacuo* and in hydrogen from 325°.[39] Pre-adsorbed hydrogen completely poisons the activity at −196°, and this is further evidence for the association of low-temperature activity with Type C hydrogen and the poisoning effect of Type A hydrogen. At −20°, however, pre-adsorbed hydrogen causes a slight activation (except for pure nickel), the effect being greatest for the alloy containing 60 per cent copper where the rate is about ten times faster than when the sample is cooled *in vacuo*. At −196°, the specific activity is independent of composition between 5 and 92 per cent copper; this level of activity is about 10^3 times less than that for pure nickel and about ten times greater than for copper. At −20°, the activity decreases slowly and linearly within this composition range: the activity of nickel is about five times greater than for the 5 per cent copper alloy, and the activity falls by a factor of 10^5 on passing from the 92 per cent copper alloy to pure copper. Thus copper appears to be *more* active at −196° than at −20°, and this suggests that the paramagnetic mechanism may be contributing at the low temperature. Activation energies are: 6 kcal. mole^{-1} for nickel, 15 kcal. mole^{-1} for copper and 9 kcal. mole^{-1} between 5 and 92 per cent copper. The frequency factor shows parallel trends, but the compensation is not complete, and the high activity of nickel and the low activity of copper are thus due chiefly to the magnitude of their activation energies. In this system therefore there are no abrupt changes in either the rate or the activation energy at the composition where the *d*-band is expected to be filled; the heats of adsorption of hydrogen parallel the activity changes.[52]

Studies on the activity of platinum–gold alloys[22] are complicated by the existence of a miscibility gap between 15 and 75 per cent gold. Specific activities for hydrogen–deuterium equilibration at 180° have been measured: the activity of a 9.5 per cent gold alloy is slightly less than that of pure platinum, while a 90 per cent gold alloy is about as active as pure platinum and ten times more active than pure gold. Activities greater and less than these values are reported for compositions within or on the edge of the heterogeneous region, but the results are difficult to interpret.

The foregoing results are not entirely consistent, but except for those on the nickel–copper alloy powders, they lend general support to the concept of the importance of *d*-band vacancies in determining catalytic activity. A fuller discussion of the electronic factor is reserved for later in this book (see Chapter 21), when similar studies on other reactions have been described.

8.4 The Formation and Recombination of Hydrogen Atoms at Metal Surfaces

8.41 The Atomization of Hydrogen on Metallic Filaments

Two mechanisms have been proposed for the atomization of molecular hydrogen at tungsten filaments; these may be formulated as

$$H_2 + 2* \rightarrow 2\underset{*}{H}; \quad \underset{*}{H} \rightarrow H\bullet + * \tag{h}$$

and

$$H_2 + * \rightarrow \underset{*}{H} + H\bullet . \tag{i}$$

The experimental method is to heat a tungsten filament to temperatures above about 1000° in a small pressure of hydrogen: the hydrogen atoms are then trapped, either on the glass walls of the vessel which is cooled to $\sim -190°$[53, 54] or more reliably and efficiently on films of potassium[55, 56] or molybdenum trioxide.[55, 57] In the earlier work, temperatures between 1200 and 1400°K and hydrogen pressures between 10^{-2} and 10^{-3} were used, but recently these conditions have been extended to 1800°K and 10^{-6} mm.[57] The rate of atomization has been found to be proportional to $P_{H_2}^{0.5}$, and activation energies of 45,[55], ~40[56] and 52.6 kcal. mole^{-1} [57] have been reported. Theoretical considerations have shown[58] that the half-power law would be obeyed with mechanism (h) at low coverages and with mechanism (i) at high coverages. Bosworth[59] determined the coverage at 1000°K and 3×10^{-3} mm. pressure to be about 80 per cent, and this has led to the acceptance until recently of mechanism (i). This conclusion has been supported by Absolute Rate Theory calculations.[60]

However, the figure of 80 per cent for the coverage at 1000°K and low pressure is almost certainly much too high, and it is now believed that mechanism (h) operates.[57] The lower activation energies found in the earlier work are attributed to the use of poisoned surfaces, and it has been shown[57] that an activation energy of 44.5 kcal. mole^{-1} results when the tungsten filament is not protected from tap-grease vapour by a cold trap. Poisoning of the filament with ethylene lowers the rate of atomization, but does not affect the activation energy. The foregoing view of the mechanism by the atomization of hydrogen over tungsten has since been elegantly confirmed by use of the flash-filament technique,[61] and the two sets of results are in substantial agreement.

Similar measurements have recently been made[57] using platinum and gold filaments between 1200 and 1800°K, and in the lower temperature regions the rate is again proportional to $P_{H_2}^{0.5}$: activation energies are close to 51 kcal. mole^{-1}, but the pre-exponential factor is lower for gold than for platinum and tungsten, presumably because the condensation coefficient for hydrogen on gold is comparatively low.

8.42 The Recombination of Hydrogen Atoms at Metal Surfaces

Possible mechanisms for this process are:

$$2H\bullet + 2* \rightarrow 2\underset{*}{H} \rightarrow H_2 + 2* \tag{j}$$

and

$$H\bullet + * \rightarrow \underset{*}{H}; \quad H\bullet + \underset{*}{H} \rightarrow H_2 + * . \tag{k}$$

On those metals which adsorb hydrogen atoms readily the coverage will be high, so that mechanism (j) should be zero order in [H•] and (k) first-order in [H•]. The experimental method generally used is based on measuring the efficiency of a metal for the reaction by the heat liberated: this has been accomplished by coating a thermometer bulb with a deposit of metal,[62] by using wires as resistance thermometers[63] and by coating a thermocouple sheath with a metal film.[64] In the last case, the temperature rise was found to be proportional to the atom concentration, and this clearly favours mechanism (k).

There have been several measurements of the relative efficiencies of metals for hydrogen-atom recombination.[62–66] The results are summarized in Table XII, which contains three kinds of information: (i) whether or not a metal is able to catalyse the process,[65] (ii) the sequence of efficiencies,[62] and (iii) numerical values of relative efficiencies.[63, 64, 66] With regard to this last category, the results from Refs. 63 and 64 are placed relative to Pt = 100, this being the most active metal yet studied, although even here the recombination coefficient (defined as the probability that the collision of an atom with a surface will lead to recombination) is only 0.25.[64] Figures in the last rows, derived from Ref. 66, are placed relative to Ni = 72, since a value was

TABLE XII. *Relative Efficiencies of Metals for Hydrogen–atom Recombination*

The first lines in each group show whether the metal is active (+) or not (−): the second lines give the sequence of efficiency, and the third, fourth and fifth lines give the relative efficiencies (see text).

Ref.	Al	Ti	V	Cr	Mn	Fe	Co	Ni	Cu	Zn
65	—	.	.	.	.	.	.	+	+	—
62	.	.	.	5	.	4	.	.	7	.
63	.	.	.	70	.	81.5	98	90	70.5	32
64	0.4	40	60	64	80	68	72	72	76	.
66	.	60	.	51	47.5	71	85	72	42.5	.

Ref.	Mo	Pd	Ag	Cd	Sn	Sb
65	—	.	—	+	—	+
62	.	2	6	.	.	.
63	.	.	.	66	9	.
64	.	80	52	.	.	.
66	61	.	.	.	.	.

Ref.	Ta	W	Pt	Au	Hg	Pb	Bi
65	.	.	+	.	—	+	—
62	.	3	1	.	.	8	.
63	.	.	100	.	.	.	.
64	.	.	100	40	.	.	.
66	63.5	60.5	.	.	.	.	.

not found for platinum in this work, and this value for nickel[64] is probably better than the value of 98.[63] If we bear in mind that different metal preparations are involved, the agreement between the three sets of figures is satisfactory (especially for Cr, Fe, Co and Ni), although there are some wide discrepancies (e.g. for Mn and Cu). There are strong indications that cobalt is more active than either iron or nickel. For further discussion, it is convenient to consider the Transition and non-Transition metals separately.

For the Transition metals, regardless of which mechanism is operative, there is to be expected an inverse correlation between efficiency for atom recombination and strength of binding. If we take the latter to be proportional to the initial heat of adsorption of hydrogen, we obtain in Fig. 10 the expected relation: here a selection of the results from Refs. 64 and 66 are

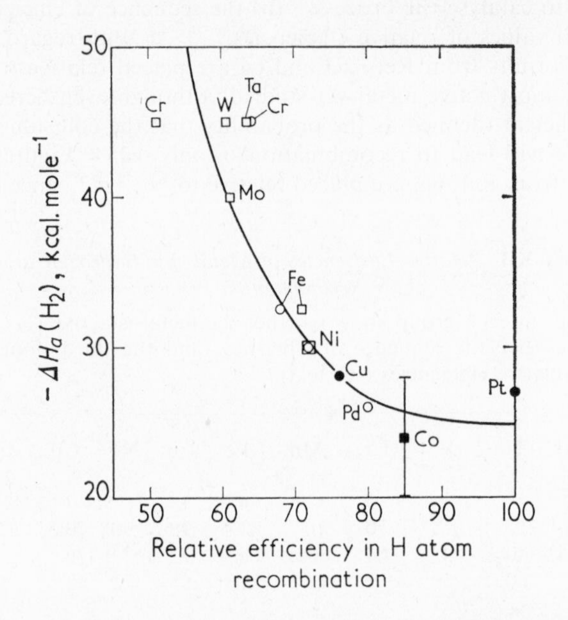

FIG. 10. Relative efficiencies of metals in hydrogen-atom recombination as a function of their initial heat of adsorption of hydrogen.

Circles, ref. 64; squares, ref. 66. Open points, heats measured on evaporated films; filled points, heats for silica-supported metals.

plotted against the heats quoted in Chapter 5, using where possible the values appropriate to films. The general success of this correlation suggests for example that the low values for copper and manganese are probably incorrect, although the latter may be a genuine exception.

The form of the relation in Fig. 10 is reminiscent of that between the heat of adsorption of hydrogen and the percentage *d*-bond character of the metal, δ (see Fig. 7 in Chapter 5). There is indeed a good linear relation between relative efficiency in hydrogen-atom combination and δ, the exceptions being that copper (with a δ of 36 per cent) is more active than expected, and that palladium and platinum are in the wrong order. The parallelism between relative efficiency and latent heat of sublimation (L_s) has been noted,[66] and since attention has recently been drawn[34] to the connection between efficiency in *para*-hydrogen conversion and L_s, it is of interest to compare the available results for the recombination and conversion reactions. From Refs. 18, 33 and 34 we would assess the activity sequence for *para*-hydrogen conversion to be

$$\text{Pt} > \text{Pd} > \text{Co} \geqslant \text{Ni} > \text{Fe} \doteqdot (\text{Ti, Cr}) > \text{Mn},$$

and for recombination efficiency from Refs. 64 and 66,

$$\text{Pt} > \text{Co} > \text{Pd} > \text{Ni} \doteqdot (\text{Ti, Cr}) > \text{Mn}(?).$$

The correlation is excellent, especially if the lower activity of palladium in the latter sequence is attributed to poisoning by dissolved hydrogen atoms. In view of the general success of these correlations, there is scope for a thorough investigation of the heats of adsorption, and of the efficiencies in atom recombination and hydrogen equilibration reactions, shown by those metals for which no quantitative or unambiguous information is available (e.g. tungsten, ruthenium, osmium, rhodium, iridium and manganese).

Relative rates of hydrogen-atom recombination have been measured in different faces of single metal crystals. For nickel the activity sequence is

$$(110) \doteqdot (100) > (111)$$

while similar sequences, with (110) > (100), have been reported for copper and silver.[67] These results do not, however, greatly aid our understanding of the process.

With the *sp*-metals, atom-recombination efficiencies are generally lower than for the *d*-metals (Table XII); the two notable exceptions are copper and cadmium. Thus on passing from Group VIII to Group IB, there is a slight increase in activity from nickel to copper, but a substantial decrease from palladium to silver and from platinum to gold. A study of atom-recombination efficiency on a series of, for example, palladium–silver alloy wires would be valuable. Within Group IB, the activity falls in the same sequence as does activity for *para*-hydrogen conversion.

8.5 The Mechanism of Hydrogen Evolution during Electrolysis: Hydrogen Overpotential

The literature on the mechanism of hydrogen evolution in electrolysis is very extensive, and it would be impossible and indeed inappropriate to try to do justice to it here. We shall therefore confine our attention to a statement of possible mechanisms, and to a discussion of the relations between the experimentally observable quantities and other parameters of metals.

When an electrolytic solution contains metallic cations which are discharged as metal at the cathode, the electrode reaction in the case of irreversible electrodes is normally the discharge of hydrogen ions to form molecular hydrogen. With most metallic cathodes operating at small current densities, the potential becomes much more negative when current flows. The difference between the actual and the reversible electrode potential is the *overpotential*, given the symbol η. The overpotential is related to the current density I by the Tafel equation

$$\eta = a + b \log I,$$

where a and b are constants. The current density is a measure of the rate of conversion of ions into molecular hydrogen, and the form of the Tafel equation suggests that some stage of this process takes place slowly, and requires an activation energy. There has been much controversy over the nature of this rate-limiting step, and it is probable that it is not the same for all metals.

Almost certainly the first step is the discharge of the ion:

$$H_3O^+ + e^- + * \rightarrow \underset{*}{H} + H_2O. \qquad (l)$$

This may be followed by the combination of the adsorbed hydrogen atoms,

$$2\underset{*}{H} \rightarrow H_2 + 2* \qquad (m)$$

or by the so-called "electrochemical" or ion + atom reaction

$$H_3O^+ + e^- + \underset{*}{H} \rightarrow H_2 + H_2O + *. \qquad (n)$$

All three steps have at some time been thought to be rate-limiting in particular systems. Thus for example Conway and Bockris[68] have stated that with metals having overpotentials at 10^{-3} A. cm.$^{-2}$ in normal HCl at 25° more positive than about —0.8 V., (n) is rate-limiting, whereas with the few metals (Hg, Pb, Tl) having overvoltages more negative than this, (l) is rate-limiting. Parsons has recently discussed the problem.[69]

A naïve appraisal of the situation would lead one to expect a relation between overpotential and work function if step (l) were the slowest one: there is no evidence for such a relation.[70] If step (m) were the slowest, a relation between overpotential and heat of adsorption of hydrogen or activity in hydrogen reactions might be expected. If step (n) were slowest, both work function and heat of adsorption should be important. Direct evidence in favour of step (m) comes from comparing the activity of several metals for (i) hydrogen ion discharge and (ii) *para*-hydrogen conversion in the gas-phase;[71] the results are shown in Table XIII. There is a good linear relation between log$k$ and log$I$, except for molybdenum, whose activity in *para*-hydrogen conversion is unexpectedly high. Further evidence claiming to support step (m) as the slow step comes from a comparison of calculated heats of adsorption of hydrogen atoms with overpotentials measured under the standard conditions referred to above. Rüetschi and Delahay[70] have calculated heats of atom-adsorption for a number of metals by the Eley method (but ignoring the electronegativity-difference term) and find a linear increase of the negative overpotential in the range —0.2 – —1.0 V. with increasing heat of adsorption. The correlation as it stands at the moment

TABLE XIII. *Comparison of the Rates of* Para-*hydrogen Conversion (in cm.$^{-2}$ min.$^{-1}$) and Hydrogen-ion Discharge (in cm.$^{-2}$ at η = 0.3 V.) for some Catalytic Materials*[71]

Catalyst	*Form, pretreatment*	*log k at 20°*	*log I*
Cu	foil, rolled	< -6	-3.92
Cu	powder, unsintered	~ -6	-3.37
Ni	foil, rolled	-5.96	-3.58
Hastalloy (Ni–Fe–Mo)	foil, rolled	-4.70	-1.45
Ni	powder, sintered	-3.92	-1.59
Mo	powder, unsintered	-1.7	-1.65
Co	powder, sintered	-2.75	-1.0
Ni	powder, unsintered	-2.13	0.0

is not convincing for the following reasons: (i) chosen values of the overpotentials are sometimes the mean of widely discordant values; (ii) the Eley method of calculation is not yet sufficiently refined to permit accurate values of heats of adsorption (see Chapter 5). For only four metals (Cr, Fe, Ni and Cu) is it possible to test the relation using accurate experimental heats; this is clearly a quite insufficient sample. Metals showing overpotentials of less than -0.5 V. are chiefly *sp* in character, and for these metals there are no measurements of heats of adsorption.

No attempt will be made to pass judgment in this confused field. We must be content to note the manner in which the electronic character of metals impinges on the field of electrochemistry, and the possible correlations between electrochemical and catalytic phenomena.

REFERENCES

1. A. Farkas, "Light and Heavy Hydrogen", (Cambridge University Press, 1935).
2. R. E. Dodd and P. L. Robinson, "Experimental Inorganic Chemistry" (Elsevier, Amsterdam, 1954).
3. E. Fajans, *Z. phys. Chem.* (*Leipzig*) **28B,** 239, 252 (1935).
4. K. F. Bonhoeffer, F. Bach and E. Fajans, *Z. phys. Chem.* (*Leipzig*) **168A,** 313 (1934).
5. A. Farkas and L. Farkas, *J. Amer. Chem. Soc.* **60,** 22 (1938).
6. A. Farkas, *Trans. Faraday Soc.* **32,** 416 (1936).
7. D. D. Eley and E. K. Rideal, *Proc. Roy. Soc.* **A178,** 429 (1941).
8. K. F. Bonhoeffer and A. Farkas, *Z. phys. Chem.* (*Leipzig*) **12B,** 231 (1931).
9. A. F. Benton and T. A. White, *J. Amer. Chem. Soc.* **52,** 2325 (1930).
10. A. J. Gould, W. Bleakney and H. S. Taylor, *J. Chem. Phys.* **2,** 362 (1934).
11. W. Frankenburger and A. Hodler, *Trans. Faraday Soc.* **28,** 229 (1932).
12. E. K. Rideal, *Proc. Cambridge Phil. Soc.* **35,** 130 (1939).
13. J. K. Roberts, *Proc. Cambridge Phil. Soc.* **34,** 399 (1938).
14. A. Couper and D. D. Eley, *Discuss. Faraday Soc.* **8,** 172 (1950).
15. W. G. Frankenburg, *J. Amer. Chem. Soc.* **66,** 1827, 1838 (1944).
16. E. K. Rideal and B. M. W. Trapnell, *Discuss. Faraday Soc.* **8,** 114 (1950); *Proc. Roy. Soc.* **A205,** 409 (1951); B. M. W. Trapnell, *Proc. Roy. Soc.* **A206,** 39 (1951).
17. A. Couper and D. D. Eley, *Proc. Roy. Soc.* **A211,** 536 (1952).

18. A. Couper, D. D. Eley, M. J. Hulatt and D. R. Rossington, *Bull. Soc. chim. belges* **67,** 343 (1958).
19. A. Farkas and L. Farkas, *J. Amer. Chem. Soc.* **64,** 1594 (1942).
20. A. Farkas, *Z. phys. Chem. (Leipzig)* **14B,** 371 (1931).
21. A. Farkas, *Trans. Faraday Soc.* **32,** 416 (1936).
22. M. A. Avdeenko, G. K. Boreskov and M. G. Slin'ko, In "Problems of Kinetics and Catalysis", edited by S. Z. Roginskii (U.S.S.R. Acad. Sci. Press, Moscow, 1957), **9,** 61.
23. J. H. Singleton, *J. Phys. Chem.* **60,** 1606 (1956).
24. G.-M. Schwab and E. Killmann, Proc. 2nd International Congress on Catalysis (Editions Technip, Paris, 1961), **1,** 1047.
25. G. Reinäcker and G. Vormum, *Z. anorg. Chem.* **283,** 287 (1956).
26. E. Cremer, *Adv. Catalysis* **7,** 75 (1955); E. Cremer and R. Kerber, *Z. Elektrochem.* **57,** 757 (1953).
27. A. Farkas, *Trans. Faraday Soc.* **32,** 1667 (1936).
28. G. Rienäcker and B. Sarry, *Z. anorg. Chem.* **257,** 41 (1948).
29. A. Farkas, *Trans. Faraday Soc.* **32,** 922 (1936).
30. D. D. Eley, "Catalysis and the Chemical Bond", (University of Notre Dame Press, Notre Dame, 1954).
31. D. D. Eley, *Discuss. Faraday Soc.* **8,** 191 (1950).
32. A. Couper and D. D. Eley, *Proc. Roy. Soc.* **A211,** 544 (1952).
33. G. C. A. Schuit and L. L. van Reijen, *Adv. Catalysis* **10,** 242 (1958).
34. D. D. Eley and D. Shooter, *Proc. Chem. Soc.* 315 (1959).
35. P. H. Emmett, *J. Phys. Chem.* **63,** 449 (1959).
36. B. M. W. Trapnell, *Trans. Faraday Soc.* **48,** 160 (1952).
37. D. D. Eley and D. R. Rossington (1957), In "Chemisorption", edited by W. E. Garner, (Butterworths, London 1957), p. 137.
38. R. J. Mikovsky, M. Boudart and H. S. Taylor, *J. Amer. Chem. Soc.* **76,** 3814 (1954).
39. P. B. Shallcross and W. W. Russell, *J. Amer. Chem. Soc.* **81,** 4132 (1959).
40. D. D. Eley, *Proc. Roy. Soc.* **A178,** 452 (1941).
41. B. M. W. Trapnell, In "Catalysis", edited by P. H. Emmett (Reinhold, New York, 1955), **3,** 1.
42. G. K. Boreskov and A. A. Vassilievitch, Proc. 2nd International Congress on Catalysis (Editions Technip, Paris, 1961), **1,** 1095.
43. J. T. Kummer and P. H. Emmett, *J. Phys. Chem.* **56,** 258 (1952).
44. P. M. Gundry, Proc. 2nd International Congress on Catalysis (Editions Technip, Paris, 1961), **1,** 1083.
45. P. H. Emmett and R. W. Harkness, *J. Amer. Chem. Soc.* **57,** 1624 (1935).
46. J. E. Lennard-Jones and A. F. Devonshire, *Proc. Roy. Soc.* **A156,** 6 (1936).
47. K. J. Laidler, *J. Phys. Chem.* **57,** 318, 329 (1953).
48. Y. L. Sandler, *J. Chem. Phys.* **21,** 2243 (1953).
49. G. D. Halsey, *Trans. Faraday Soc.* **47,** 649 (1951).
50. D. D. Eley, *Trans. Faraday Soc.* 44, 216 (1948).
51. J. C. P. Mignolet, *Bull. Soc. chim. belges* **67,** 358 (1958).
52. L. S. Shield and W. W. Russell, *J. Phys. Chem.* **64,** 1592 (1960).
53. I. Langmuir, *J. Amer. Chem. Soc.* **34,** 1310 (1912); **37,** 417 (1915).
54. N. S. Zaitsev, *Zhur. fiz. Khim.* **14,** 644 (1940).
55. G. Bryce, *Proc. Cambridge Phil. Soc.* **32,** 648 (1936).
56. T. Ivanoiskaya and I. Mochan, *Zhur. fiz. Khim.* **22,** 439 (1948).
57. D. Brennan and P. C. Fletcher, *Proc. Roy. Soc.* **A250,** 389 (1959); *Trans. Faraday Soc.* **56,** 1662 (1960).
58. J. K. Roberts and G. Bryce, *Proc. Cambridge Phil. Soc.* **32,** 653 (1936).
59. R. C. L. Bosworth, *Proc. Cambridge Phil. Soc.* **33,** 394 (1937).
60. K. J. Laidler, In "Catalysis", edited by P. H. Emmett (Reinhold, New York, 1954), **1,** 178, 210.
61. G. Ehrlich, *J. Chem. Phys.* **31,** 1111 (1959); T. W. Hickmott, *Ibid.* **32,** 810 (1960).

62. K. F. Bonhoeffer, *Z. phys. Chem. (Leipzig)* **113,** 199 (1924).
63. S. Katz, G. B. Kistiakowsky and R. F. Steiner, *J. Amer. Chem. Soc.* **71,** 2257 (1949).
64. B. J. Wood and H. Wise, *J. Chem. Phys.* **29,** 1416 (1958).
65. G. L. Wendt and L. Landauer, *Z. Physik.* **14,** 18 (1923).
66. K. Nakada, *Bull. Chem. Soc. Japan* **32,** 809 (1959).
67. T. Kwan, *Adv. Catalysis* **6,** 67 (1954); S. Sato, K. Nakada and S. Shida, *J. Chem. Soc. Japan* **76,** 1313 (1955); K. Nakada, *Bull. Chem. Soc. Japan* **81,** 4132 (1959).
68. B. E. Conway and J. O'M. Bockris, *Naturwiss.* **43,** 446 (1956).
69. R. Parsons, *Trans. Faraday Soc.* **54,** 1053 (1958).
70. P. Rüetschi and P. Delahay, *J. Chem. Phys.* **23,** 195 (1955).
71. E. Cremer and R. Kerber, *Z. Elektrochem.* **57,** 757 (1953).

Chapter 9

Exchange Reactions of Saturated Hydrocarbons with Deuterium

9.1 The Adsorption and Decomposition of Saturated Hydrocarbons at Metal Surfaces

Since saturated hydrocarbons contain electrons only in σ-bonds, their mode of adsorption must necessarily be dissociative; this view is widely held and has never been questioned. In hydrocarbons containing two or more carbon atoms, the dissociation may involve either the carbon–hydrogen or carbon–carbon bonds. In fact, the former is the favoured process, although fission of carbon–carbon bonds is possible at high temperatures; however, this process is probably never the initial one.

There are two possible adsorption mechanisms, and these may be illustrated by reference to methane: they are

$$CH_4 + 2{*} \rightarrow \underset{*}{CH_3} + \underset{*}{H} \quad \text{(a)}$$

and

$$CH_4 + \underset{*}{H} \rightarrow \underset{*}{CH_3} + H_2\,. \quad \text{(b)}$$

Mechanism (b) may use adsorbed hydrogen either formed in step (a) (which must occur initially when methane is exposed to a bare metal surface) or deriving from molecular hydrogen if it is present. Evidence for and against these possible mechanisms will be presented later.

When a saturated hydrocarbon contains two or more non-equivalent carbon–hydrogen bonds, the question arises as to which bond is broken in the act of adsorption. To this question there is no easy answer. In the case of propane, for example, the secondary carbon–hydrogen bond is the more readily broken, but adsorption by fission of the primary bond should also be possible. However, even if one mode were quite forbidden, mechanisms are available whereby the adsorbed species may be brought into equilibrium.

To describe the adsorbed state of more complex molecules, Burwell has found it convenient to introduce a terminology based on regarding the catalyst as a substituent on the hydrocarbon radical.[1] This system has considerable merits, and it will be used where appropriate. The following examples illustrate the method.

TABLE I. *Terminology of Adsorbed Hydrocarbon Radicals*

Hydrocarbon	*Adsorbed structure*	*Name*
C_2H_6	$CH_3—\underset{*}{CH_2}$	monoadsorbed ethane
C_2H_6	$CH_3—\underset{**}{CH}$	1,1-diadsorbed ethane
C_3H_8	$CH_3—\underset{*}{CH}—CH_3$	2-adsorbed propane

There is little doubt that the first hydrocarbon radical formed on adsorption of ethane is the ethyl radical, and that this is capable of losing a further hydrogen and forming 1,2-diadsorbed ethane (or adsorbed ethylene) on most metals, even at temperatures very much lower than those at which the thermodynamic stability of ethylene approaches that of ethane. These processes are reversible, and more extensive dehydrogenation (for example, to adsorbed acetylene) is improbable.[2] However, on certain metals, and more especially on those which readily form carbides (for example, tungsten and nickel), further reactions occur leading to the formation of methane: a possible formulation is

$$\underset{*}{CH_2}—\underset{*}{CH_2} \rightarrow 2\,\underset{**}{CH_2} \rightarrow \underset{****}{C} + CH_4. \qquad (c)$$

Since adsorption and decomposition are not always clearly separable, it is convenient to consider the two phenomena together.

Adsorption and decomposition of methane and ethane have been studied using evaporated films of a number of metals;[3, 4, 5] in all circumstances ethane is the more easily adsorbed of the two. Films of the following metals readily adsorb small amounts of both gases:[4] Ti, Ta, Cr, Mo, W, Rh and Pd. Amounts adsorbed tend to rise with temperature, but the coverages are nothing like complete at the temperatures at which decomposition starts. Tungsten shows the highest ability to adsorb, but even in this case the maximum amount of hydrocarbon taken up is much less than the amount of hydrogen required to form a monolayer.[3] The heats of adsorption must fall, and the activation energies rise, rapidly with increasing coverage. Tungsten readily adsorbs methane at 0°, but the decomposition temperature is ≥ 60°; the processes of adsorption and decomposition are thus clearly distinguishable in this case. On iron and nickel films, however, both processes become observable together at the minimum temperatures of 170° and 140° respectively. Tungsten and nickel both adsorb ethane at 0°, with very slight decomposition; the minimum adsorption temperature for ethane on iron is 77°, at which temperature the decomposition rate is low.[3]

The interpretation of these findings is briefly as follows. The higher activity of ethane is attributable, at least in part, to the dissociation energy of the carbon–hydrogen bond being about 5 kcal. $mole^{-1}$ less than in methane. The higher activity of tungsten in these reactions parallels the higher heats of adsorption which this metal shows for a number of gases (see Chapter 5): the rapid fall in activity with coverage is partly to be ascribed to steric hindrance of adsorption sites adjacent to those formally "occupied." The rate-limiting step in decomposition is normally the breakdown of the first-formed hydrocarbon radical, although in the methane–tungsten system it may be the recombination of adsorbed hydrogen atoms, and in the ethane–iron system the adsorption of the hydrocarbon.

On tungsten and nickel films, the activation energies for ethane decomposition are[3] respectively 16 and ~19.5 kcal. $mole^{-1}$, the frequency factors being identical (5×10^{21} mol. $cm.^{-2}$ $sec.^{-1}$) On iron and alkali-promoted iron powders, a value of ~20 to 25 kcal. $mole^{-1}$ has been recorded. The progressive addition of alkali (K_2O) to iron has the effect of progressively reducing the dehydrogenation power of the surface, i.e. of increasing the mean number of hydrogen atoms retained by the adsorbed hydrocarbon.[6]

The mean number of hydrogen atoms released by several hydrocarbons on adsorption by silica-supported nickel has been estimated by exchanging them with deuterium, and determining the change in the isotopic composition of the gas.[7] It was shown that this process is much faster than the subsequent exchange between deuterium and the retained hydrogen atoms.

9.2 Experimental Methods for Exchange Reactions[8, 9]

Since exchange reactions involve no chemical transformation, refined physical methods of analysis are called for to follow their progress. For the exchange reaction between a "light" hydrocarbon and deuterium, measurements may be made on either (i) the increase in the deuterium content of the hydrocarbon, or (ii) the increase in the hydrogen content of the deuterium, or of course ideally, as a check, (iii) both simultaneously. Measurements of type (ii) may be made, after removing the hydrocarbon, by thermal conductivity, or pyknometrically on the water to which the gas may be oxidized. Measurements of type (i) may be made similarly, and in addition by infrared spectroscopy.[10–12] The deuterium content so determined is, however, only a mean value, and no information is revealed on the nature and number of the individual species present. In acquiring this information, there is no substitute for mass-spectrometry.

A short description of the mass-spectrometric technique is in order, particularly in regard to the calculations which must be performed on the basic results. These calculations always involve certain assumptions; these will affect the results obtained, and they must therefore be justified. In the mass-spectrometer, the molecules are ionized by means of fast-moving and (ideally) monoenergetic electrons, and the resulting positive ions resolved according to their mass by passage through a magnetic field. The deflection produced by this field is determined by the e/m ratio of the ion, but since ions more than singly charged are formed only at high electron energies, this deflection is in practice determined solely by the mass of the ion. Continual variation of the magnetic field strength results in one ion after another encountering the collector where the ions are discharged, and the resulting positive ion current is very substantially magnified and fed into an automatic or other recording device.

The ionization process is unfortunately not simple. When the energy of the electrons is below the ionization potential of the molecule, no ions are of course formed. When their energy is significantly greater than the ionization potential I, secondary processes involving the dissociation of the hydrocarbon occur. In these secondary processes, carbon–hydrogen and carbon–carbon bonds may be broken: by way of illustration, Fig. 1 shows the

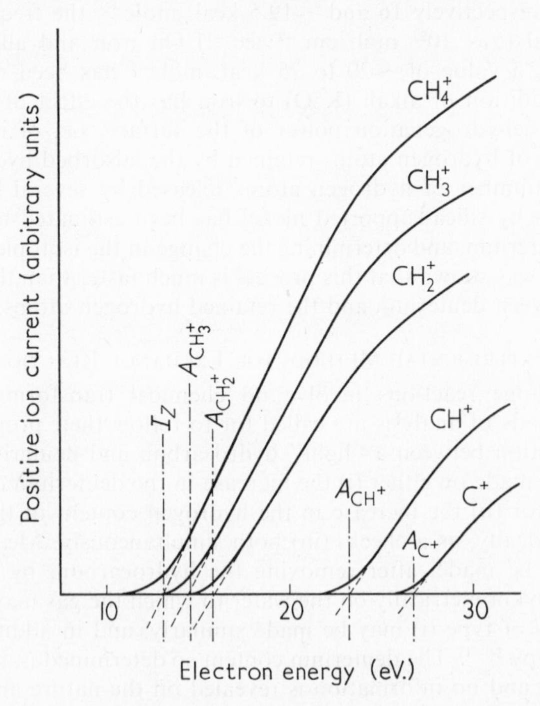

FIG. 1. The variation with electron energy of positive currents due to ions deriving from methane.

ionization efficiency curves (dependence of ion current on electron energy) for ions derived from methane. The minimum electron energy required to form a given ion J^+ from a hydrocarbon K is termed the appearance potential of that ion in that hydrocarbon, and is given the symbol $A_{J^+}(K)$. The following values in eV. have been recorded for methane:[13] I, 13.1; $A_{CH_3^+}$, 14.4; $A_{CH_2^+}$, 15.7; A_{CH^+}, 23.3; A_{C^+}, 26.7. The relative values of the ion currents due to the various ions at a given voltage is designated the mass spectrum of the compound at that voltage; the ion currents are normally expressed as percentages of the most abundant ion. Inspection of Fig. 1 shows that the mass spectrum will vary with electron energy up to a certain value, whereafter it will be constant.

Ethane presents a special case in that the process

$$C_2H_6 \rightarrow C_2H_4^+ + H_2 + e^- \qquad \text{(d)}$$

is particularly favoured, and the appearance potential $A_{C_2H_4^+}(C_2H_6)$ is only slightly greater than the ionization potential of ethane; the values are 12.7 and 11.6 eV. respectively.[14] It is therefore virtually impossible to obtain with ethane an ion current at mass 30 ($C_2H_6^+$) of measurable intensity without simultaneously forming the $C_2H_4^+$ ion of mass 28.

Refs. 15 and 16 should be consulted for further information on the theory and practice of the mass spectrometry of hydrocarbons.

The central problem in the application of this technique to the exchange reactions of hydrocarbons is the analysis of a mixture of deuterated paraffins. Thus for example the reaction of methane with deuterium affords CD_4, CHD_3, CH_2D_2 and CH_3D, and unchanged "light" methane will also be found. The same principle holds for higher hydrocarbons, with the number of possible products increasing with the number of exchangeable hydrogens, but the added complication of positional isomerism is also encountered. For example, a deuterated propane $C_3H_3D_2$ of mass 46 may have only one of the following structures: CH_3—CD_2—CH_3; CHD_2—CH_2—CH_3; CH_2D—CHD—CH_3; CH_2D—CH_2—CH_2D. These compounds are distinguishable only by their differing fragmentation patterns, i.e. by the different fragment ions to which they give rise. As and when the quantitative analysis of positional isomers becomes possible, much more information on the mechanisms of exchange reactions will become accessible.

Eminently the most satisfactory method of analysing a mixture of deuterated hydrocarbons is to operate below the appearance potentials of all fragment ions: it is then only necessary to convert the relative currents due to the parent ions into a percentage composition. This conversion involves only the assumption that the observed ion current is proportional to the number fraction of that species in the mixture. This assumption is not true for methane when electron energies only slightly greater than the ionization potential are used; this is because the ionization potentials of the five methanes are not the same. The following values in eV. have been recorded:[17] CH_4, 13.07; CH_3D, 13.12; CH_2D_2, 13.14; CHD_3, 13.18; and CD_4, 13.25.

No information is available on the ionization potentials of higher deuterated paraffins, although similar differences are likely to exist. Completely accurate analysis therefore demands a knowledge of the yield of parent ion from each species at the electron energy used.

The practical disadvantage of the foregoing method is that the yields of the parent ions may be too small for accurate measurement at the necessary low electron energies. At the other extreme, the use of electron energies of 50 eV. or greater leads to all conceivable fragment ions, and greatly complicates the subsequent computations. In practice, the use of low energies (12 to 20 eV.) is a reasonable compromise, and the calculations are quite simple if only two or three fragment ions are formed.[18] The basis of the calculation may be illustrated as follows. In a mixture of deuterated ethanes, masses 36 and 35 ($C_2D_6^+$ and $C_2HD_5^+$) are uncomplicated by contributions from other sources. However, at mass 34, we have the parent ion $C_2H_2D_4^+$ together with $C_2D_5^+$ formed both by loss of a hydrogen atom from $C_2HD_5^+$ and by loss of a deuterium atom from $C_2D_6^+$: it is therefore necessary to estimate and to subtract from the observed total ion current at each mass the contributions of all fragment ions to that mass, in order to derive the contribution of the parent ion.

This may be readily done if the mass-spectrum of each individual species under the operating conditions is known, but this is not generally the case. Alternatively the mass-spectrum of each species must be calculated. We will suppose at the obtaining electron energy that ethane forms $C_2H_6^+$, $C_2H_5^+$ and $C_2H_5^+$ in the ratio $1 : u : v$. If this ratio is independent of isotopic composition, then the mass spectrum of any species may be obtained by purely statistical reasoning. Thus the mass-spectrum of $C_2H_3D_3$ would be estimated as:

33	32	31	30	29
1	$\frac{1}{2}u$	$\frac{1}{2}u + \frac{1}{4}v$	$\frac{1}{2}v$	$\frac{1}{4}v$.

This procedure ignores the differences which undoubtedly exist between the various isomers of this species. There is, however, good evidence to show that it is not equally easy to remove a hydrogen or deuterium atom, or to remove H_2, HD or D_2 and further that the probability of loss is not independent of isotopic composition.[19] We may adopt the convention of allowing $P_i(K)$ to represent the probability of loss of the species i from the hydrocarbon K. It has been found[20] that at an electron energy of 16 eV., $P_D(C_3D_8)$ is 0.66 while $P_H(C_3H_8)$ is 0.82. The values of P_H and P_D for the deuterated methanes are well-represented by the relations:

$$P_H(CH_{4-x}D_x) = 1.22^x$$

and

$$P_D(CH_{4-x}D_x) = 0.87^{5-x}.$$

The observed[19] and calculated values are compared in Table II.

TABLE II. *Observed and Calculated Probabilities of Loss of H and D Atoms from Deuterated Methanes*[19]

Compound	P_H *observed*	P_H *calculated*	P_D *observed*	P_D *calculated*
CH_4	1.00	—	—	—
CH_3D	1.23	1.22	0.55	0.57
CH_2D_2	1.48	1.49	0.65	0.66
CHD_3	1.80	1.82	0.76	0.76
CD_4	—	—	0.90	0.87

Information of this type is much less complete for higher hydrocarbons, but Refs. 19 and 21 may be consulted in this connection.

When it is required to estimate the relative chances of loss of H_2 and D_2, it is necessary to multiply the statistical chances by P_H^2 and P_D^2 respectively. For HD it is usually sufficient to assume that $P_H \times P_D$ is about unity (see however Ref. 22).

However, it has been noted[18, 20] that the use of weighting factors to modify the statistical chances is unnecessary unless the distribution is weighted heavily in favour of the more completely deuterated species. The reason for this is straightforward. If we consider a symmetrical binomial distribution of ethanes, the current at mass 33 (the mass of the most abundant parent ion $C_2H_3D_3^+$) will be made up predominantly (~90 per cent) of the parent ion's contribution; any change in the variables of the calculation will only affect the remaining 10 per cent contributed by fragment ions, and will thus only change the result insignificantly. However, errors due to the use of an incorrect model for the calculation will accumulate, and may quite seriously affect the results for the "light" hydrocarbon and the slightly deuterated species, at which masses the fragment ions make the predominant contribution.[18, 23, 24]

This failure shows up in two ways: (i) a satisfactory isotopic mass balance is not obtained, and (ii) the calculated ion currents at masses less than that of the lightest parent ion do not compare well with those observed. The situation is somewhat less serious with propane than with ethane, where the ready formation of the ethylene ion makes for very large fragment ion contributions. However, the success or otherwise of these two critical tests provides the ultimate judgment on the method. Finally, of course, it is necessary to take account of the naturally occurring ^{13}C in hydrocarbons.

In this book we shall use the Boughton convention for naming deuterated hydrocarbons. The following few examples will be sufficient to indicate the principles involved.

$CH_3—CHD_2$	$CH_2D—CHD_2$	C_3D_8
ethane-1-1,d_2	ethane-1,1,2-d_3	propane-d_8

Where the positions of the substituent deuterium atoms are unknown, the place-designating numbers are simply omitted; thus C_3H_7D is propane-d_1.

9.3 Mechanisms of Exchange Reactions[8, 9, 22]

The hydrogen atoms in saturated hydrocarbons exchange with molecular deuterium homogeneously only above about 600°, although they exchange with deuterium *atoms* at much lower temperatures. The heterogeneous reaction occurs on a variety of metals between —100 and 300°, depending on their form and catalytic efficiency. If allowed to do so, it will continue to equilibrium, where the hydrogen and deuterium atoms will be shared between the "hydrogen" and the hydrocarbon as determined by the several equilibrium constants. Insufficient information is available for the calculation by statistical mechanics of the equilibrium constants in exchange reactions except in the simplest cases.[25] Kemball has measured the several equilibrium constants for the deuteromethanes,[25] deuteroethanes[26] and deuteropropanes[27] and has found that they compare well with the classically expected values: the n-deuterobutanes behave similarly.[28]

The kinetics of hydrocarbon exchange reactions are more complicated than those of the hydrogen equilibration reactions, in as much as two species rather than one take part; they are, however, uncomplicated by the formation of a chemically different product. Hydrogen is more strongly adsorbed than saturated hydrocarbons, and so we expect to find positive orders up to unity for the hydrocarbons and zero or negative orders for hydrogen. There is little doubt that exchange takes place by processes of the following kind:

$$\left.\begin{array}{l} RH + 2* \rightarrow \underset{*}{R}\,\underset{*}{H} \\ D_2 \;+ 2* \rightarrow 2\underset{*}{D} \end{array}\right\} \rightarrow RD + HD + 4*. \qquad (e)$$

RH represents the hydrocarbon. The rates of adsorption and desorption of the deuterium and hydrogen deuteride are certainly rapid compared with the corresponding rates for the hydrocarbon, so that the released hydrogen atom is rapidly replaced by a deuterium atom. The rate of exchange is thus limited by the rates of adsorption and desorption of the hydrocarbon.

If in the exchange of the saturated hydrocarbon C_nH_m the fraction of the species $C_nH_{m-x}D_x$ present at time t is f_x, then the extent of the exchange reaction may be expressed in terms of the function φ defined as

$$\varphi = f_1 + 2f_2 + 3f_3 \ldots + xf_x \qquad (1)$$

and, if all isotopic species react at identical rates, the course of the reaction will follow the first-order rate law:

$$-\log(\varphi - \varphi_\infty) = \frac{k_\varphi t}{2.303\,\varphi_\infty} + C, \qquad (2)$$

where C is a constant, φ_∞ the equilibrium value of φ and k_φ a rate constant equivalent to the number of deuterium atoms entering 100 molecules of hydrocarbons per unit time. The equation requires modification if the hydrocarbon contains more than one kind of carbon–hydrogen bond.[26] The rate of disappearance of the "light" hydrocarbon is also found in practice to follow the similar rate law:

$$-\log(f_{0,t} - f_{0,\infty}) = \frac{kt}{2.303(100 - f_{0,\infty})} + C', \tag{3}$$

where C' is another constant, and $f_{0,t}$ and $f_{0,\infty}$ are respectively the fractions of light hydrocarbon present at times t and infinity. The ratio of the two rate constants, k_φ/k, is designated M, and this represents the mean number of deuterium atoms initially entering each hydrocarbon molecule.

Mechanism (e) would appear to suggest that it is only possible to exchange one hydrogen atom of the hydrocarbon at each residence. The formation of the dideutero-hydrocarbon could then only proceed through the readsorption and further exchange of the monodeuterated species, and so on. This process will be referred to as *step-wise exchange*, and when it occurs the following criteria will be obeyed. (i) The value of M will be found to be unity, and only the monodeuterated species will be observed initially. (ii) The distribution of the various hydrocarbon species at any time calculated on the supposition that equilibrium is maintained between them will be found to be in agreement with the observed distribution if all the hydrogen atoms in the hydrocarbon are equivalent. The reaction between neopentane and deuterium on palladium and nickel films proceeds by step-wise exchange.

There is, however, ample evidence to show that it is sometimes possible to exchange many or all of the hydrogen atoms in a hydrocarbon in one residence. When more than one hydrogen atom is exchanged at a time, the process is referred to as *multiple exchange*, and this is characterized by (i) a value of M greater than unity and (ii) the initial appearance of species containing more than one deuterium atom. Although such a process occurs with methane, it is more readily understood by reference to ethane, and since the mechanism is also applicable to most higher hydrocarbons it may be discussed at this juncture.

The adsorbed ethyl radical formed from ethane is capable of losing another hydrogen and forming adsorbed ethylene which, however, must necessarily regain two "hydrogen" atoms and revert to ethane. We may represent the situation as follows, omitting hydrogen atoms.

$$C_2H_6 \underset{4}{\overset{1}{\rightleftarrows}} \underset{*}{C_2H_5} \underset{3}{\overset{2}{\rightleftarrows}} \underset{*\ *}{C_2H_4}$$

Now, as we have seen, when deuterium is present each ethane-ethyl-ethane cycle will lead in general to the formation of an ethane molecule containing one more deuterium atom than its precursor. If, however, the ethyl–ethylene–ethyl cycle occurs, the ultimate ethane will possess *two* more deuterium atoms than its precursor. Thus in a situation where the rates of steps 2 and 3 are rapid compared with 1 and 4, reiteration of steps 2 and 3 may lead to a completely exchanged ethyl radical, and hence to ethane-d_6, all within one period of residence. The observed initial degree of exchange is, therefore, simply determined by the ratio k_2/k_4, to which quantity the symbol $\mathscr{P}$ has been applied:[26] a low value of $\mathscr{P}$ would imply that the principal initial product would be ethane-d_1, while a high value of $\mathscr{P}$ would imply the preponderant formation of ethane-d_6. The mean number of deuterium atoms M in ethane molecules which have suffered exchange is related to $\mathscr{P}$ by a sigmoid curve[26] such that M is about four when $\mathscr{P}$ is ten, and about 5.5 when $\mathscr{P}$ is one hundred. It is sometimes found that two processes, one having a high $\mathscr{P}$ value and the other a low $\mathscr{P}$ value, can proceed simultaneously. The procedure for calculating the theoretical initial ethane distribution appropriate to any value of $\mathscr{P}$ has been described.[26, 29]

In the next Section, we shall consider the detailed experimental findings, with the objects of further understanding the reaction mechanisms and of relating the parameters of the exchange reaction to the structure of the catalytic metal. The results are especially valuable from the last standpoint, since not only is it possible to correlate in the usual way the rates and activation energies with metal structure, but also it is possible to use the value or values of $\mathscr{P}$, which constitute an internal measure of the efficiency of the reaction, to the same end. The results are valuable also for correlation with those of the hydrogenation of olefins, since the same adsorbed intermediates are thought to be involved.

Certain themes will be found to pervade the following sections, the chief of these being (i) the relative reactivities of hydrocarbons under fixed experimental conditions, and (ii) the role of the metal in determining the course of the exchange reaction. With regard to (i), there is a large measure of agreement between studies using various catalyst preparations, and the order of reactivity is:

$$\text{methane} < \text{neopentane} < \text{ethane} < \text{propane} \doteqdot \text{isobutane}$$
$$< \text{n-butane} \doteqdot \text{all higher hydrocarbons.}$$

Undoubtedly this order reflects the strength of the carbon–hydrogen bond which is broken in the rate-determining step. With regard to the second point, a short summary of the role of the metal is attempted in Section 9.48.

Especially when multiple exchange predominates, the reaction releases much hydrogen deuteride to the gas phase, and it is important to operate under conditions where its chance of re-entry into the reaction is minimized. This may be achieved either by using a large excess of deuterium[30] or by carrying the reaction only to very low conversion.

9.4 Experimental Results, and Correlations with Metal Structure

9.41 Methane

The first evidence for the exchange of methane with deuterium came from the observation that infra-red absorption bands due to C–D bonds arose when the reactants were exposed to nickel–kieselguhr at temperatures greater than about 140°: an activation energy of ~28 kcal. mole^{-1} was reported.[11] In the earliest application of mass-spectrometry to exchange processes, it was found[31] that the distribution of exchanged methanes from the reaction over a cobalt–thoria–magnesia–kieselguhr catalyst at 183° was as follows:

$$CD_4,\ 15.5\%;\ CHD_3,\ 1.0\%;\ CH_2D_2,\ 0\%;\ CH_3D,\ 83.5\%.$$

It appeared that step-wise and multiple exchange processes were operating simultaneously.

Very thorough studies of the exchange of methane with deuterium over evaporated metal films have been made by Kemball.[25, 32] In the earlier investigation[25] it was shown that CD_4 was the most abundant initial product over nickel, and the orders of reaction and activation energies determined for each product clearly indicated that CH_3D was formed by the stepwise exchange:

$$\left.\begin{array}{l} CH_4 + 2* \rightarrow \underset{*}{CH_3} + \underset{*}{H} \\ D_2 \quad + 2* \rightarrow 2\underset{*}{D} \end{array}\right\} \rightarrow CH_3D + HD + 4*, \qquad \text{(f)}$$

while the other products were all formed through a multiple exchange process probably involving methylene radicals, whose hydrogen atoms are easily exchanged. This last process does not proceed through intermediate methyl radicals, and so the process may be formulated as

$$CH_4 + 4* \rightarrow \underset{**}{CH_2} + 2\underset{*}{H} \rightarrow \underset{**}{CH_2} + \overset{H_2}{\vdots} + 2* \qquad \text{(g)}$$

$$\underset{**}{CH_2} + 2* \rightarrow \underset{***}{CH} + \underset{*}{H};\quad \underset{***}{CH} + \underset{*}{D} \rightarrow \underset{**}{CHD} + 2* \text{ etc.} \qquad \text{(h)}$$

$$\underset{**}{CH_2} + 2\underset{*}{D} \rightarrow \overset{CH_2D_2}{\vdots} + 4*;\quad \underset{**}{CHD} + 2\underset{*}{D} \rightarrow \overset{CHD_3}{\vdots} + 4* \text{ etc.} \qquad \text{(i)}$$

Increasing the ratio of the deuterium pressure to the methane pressure increased the yield of CD_4 relative to that of CHD_3 and CH_2D_2 because the chance of obtaining a deuterium atom was increased. The ratio of the chance of a methylene radical's acquiring a deuterium atom to its chance of retaining a hydrogen atom was proportional to $P_{D_2}^{1/2}P_{CH_4}^{-1/3}$: this may indicate that in this process the methane initially dissociates into three fragments as shown in step (g) above.

The reaction has also been studied[32] on evaporated films of several other metals, of which only iron was quite inactive. The activation energies and frequency factors are plotted as a compensation effect in Fig. 2; it is noteworthy that the values of each are much lower for tungsten than for the remaining metals. Table III gives the orders of reaction for both processes, and other information. The rates of exchange at 200° increase roughly in proportion to the percentage *d*-character of the metal, although tungsten is

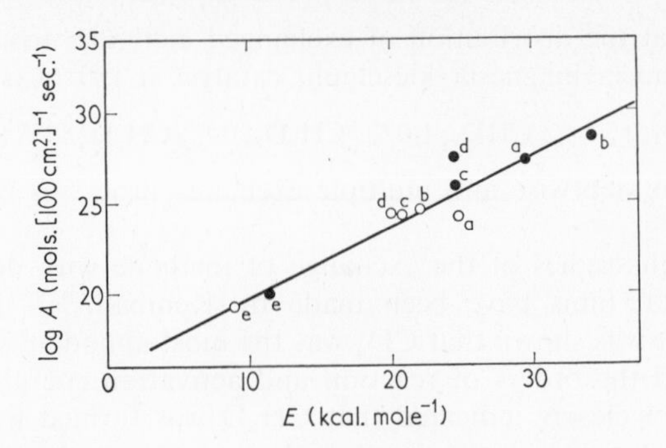

FIG. 2. Compensation effect in the exchange between methane and deuterium over evaporated metal films.[25, 32]

○ Values for stepwise exchange; ● values for multiple exchange.

a, Ni; b, Pd; c, Pt; d, Rh; e, W.

The temperature ranges used are given in Table III.

much more active in stepwise exchange, and palladium much less active in multiple exchange, than expected.[33] There is also a fair correlation between rates of exchange and rates of adsorption.[4]

Laidler and his associates have carried out Absolute Rate calculations for the reaction over nickel films, based on the mechanisms outlined above, and have obtained[34] very good agreement with the observed rates by using a value of 24.0 kcal. mole^{-1} for E_{sw} and 33.0 for E_m. Miyahara[35] has also offered a theoretical discussion of this reaction, and the Power Rate Law has been applied[36] to Kemball's results.

TABLE III. *Kinetic Results for the Exchange Between Methane and Deuterium over Evaporated Metal Films*[25, 32]

		Stepwise exchange			*Multiple exchange*		
Metal	*Temp. range (°C)**	*Order in H_2*	*Order in CH_4*	*logr at 200°C†*	*Order in H_2*	*Order in CH_4*	*logr at 200°C†*
Ni	206–255	1.0	−0.5	13.3	1.0	−1.0	13.8
Pd	243–308	1.0	−0.5	14.5	1.0	−0.9	12.8
Pt	159–275	0.6	−0.4	14.7	0.8	−0.8	14.6
Rh	138–217	0.4	−0.2	15.2	0.4	−0.7	16.2
W	92–174	0.3	−0.1	15.2	0.3	−0.5	14.7

* Used in determining activation energies.
† Rate in molecules cm.$^{-2}$ sec.$^{-1}$.

9.42 Ethane

The minimum temperature at which the exchange of ethane with deuterium is detectable over nickel–kieselguhr is[10] 100°; this is some 40° lower than the minimum temperature for methane, and the reported activation (15 kcal. mole^{-1}) is also lower than for methane. The first mass-spectrometric study of ethane exchange revealed that ethane, like methane, is capable of undergoing multiple exchange. The distribution of deuterated ethanes arising from the reaction over a cobalt–thoria Fischer–Tropsch catalyst at 183° is:

C_2D_6, 40 %; C_2HD_5, 7 %; $C_2H_2D_4$, 0 %; $C_2H_3D_3$, 5 %; $C_2H_4D_2$, 44%; C_2H_5D, 0%.

The work of Anderson and Kemball[26] on this reaction over evaporated metal films has confirmed the readier exchange of ethane, and the widespread occurrence of multiple exchange. Of the metals investigated, manganese and silver were inactive up to 370° (presumably because of their inability to chemisorb the reactants); iron films at this temperature formed only deutero-methanes, while cobalt and nickel showed simultaneous exchange and cracking at temperatures above 300° and 160° respectively. Table IV gives the values for the activation energies, frequency factors and rates at 150°.

TABLE IV. *Activation Energies, Frequency Factors and Rates at 150° for the Ethane–Deuterium Exchange over Evaporated Metal Films*[26]

Metal	*Temp. range (°C)*	*E(kcal. mole^{-1})*	*logA*†	*logr at 150°*†
W	−80−−29	8.2	23.7	19.5
Mo	−50–0	7.0	21.5	17.9
Ta	−44–0	7.8	21.9	17.8
Zr	158–192	15.4	23.5	15.6
Cr	149–215	23.4	23.4	16.2
V	102–260	20.7	26.8	16.1
Ni	162–195	18.0	23.8	14.5
Pt	134–192	12.5	22.3	15.9
Pd	145–207	21.4	25.8	14.8
Rh	0–70	11.7	24.0	18.0

† A and r in mol (10 mg.)$^{-1}$ sec.$^{-1}$.

Tungsten, molybdenum and tantalum all show outstandingly low activation energies, probably because the activation energies for the adsorption of ethane on them is also low. All three metals are body-centred cubic in structure. In the remaining metals, there is no obvious correlation between activation energy and any other parameter, but the existence of a reasonable compensation effect makes it possible that in this case the rate at a given temperature is more fundamental than the separate Arrhenius parameters. Figure 3 shows a plot of the log of the rate of ethane exchange at 150° as a function of the percentage *d*-character of the metals. It is possibly significant that the values for the face-centred cubic metals of Group VIII appear to form one series and the other transition metals a second series. We may in fact be witnessing the combined effects of electronic structure and geometric structure in this system.

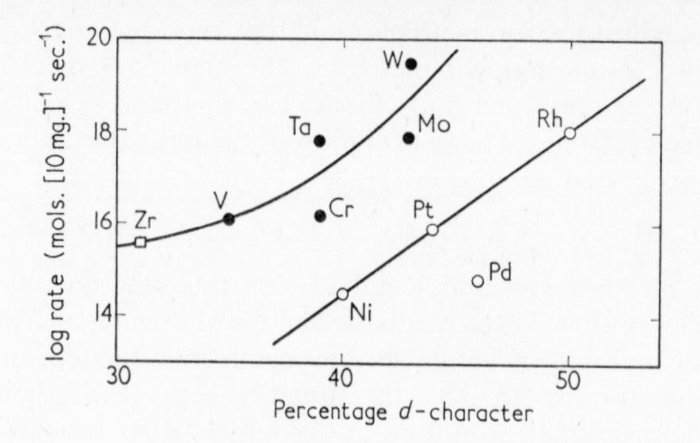

FIG. 3. Dependence of the rate of ethane exchange[26] on the percentage *d*-character of the metal.

○ Face-centred cubic metals.
□ Close-packed hexagonal metals.
● Body-centred cubic metals.

Orders of reaction based on the rates of removal of "light" ethane were determined for tungsten, rhodium and palladium, with the results shown in Table V.

TABLE V. *Orders of Reaction for the Ethane–Deuterium Exchange over Evaporated Metal Films*[26]

Metal	*Order in* C_2H_6	*Order in* H_2
W	0.1	−0.1
Rh	0.8	−0.7
Pd	0.8	−0.8

Table VI shows the temperature-independent initial distributions of deuteroethanes (expressed as percentages) found for the various metals. Ruthenium films were active between 0 and 50°, but the results were not reproducible, although they appeared to resemble those for platinum. The values quoted for nickel are those obtained with a film of standard weight, which was active at temperatures where cracking also occurred. Much heavier films were active between 0 and 75°, but whether "oriented" or not give little or no multiple exchange. However, in view of the work described in Chapter 3, it seems probable that both kinds of the heavier films were in fact substantially oriented and that the chief difference between the normal and the heavy films is to be ascribed to differences in mean particle size.[8]

The results presented in Table VI have been interpreted along the lines indicated in Section 9.3. In the case of the metals molybdenum, tantalum, palladium and rhodium one value of the parameter $\mathscr{P}$ suffices to describe the

TABLE VI. *Initial Distributions of Deuteroethanes from the Ethane–Deuterium Exchange over Evaporated Films of Various Metals*[26]

Metal	Percentage composition						M
	C_2H_5D	$C_2H_4D_2$	$C_2H_3D_3$	$C_2H_2D_4$	C_2HD_5	C_2D_6	
W	79.1	12.2	5.2	2.0	0.9	0.6	1.30
Mo	82.2	14.1	3.0	0.7	0	0	1.16
Ta	81.3	15.0	3.1	0.6	0	0	1.15
Zr	52.4	17.1	5.1	4.3	7.0	14.1	2.3
Cr	47.2	18.0	6.6	6.0	7.2	15.0	2.5
V	46.3	19.2	5.7	5.1	7.5	16.2	2.6
Ni	40.4	10.1	4.0	5.1	10.1	30.3	3.1
Pt	19.4	17.3	12.2	10.2	15.3	25.5	3.5
Pd	5.0	5.9	7.9	10.9	18.8	51.5	4.8
Rh	4.8	2.9	4.3	7.1	17.1	63.8	5.0
Co	—	—	5.3	10.5	21.0	63.2	5.4

distribution of ethanes: the values are respectively 0.25, 0.25, 18.0 and 28.0. For the other metals it is necessary to suppose that two mechanisms (designated A and B) having different $\mathscr{P}$ values ($\mathscr{P}_A$ and $\mathscr{P}_B$) coexist and contribute to the total process to varying extents. Table VII gives the values of the parameters which lead to optimal agreement with the observed values, which agreement is illustrated by selected examples in Table VIII.

It is now necessary to examine the foregoing results with a view to finding what correlations may exist between them and other parameters of the metals already encountered. Figure 4 shows plots of the mean deuterium number M (Table VI) as a function of (a) the percentage d-character of the metals, δ, and (b) the heats of adsorption of hydrogen. Excluding the body-centred cubic metals of the second and third long periods, M increases with δ and decreases with increasing heat of adsorption. Examination of the material in Table VII shows that there is no observable correlation between either $\mathscr{P}_B$ or the contribution of process B and any other quantities, although both $\mathscr{P}_A$

TABLE VII. *Best-fit Parameters used in Calculating Ethane Distributions*[26]

Metal	Process A		Process B	
	Contribution (%)	$\mathscr{P}_A$	Contribution (%)	$\mathscr{P}_B$
W	6.5	4.0	93.5	0.20
Zr	29.7	13.5	70.3	0.36
Cr	35.3	13.2	64.7	0.48
V	38.1	14.0	61.9	0.45
Ni	51.4	16.0	48.6	0.50
Pt	50.0	18.0	50.0	2.0

TABLE VIII. *Comparison Between Observed and Calculated Ethane Distributions*[8]

Metal		Percentage composition					
		C_2H_5D	$C_2H_4D_2$	$C_2H_3D_3$	$C_2H_2D_4$	C_2HD_5	C_2D_6
Mo	Observed	82	14	3.0	0.7	0	0
	Calculated, P = 0.25	80.0	17.2	2.5	0.3	0	0
Pd	Observed	5	6	8	11	19	51
	Calculated, P = 18	5.3	7.3	8.7	11.2	16.9	50.6
Pt	Observed	20	17	12	10	15	26
	Calculated, P_B = 2 (50%)	16.6	14.3	9.5	5.7	2.9	1.0
	Calculated, P_A = 18 (50%)	2.6	3.6	4.4	5.6	8.4	25.4
	Calculated, total	19.2	17.9	13.9	11.3	11.3	26.4

and the contribution of process A increase with δ. These relations are shown in Fig. 5, where M_A per cent (the percentage deuterium content of the distribution corresponding to $\mathscr{P}_A$, defined as $(M_A/6) \times 100$) is used in place of $\mathscr{P}_A$ to facilitate comparison with work to be described later.

The dependence of the parameter $\mathscr{P}$ on the reactant pressures was studied in three cases. Over tungsten, rhodium and palladium, $\mathscr{P}$ varied as the 0.2 power of the ethane pressure, and as the powers —0.5, —0.9 and —0.9 respectively of the deuterium pressure.

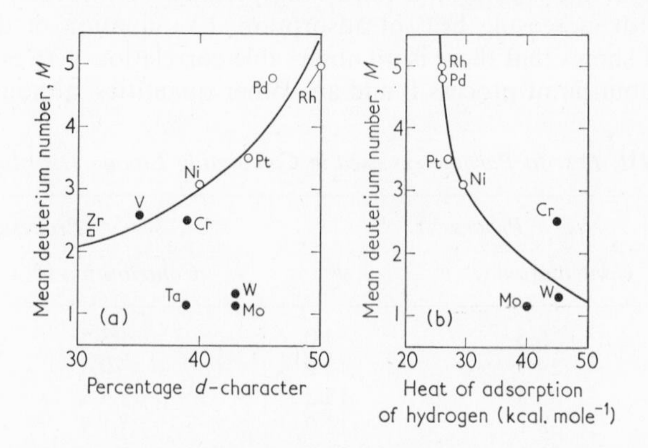

FIG. 4. Dependence of mean deuterium number in ethane exchange[26] on (a) percentage *d*-character, and (b) the heat of adsorption of hydrogen.

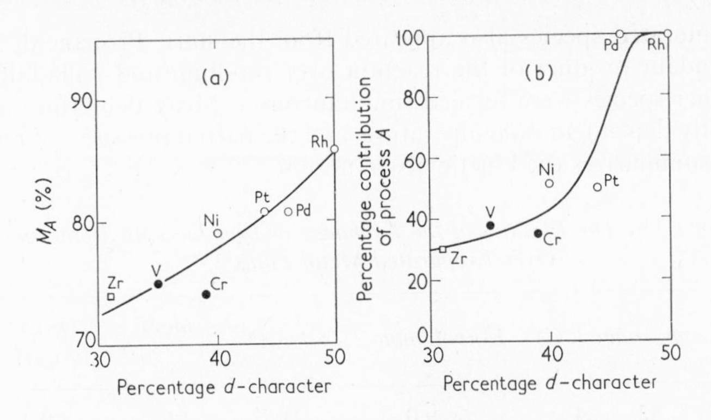

FIG. 5. (a) Dependence of M_A% (the percentage deuterium content of ethanes formed by process A) on percentage *d*-character. (b) The dependence of the contribution of process A on percentage *d*-character.

Arguments have been brought forward to suggest that the mechanism on tungsten differs from that operating over rhodium and palladium. On tungsten, the adsorbed species are believed to be formed by loss of hydrogen atoms from ethane by successive interaction with adsorbed deuterium atoms, with the formation of hydrogen deuteride, while on rhodium and palladium the hydrogen atoms lost are thought to be acquired by adjacent vacant sites. In the former case, the interaction with deuterium atoms may be necessitated by the strong adsorption of hydrogen on tungsten, and hence by the small concentration of vacant sites.

Miyahara[35] has offered an alternative mechanistic interpretation of ethane exchange, involving species more dehydrogenated than the ethyl radical, but his views have been strongly criticized.[2]

9.43 *Propane*

Propane exchanges with deuterium more readily than either methane or ethane over nickel–kieselguhr,[12] platinum foil[37] and evaporated metal films.[27] Over nickel–kieselguhr, the activation energy is about 19 kcal. mole^{-1} and the rate expression is

$$r = k\,[C_3H_8]^{0.62}\,[D_2]^{-0.76}.$$

Over platinum foil, the activation energy decreases from 11.6 to 8.8 kcal. mole^{-1} between 26 and 126°: there is evidence that over this catalyst the secondary hydrogen atoms exchange more rapidly than the primary hydrogens.[38] Multiple exchange has been detected over a cobalt–thoria catalyst at 183°.[31]

The reaction has also been studied over evaporated films of tungsten, rhodium, palladium and nickel[22, 27] and over pumice-supported platinum, palladium, rhodium and iridium.[30] Propane-2-d_1 was the most abundant initial product over tungsten and nickel films, although in both cases more highly deuterated species also appeared from the start. Propane-d_8 was the most abundant product of the reaction over rhodium and palladium films, but all other species were formed simultaneously. Mean deuterium numbers were slightly dependent on temperature, and the partial pressures of reactants. Table IX summarizes the kinetic observations.

TABLE IX. *The Kinetics of the Exchange of Propane with Deuterium Over Evaporated Metal Films*[22, 27]

Metal	*Temp. range* (°C)	*E*(*kcal. mole*$^{-1}$)	*log A**	*log r at* −20°*	*Order in* C_3H_8	*Order in* D_2
W	−82–−24	9.0	21.7	14.1	−0.4	−0.4
Rh	−25–−16	13.3	25.0	13.5	0.5	−0.8
Ni	−47–0	10.4†	21.7	12.7	1.0	−0.6
Pd	146–185	23.7	26.0	5.6	—	—

*; *A* and *r* in mol. cm.$^{-2}$ sec.$^{-1}$:
†; for exchange of secondary hydrogen atoms.

Primary and secondary hydrogen atoms apparently exchanged at equal rates over tungsten, but over nickel the secondary hydrogens exchanged ten times faster: with rhodium and palladium, the large amount of multiple exchange obscured any difference which might have existed. Table X shows the observed propane distributions over rhodium and palladium films. The existence of a second maximum at propane-d_3 in the case of rhodium shows that two processes having different $\mathscr{P}$ values must be proceeding concurrently: the deuterated *ethanes* formed over rhodium, however, only needed one value of $\mathscr{P}$ for their description. The absence of any significant multiple exchange over nickel implies that comparison should be made with the results for ethane obtained with the heavier films.

TABLE X. *Initial Distributions of Deuterated Propanes Formed Over Metal Films*[22, 27]

Metal	*Temp.* (°C)	d_1	d_2	d_3	d_4	d_5	d_6	d_7	d_8	*M*
Rh	−24	6.0	7.5	10.0	7.5	5.0	13.3	23.1	27.6	5.7
Pd	146	1.0	0.6	0.4	0.5	1.0	3.5	12.5	80.5	7.6
Pd	185	1	1	<0.5	<0.7	1	4	12	81	7.7

The propane distributions resulting from the exchange of propane with deuterium over pumice-supported metals[30] were independent of the partial pressures of reactants, and generally showed three maxima, at C_3D_8, about $C_3H_4D_4$ and C_3H_7D. C_3D_8 was the most abundant product with all metals except over platinum at low temperatures. It was found that each of the observed distributions could be described as the sum of three separate distributions, whose contributions are designated ΣA, ΣB and ΣC: the three distributions were obtained by random sampling from pools of hydrogen and deuterium atoms whose deuterium contents were δ_A, δ_B and δ_C. Thus for example, random sampling from a pool containing 50 per cent deuterium atoms led to a binomial distribution of propanes symmetrical about $C_3H_4D_4$, and therefore corresponding approximately to distribution B. To describe distribution A, values of δ_A were required to be about 98 per cent, and scrambling of this pool led to about 80 per cent C_3D_8, 15 per cent C_3HD_7 and 5 per cent $C_3H_2D_6$, and no less deuterated species. Values of δ_C were between 3 and 16 per cent. The δ-values were usually independent of temperature (except notably with platinum), while the contributions of each distribution were usually temperature-dependent. Table XI gives the best-fit values of the parameters, and the temperature range in which measurements were made: where two values of any parameter are quoted, these are respectively the values obtaining at the lowest and highest temperatures employed. This method of interpretation has, however, been repeatedly criticized.[8, 22, 39, 40]

TABLE XI. *Best-fit Parameters Used to Reproduce the Propane Distributions Observed in Propane Exchange Over Pumice-supported Metals*[30]

Metal	*Temp. range (°C)*	*ΣA*	*ΣB*	*ΣC*	δ_A	δ_B	δ_C
Pd	100–200	58→68	25→14	~17.5	96.9	49	16
Rh	50–200	50→~60	28→17	~22.5	97.4	50	9.5
Ir	100–200	70	19→30	11→0*	97.9	50→65	3*
Pt	100–250	32→46	44→36	24→18	90→95.4	45→50	15→3

* Distribution C appeared only at 100°.

We may now compare these results with those found for ethane and propane with evaporated films, and this is done in Table XII, where *M* per cent represents the percentage deuterium content of the whole observed distribution and M_A per cent the deuterium content of the A distribution, obtained

TABLE XII. *Comparison of the Parameters Describing Distributions Arising from the Exchange of Ethane and Propane*

	Propane exchange at 200° over pumice-supported metals		*Propane exchange over evaporated films*		*Ethane exchange over evaporated films*	
Metal	δ_A	*M*(%)	δ_A	*M*(%)	M_A(%)	*M*(%)
Ir	97.9	84.5	—	—	—	—
Rh	97.5	89.0	89	71	85.7	83.5
Pt	94.8	75.5	—	—	80.7	58.2
Pd	96.8	89.7	98	96	80.7	80.0

in the manner of Anderson and Kemball. Comparison of the columns headed *M* per cent shows (i) that significantly more multiple exchange usually occurs over pumice-supported metals at 200° than over metals in the form of films, and (ii) that in each case the amount of multiple exchange is much less over platinum than over the other metals. The *efficiency* of multiple exchange is given by the columns headed δ_A and M_A, comparison of which shows that in most cases the exchange is more efficient over the pumice-supported metals than over films. With the former, δ_A increases with percentage *d*-character of the bonds in the metal, except that the order of rhodium and iridium is reversed.

The Arrhenius parameters and the rates at 200° found for propane exchange over pumice-supported metals are given in Table XIII. The activity order does not follow the percentage *d*-character, but is the same as that found for ethane exchange over films.

TABLE XIII. *Arrhenius Parameters and Rates at 200° for Propane Exchange over Pumice-supported Metals*[30]

Metal	*E(kcal. mole^{-1})*	*logA**	*logr**
Rh	17.3	10.7	2.5
Pd	17.2	9.5	1.4
Ir	17.7	11.8	3.6
Pt	18.2	10.2	1.6

* *A* and *r* in % reaction (g. catalyst)$^{-1}$ hr.$^{-1}$.

The mechanism of propane exchange is likely to be similar to that proposed for ethane, with the difierence that two distinguishable forms of the adsorbed propyl radical (viz. the n- and the iso-forms) are possible. The isopropyl radical is the more readily formed, and the multiple exchange must result through reiteration of the sequence

$$\underset{*}{CH_3\text{–}CH\text{–}CH_3} \underset{+H}{\overset{-H}{\rightleftharpoons}} \underset{*\quad\quad *}{CH_2\text{–}CH\text{–}CH_3} \underset{-H}{\overset{+H}{\rightleftharpoons}} \underset{*}{CH_2}\text{–}CH_2\text{–}CH_3 \quad (j)$$

the hydrogen atoms lost by the radicals appearing as hydrogen deuteride, and being replaced by deuterium atoms. It has been suggested[30] that the several distributions which apparently arise over the pumice-supported metals are caused by reactions occurring on different crystal faces. Assuming that propylene is adsorbed by adjacent metal atoms, a propyl radical can make the second contact in six directions on the (111) plane, in four directions on the (100) plane, and in two directions on the (110) plane of a face-centred cubic metal. These planes may be responsible respectively for the A, B and C distributions. This view is supported by the finding[26] that stepwise exchange (corresponding to distribution C) is the principal reaction over (100)-oriented nickel films, and might suggest that in such films this face is indeed the one predominantly exposed, despite arguments to the contrary.[41] A study of the exchange reactions of hydrocarbons on well-defined faces of single metal crystals should prove rewarding.

An alternative theoretical treatment of the foregoing results has been published,[39] and the possible role of triadsorbed species noted.

9.44 *Butanes*

n-Butane exchanges its hydrogen atoms with deuterium over platinized platinum foil with an activation energy which decreases with increasing temperature between 26 and 95°.[37] The reaction proceeds more readily than the corresponding reaction with propane.[31, 37] Over a cobalt–thoria catalyst at 183°, extensive exchange of n-butane occurred when a 6 : 1 deuterium: hydrocarbon mixture was passed at a space velocity of 150 hr.$^{-1}$: the exchanged butane contained 82.7 per cent deuterium, but the actual distribution is not meaningful since some back-exchange of the liberated hydrogen had taken place. When the space velocity was raised to 750 hr.$^{-1}$, the deuterium content of the exchanged butane rose to 92.9 per cent, the distribution being

$$C_4D_{10}, 45\%; C_4HD_9, 40\%; C_4H_2D_8, 15\%,$$

no others being observed.[31]

The exchange reaction between n-butane and deuterium has been examined[28] using a series of supported-platinum catalysts containing 0.35 to 0.59 per cent platinum by weight. Unfortunately the non-equilibrium (initial) distributions of the deuterated butanes were not determined, although values of *M*, the mean number of deuterium atoms initially entering each butane molecule, were derived from low conversion results by the velocity constant method. They do not, however, differ from one support to another to a significant degree. Table XIV details the supports used and the chlorine contents of the

TABLE XIV. *Arrhenius Parameters for the Exchange of Butane With Deuterium over Supported Platinum Catalysts*[28]

Number	*Support*	*% Cl (wt.)*	*Temp. range (°C)*	*E(kcal. mole^{-1})*	*log A**	*log r at 100°**	*M*
1	η–Al_2O_3	0.15	75–200	14.8	9.0	0.3	2.6
2	η–Al_2O_3	0.69	100–200	2.8	2.4	1.0	3.7
3	η–Al_2O_3	0.01	75–200	17.4	9.5	−0.5	3.4
4	η–Al_2O_3	0.35	100–200	8.1	5.2	0.4	4.0
5	Al_2O_3(F–10)	1.0	100–231	8.2	4.8	0.0	3.7
6	SiO_2–10% Al_2O_3	—	50–100	10.0	6.9	1.0	4.3
7	As 6, K_2CO_3 treated	—	50–150	6.6	3.9	0.0	2.0
8	SiO_2	—	75–150	10.4	6.2	0.1	3.3
9	Activated C	—	230–320	26.0	11.1	−4.2	2.1

* Rate in % exchange g.$^{-1}$ sec.$^{-1}$.

catalysts, and quotes the Arrhenius parameters and the values of M. Surface areas varied from 90 $m.^2$ $g.^{-1}$ (number 5) to 1080 $m.^2$ $g.^{-1}$ (number 9), but these appear to be without effect on any of the observed quantities. The lowest activity and highest activation energy is shown by the carbon-supported platinum. In the η-Al_2O_3-supported catalysts, the activation energy increases, and the activity decreases, with increasing chlorine content.

The back-exchange of liberated hydrogen was encountered in the exchange of isobutane with deuterium over cobalt–thoria at 183°.[31] Table XV shows the dependence of the deuterium content on space velocity. The distribution observed at the highest space velocity used was

$$C_4D_{10},\ 30\%;\ C_4HD_9,\ 39\%;\ C_4H_2D_8,\ 31\%,$$

and no others were detected.

TABLE XV. *Dependence of Deuterium Content of Exchanged Isobutane on Space Velocity over a Cobalt–Thoria Catalyst at 183°.* [31]
($D_2 : C_4H_{10} = 6 : 1$)

Space velocity (hr^{-1})	150	200	500
Deuterium content	50.5	79.2	90.0

Isobutane was found to exchange at about the same rate as propane over films of several metals, and over nickel the tertiary hydrogen atom exchanged faster than the primary hydrogens.[27] Isobutane-d_1 was also the chief product of the reaction over tungsten, and the following percentage distribution was found over a rhodium film at −27°:

d_{10}	d_9	d_8	d_7	d_6	d_5	d_4	d_3	d_2	d_1
24.0	10.0	7.5	5.4	3.7	5.7	12.5	10.0	12.5	8.7

Values for the activation energy and the log of the frequency factor were respectively, for tungsten, 7.9 kcal. $mole^{-1}$ and 20.1 (mols. $cm.^{-2}$ $sec.^{-1}$) between −80 and −27°, and for the exchange of the primary hydrogen atom over nickel, 9.0 kcal. $mole^{-1}$ and 20.5 (mol. $cm.^{-2}$ $sec.^{-1}$) between −47 and 0°.

9.45 Neopentane

Neopentane, $C(CH_3)_4$, like methane, contains only primary hydrogen atoms, and moreover the normal kind of multiple exchange mechanism, often referred to as α–β exchange, is impossible with this molecule. A process leading to the simultaneous introduction into the molecule of more than one deuterium atom must therefore involve either α–α exchange (as occurs with methane) or α–γ exchange.

Neopentane exchanges with deuterium over evaporated metal films somewhat less readily than does ethane.[29] Since the parent ions are unstable, analyses were of necessity based on the fragment ions formed by loss of a methyl group. Only stepwise exchange occurs over palladium and nickel,[29, 42] but over rhodium and tungsten slight multiple exchange (which increases in extent with rising temperature) has been found.[29] It is believed that at low temperatures this multiple exchange proceeds through the α–α mechanism, and requires a larger activation energy than does stepwise exchange; the α–γ mechanism, requiring a yet higher activation energy, probably contributes over rhodium. Arrhenius parameters, based on rates of removal of "light" neopentane, are shown in Table XVI.

TABLE XVI. *Arrhenius Parameters for the Exchange of Neopentane over Evaporated Metal Films*[29]

Metal	*Temp. range (°C)*	*E(kcal. mole^{-1})*	*logA**	*logr at 50°**
W	0–45	10.3	20.2	13.2
Pd	112–174	33	30.0	7.7
Rh	0–76	14.3	23.4	13.7

*; *A* and *r* in mol. cm.$^{-2}$ sec.$^{-1}$

9.46 n-Pentane, Hexanes and Higher Homologues: Stereochemical Aspects of Hydrocarbon Exchange

The exchange of n-pentane with deuterium over palladium films[22] gives rise to distributions of deuterated pentanes resembling the propane distributions recorded in Table X, although the mean deuterium content of the exchanged molecules is slightly higher for the former (98 per cent as against 95.5 per cent). The results are contained in Table XVII: pentanes contained from two to eight deuterium atoms constitute less than 0.2 per cent of the total.

TABLE XVII. *Initial Distributions of Deuterated Pentanes from the Exchange of n-Pentane over Palladium Films*[22]

Temp. (°C)	d_1	d_9	d_{10}	d_{11}	d_{12}	*M*
83	0.9	0.2	0.9	8.5	89.5	11.8
116	1.4	0.5	1.6	10.5	86.0	11.7

The activation energy is 14.5 kcal. mole^{-1} and log*A* is 22.4 (mol. cm.$^{-2}$ sec.$^{-1}$). Over a rhodium film at 0°, pentane-d_{12} is still the major product, but it is only 28 per cent the whole, and pentane-d_2 (23.5 per cent) is also an important product: all intermediate pentanes were detected, the value of *M* being 7.1.

The results for n-hexane[22] present a similar aspect. Over a palladium film at 60°, hexane-d_{14} is 85 per cent of the initial products, whose mean deuterium content is 98 per cent (see Fig. 6). The activation energy is 16.8 kcal. mole^{-1} and log*A* is 23.7 (mol. cm.$^{-2}$ sec.$^{-1}$). Over rhodium films, hexane-d_2 is the major product between −7 and −35°, but all the deuterated hexanes are formed in small yield (Fig. 6). After being poisoned by a reaction at 50°, or by adsorbed oxygen, rhodium films are less active for multiple exchange (Fig. 6), but a film poisoned by presorbed ether shows much enhanced multiple exchange at 250°, where hexane-d_{14} is some 65 per cent of the initial products.

n-Hexane, n-heptane and 3-methylhexane may exchange all their hydrogen atoms: similar distributions of deuterated products have been recorded for nickel–kieselguhr (90–130°)[43], nickel films (130–200°),[42] nickel powder

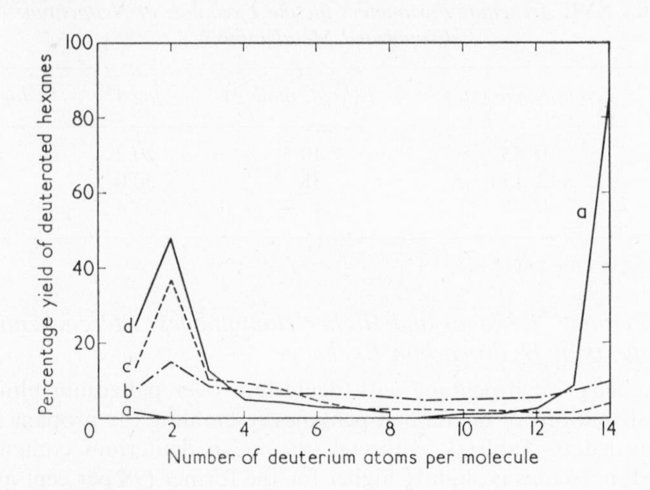

FIG. 6. Distributions of deuterated hexanes from the n-hexane-deuterium exchange reaction.[22]
(a) Over Pd film at 60°.
(b) Over Rh film at −7°.
(c) Over Rh film at −35°.
(d) At 0° over Rh film poisoned by reaction at 50°.

(156–210°)[42] and nickel–silica (86–156°).[44] Some degree of multiple exchange was observed with all these forms of nickel, and this has been found to increase with the degree of sintering (and hence with increasing particle size) in the case of the nickel–silica catalysts, which were characterized by the magnetic technique described in Chapter 3. Results obtained with these three hydrocarbons using palladium–alumina[45] at about 150° closely resemble those found with the higher particle size form of nickel–silica, but it shows much more multiple exchange between 0 and 60°. 2,3-Dimethylbutane also exchanges all its hydrogen atoms over a nickel film at 200°, but with 3,3-dimethylhexane, 2,2,3-trimethylbutane and 3,3-dimethylpentane, the maximum numbers of hydrogen atoms exchangeable at one residence are respectively seven, seven and five. Thus while the point of attachment of the hydrocarbon to the surface may migrate freely past a secondary or tertiary carbon atom, it is effectively halted by a quaternary carbon atom. These findings, therefore, substantiate the results obtained with neopentane[29, 42] and confirm that α–β exchange is the predominant mechanism.

Very complete exchange of n-heptane occurs over rhodium–alumina at 100 and 150°.[45] The species containing fourteen to sixteen deuterium atoms account for about 95 per cent of the products. An interesting effect arises when n-heptane and ethyl butyl ether are exchanged simultaneously. The ether reduces the rate of the heptane exchange (see Chapter 10) but also affects the distribution, in that a broad peak having its maximum at $C_7H_7D_9$ appears, and the exchange is therefore less complete. The effect was found to persist in some degree in a subsequent run in which some of the adsorbed ether had remained from the previous experiment, but complete removal of the ether restored the normal behaviour.

(+)3-Methylhexane racemizes during exchange.[42–45] Over nickel–kieselguhr[43] the rate of racemization is about the same whether hydrogen or deuterium is used, and the rate expression at 122° is

$$r \propto P_{\mathrm{MH}}^{0.33} P_{\mathrm{H_2}}^{-0.6}.$$

The activation energy is 26 kcal. mole^{-1} between 103 and 154°, and the dissociative adsorption of the hydrocarbon has been suggested as the slow step. Over the several forms of nickel used, the ratio of the rates of exchange and racemization varies from 1.1 to 1.9,[42] and over palladium–alumina and palladium films between 110° and 200°, the values range between 0.9 and 1.3. The higher values tend to be found at lower temperatures.[44, 45] A rhodium film at 100° gave the high value of 3.1. It thus appears that nearly every molecule in which the tertiary hydrogen is exchanged (and this is, of course, the most reactive one), undergoes an inversion of configuration. The generally accepted mechanisms do not accommodate this possibility, and it has been stressed than an intermediate in which the configuration about the tertiary carbon atom is planar is vital. The structure of the proposed intermediate has been represented[1, 44, 45] as

```
         C                        C
         |                        |
   C     C                  C     C•
    \   //\                  \   / \
     C     C····     ⇌        C     C····      (k)
     |                        ||
     *                        **
```

but the manner of its formation has not been made clear.

9.47 *Cyclic Hydrocarbons*

Instructive information has resulted from studies of the exchange of cyclic hydrocarbons with deuterium. The exchange and hydrogenation of cyclopropane occur at comparable rates over a rhodium film at −100°,[47] but over pumice-supported platinum the exchange is much the slower reaction at and above room temperature.[48] Ethylcyclobutane exchanges all its hydrogen atoms over evaporated nickel at 150°, but here also quantitative study is rendered difficult by the simultaneous occurrence of ring fission.[42]

The exchange of cyclopentane has been studied over evaporated films of rhodium,[47] palladium,[47] nickel[42] and over palladium–alumina[42] and nickel–silica.[44] Table XVII gives some kinetic parameters for the first two of these metals.

TABLE XVIII. *Kinetic Parameters for the Exchange of cyclopentane over Evaporated Metal Films*[47]

Metal	*Temp. range* (°C)	*E*(*kcal. mole*$^{-1}$)	log*A* (*mol. cm.*$^{-2}$ *sec.*$^{-1}$)	*M*
Rh	−85	—	—	1.86
Pd	0–37	14.2	22.7	4.47 (0°C)
				5.71 (37°C)

Over rhodium at −85°, no species containing more than five deuterium atoms accounts for more than 0.5 per cent of the exchanged hydrocarbon. Fig. 7 shows some of the distributions obtained with palladium catalysts: the similarities are quite evident, and the sharp decrease in the yield from cyclopentane-d_5 to cyclopentane-d_6 is marked in each case. This break

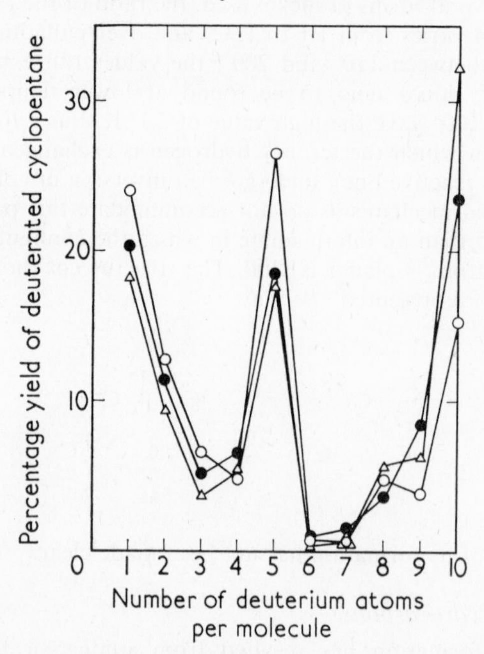

FIG. 7. Distributions of deuterated cyclopentanes from cyclopentane–deuterium exchange over palladium catalysts.[45, 47]

○ Over Pd film at 0°.
△ Over Pd film at 25°.
● Over Pd–Al_2O_3 at 50°.

becomes less distinct with increasing temperature when palladium–alumina, rhodium–alumina[46] and nickel catalysts are used; it is detected over nickel–silica at 68°,[44] but is entirely absent from the distribution arising from reactions over a nickel film at 150 and 200°.[42]

This break in the distribution is accounted for as follows. Cyclopentane is assumed to be chemisorbed as a cyclopentyl radical: multiple exchange may then occur by a mechanism akin to that proposed for ethane, with the point of attachment circulating the ring, but only on the same side as the original point of attachment. Five hydrogen atoms are readily substituted in this way. However, the amounts of the cyclopentanes containing six to ten deuterium atoms are too large to be accounted for by the readsorption of molecules which have suffered exchange at one side. There clearly must be some mechanism whereby an adsorbed molecule may "turn over" in the period of one residence to permit exchange on the other side. The fact that the break in the distribution exists, and that the proportions of the more highly deuterated species increase with temperature, show that the turning over process requires a higher activation energy than the normal multiple exchange.

The mechanism by which this inversion takes place is not yet certain, but it seems likely that an α,d-diabsorbed radical is the intermediate. The inversion process may then be represented as:

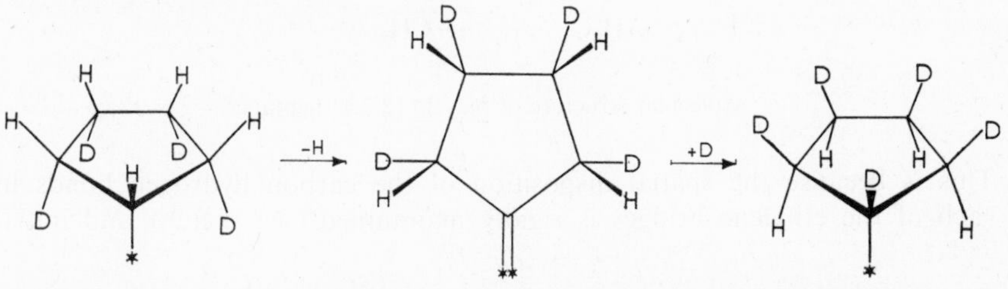

All the hydrogen atoms of methylcyclopentane are exchangeable in one residence on nickel films.[42] In the product distribution of the species arising from the exchange of 1,1-dimethylcyclopentane over palladium–alumina at 60°, there is a significant break between the d_4- and the d_5-species.[45] This implies that four hydrogen atoms on one side are easily exchanged, and that, as above, difficulty is experienced in inverting the molecule: no more than eight deuterium atoms are initially introduced into this molecule.

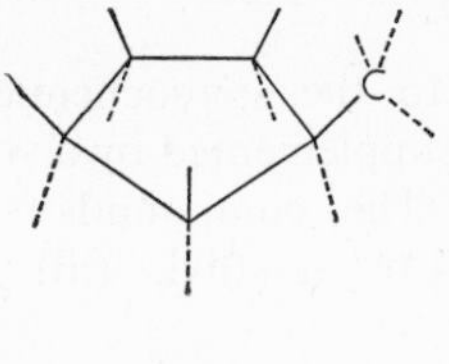

The results obtained with methylcyclopentane over palladium–alumina at 50° are especially revealing.[45] The product distribution shows very sharp breaks between the d_4- and the d_5-species and also between the d_8- and the d_9-species. Consideration of the molecular geometry (see diagram below) shows that there are four hydrogen atoms on the same side of the ring as the methyl group (solid lines): now on steric grounds it is impossible for the point of attachment to transfer from one of these positions to the methyl group and so initial adsorption by fission of a carbon–hydrogen bond *cis* to the methyl group can lead at most to the d_4-species. However, there is no such steric objection to transferring the point of attachment from a position *trans* to the methyl group to the methyl group itself, so that initial adsorption on the side opposite to the methyl group may lead to the d_8-species (dotted lines). A combination of these processes involving the inversion of the molecule leads to species containing from nine to twelve deuterium atoms, and indeed the latter is the most abundant exchanged species. Bicyclo[2.2.1]heptane (whose molecular structure is shown below) exchanges only two of its hydrogens at one residence.[45]

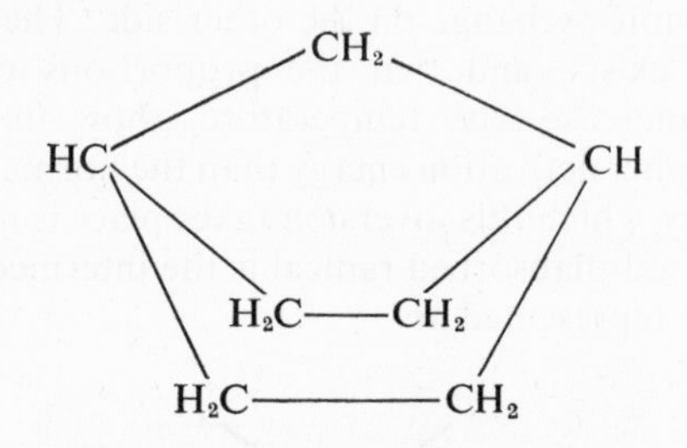

Molecular structure of bicyclo [2.2.1] heptane.

This is because the spatial disposition of the carbon–hydrogen bonds in each of the ethylene bridges is rigidly maintained (see sketch), and initial

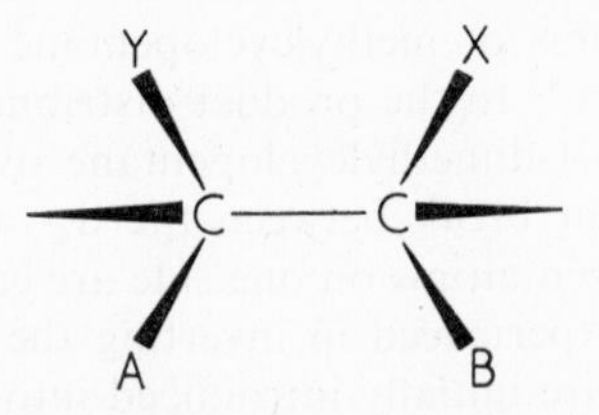

Spatial disposition of carbon-hydrogen bonds.

adsorption at point *A* can only be followed by second-point adsorption at *B*, and not at *X*, for the distance *A* . . . *X* would be prohibitively great. Hence only the hydrogen atoms in positions *A* and *B* (or *X* and *Y*) are readily exchangeable.

This kind of approach to the stereochemical aspects of hydrocarbon exchange has recently been supplemented by a study of the exchange of some polymethylcyclopentanes.[49] The compounds studied were the (i) 1,1,3-trimethyl, (ii) *trans*-1,1,3,4-tetramethyl, (iii) *cis*-1,1,3,4-tetramethyl, (iv)

1,1,3,3-tetramethyl and (v) 1,1,3,3,4-pentamethyl derivatives of cyclopentane. Table XIX shows the major initial products expected on the basis of the foregoing arguments, together with those observed in their reaction with deuterium over palladium films between 40 and 80°. The amounts of products not reported totalled less than 1 per cent. The agreement between prediction and observation is excellent.

TABLE XIX. *Expected and Observed Initial Products from the Exchange of Polymethylcyclopentanes with Deuterium over Palladium Films*[49]

Compound	*Expected major initial products*	*Observed products*								
		d_1	d_2	d_5	d_6	d_7	d_9	d_{10}	d_{11}	d_{12}
1,1,3-trimethyl	d_1, d_2, d_7, d_{10}	2.4	1.4	—	1.0	4.8	8.2	82.2	—	—
trans-1,1,3,4-tetramethyl	d_1, d_5, d_{12}	5.5	—	6.5	—	—	—	<2	7.5	80.5
cis-1,1,3,4-tetramethyl	d_1, d_{10}, d_{12}	<2	—	—	—	—	—	<2	7.5	92.5
1,1,3,3-tetramethyl	d_1, d_2	43	57	—	—	—	—	—	—	—
1,1,3,3,4-pentamethyl	d_1, d_5, d_6	50	1	5	44	<2	—	—	—	—

Considerable attention has been paid to the exchange of cyclohexane. This reaction has been studied on evaporated films of tungsten,[47, 50] molybdenum,[50] nickel,[42, 47] rhodium,[45, 47] palladium,[45, 47] and platinum,[47] and also on nickel powder,[42] nickel–silica,[44] palladium–alumina[45] and platinum foil.[51] Reported kinetic parameters are presented in Table XX, and, except for the values of *M*, are based on the rate of disappearance of "light" cyclohexane. There is a

TABLE XX. *Kinetic Parameters for the Exchange of cyclohexane over Evaporated Metal Films*

Metal	*Temp. range (°C)*	*E(kcal. mole⁻¹)*	*logA*	*logr at 0°C**	*M*	*Ref.*
W	−69–−48	11	23.4*	14.6	2.1 (−66°); 1.5 (−48°)	47
W	84–111	7.9	8.16†	—	—	50
Mo	75–102	6.2	6.25†	—	—	50
Ni	−35–0	10.8	21.9*	13.3	1.2	47
Rh	−48–0	10.4	22.5*	14.2	4.8 (−48°); 3.8 (0°)	47
Pd	18–82	13.0	21.4*	11.0	6.5 (18.5°); 10.4 (81°)	47
Pt	0–31	12	22.5*	12.9	2.1 (0°); 2.5 (31°)	47

*; A and r in mol. cm.$^{-2}$ sec.$^{-1}$: †; A in mol. (10 mg.)$^{-1}$ sec.$^{-1}$.

Metal	*Order in C_6H_{12}*	*Order in D_2*	*Ref.*
Mo	1.0	−0.6	50
Pd	0.9	−1.0	47

tendency, as in ethane exchange, for the body-centred cubic metals tungsten and molybdenum to show low activation energies. Cyclohexane is weakly adsorbed, and deuterium quite strongly.

Distributions arising from the reactions over rhodium and palladium films at several temperatures are shown in Figs. 8 and 9. Significant breaks in

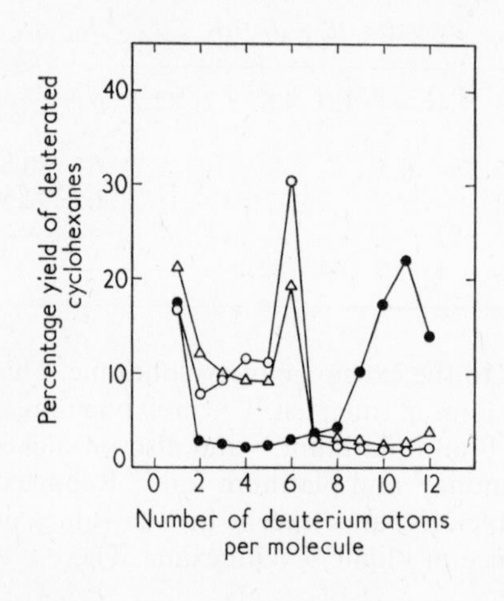

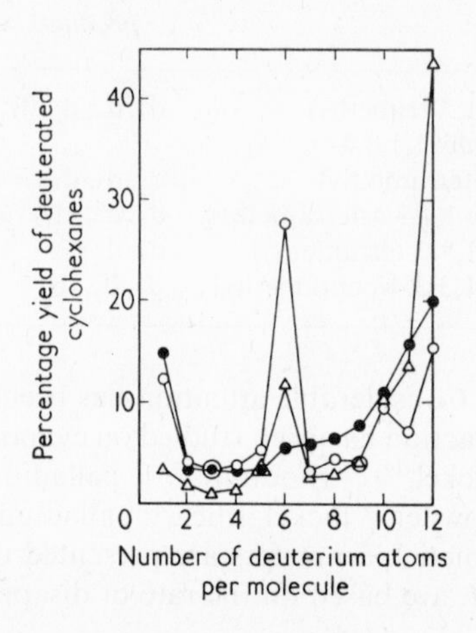

FIG. 8 (Left). Distributions of deuterated cyclohexanes from the exchange of cyclohexane over rhodium films.[45, 47]

○, −48°; △, −28°; ●, 100°.

FIG. 9 (Right). Distributions of deuterated cyclohexanes from the exchange of cyclohexane over palladium films.[45, 47]

○, 18.5°; △, 44°; ●, 150°.

the distributions occur between the d_6- and the d_7-species at temperatures below about 50°, but are absent at higher temperatures: as with cyclopentane, the sharpness of the break decreases, and the yields of the more highly deuterated species tend to increase, with rising temperature. The distribution found from the reaction over palladium–alumina at 60° shows a slight break, but there is none at 170°.[45] Similar results have been obtained with nickel powder[42] and nickel–silica;[44] oriented and unoriented nickel films at −34° show little tendency to cause multiple exchange, and no products containing more than four and five deuterium atoms respectively are found.[47] There is no break in the distribution obtained over tungsten at −69°,[47] and it has been claimed that there is no evidence of breaks in the distributions found over tungsten and molybdenum films at much higher temperatures:[50] the value of this latter work is, however, uncertain because of the low deuterium content of the "deuterium" used. Methyl- and 1,1-dimethylcyclohexane behave analogously to the parent compounds.[42] In the case of nickel–silica catalysts, multiple exchange is favoured by large nickel particles, as was the case with the straight-chain hydrocarbons.

The interpretation of these results follows closely that advanced in the case of cyclopentane. The often-found breaks in the distributions strongly suggested that all six hydrogen atoms on one side of the cyclohexane ring are readily exchangeable by repeated second-point adsorption. Inversion of the ring to permit exchange of the other six hydrogen atoms is energetically difficult, but takes place with increasing ease as the temperature is raised: an α,α-diadsorbed radical may again intervene. Distributions have been described in terms of $\mathscr{P}$ values by appropriate modification of the general theory outlined earlier for ethane, and it appears that all metals except nickel require one high value of $\mathscr{P}$ and one low value to describe their distributions.[45] Two low values may be required by nickel, but one of these is unnecessary when oriented films are used. The use of (110) oriented rhodium films leads to a decrease in the contribution of the process having a low value of $\mathscr{P}$: this is to be contrasted with the apparent effect of orientation on nickel in ethane exchange.[26]

Cycloheptane and cyclo-octane both exchange all their hydrogen atoms with ease:[45] at about 60° and above, no breaks in the distributions corresponding to half-exchange are observed and there is very considerable multiple exchange. These molecules, therefore, seem to invert with a greater facility than do cyclopentane and cyclohexane, the reason probably being that their rings are sufficiently flexible to admit adjacent (α,β) two-point adsorption on opposite sides of the ring.

9.48 Influence of the Nature of the Metal on the Course of Exchange Reactions

The object of this Section is to summarize the role of the metal in determining the course of exchange reactions, as revealed by the foregoing results. Certain broad patterns of behaviour are suggested, and it is gratifying that there is a large measure of consistency between results given by evaporated films and supported catalysts of the same metal. This lends confidence to the view that the basic catalytic properties of a metal are shown in whatever form of preparation is employed. The reactions of ethane and higher hydrocarbons (both straight chain and cyclic) not containing a quaternary carbon atom over a given metal have some features in common, and the behavioural patterns may be described in terms of these common features. The following remarks, therefore, have regard to the efficiency of multiple exchange by the mechanism of repeated second-point (α,β) adsorption.

The outstanding feature shown by all the relevant hydrocarbons is that multiple exchange is most extensive and most efficient on the noble metals of Group VIII (Rh, Pd, Ir and Pt). These are the metals which show the highest percentage *d*-character, and what is perhaps more relevant, the lowest heats of adsorption of hydrogen and of ethylene. There are some differences between these four metals: palladium, which is often the least *active* metals of this group, often shows the most efficient multiple exchange, while on platinum and rhodium multiple exchange is sometimes less extensive than on the other metals. Cobalt and nickel show less extensive and less efficient multiple exchange than the other Group VIII metals. Metals in Groups IVA, VA and VIA have little tendency to show multiple exchange, and this may be at least partly ascribed to their not possessing the face-centred cubic structure. Empirical correlations between activity and efficiency in multiple exchange, and percentage *d*-character show some success, although much more information is needed before any of the proposed correlations is regarded as established. The outline of a general pattern is, however, emerging.

9.5 The Exchange Reaction between Light and Deuterated Hydrocarbons

It is appropriate to conclude with a short description of the few investigations which have been made between light and deuterated hydrocarbons of the same structure. It may be said at once that this approach to the problem of the mechanism of surface reactions is less informative than the more widely used method described above. The process if unaccompanied by decomposition of the hydrocarbon may be formulated as, for example,

$$\left.\begin{array}{l} CH_4 + 2* \rightarrow \underset{*}{CH_3} + \underset{*}{H} \\ CD_4 + 2* \rightarrow \underset{*}{CD_3} + \underset{*}{D} \end{array}\right\} \rightarrow CH_3D + CHD_3 + 4*. \qquad (1)$$

Over nickel–kieselguhr at 184°,[11] this process is faster than the methane–deuterium reaction, and has an activation energy of 19 kcal. mole^{-1}. A more detailed investigation[52] using a nickel–20 per cent chromia catalyst between 100 and 255° has found poisoning due to decomposition at all temperatures, and an activation energy of 20.8 kcal. mole^{-1} was recorded. CH_2D_2 and CHD_3 were formed according to a first-order rate law, and this suggests that CH_2D_2 is formed, not from CHD_3 and CH_3D, but by an independent process, slower than that formulated above, and perhaps involving methylene radicals:

$$\left.\begin{array}{l} CH_4 + 4* \rightarrow \underset{**}{CH_2} + \underset{*}{2H} \\ CD_4 + 4* \rightarrow \underset{**}{CD_2} + \underset{*}{2D} \end{array}\right\} \rightarrow 2CH_2D_2 + 8*. \qquad (m)$$

The exchange reaction between n-butane and a mixture of deuterated butanes has been studied over the same series of supported platinum catalysts as that with which the butane–deuterium reaction was investigated.[28] The results are given in Table XXI. Only for two catalysts (numbers 5 and 9) is the activity for the former reaction the greater. There is no apparent correlation between any of the kinetic parameters and any property of the catalysts, but a reasonable compensation effect between activation energy and the log of the frequency factor exists.

TABLE XXI. *Kinetic Parameters for the Exchange between* n-*Butane and Deuterated Butanes over Supported-platinum Catalysts*[28] (see Table XIV for details of these)

Catalyst number	*Temp. range (°C)*	*E(kcal. mole⁻¹)*	*logA**	*logr at 100°C**
1	50–150	7.0	3.7	−0.4
2	50–150	8.5	4.7	−0.3
3	75–200	5.6	2.4	−0.9
4	100–200	4.7	1.6	−1.2
5	75–144	20.1	10.6	0.4
6	75–144	18.2	10.4	0.3
7	75–319	5.3	2.0	−1.1
8	230–320	14.3	5.5	−2.9
9	230–230	13.5	4.6	−3.4

* Rate in % exchange $g.^{-1}$ $sec.^{-1}$.

REFERENCES

1. R. L. Burwell, *Chem. Rev.* **57,** 895 (1957).
2. C. Kemball, *J. Res. Inst. Catalysis, Hokkaido Univ.* **4,** 222 (1957).
3. P. G. Wright, P. G. Ashmore and C. Kemball, *Trans. Faraday Soc.* **54,** 1692 (1958).
4. B. M. W. Trapnell, *Trans. Faraday Soc.* **52,** 1618 (1956).
5. R. Coekelbergs, J. Decot, A. Frennet, A. Jelli and G. Lienard, Proc. 2nd International Congress on Catalysis (Editions Technip, Paris, 1961). **1,** 427.
6. A. Cimino, M. Boudart and H. S. Taylor, *J. Phys. Chem.* **58,** 796 (1954).
7. A. K. Galwey and C. Kemball, *Trans. Faraday Soc.* **55,** 1959 (1959).
8. C. Kemball, *Bull. Soc. chim. belges* **67**· 373 (1958); *Adv. Catalysis* **11,** 223 (1959); *Proc. Chem. Soc.* 264 (1960).
9. T. I. Taylor, In "Catalysis", edited by P. H. Emmett (Reinhold, New York 1957), **5,** 257.
10. K. Morikawa, W. S. Benedict and H. S. Taylor, *J. Amer. Chem. Soc.* **58,** 1795 (1936).
11. K. Morikawa, W. S. Benedict and H. S. Taylor, *J. Amer. Chem. Soc.* **57,** 592 (1935); **58,** 1445 (1936).
12. K. Morikawa, N. R. Trenner and H. S. Taylor, *J. Amer. Chem. Soc.* **59,** 1103 (1937).
13. L. G. Smith, *Phys. Rev.* **51,** 263 (1937).
14. J. A. Hipple, *Phys. Rev.* **53,** 530 (1938).
15. A. J. B. Robertson, "Mass Spectrometry" (Methuen, London 1954).
16. W. J. Dunning, *Quart. Rev.* **9,** 23 (1955).
17. A. W. Tickner, W. A. Bryce and F. P. Lossing, *J. Amer. Chem. Soc.* **73,** 5001 (1951); *J. Chem. Phys.* **19,** 1254 (1951); **20,** 537 (1952).
18. G. C. Bond, In "Applied Mass Spectrometry" (Institute of Petroleum, London, 1954), p. 91.

19. M. W. Evans, N. Bauer and J. Y. Beach, *J. Chem. Phys.* **14,** 701 (1946); J. Turkevich, L. Friedman, E. Solomon and F. M. Wrightson, *J. Amer. Chem. Soc.* **70,** 2638 (1948); D. O. Schissler, S. O. Thompson and J. Turkevich, *Discuss. Faraday Soc.* **10,** 46 (1951); M. Krauss, A. L. Wahrhaftig and H. Eyring, *Ann. Rev. Nuclear Sci.* **5,** 241 (1955).
20. J. Addy, M.Sc. thesis. Leeds (1956).
21. D. P. Stevenson and C. D. Wagner, *J. Chem. Phys.* **19,** 11 (1951); F. E. Condon, H. L. McMurry and V. Thornton, *Ibid.* **19,** 1010 (1951); F. E. Condon, *J. Amer. Chem. Soc.* **73,** 4675 (1951).
22. F. G. Gault and C. Kemball, *Trans. Faraday Soc.* **57,** 1771 (1961).
23. G. C. Bond, *Trans. Faraday Soc.* **52,** 1235 (1956).
24. J. N. Wilson, J. W. Otvos, D. P. Stevenson and C. D. Wagner, *Ind. Eng. Chem.* **45,** 1480 (1953).
25. C. Kemball, *Proc. Roy. Soc.* **A207,** 539 (1951).
26. J. R. Anderson and C. Kemball, *Proc. Roy. Soc.* **A233,** 361 (1954).
27. C. Kemball, *Proc. Roy. Soc.* **A233,** 377 (1954).
28. C. G. Myers, D. J. Sibbett and F. G. Ciapetta, *J. Phys. Chem.* **63,** 1032 (1959).
29. C. Kemball, *Trans. Faraday Soc.* **50,** 1344 (1954).
30. J. Addy and G. C. Bond, *Trans. Faraday Soc.* **53,** 368, 383, 388 (1957).
31. S. O. Thompson, J. Turkevich and A. P. Irsa, *J. Amer. Chem. Soc.* **73,** 5213 (1951).
32. C. Kemball, *Proc. Roy. Soc.* **A216,** 376 (1953).
33. B. M. W. Trapnell, *Quart. Rev.* **8,** 404 (1954).
34. M. C. Markham, M. C. Wall and K. J. Laidler, *J. Phys. Chem.* **57,** 321 (1953).
35. K. Miyahara, *J. Res. Inst. Catalysis, Hokkaido Univ.* **4,** 143 (1956); **4,** 177 (1957).
36. L. L. van Reijen and G. C. A. Schuit, *Bull. Soc. chim. belges* **67,** 489 (1958).
37. A. Farkas, *Trans. Faraday Soc.* **36,** 522 (1940).
38. L. N. Kauder and T. I. Taylor, *Science* **113,** 238 (1951).
39. C. Kemball and I. Woodward, *Trans. Faraday Soc.* **56,** 138 (1960).
40. J. R. Anderson, *Adv. Catalysis* **9,** 86 (1957); C. Kemball, *Ibid.* **9,** 87 (1957).
41. W. M. H. Sachtler, G. J. H. Dorgelo and W. van der Knapp, *J. Chim. phys.* **51,** 491 (1954).
42. H. C. Rowlinson, R. L. Burwell and R. H. Tuxworth, *J. Phys. Chem.* **59,** 225 (1955).
43. R. L. Burwell and W. S. Briggs, *J. Amer. Chem. Soc.* **74,** 5096 (1952).
44. R. L. Burwell and R. H. Tuxworth, *J. Phys. Chem.* **60,** 1043 (1956).
45. R. L. Burwell, B. K. C. Shim and H. C. Rowlinson, *J. Amer. Chem. Soc.* **79,** 5142 (1957).
46. J. M. Forrest, R. L. Burwell and B. K. C. Shim, *J. Phys. Chem.* **63,** 1016 (1959).
47. C. Kemball and J. R. Anderson, *Proc. Roy. Soc.* **A226,** 472 (1954).
48. G. C. Bond and J. Turkevich, *Trans. Faraday Soc.* **50,** 1335 (1954).
49. J. J. Rooney, F. G. Gault and C. Kemball, *Proc. Chem. Soc.* 407 (1960).
50. T. Hayakawa and T. Suguira, *Bull. Chem. Soc. Japan* **31,** 180, 186, 190 (1958).
51. R. K. Greenhalgh and M. Polanyi, *Trans. Faraday Soc.* **35,** 520 (1939).
52. M. M. Wright and H. S. Taylor, *Canad. J. Res.* **B27,** 303 (1949).

Chapter 10

Exchange Reactions of Other Molecules with Deuterium

10.1 The Exchange Reaction between Deuterium and Water

The exchange of "hydrogen" atoms between molecular "hydrogen" and water has been studied with both liquid water and with water vapour, chiefly using the system $H_2O + D_2$; the deuterium content of the hydrogen has sometimes been quite low (~5 per cent). The progress of the reaction has been followed by measurements of the change (a) in the density of the water, by micropyknometry, and (b) in the thermal conductivity of the hydrogen. Simultaneous measurements of the rate of *para*-hydrogen or *ortho*-deuterium conversion have also been achieved.[1, 2]

Equilibrium is attained in one to two hours at room temperature when palladium or platinum black is used in liquid water.[3] This, combined with the use of platinum wire in the vapour phase at higher temperatures, has enabled the positions of the relevant equilibria to be determined experimentally between about 0 and 450°, and the values so obtained compare very satisfactorily with those calculated by statistical mechanics.[3] These equilibria may be defined by reference to the following three basic processes:

$$H_2 + D_2 \rightleftharpoons 2HD \quad \ldots\ldots \quad K_1$$
$$H_2O + D_2O \rightleftharpoons 2HDO \quad \ldots\ldots \quad K_2$$
$$H_2O + HD \rightleftharpoons HDO + H_2 \quad \ldots \quad K_3$$

The equilibrium constants for other systems may then be expressed as combinations of K_1, K_2 and K_3, viz.

$$H_2O + D_2 \rightleftharpoons D_2O + H_2 \quad \ldots \quad K_4 = K_3^2 K_1 K_2^{-1}$$
$$H_2O + D_2 \rightleftharpoons HDO + HD \quad \ldots \quad K_5 = K_3 K_1$$
$$HDO + HD \rightleftharpoons D_2O + H_2 \quad \ldots \quad K_6 = K_3 K_2^{-1}$$
$$D_2O + HD \rightleftharpoons HDO + D2 \quad \ldots \quad K_7 = K_2 K_3^{-1} K_1^{-1}.$$

The temperature dependence of the constants K_1, K_2 and K_3 is given by the following relations, the water being in the liquid state:

$$\log K_1 = \frac{-155}{2.303RT} + 0.6276 \qquad (1)$$

$$\log K_2 = \frac{-162}{2.303RT} + 0.6231 \tag{2}$$

$$\log K_3 = \frac{+750}{2.303RT} - 0.1335. \tag{3}$$

The heat terms represent the zero-point energy differences between the two sides of the equilibria. K_3 is 3.05 at 20° for liquid water, but 2.67 for water vapour.

The rate of this exchange is much faster when the water is present as vapour than when the catalyst is immersed in liquid water: with platinized platinum foil at 18°, the rates differ by a factor of fourteen.[4] The mechanisms in the two cases are not necessarily the same, so results obtained with each system will be considered in turn.

Over platinum wire at 236°, the exchange obeys the first-order rate law. The rates of *para*-hydrogen and *ortho*-deuterium conversion in the presence of 10 mm. water vapour are eight to ten times faster than the exchange between 186 and 327°,[2] although the factor is only 1.8 over platinum foil at 18°.[4] It is at once evident that the dissociation and recombination of the "hydrogen" cannot determine the rate of the exchange. Water vapour inhibits *para*-hydrogen conversion: at about 185°, 10 mm. of water vapour causes a ten-fold decrease in the rate, but this effect is readily reversible. Between 140 and 248°, the conversion rate is proportional to the *para*-hydrogen pressure and to some negative power of the water vapour pressure: the inhibiting power of the water decreases with increasing temperature.[2] Similar inhibition has been detected at room temperature. The activation energy is also affected, as may be seen from Table I. The rate of the exchange

TABLE I. *Activation Energies for Water Exchange and* Para-*Hydrogen Conversion over Platinum Wire*[2]

Temp. range (°C)	$P_{p\text{-}H_2}$(*mm.*)	P_{D_2}(*mm.*)	P_{H_2O}(*mm.*)	*E*(*kcal. mole*$^{-1}$)
142–217	20	—	—	6.4
186–322	20	—	10	10.8
252–535	—	20	10	13.5

is proportional to deuterium pressure and independent of water vapour pressure at 296°, although inhibition by the latter at pressures above about 5 mm. is apparent at room temperature. On a platinum wire activated by flashing or by heating in hydrogen to 300°, very strong and irreversible adsorption of water occurs, and the activation energy for *para*-hydrogen conversion with 4.5 mm. of water vapour is raised to 13.7 kcal. mole^{-1}.

The following mechanisms are suggested for the room temperature reaction over platinum foil and for the high temperature reaction over platinum wire. For exchange to occur, it is probably necessary for water to be dissociatively adsorbed, and so the reaction may be represented as

$$\left.\begin{array}{l} H_2O + 2* \rightleftarrows \underset{*}{HO} + \underset{*}{H} \\ D_2 \quad + 2* \rightleftarrows 2\underset{*}{D} \end{array}\right\} \rightarrow HDO + HD + 4*. \qquad (a)$$

An alternative possible mode of adsorption of water involves the donation of an electron pair to the collective vacant *d*-band of the metal:

$$H_2O + * \rightarrow \underset{\underset{*}{\downarrow}}{H\ddot{O}H}. \qquad (b)$$

This second path probably leads to a more strongly adsorbed state. Now at room temperature, variation of the water vapour-pressure affects the rates of exchange and of *para*-hydrogen conversion almost equally: both reactions must therefore proceed on that fraction of the surface not covered by water strongly adsorbed as in (b). The objection to mechanism (a) is that if the slow step is taken to be the reaction of HO with D, the rate should depend on the one-half power of the deuterium pressure, and not on its first power, as observed. If the dissociative adsorption of the water were rate-limiting, the deuterium would inhibit. A possible explanation is that a Rideal–Eley mechanism is operating:

$$\left.\begin{array}{l} H_2O + 2* \rightarrow \underset{*}{HO} \quad + \underset{*}{H} \\ \underset{*}{HO} \quad + D_2 \rightarrow HDO + \underset{*}{D} \\ \underset{*}{H} \quad + \underset{*}{D} \rightarrow HD \quad + 2* \end{array}\right\}. \qquad (c)$$

This would require first-order dependence on deuterium pressure.

At higher temperatures, the dependence of the two rates on water vapour-pressure is not the same, and hence the exchange reaction cannot involve sites not covered by water. A possible process is

$$\underset{\underset{*}{\downarrow}}{H\ddot{O}H} + D_2 \rightarrow \underset{\underset{*}{\downarrow}}{H\ddot{O}D} + HD. \qquad (d)$$

Thus while mechanisms (a) and (c) could only lead to stepwise replacement of the hydrogen atoms of the water, (d) could lead to multiple exchange. The application of mass-spectrometry to this system would be illuminating. No measurements of the relative activities of metals for this reaction have yet been reported.

Exchange and *para*-hydrogen conversion occur slowly, and at equal rates, over platinized platinum foil immersed in liquid water at 18°.[4] The diffusion of "hydrogen" through the water is probably the slow step in each case. In decinormal acid at 0° with platinum black, the order in deuterium is[1] 0.85, and this further suggests diffusion limitation. Studies of this type yield little information on the detailed mechanism, but the observations[1] that the rate is four times faster in decinormal acid than in decinormal alkali and that the activation energies differ, suggest the ionic species in the solution play some role. A possible mechanism is:

$$\left.\begin{array}{l} D_2 + 2* \xrightarrow{\text{slow}} 2\underset{*}{D} \\ \\ H_3O^+ + \underset{*}{D} \xrightarrow{\text{fast}} H_2DO^+ + \underset{*}{H} \end{array}\right\}. \quad \text{(e)}$$

10.2 The Exchange Reactions between Deuterium and Alcohols

Ethanol, n-butanol and 2-ethylhexanol have been found to exchange their hydroxylic hydrogen atoms at comparable rates over platinum foil at room temperature: the rates are somewhat greater than for water exchange, and the rate of simultaneous *para*-hydrogen conversion is in each case about twice the rate of the exchange.[4] Platinum black catalyses the reaction between deuterium and 98 per cent ethanolic decimolar potassium hydroxide at room temperature. Orders of reaction in deuterium of 0.5 and 0.6, and activation energies of 10.2 and 8.5 kcal. mole^{-1} near room temperature, have been recorded.[1, 5, 6]

The vapour-phase reaction between deuterium and various alcohols has been studied over evaporated films of a number of metals.[7] In confirmation of the earlier work, it was found that the monodeuterated alcohol was invariably the most abundant product: indeed, with methanol over nickel, iron and palladium films at 0°, methanol-d$_1$ was the only product observed, but with these metals at higher temperatures, and with rhodium at 0°,

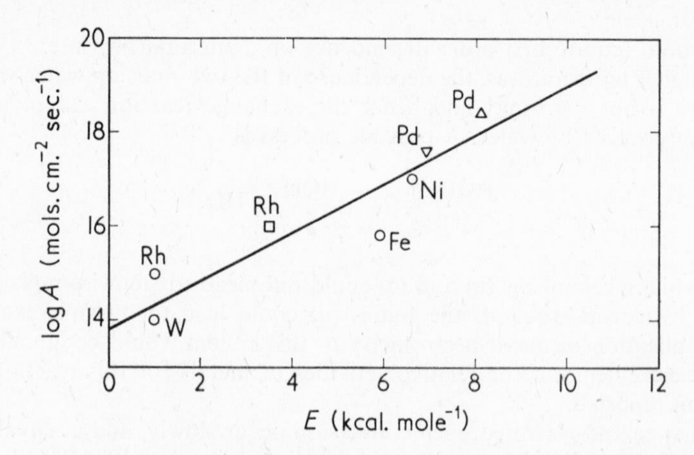

Fig. 1. Compensation effect in the exchange of alcohols over evaporated metal films.[7] The exchanged atoms are the hydroxylic hydrogens, except for isopropanol, where the methylenic hydrogen is exchanged.

○ CH_3OH; □ C_2H_5OH; △ iso-C_3H_7OH; ▽ t-C_4H_9OH.

tungsten at 88° and silver at 262°, all products up to methanol-d_4 were found. The activation energy for replacement of the methyl hydrogen atoms was 8 to 10 kcal. $mole^{-1}$ larger than for hydroxyl exchange. Similar results were found for ethanol; over rhodium, very little exchange of the ethyl hydrogen atoms occurred at 0 to 40°, although extensive exchange took place at 100°. Isopropanol and t-butanol were briefly studied. Activation energies and frequency factors for the exchange are shown in the form of a compensation effect in Fig. 1. The rate expression for the exchange of methanol over nickel was found to be

$$r \propto P_{CH_3OH}^{0.6} P_{D_2}^{0.4}. \tag{4}$$

Poisoning by decomposition products (probably carbon monoxide) was frequently encountered.

The mode of adsorption and the mechanism of the exchange are not entirely clear. As with water, two types of adsorption are conceivable:

$$CH_3OH + 2* \rightarrow CH_3\underset{*}{O} + \underset{*}{H} \tag{f}$$

and

$$CH_3OH + * \rightarrow CH_3\underset{\overset{\downarrow}{*}}{\ddot{O}}H. \tag{g}$$

Of the two, (f) is the more likely to result in the ready exchange of the hydroxylic hydrogen atom. Exchange of the methyl hydrogen atoms must involve adsorption at the carbon atom, but whether this is an independent process, e.g.

$$CH_3OH + 2* \rightarrow \underset{*}{C}H_2OH + \underset{*}{H}, \tag{h}$$

or whether either the type (f) or (g) adsorbed states intervene, as

$$CH_3\underset{*}{O} + 2* \rightarrow \underset{*}{C}H_2\text{—}\underset{*}{O} + \underset{*}{H} \rightarrow \underset{*}{C}H_2OH + 2* \tag{i}$$

or

$$CH_3\underset{\overset{\downarrow}{*}}{\ddot{O}}H + 2* \rightarrow \underset{*}{C}H_2\text{—}\underset{\overset{\downarrow}{*}}{\ddot{O}}H + \underset{*}{H} \rightarrow \underset{*}{C}H_2OH + \underset{*}{H} + *, \tag{j}$$

is uncertain. Once the species $\underset{*}{C}H_2OH$ is formed, the exchange may proceed as for methane. The corresponding species from ethanol is $CH_3\underset{*}{C}HOH$ and once formed enables the exchange to proceed as for ethane. The activity order, based on the temperatures required to effect a rate of 1 per cent exchange $min.^{-1}$, is

$$Pt > Rh > Pd > Ni > Fe \doteqdot W > Ag;$$

this order, which is quite different from that found for ethane, throws no further light on the mechanism at the moment.

10.3 The Exchange Reactions between Deuterium and Ethers

The exchange reaction between diethyl ether vapour and deuterium over platinum foil at room temperature is more than twenty times slower than the exchange of ethanol, but the rate of simultaneous *para*-hydrogen conversion is about five times more rapid.[4] The low rate of exchange is, therefore, to be attributed to the reluctance of the ether to be chemisorbed under these conditions.

The exchange of diethyl ether has been studied over evaporated films of a number of metals.[8] The essential feature of the results is that multiple exchange is unable to propagate past the oxygen atom: thus the most highly deuterated species formed in one residence is ether-d_5. The principal results are given in Table II. Poisoning, due to products of a decomposition process,

TABLE II. *Kinetic Parameters for the Exchange of Diethyl Ether over Evaporated Metal Films*[8]

Metal	*Temp. range (°C)*	*M*	*E(kcal. mole⁻¹)**	*logA†**	*Min. temp. for poisoning (°C)*
W	12	1.17	—	—	0
Fe	165	1.25	—	—	160
Pt	14	1.75	—	—	—
Ni	62–104	1.75	28.6	29.1	104
Pd	16–63	4.0	17.9	23.8	64

* Based on disappearance of ether-d_0; †, A in mols. (10 mg.)$^{-1}$ sec.$^{-1}$.

occurred above the temperatures quoted in the last column; in the case of platinum, poisoning took place even at −8°, and rhodium films lost their activity so rapidly that little work could be done with them. The distributions, which are not given in full, show the following features.

Ni: both stepwise and multiple exchange appear to occur, in extents not dependent on temperature.

Pd: mainly multiple exchange, ether-d_5 being the principal product: no effect of temperature.

Pt: shows a mixture of stepwise and multiple exchange, and the mean deuterium number increases from 1.4 at −8° to 1.92 at 23°.

Rh: also shows both stepwise and multiple exchange, the latter being more important than it is over nickel.

W, Fe: show mainly stepwise exchange.

The exchange of ethers with deuterium has also been studied over a rhodium–alumina catalyst.[9] The difference between this catalyst and rhodium films is startling: while, as mentioned above, the films poison extremely rapidly, the supported catalyst remained active for six months, with occasional reactivation. Diethyl ether only started to decompose over this catalyst above 200°, and with higher ethers the decomposition was only slight at 150°. It was confirmed that the oxygen atom arrests the progress of multiple exchange: at 150°, both n- and isopropyl ethers exchanged at most seven hydrogen atoms in one residence, while with ethyl butyl ether maxima appeared in the distributions corresponding to the exchange of five and nine hydrogen atoms. Ethers are strongly chemisorbed, probably by electron pair donation from the oxygen atom, and the subsequent exchange of hydrocarbons is thereby poisoned, but the effect is removable by hydrogen treatment at 150°. The order of poisoning efficiency is

dioxan > tetrahydrofuran > straight-chain ethers.

In the simultaneous exchange of ethyl butyl ether and n-heptane, the exchange of the latter is six times slower than exchange of the ether; in a following experiment, the rate of exchange of heptane in the absence of the ether was twice its previous value, and after hydrogen treatment at 150°, thirty times its previous value. The distribution of deuterated ethers was unaffected by the presence of the heptane. Tetrahydrofuran reduced the rate of cyclopentane exchange by a factor of 10^3.

Methyl amyl ether yielded a large amount of a monodeuterated product, through stepwise exchange on the methyl group: there was no maximum at the ether-d_3 (corresponding to complete exchange on the methyl group), but a maximum occurred at the ether-d_{11} due to complete exchange of the amyl group. The four *cis*-hydrogen atoms of tetrahydrofuran exchanged readily, but more completely deuterated products were also formed indicating that inversion (as with cyclopentane) is possible.

10.4 The Exchange Reaction between Ammonia and Deuterium

This reaction occurs on promoted iron[10] and on rhenium[11] at temperatures significantly below that at which the decomposition of ammonia is detectable. Because of the possible relation getween exchange, on the one hand, and decomposition and synthesis on the other, several kinetic studies of the exchange reaction have been made over iron catalysts: the results are summarized in Table III. Table IV provides similar information for evaporated films of a number of metals.

The hydrogen equilibration reactions proceed over an evaporated iron film at room temperature, whereas temperatures greater than about 160° are

Table III. *Kinetics of the Exchange Reaction between Ammonia and Deuterium over Iron Catalysts*

Form	*Temp. range (°C)*	*E(kcal. mole^{-1})*	*Order in NH_3*	*Order in D_2*	*Ref.*
Powder	210–319	17.5	zero	first	12
Singly prom.	122–164	~13*	(see text)	0.5	13
Film	164–234	16 ± 3	zero	0.5	14
Film	(~300)	20.3 ± 1.0	negative	first	15
Film	(~135)	12.5	—	—	16

* Slightly dependent on ammonia pressure.

needed to effect the ammonia exchange reaction.[14] *para*-Hydrogen conversion is inhibited by ammonia at 80°, and less strongly at 120°. When *ortho*-deuterium conversion is studied simultaneously with the exchange of ammonia at 80°, the former is complete in 30 min. while the latter is not detectable in that time. Ammonia is evidently quite strongly chemisorbed at these temperatures.

TABLE IV. *Kinetics of the Exchange Reaction between Ammonia and Deuterium over Evaporated Metal Films*

Metal	*Mean temp. (°C)*	*E (kcal. mole⁻¹)*	*log A**	*log r at 77°C**	*Order in NH_3*	*Order in D_2*	*Ref.*
W	120	9.2	20.1	14.4	—	—	16
Fe	135	12.5	21.5	13.3	—	—	16
Ni	66	9.3	21.1	15.3	(0.6)	0.5	16, 17
Ni	280	15.1	—	—	zero†	(0.5)†	15
Rh	13	6.7	21.4	17.2	—	—	16
Pd	29	8.5	21.9	16.6	—	—	16
Pt	−38	5.2	21.2	17.9	—	—	16
Cu	212	13.4	21.3	12.9	—	—	16
Ag	271	14.1	21.2	12.4	—	—	16

* Rate in mol. $(100\ cm.^2)^{-1}\ sec.^{-1}$; †, see text.

We may proceed to comment on the Arrhenius parameters shown in Tables III and IV. The activation energies for the reaction over iron and nickel films increased with increasing temperature of operation, probably as a result of sintering. The values obtained with evaporated films have been correlated with the work function of the metals,[16] but there is an equally satisfactory and perhaps more soundly based correlation with percentage *d*-character.[18] The log of the rate at 77° also tends to increase with increasing *d*-character of the metal. The constancy of the pre-exponential factor (Table IV) is striking; and this system is, therefore, an example of the Case II "no compensation" effect described in Chapter 7.

The detailed reaction mechanism is not yet established. Analysis by mass-spectrometry of the deuterated ammonias formed in this reaction clearly shows that only stepwise exchange is possible. A somewhat varied collection of reaction orders is given in Tables III and IV. In addition to the values quoted, the rate expression

$$r \propto \frac{P_{NH_3} P_{D_2}^{0.5}}{(1 + aP_{NH_3})^2} \tag{5}$$

is obeyed over singly promoted iron between 122 and 164°.[13] For the reaction over a nickel film at 263°, the order in ammonia is zero, but it becomes fractionally positive at 300°: at 272°, the order in deuterium is approximately one-half, although the results contain complicating features.[15] It may be significant that the first orders in deuterium have only been observed well above 200°. Extensive discussions of possible mechanisms have been given,[13,16] and these may be briefly summarized. The fact that the rate passes through a maximum as the ammonia pressure is increased has been taken[13] as evidence for a Langmuir–Hinshelwood mechanism in which the slow step is perhaps

$$\underset{*}{\overset{NH_3}{\downarrow}} + \underset{*}{D} \rightarrow \underset{*}{\overset{NH_2D}{\downarrow}} + \underset{*}{H}, \qquad (k)$$

and as evidence against a Rideal–Eley mechanism involving gaseous ammonia molecules. The argument is, however, not conclusive unless the former proceeds on only one site.[16] The above mechanism could, however, conceivably result in multiple exchange. Other possible rate-controlling steps are

$$\underset{*}{\overset{NH_3}{\vdots}} + \underset{*}{D} \rightarrow \underset{*}{\overset{NH_2D}{\vdots}} + \underset{*}{H}$$

or

$$\underset{*}{NH_2} + \underset{*}{\overset{D_2}{\vdots}} \rightarrow \underset{*}{\overset{NH_2D}{|}} + \underset{*}{D}. \qquad (m)$$

These processes and other combinations of them are kinetically indistinguishable. The first orders in deuterium observed at the higher temperatures may imply that the chemisorption of deuterium is rate-limiting under those conditions.

Values of the equilibrium constants

$$K_1 = \frac{[NH_2D]^2}{[NH_3]\,[NHD_2]} \text{ and } K_2 = \frac{[NHD_2]^2}{[ND_3]\,[NH_2D]}$$

have been determined to be close to 2.9 at about 300°, and to have no detectable temperature dependence. The classically expected value is 3.0 in each case.

10.5 The Exchange Reactions between Amines and Deuterium

The exchange reaction of deuterium with mono-, di- and trimethylamines has been studied over evaporated films of a number of metals:[19] the essential kinetic observations are summarized in Table V. Only methylamine-d_1 and -d_2 were formed from methylamine and deuterium over palladium and platinum: this is in keeping with the high activity of these metals in ammonia exchange (Table IV) and their somewhat modest activity in methane exchange (Chapter 9). Over iron, nickel and tungsten, there is evidence for exchange of the methyl hydrogen atoms, a process which increases with rising temperature. The behaviour of nickel and tungsten is understandable; thus for example, tungsten is very active for the exchange of hydrocarbons, but relatively inactive for the exchange of ammonia. The behaviour of iron is, however, surprising, in view of its complete inactivity in hydrocarbon

TABLE V. *Kinetic Parameters for the Exchange of Methylamines with Deuterium over Evaporated Metal Films*[19]

Amine	*Metal*	*Temp. range (°C)*	*Min. temp. for poisoning (°C)*	*E(kcal. mole⁻¹)*	*logA**
CH_3NH_2	Pd	−20–60	30	10.9	21.20
CH_3NH_2	Pt	−48–−20	−48	10.9	22.42
CH_3NH_2	W	61–202	180	7.6	15.86
CH_3NH_2	Ni	32–180	60	13.3	21.53
CH_3NH_2	Fe	25–79	—	9.2	18.08
$(CH_3)_2NH$	Pd	−28–22	0	7.3	18.61
$(CH_3)_2NH$	W	51–91	90	5.4	14.58
$(CH_3)_2NH$	Fe	139–199	—	15.7	20.00
$(CH_3)_2NH$	Ni	39–70	—	6.2	16.67
$(CH_3)_3N$	Pd	60–117	†	22.4	26.20
$(CH_3)_3N$	W	0–90	†	13.5	21.20
$(CH_3)_3N$	Fe	96–151	†	18.9	23.00

* *A*, in molecules $cm.^{-2}$ $sec.^{-1}$; †, no poisoning detected.

exchange. Dimethylamine gives rise to similar phenomena. Dimethylamine-d_1 is the only product over palladium, while up to six hydrogen atoms are exchanged over tungsten and iron: these are presumably those of the two methyl groups. Nickel shows a progressively-increasing tendency to exchange the methyl hydrogen atoms with rising temperature, and all possible products, including the d_7-species, are formed at 70°.

Further evidence for the ease with which palladium causes the exchange in the =N—H system comes from the observation (Table V) that, while tungsten and iron are equally or more active for trimethylamine exchange than for the other amines, palladium is decidedly less active. It is, however, more active in trimethylamine exchange than in neopentane exchange.

Three possible mechanisms commend themselves.

(i) The α–α mechanism (as in methane) probably contributes in all cases where multiple exchange occurs.

(ii) The α–β mechanism (as in ethane) may account for the near-complete exchange of methylamine (W, Fe, Ni) and the complete exchange of dimethylamine (Ni). The detailed mechanisms may be analogous to those proposed for ethane and propane in Chapter 9, e.g.

$$
\begin{array}{ccc}
 & CH_3-\overset{}{\underset{*}{N}}H & \\
(a)\ \rightleftharpoons & & \rightleftharpoons \\
CH_3-NH_2 & & \underset{*}{C}H_2-\underset{*}{N}H \\
(b)\ \rightleftharpoons & & \rightleftharpoons \\
 & \underset{*}{C}H_2-NH_2 &
\end{array}
$$

Process (a) is the favoured initial step in palladium, and (b) on tungsten.

(iii) The α–β mechanism is impossible with trimethylamine, and so either the α–α mechanism, or the α–γ mechanism (as with neopentane) must operate in this case.

Mono- and dimethylamine have been found to exchange only the hydrogen atoms attached to the nitrogen atom over iron powder between 240 and 290°.[20]

References

1. D. D. Eley and M. Polanyi, *Trans. Faraday Soc.* **32,** 1388 (1936).
2. A. Farkas, *Trans. Faraday Soc.* **32**, 922 (1936).
3. A. Farkas and L. Farkas, *Trans. Faraday Soc.* **30,** 1071 (1934).
4. A. Farkas and L. Farkas, *Trans. Faraday Soc.* **33,** 678 (1937).
5. J. Horiuti and M. Polanyi, *Nature* **132,** 819, 931 (1933).
6. J. Horiuti and M. Polanyi, *Mem. Proc. Manchester Lit. Phil. Soc.* **78,** 47 (1934).
7. J. R. Anderson and C. Kemball, *Trans. Faraday Soc.* **51,** 966 (1955).
8. J. K. A. Clarke and C. Kemball, *Trans. Faraday Soc.* **55,** 98 (1959).
9. J. M. Forrest, R. L. Burwell and B. K. C. Shim, *J. Phys. Chem.* **62,** 1017 (1959).
10. H. S. Taylor and J. C. Jungers, *J. Amer. Chem. Soc.* **57,** 660 (1935).
11. J. P. McGeer and H. S. Taylor, *J. Amer. Chem. Soc.* **73,** 2743 (1951).
12. J. R. Gutman, *J. Phys. Chem.* **57,** 309 (1953).
13. J. Weber and K. J. Laidler, *J. Chem. Phys.* **19,** 1089 (1951).
14. A. Farkas, *Trans. Faraday Soc.* **32,** 416 (1936).
15. J. H. Singleton, E. R. Roberts and E. R. S. Winter, *Trans. Faraday Soc.* **47,** 1318 (1951).
16. C. Kemball, *Proc. Roy. Soc.* **A214,** 413 (1954).
17. C. Kemball, *Trans. Faraday Soc.* **48,** 254 (1952).
18. M. McD. Baker and G. I. Jenkins, *Adv. Catalysis* **7,** 1 (1955).
19. C. Kemball and F. J. Wolf, *Trans. Faraday Soc.* **51,** 1111 (1955).
20. J. R. Gutman, *J. Phys. Chem.* **59,** 478 (1955).

Chapter 11

The Hydrogenation of Mono-olefins and Alicyclic Molecules

11.1 The Chemisorption of Olefins

11.11 Mechanisms of Chemisorption and the Reactivity of Adsorbed Species

The chief purpose of this Chapter is to discuss the mechanisms through which olefins are hydrogenated on metal surfaces. While a knowledge of what species are formed when olefins become chemisorbed is clearly relevant to such a discussion, it is worth while giving a word of warning at the outset concerning the generality of the results to be described in this Section.

In the first place, the fact that certain processes occur when olefins are chemisorbed by some kinds of metal surface is no guarantee that identical processes will also occur on other kinds of surface. Second, the fact that certain species appear to be formed in the chemisorption of a reactant is no guarantee that the same species will also exist as an intermediate during a reaction, when two reactants are amply present in the gas phase. It will, therefore, be necessary to scrutinize carefully the material which follows to decide its precise relevance to reaction conditions. Third, most of the work to be described has been carried out with ethylene, and our ignorance of what happens in the case of other olefins is almost complete. Further, most workers have used evaporated films, and less is known concerning the chemisorption of olefins on other kinds of surface.

We turn first to consider briefly the chemisorption of ethylene on evaporated metal films; this has been studied volumetrically on films of nickel,[1, 2] palladium[3] and tungsten.[4] All the metals show certain common features, which may be generalized as follows.

The first increments of ethylene, admitted to the clean film at or near room temperature, are adsorbed to a very low residual pressure until some 1 to 5 $\times 10^{16}$ mol. mg.$^{-1}$ of film have been added (point *A* in Fig. 1): this corresponds to about 25 per cent of the low-temperature hydrogen monolayer

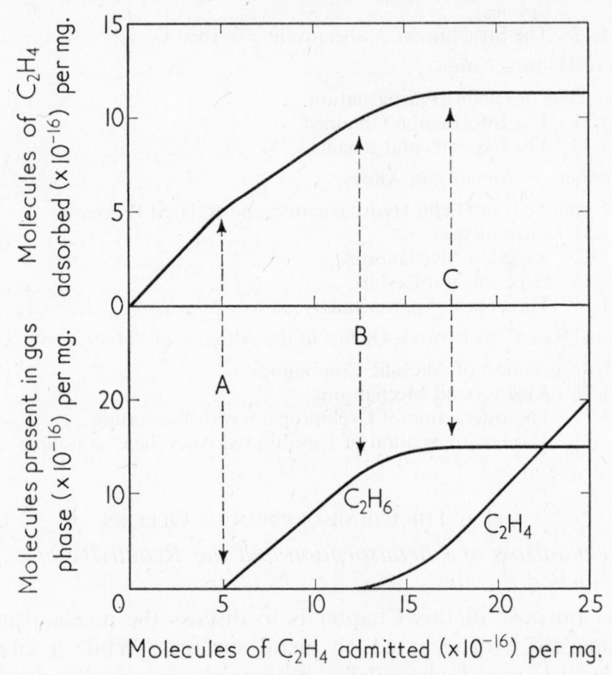

FIG. 1. The chemisorption of ethylene on evaporated metal films (the scales relate to nickel[1]).

capacity. Further increments of ethylene give rise to a progressively increasing residual pressure, but the gas causing this pressure is chiefly or entirely ethane. At point *B*, ethylene appears in the gas phase, and the number of ethane molecules equals the number of ethylene molecules adsorbed. Beyond this point, ethylene adsorption continues more slowly until the limit is reached at *C*.

The interpretation of these findings is as follows. In these systems, ethylene must first chemisorb dissociatively, freeing hydrogen atoms which, however, remain adsorbed. There is evidence that this initial process requires four sites, and it may be formulated as

$$C_2H_4 + 4* \rightarrow \underset{*\;*}{C_2H_2} + \underset{*}{2H}. \qquad \text{(a)}$$

The precise structure of the $\underset{*}{C}_2\underset{*}{H}_2$ entity, variously referred to as an "acetylenic residue" or "surface complex," is immaterial for the moment. The further adsorption of ethylene by this mechanism does not occur beyond point *A*, but instead the adsorbed hydrogen atoms begin to react, either with gaseous ethylene[1, 2] as

$$C_2H_4 + 2\underset{*}{H} \rightarrow C_2H_6 + 2* \qquad \text{(b)}$$

or, with the complex,[3] as

$$\underset{*}{C}_2\underset{*}{H}_2 + 4\underset{*}{H} \rightarrow C_2H_6 + 6*, \qquad \text{(c)}$$

creating free sites upon which further molecules of ethylene may be chemisorbed. It has been shown[2] that reaction (b) proceeds rapidly, and (c) only relatively slowly, over nickel films, although Stephens has stated[3] that (c) is the important process over palladium. At point *B*, the net process is given by the equation

$$2\,C_2H_4 \rightarrow C_2H_{2(a)} + C_2H_6 \qquad \text{(d)}$$

and, beyond this point, the process continues until most[2, 3] or all[4] of the surface is covered by complexes (assumed to be held by two-point attachment). Reaction (d) is referred to as a "self-hydrogenation" reaction. This process is absent from ethylene chemisorption on nickel films at −78°[1] and is of small importance over palladium at this temperature[3] where most of the ethylene is probably held by associative attachment, in which the π-bond is broken and two carbon-metal bonds are formed (see Section 11.12). There are no corresponding studies of the chemisorption of other olefins.

It is now necessary to review the work carried out using supported metals. This has been done using the technique of magnetization changes on nickel–kieselguhr and nickel–silica[5] and the technique of infra-red spectroscopy on nickel–silica[6] and palladium–silica.[7]

Assuming that the formation of a nickel–carbon bond affects the magnetization of nickel in the same way as a nickel–hydrogen bond, the chemisorption of ethylene on supported nickel at room temperature results in the nickel's gaining on average slightly more than two electrons per molecule.[5] This is interpreted as implying that most of the ethylene is associatively chemisorbed, but that a "moderate fraction" is held in a dissociative form requiring four or more sites. At 100°, ethylene is more extensively dissociated than at room temperature, and each molecule ultimately forms six bonds to the surface, a process which may perhaps be formulated as

$$C_2H_4 + 6* \rightarrow 2\,\underset{*}{H} + \underset{**}{\overset{\text{HC}}{\wedge}}\!\!\text{—}\!\!\underset{**}{\overset{\text{CH}}{\wedge}}\,. \qquad \text{(e)}$$

Eischens and Pliskin[6] have found that the species formed when ethylene interacts with the surface of nickel–silica depends on the temperature, the partial pressure of hydrogen, and the presence or absence of a layer of pre-adsorbed hydrogen. When ethylene is admitted to a nickel surface covered by a layer of preadsorbed hydrogen at 35°, the associative form results. The implication is that ethylene can displace adsorbed hydrogen without reacting with it, but is unable to dissociate while the rest of the surface remains covered with hydrogen: vacant sites are required to accommodate the hydrogen atoms which would be released by dissociation before this process can occur. On a bare nickel surface at 35° or on a hydrogen-covered nickel surface at 150° however, ethylene on chemisorption forms complexes in which the carbon/hydrogen ratio is variable (see also Ref. 1) and the carbon atoms are mainly saturated. The species formed in process (e) above, in which each carbon atom is singly bonded to two different sites rather than doubly bonded to the same site, is indicated as a possibility. The spectra of the three isomeric normal hexenes when adsorbed are unexpectedly similar, and it is thought that the absence of the expected differences is caused by each species being bonded to the surface at more than two points.[8] The isomeric normal butenes behave similarly. Similar results have been found with ethylene on palladium–silica.[7]

A complex-covered surface can take up hydrogen,[2, 3] some of which becomes chemisorbed, while the remainder reacts with the complexes. This process occurs readily over supported nickel,[6] but with little release of hydrocarbon to the gas phase, and is reversed by pumping. This may be represented as

$$\text{complex} + H_2 \rightleftharpoons \underset{*\ *}{C_2H_4} \xrightarrow{H_2} C_2H_6. \qquad \text{(f)}$$

Over palladium at 0° some ethane is rapidly formed, and more is slowly liberated, perhaps by the slow disproportionation of adsorbed ethyl radicals.[3] These radicals have been shown to form when associatively adsorbed ethylene reacts with hydrogen.[6] Over nickel films at room temperature, some 20 per cent of the complexes are removed by hydrogen in one hour,[1, 2] but the products are variously reported to be pure ethane[2] or 90 per cent of polymeric saturated hydrocarbons (C_4, C_6, C_8 and higher) and 10 per cent ethane.[1] Over a palladium film at 0°, the products are: 93 per cent ethane; 3 per cent butane; and 4 per cent ethylene.[3] The detection of ethylene in this system lends support to mechanism (f) if the associatively adsorbed ethylene can desorb. The detection of polymeric hydrocarbons shows that the acetylenic complexes are able to polymerize, either by elimination of hydrogen as

```
     H—C—C—H             H—C—C—C—C—H
2     /\ /\       →        /\ /\ /\ /\      + H2      (g)
     ** **                 ** ** ** **
```

or in the following manner:

```
                              H  H
                             /  /
     H—C—C—H             H—C—C—C—C—H.                 (h)
2     /\ /\       →        /\ |  | /\
     ** **                 ** *  * **
```

Infra-red studies have provided evidence for both the monomeric and polymeric structures.[6, 7, 9] The complexes formed on nickel films are more reactive than chemisorbed acetylene,[1] but this information is of little use since the structure of the latter is not known. Table I summarizes the available information on the rates of removal of adsorbed complexes from films of various metals by hydrogen: the order of reactivities is Rh > Pd > Ni.

TABLE I. *Rates of Removal of Adsorbed Complexes by Hydrogen from Evaporated Metal Films*

Metal	*Temp.* (°C)	*Reaction time*	% *removed*	*Ref.*
Rh	23	1 min.	60	1
Rh	23	long	100	1
Pd	0	5 min.	50–60	3
Ni	20	1 hr.	20	1, 2

The present position may be summarized in the following way. When ethylene chemisorbs on evaporated metal films or on bare supported nickel at or near room temperature, it dissociates into adsorbed hydrogen and a complex, C_2H_2. Attempted calculations of the heat of adsorption assuming the complex to have the structure $\overset{}{\underset{*}{HC}}=\underset{*}{CH}$ (which is the structure of associatively adsorbed acetylene) are not very successful[10, 11] (see Chapter 5). More probable structures are either

$$\begin{array}{ccc} HC\text{———}CH & & HC\text{———}CH \\ \wedge \quad\quad \wedge & \text{or} & \| \quad\quad\quad \| \\ MM \quad MM & & M \quad\quad\quad M \end{array}$$

The complexes may polymerize (perhaps relatively slowly) and higher paraffins sometimes result when they are removed from the surface by hydrogen. It is worth stressing that there is evidence for these species only when there is no sensible pressure of hydrogen in the gas phase. There is considerable evidence for the associative form $H_2\underset{*}{C}—\underset{*}{C}H_2$ existing after ethylene chemisorption (i) on hydrogen-covered nickel–silica and (ii) on films and nickel–silica when the resulting complex is exposed to hydrogen.

We are now in a position to understand why the rates of bulk hydrogenation reactions often depend critically on the order of addition of the reactants to the catalyst. The observation is briefly this: when the olefin is admitted first (especially to nickel) the rate is in some degree smaller than when hydrogen is admitted first, and complete inhibition sometimes results.[12–14] Beeck[1] gives the following figures for the rates of ethylene hydrogenation at 0° after pretreatment of the metal film by ethylene, as a percentage of the rate before this treatment:

Ta, 10%; W, 20%; Ni, 40%; Pt and Rh, 95%.

The figures for nickel, platinum and rhodium conform to experience with other metal forms. The explanation is this: that especially over tantalum and tungsten, and to a certain extent over nickel, the ethylene pretreatment or the prior addition of olefin results in the formation of complexes which reduce the active area and which probably remain unaffected during the bulk reaction. With platinum and rhodium, such complexes, while they may be initially formed, are hydrogenated very quickly after the hydrogen is admitted, and most of the surface is then active. If hydrogen is admitted first, and the olefin subsequently, then there is no opportunity for complexes to form and a more rapid reaction ensues.

In order to present a coherent discussion on mechanisms of olefin hydrogenation, it is now necessary to come to some decision as to what the nature of chemisorbed olefins will be assumed to be. In view of the foregoing results and of the general success which has attended interpretation based on this model, it will be assumed that it is the associative form of chemisorbed olefin which exists on the surface when both reactants are substantially present in the gas phase and which participates in the bulk reaction. While there is some contrary evidence,[2] most of the evidence is not opposed to this view. We may now, therefore, start a more detailed examination of the associatively adsorbed state.

11.12 The Structure of Associatively Adsorbed Olefins

Associatively adsorbed ethylene is commonly assumed to have an ethane-like structure, in which the carbon–carbon distance is 1.54 Å and the bonds are tetrahedrally disposed about the carbon atoms (Fig. 2). The alternative

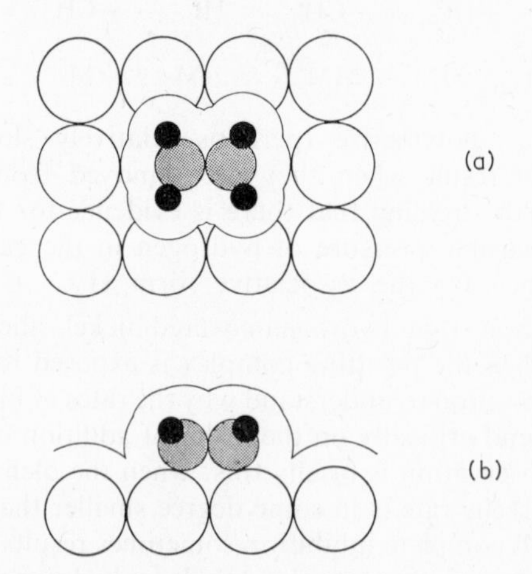

FIG. 2. Ethylene associatively chemisorbed on the (100) face of nickel: (a) plan and (b) side elevation. The following interatomic distances and radii were used in constructing this and the following two figures: C–C, 1.54 Å; C–H, 1.09 Å; C–Ni, 2.0 Å; C (van der Waals). 1.75 Å; H (van der Waals), 1.20 Å.

idea that olefins are held by a π-bond donor mechanism ("Dewar bond") was mentioned in Chapter 5, but will not be pursued. It is now necessary to decide what value to take for the carbon–metal distance: this has variously been taken as 1.82 Å (as in nickel carbonyl)[15] and more plausibly as 2.0 Å, the sum of the covalent radii.[16] Taking the smaller value, it has been calculated[15] that the ideal metal–metal distance is 2.73 Å, and hence it has been inferred that ethylene is associatively chemisorbed on the shorter of the two metal–metal spacings available in face-centred cubic metals. This spacing is twice the metallic radius and values range from about 2.5 Å for nickel to about 2.8 Å for platinum. According to this model, if ethylene were chemisorbed on nickel, the carbon and nickel atoms being in one plane, the Ni—C—C angle would be about 105° instead of the normal tetrahedral angle of $109\frac{1}{2}$°. The strain introduced into the system is thus quite small, and the same is true for all the metals which are active as hydrogenation catalysts. Burwell[17] has argued convincingly that the conformation of the bonds about the carbon atoms is more likely to be eclipsed than staggered.

The short metal–metal spacings are present in all the three low index planes of face-centred cubic metals. It was originally concluded[15] that on (111) faces there would be substantial overlap between adjacently adsorbed molecules, but no overlap on (110) faces; the latter conclusion may require

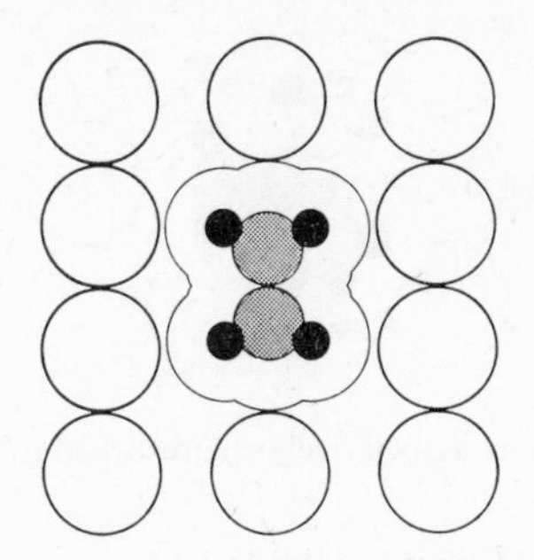

FIG. 3. Plan of ethylene associatively chemisorbed on the (110) face of nickel.

revision, since the effect of the van der Waals envelope seems to have been underestimated (see Fig. 3). No conclusions were drawn concerning the (100) face (claimed to be catalytically inactive), but it is evident that there should be considerable overlap (Fig. 2).

The claim[1] that the (110) face of nickel has an activity superior to other faces has often been repeated, and has given rise to speculation concerning the detailed effect of surface geometry on reaction mechanism. The original claim was, however, almost certainly unjustified, as has already been discussed (Chapter 3). Measurements of the rates of ethylene hydrogenation on the different faces of a nickel single crystal[18] are difficult to interpret, and do not contribute significantly to our understanding of the problem. There should nevertheless be in principle differences between the activities of different faces, and the following considerations may be relevant. We may assume that for optimum reactivity the simultaneous and adjacent adsorption of both reactants is required. Thus on any face on which ethylene may be packed tightly, with no mutual interference, hydrogen will generally have only a small chance of getting adsorbed by reason of the stronger adsorption of ethylene, but on a face, such as the (111) or (100), where mutual interference is substantial, the ethylene layer may contain gaps in which hydrogen can readily adsorb. This approach assumes that both reactants are adsorbed on the same kind of sites, but there is impressive evidence to the contrary.[5] Thus for example on the (110) face there may be interstitial sites available to hydrogen but not available to ethylene. The concept of different kinds of sites has already been introduced in considering the reactions of hydrogen (Chapter 8), but it has not yet been applied to other systems. This important aspect of reaction mechanisms awaits a thorough study, and any proposed mechanism which ignores it must be deemed naïve.

With substituted ethylenes containing one or more methyl groups, mutual interference between adjacently adsorbed molecules is much greater than with ethylene[15] (see Fig. 4). This has two consequences: (i) the concentration of adsorbed molecules will be smaller than with ethylene, and (ii) there may

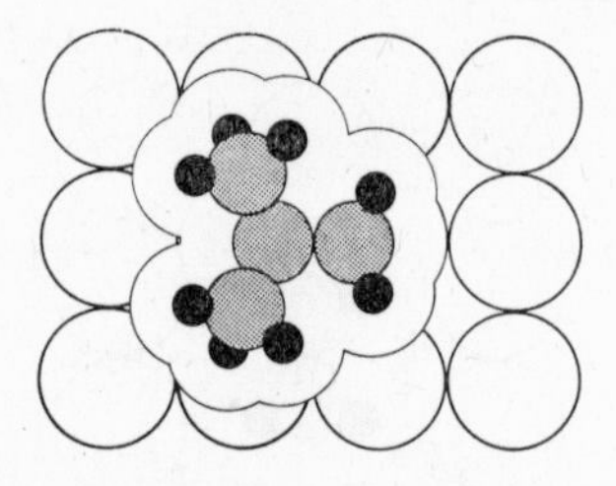

FIG. 4. Plan of isobutene associatively chemisorbed on the (100) face of nickel.

be a substantial number of sites available to hydrogen which are not available to the olefin. The existence of such sites has been elegantly demonstrated by examining the extent to which the various methylethylenes are capable of inhibiting *para*-hydrogen conversion:[15] increasing the number of substituted methyl groups markedly decreases the olefin's inhibiting power. We may, therefore, expect to find important differences between the reactivity and the kinetics shown by various olefins depending on their ease of packing on a given surface. The formulation of rate expressions will be more complicated where independent adsorption of hydrogen is possible. Thus the expression for the concentration of adsorbed hydrogen will consist of two terms, the first dealing with hydrogen adsorbed in competition with the olefin and the second pertaining to hydrogen adsorbed without competition. We may, therefore, expect that for any olefin the *kinetics* of its hydrogenation will vary from one crystal face to another, but there is as yet no experimental evidence on this point.

11.2 Heats of Hydrogenation[21]

According to the Law of Constant Heat Summation, the heat content change accompanying a chemical reaction is independent of the path through which the reaction proceeds. This principle has been widely employed in the determination of the heats of hydrogenation of a number of unsaturated molecules, for the use of catalysts enables the reactions to occur at moderate temperatures (20°–100°) where standard calorimetric techniques may be used. The corresponding homogeneous reactions only proceed at elevated temperatures (~600°) where calorimetry would be exceedingly difficult, where side reactions may interfere, and where the reaction may not go to completion. The value for a heat of reaction obtained calorimetrically may be checked against the values found by two other methods, viz. (i) from the difference between the heats of formation of reactants and products as deduced from heats of combustion, and (ii) from the temperature-dependence of the equilibrium constant. All three methods have been applied[22] to the hydrogenation of ethylene with the following results at 25°: $-\Delta H°$, 32.57 kcal. $mole^{-1}$ (calorimetric); 32.78 kcal. $mole^{-1}$ (calculated from heats of combustion); −32.60 kcal. $mole^{-1}$ (from equilibrium constants). The agreement between calorimetric and calculated values is usually equally satisfactory. Skinner's monograph[20] summarizes the experimental methods and tabulates the available results: more recent work is described in Ref. 23.

The measurement of heats of hydrogenation does not, of course, directly further our understanding of reaction mechanisms, but rather it yields valuable information concerning the molecular structure of the molecules studied. The strength of the π-bond may be deduced, and its response to its environment examined, and these considerations are pertinent to the present Chapter because this is the bond believed to be broken in forming the associatively chemisorbed state. It is worth emphasizing that this state resembles the saturated hydrocarbon more closely than the olefin, and that the catalyst has performed a significant part of its functions in facilitating this transformation. The breaking of carbon–metal bonds by hydrogen requires no substantial re-arrangements.

We might thus expect to find a parallelism between the heat of hydrogenation and the heat liberated in forming the associatively adsorbed state. Unfortunately the latter information is entirely lacking. As we have seen, the heats of adsorption of ethylene on films (discussed in Chapter 5) almost certainly refer to a dissociative state of adsorption, and it would be of enormous interest to have measurements of heats of adsorption of a series of olefins made at low temperature where the associative state is probably formed. However, variations in heats of adsorption may be manifested indirectly through the equilibrium coverage of a surface by olefin during hydrogenation reactions. As the heat of hydrogenation (and of adsorption) decreases, so will the coverage under fixed conditions, and this may affect the kinetics, although this effect is probably masked by the steric considerations mentioned in the last Section.

We may now shortly consider the salient observations, which are two-fold.

(i) In a series of straight-chain α-olefins, the heat of hydrogenation (apart from ethylene) is constant at about 30.1 kcal. mole^{-1}. This clearly shows that the maximum stabilization of the π-bond by hyperconjugation occurs when a methyl group is substituted, and that lengthening the alkyl chain produces no additional effect. (ii) When methyl groups are progressively substituted about the double bond, there is a continuous decrease in the heat of hydrogenation: the results are shown in Table II. Here the first methyl group produces the largest stabilization, and the fourth the smallest.

TABLE II. *Heats of Hydrogenation (kcal. mole^{-1}) of Methylethylenes at 82°* [19]

$H_2C{=}CH_2$ 32.8	$CH_3CH{=}CH_2$ 30.1	$(CH_3)_2C{=}CH_2$ 28.4
$(CH_3)_2C{=}CH{-}CH_3$ 26.9	$(CH_3)_2C{=}C(CH_3)_2$ 26.6	$CH_3{-}CH{=}CH{-}CH_3$ *cis*: 28.6 *trans*: 27.6

There is one other kind of system which produces relevant information. The silver ion is isoelectronic with the palladium atom, and the former is known to form complexes with olefins, involving Dewar bonds: there may, therefore, be some relation between the stability of a complex and the strength of adsorption of the olefin on a metal surface, regardless of the precise manner in which it is held. Such a correlation cannot, of course, be established at the moment, but a linear relation has been shown to exist between the logarithm of the stability constant of complexes at 25° and the heats of hydrogenation of the corresponding olefins[24] (Fig. 5). Increasing hyperconjugative stabilization of the olefin decreases the stability of the

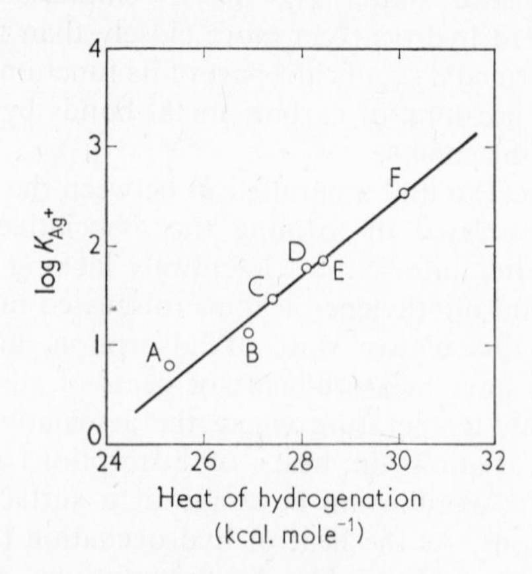

FIG. 5. The relation between the log of the stability constant for silver ion complex formation (K_{Ag^+}) and the heat of hydrogenation (both at 25°) for selected olefins.
A, 2,4-dimethyl-2-pentene; B, 2-methyl-2-butene; C, *trans*-2-butene; D, isobutene; E, *cis*-2-butene; F, 1-octene.

complex, presumably because of the decreasing electron density at the double bond. This relation gives some slight support to the concept of an adsorbed state resembling the saturated hydrocarbon: at least it may be safely said that the same basic facets of molecular structure are reflected in the heat of hydrogenation, in complex stability and in strength of adsorption. Stability constants, together with the standard enthalpies and entropies of formation, are known for complexes involving a number of cyclic olefins,[25] but the correlation with heats of hydrogenation is far less satisfactory than for the open-chain olefins as depicted in Fig. 5. The reason for this is not clear, but it is possible that steric effects obtrude and confuse the issue.

11.3 The Kinetics of Olefin Hydrogenation[26–31]

11.31 The Information Obtained

The purpose of this sub-section is to summarize the motives underlying the measurement of rates of olefin hydrogenation and their dependence on temperature and reactant pressures, and to indicate the limits of the significance to be attached to such measurements. Much of the relevant published work records only the rates observed in chosen systems under fixed conditions. Problems investigated include the determination of the conditions of catalyst preparation for optimum activity and the effect of treatments such as sintering or ion bombardment on the activity. Many measurements have also been made on the relative rates shown by different olefins and in particular their dependence on the degree of substitution about the double bond. The observed rates are, however, only rarely referred to a definite surface area. This kind of information has a limited wider significance, since (i) the phenomena are often not exactly reproducible and (ii) a knowledge of the activation energy and the specific frequency factor is lacking.

Numerous values for the activation energies in olefin hydrogenation are quoted in the literature, and some of these will be given in the next sub-section. Their wide variation between even quite similar systems at once makes them suspect. The following causes may be responsible for these variations. (i) The possible existence of a compensation effect, which, of course, is not revealed unless the properly defined frequency factors are also available. (ii) The activation energies are "apparent," and not "true," and should be corrected for heats of adsorption as appropriate, after the manner described in Chapter 7. This is not usually possible, and apparent activation energies may, therefore, vary because the heats of adsorption are varying, and they will, therefore, reflect for example any irreversible poisoning the catalyst may have suffered. Notwithstanding these limitations, however, measurements of any or all of the activity parameters (k, E and A) even if not referred to unit metal area are of some qualitative interest, especially if one definite variable (such as the physical form of the metal, the support, or the nature of the metal) is under study. Quantitative information on the relative activities of metals when in the same physical form will be discussed in Section 11.4.

Of more basic interest are the less usually measured orders of reaction, and in particular these are rarely determined at more than one temperature. It must be remembered that the formulation of a rate expression as a "power rate law" is misleading to the extent that the powers only result from a simplification of the rate expression formulated in terms of adsorption isotherms (see Chapter 7). The temperature dependence of the powers should serve to confirm the mechanistic picture deduced from the observed powers at any one temperature. In this connection it is desirable to stress how important it is to record original rate-pressure results, since their presentation as power rate law hampers any accurate reinterpretation which may be found necessary. The method used in determining the rate is also worth stating because of the possible distinction between initial rate and "course" kinetics.

Accurate rate-pressure measurements over a wide range of conditions may lead to a knowledge of the adsorption coefficients of the reactants and their temperature dependence. This informs us of the relative reactant concentrations on the surface under the prevailing conditions, but it does not inform us concerning the detailed mechanisms by which the adsorbed reactants are converted to products. Ancillary evidence (to be described in Section 11.5) is required before full mechanistic discussions are in order. It may be stated categorically that the complete mechanism for a hydrogenation reaction may never be unambiguously derived from orders of reaction. Experience shows that for any reaction there is a seemingly inexhaustible number of combinations of unit steps which are kinetically acceptable.

It is, however, sometimes possible to decide whether a reaction is proceeding by a Rideal–Eley or a Langmuir–Hinshelwood mechanism (see Chapter 7). In olefin hydrogenation it is generally accepted that, should the former mechanism apply, it is the olefin which will be chemisorbed and the hydrogen which will react without adsorption, although the contrary view is sometimes expressed.[1, 2] A Langmuir–Hinshelwood mechanism will, of course, speak for itself: thus if, for example, the rate passes through a maximum as the pressure of either reactant is raised, it is at once clear that the reactants are competing for the same surface, and hence that this mechanism is operative.

There are, however, several formally possible situations which are not normally contemplated. Thus, for example, (i) both types of mechanism may contribute simultaneously to the total reaction: (ii) both reactants may be chemisorbed, but chemisorbed A may for some reason be inactive, so that the actual mechanism is

$$\underset{*}{\text{B}} + \underset{*}{\overset{\text{A}}{\vdots}} \rightarrow \text{C.}$$

This is the situation envisaged by Jenkins and Rideal,[2] where A is ethylene and B is hydrogen.

It is, perhaps, unfortunate that so much experimental work has involved the use of nickel as catalyst, and that so much theoretical discussion has centred on results obtained with it, for it is with this metal that the distinction between the two mechanisms is least clear. The situation with the noble Group VIII metals is far clearer, at least as far as the broad outlines of the mechanism go.

TABLE III. *Overall Kinetics of Olefin Hydrogenation: Nickel Catalysts* $r = kP^x_{H_2}P^y_O$, measured at T°C

Form	*Olefin*	*E(kcal. mole⁻¹)*	*x*	*y*	*T* (°C)	*Ref.*
Film	ethylene	10.7 (−80–150°)	1	0	?	1
Film	ethylene	8.0 (0–96°)	1	0	?	36
Film	ethylene	10.2 (20–150°)[a]	1 1	0 *L*	114° 165°	2
Film	ethylene	7 (−100– −120°)	0.5	0	∼−100°	37
Wire	ethylene	∼14 (60–100°)	1	0	156°	38
Wire	ethylene	4.6 (0–17°)	—	—	—	39
Wire	ethylene	8.2 (60–110°)	—	—	—	34
Foil	ethylene	3.2 (30–200°)[b]	—	—	—	40
Foil	ethylene	5 (400–600°)	—	—	—	41
Powder	ethylene	6 (−78–0°)	+ve	−ve	?	42
Powder	ethylene	—	1	*L*	99–165°	43
Powder	ethylene	7.5 (∼−70°)	—	—	—	44
On SiO_2	ethylene	8.4 (−78–0°)	0.67	−0.08	−40°	45
On Al_2O_3	ethylene	11.6 (30–80°)	1	*L*	70°	46
Wire	propylene	6.0 (60–110°)	—	—	—	34
Wire	1-butene	2.5 (76–126°)	0.5	0.5	?	47
Wire	1-butene	2.0 (60–135°)	0.5	0.5	?	47
Wire	2-butene	3.3 (60–110°)	—	—	—	34
Wire	*cis*-2-butene	3.5 (75–130°)	—	—	—	47
Wire	*trans*-2-butene	3.5 (75–130°)				
Wire	isobutene	3.3 (60–110°)	—	—	—	34

L: Langmuir expression (see text).
a; T_{max}, 160–165°. b; T_{max}, 137°.

TABLE IV. *Overall Kinetics of Ethylene Hydrogenation: Iron, Cobalt and Copper Catalysts*

Metal	*Form*	*E(kcal. mole⁻¹)*	*x*	*y*	*T* (°C.)	*Ref.*
Fe	on SiO_2	8.4 (? temp.)	0.91	−0.04	30°	45
Co	on SiO_2	8.4 (? temp.)	0.55	−0.19	−60°	45
Cu	on SiO_2	8.4 (? temp.)	0.69	0.06	80°	45
Cu	powder	4 (? temp.)	—	—	—	44
Cu	powder	13.2 (0–100°) 10.8 (150–200°) 7.0 (200–250°)	1 1 1	−ve 0 1	0° 100° 200°	48
Cu	foil	19.5 (550–700°)	—	—	—	41, 49

TABLE V. *Overall Kinetics of Olefin Hydrogenation: Noble Metals of Group VIII*

Metal	*Form*	*Olefin*	*E(kcal. mole^{-1})*	*x*	*y*	*T (°C.)*	*Ref.*
Pt	on Al_2O_3	ethylene	{ 9.9* (0–50°) 10.9† (0–50°) }	1.2	−0.5	0 or 18°	50
Pt	foil	ethylene	10 (0–150°)[a]	1.3	−0.8	?	51
Pt	on SiO_2	ethylene	8.4 (? temp.)	0.77	0.25	−40°	45
Pd	on SiO_2	ethylene	8.4 (? temp.)	0.66	−0.03	−30°	45
Rh	on SiO_2	ethylene	8.4 (? temp.)	0.85	−0.74	−76°	45
Ru	on SiO_2	ethylene	8.4 (? temp.)	0.95	−0.59	−70°	45
Pt	on pumice	propylene	6.3 (−18–130°)	0.5	−0.5	18°	52
Pd	on Al_2O_3	propylene	11.7 (? temp.)	—	—	—	53
Pt	on pumice	1-butene	2.9 (13–126°)	~0	0.4	100°	54
Pt	on pumice	isobutene	1.9 (84–170°)	0.4	0.5	100°	54
Pt	black	maleic acid	9.0 (20–60°)[b]	—	—	—	55
Pt	black	crotonic acid	6.7 (20–80°)[c]	—	—	—	55

* With H_2; † with D_2. a; $T_{max} \doteqdot 160°$: b; $T_{max} = 65°$: c; $T_{max} = 90°$.

11.32 The Experimental Results

A selection of the observed apparent activation energies and pressure dependences is presented in Tables III, IV and V. This compilation is not intended to be exhaustive, but it contains the most pertinent information at present available. In addition to a discussion of these results, the effect of molecular structure on activity parameters and the phenomenon of the inversion temperature also merit consideration.

A number of efforts have been made to measure the relative rates of hydrogenation of different olefins, and their temperature dependence.[27, 28] It is generally agreed that the rates decrease with the increasing substitution of alkyl groups about the double bond, at least over nickel and platinum catalysts; results for other metals are not extensive. Thus, for example, the following comparable times of half-reaction have been quoted[28] for the

TABLE VI. *The Relative Reactivities of Olefins in Hydrogenation over a Platinum Catalyst*[28]

Mixture *A*	*B*	*% A reacted*	*% B reacted*
Propylene	2-butene	90	20
1-Butene	2-butene	79	21
Isobutene	trimethylethylene	99	44

hydrogenation of olefins over a nickel–charcoal catalyst: C_2H_4, 8 min.; C_3H_6, 104 min.; 1-butene, 225 min.; and *iso*butene, 1100 min. Symmetrically disubstituted olefins often react faster than unsymmetrically substituted ones. The relative reactivities of olefins have been estimated by causing a mixture of olefins to react with an insufficiency of hydrogen and estimating the different products. Table VI shows some results obtained in this way. The substitution of aryl groups leads to anomalous effects: thus increasing substitution of these groups leads to a decrease in rate over platinum black, but to an increase over palladium black and Raney nickel.[28]

The differences between the rates increase with increasing temperature, and hence the apparent activation energies decrease with increasing alkyl substitution[34, 35] (see also Tables III and V). Although widely varying activation energies are recorded for ethylene, consistently low values are reported for the butenes. A normal compensation effect is apparently operative over nickel wire,[34] where the rates for ethylene, propylene and 2-butene are closely similar at 60°: in this system, the change in the activation energy is very roughly the same as the change in the heat of hydrogenation, and the same trend is observed with supported platinum catalysts, although strictly comparable values are not available.

The decrease in the activation energy with increasing substitution of methyl groups is not easily explained. It must be remembered that two effects are operating: (i) the heat of adsorption of the olefin decreases with increasing substitution (and here the need for accurate thermochemical measurements is keenly felt), and (ii) with increasing substitution there will be a progressively greater number of sites on which hydrogen may adsorb without competing for the olefin. It is difficult to avoid the feeling that for this reason the *true* activation energy may be changing, but the steric and thermochemical factors are not readily disentangled.

A quite general phenomenon in olefin hydrogenation is the observed temperature-dependence of activation energies. Above temperatures of about 100° in a typical system, the activation energy decreases continuously until it has a value of zero in the region of 150°, whereafter it becomes negative. The temperature at which the maximum rate is found is designated the inversion temperature T_{max}, and some values are quoted below Tables III and V. Although most of the observations have been made with nickel, the same effect has been found over platinum,[51, 55] and a declining activation energy has been reported with copper.[48] Most of the observations have, of course, been made with ethylene, although unsaturated acids in solution also show the effect.[55] T_{max} decreases with decreasing olefin pressure, and values as low as 60° are recorded;[56] for this reason, zur Strassen[56] suggested that desorption of olefin was the cause, and that above T_{max} it was necessary to subtract the heat of adsorption of olefin as well as that of hydrogen from the observed activation energy in order to obtain the true value, viz.

$$T < T_{max} : E_y = E_z - \{-\Delta H_a(H_2)\} \quad (1)$$

$$T > T_{max} : E_y = E_z - \{-\Delta H_a(H_2)\} - \{-\Delta H_a(C_2H_4)\}. \quad (2)$$

In harmony with this view, the order in ethylene is known to be higher above T_{max} than below it.[56, 57] T_{max} is, however, dependent on whether hydrogen or deuterium is used,[39] and this is not consistent with the above proposal. Other theoretical discussions of the phenomenon have been given.[26, 33]

It is finally necessary to review the observed orders of reaction in olefin hydrogenation (Tables III to V). Over a wide variety of forms of nickel below 100°, the order in hydrogen is generally found to be first or slightly less when ethylene is the olefin, and the order in ethylene zero. Propylene is stated to show the same behaviour as ethylene,[35] but very few studies of this system have been made. The hydrogenation of 1-butene over nickel wire is of half-order in each reactant,[14, 47] confirming the readier adsorption of hydrogen in this system. At temperatures between about 100° and T_{max}, the order in hydrogen is still first but the ethylene dependence is of the form: $cP_{C_2H_4}(1 + c'P_{C_2H_4})^{-1}$, c and c' being constants.[2, 43, 46] Above T_{max} the reaction with ethylene is reported to become first order in each reactant. Kinetic measurements on the reactions over other metals of the first Transition series are fragmentary (Table IV), and scarcely merit discussion.

A range of fractionally positive orders in hydrogen have been observed in the hydrogenation of ethylene[45, 51] and propylene[52] over the noble Group VIII metals, while the corresponding orders in ethylene lie between about +0.2 and −0.7 (Table V). The hydrogen order of 1.2 noted[50] for a variety of platinum catalysts is not explicable by simple considerations based on Langmuir isotherms. As with nickel, fractionally positive orders in both reactants are found with the butenes.[54]

Negative orders in olefins are rarely observed over nickel catalysts, but are common over the noble Group VIII metals, and this requires some discussion. There are two possibilities. (i) A Rideal–Eley mechanism operates over most nickel catalysts, whereas an "adjacent-adsorption" mechanism holds over noble Group VIII metals; this, while not impossible, is rather implausible, there being no obvious reason why the mechanism should not be the same on all these metals. (ii) A more likely explanation is that ethylene molecules cannot completely cover a nickel surface due to steric interactions, and that hence there are certain sites on which hydrogen is weakly adsorbed, whose concentration is independent of ethylene pressure. This view is not very dissimilar from one suggested by Rideal.[58] On the noble Group VIII metals, having a larger radius, the packing of ethylene may be more efficient, and hence only hydrogen adsorbed in competition with the ethylene is permitted. Further points of difference between nickel and the noble Group VIII metals will emerge in due course.

11.4 The Activity of Metals and Alloys

From the results presented in the last Section, it would appear that the probable order for the activity of pure metals in olefin hydrogenation is perhaps

$$Pt \simeq Pd > Ni > Fe \simeq Co > Cu,$$

but this order can only be approximate due to the differing preparations used. There have only been a very few investigations in which the activity order from metals have been quantitatively determined with the metals in the same physical form, and only in one of these[45] have orders of reaction also been measured; these have been given in Tables III to V.

The available values for the relative activities are shown in Table VII; they require some discussion. The two sets of values at 0° show remarkable consistency, particularly in view of the different natures of the catalysts; only the higher activity of the supported nickel and the low activity of supported iridium are unexpected. The activation energy for the reaction over all the silica-supported metals is 8.4 kcal. mole^{-1} and over the films, 10.7 kcal. mole^{-1}, except for tantalum and tungsten, where the value is only 2.4 kcal. mole^{-1}. Because of this, the activity of tungsten at −100° is relatively greater than at 0°.

The correlation between the activity and the percentage *d*-character of the metals was originally noted by Beeck,[1] and is shown again in Fig. 6 together with the new results at 0°.[45] The modification of this correlation, due to Schuit,[59] in which the activity is plotted against the product of the *d*-character and the metallic valency only affects those metals to which

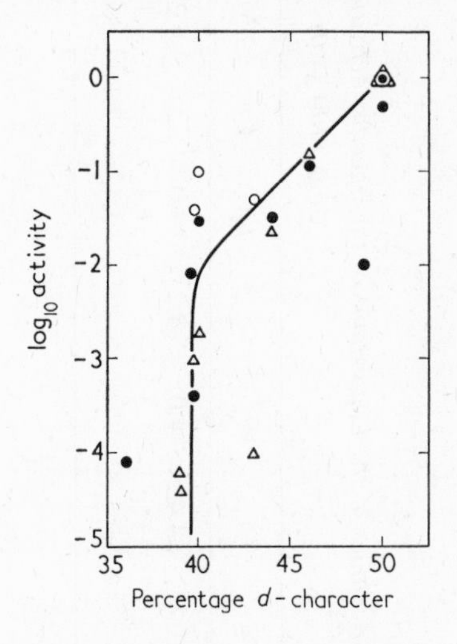

FIG. 6. Correlation of activity for ethylene hydrogenation with percentage *d*-bond character.

○ Over films at −100°.[37]
△ Over films at 0°.[1]
● Over silica-supported metals at 0°.[45]

Pauling assigned a valency of other than six. The failure of tungsten, on either treatment, to conform to the main series has occasioned much discussion, but no firm conclusion has been arrived at. The extent of the deviation

TABLE VII. *Relative Values of the Logarithms of the Specific Activities of Metals for Ethylene Hydrogenation* ($\log k_s(Rh) = 0$)

System	*Ta*	*W*	*Cr*	*Fe*	*Co*	*Ni*	*Ru*	*Rh*	*Pd*	*Ir*	*Pt*	*Cu*	*Ref.*
Metal films; H_2; 0°	−4.4	−4.0	−4.2	−3.0	—	−2.6	—	0	−0.8	—	−1.65	—	1
Metal films; D_2; −100°	—	−1.3	—	−1.4	—	−1.0	—	0	—	—	—	—	37
Metals on SiO_2; H_2; 0°	—	—	—	−3.4	−2.1	−1.5	−0.3	0	−0.9	−2.0	−1.5	−4.1	45

of this metal from the norm clearly depends on the temperature at which the observation is made.

The measurements of the orders of reaction over the silica-supported metals require comment. The hydrogen orders are irregular, but the ethylene orders are zero for metals which are active above about −50° (except for platinum); below this temperature, they become increasingly more negative with decreasing temperature.[45] The Power Rate Law has been applied to these results. The following equation (see equation 48, Chapter 7), based on the assumption of a homogeneous surface, has been used to calculate the frequency term kT/h from the observed A factor:

$$\frac{kT}{h} = A\frac{n_s}{n_g}\exp\left(-m\frac{S^0_{H^2}}{R} - n\frac{S^0_{C_2H_4}}{R}\right), \qquad (3)$$

where n_s/n_g is the ratio of the number of molecules present on the surface to that in the gas phase. The calculated frequencies are widely scattered (10^7–10^{16} sec.$^{-1}$), but average out at about $10^{11\cdot5}$, which is not too far from the expected value of 10^{13} sec.$^{-1}$. The results depend critically on the accuracy of the exponents m and n.

Equation (47) of Chapter 7 has been used[60] to calculate values of

$$-\log\left(\frac{A}{kT/h}\right)$$

for other studies of ethylene hydrogenation. The mean value from five studies is 3.62, and the mean experimental value is 3.98.

We come now to investigations of the activity of alloys for olefin hydrogenation. Ethylene hydrogenation has been studied over nickel–copper powders[44, 61] and foils;[49] the results found by Best and Russell[61] are summarized in Table VIII. The striking feature of these results is that the activity of both the alloys used is greater than that of pure nickel. The activation energies are essentially constant, and the activity differences are thus chiefly caused by differences in the pre-exponential factor: in this way, these alloys resemble the pure metals.

TABLE VIII. *The Hydrogenation of Ethylene over Nickel–Copper Powders*[61]

% Cu in alloy	0	63.1	89.7	100
Temp. range used	21–−10°	−60–−75°	−40–−70°	55–130°
E(kcal. mole^{-1})	7.5	9.5	8.6	8.0
$\log A_s$* (units arbitrary)	13.6	19.2	16.7	13.7
$\log k_s$* at −3°	0.4	2.7	1.6	−0.6

* $\log A$ and $\log k$ are expressed per m².

The extreme importance of preadsorbed hydrogen in this system has been stressed by Hall and Emmett.[44] The specific activity of alloy powders at −70° increases approximately linearly with increasing nickel content when the samples are cooled in helium from the reduction temperature. Samples cooled in hydrogen show higher activity and the promoting effect is a maximum at about 12 per cent copper. The activation energy is slightly higher for samples cooled in hydrogen than for those cooled in helium, but it is roughly constant at 4 kcal. mole^{-1} between 15 and 100 per cent nickel.

The same reaction has also been studied using foils between 400 and 600°.[49] It must be remembered, at least for nickel and probably for the nickel-rich alloys, that this is well above the usual inversion temperature, and hence results found at these high temperatures are not necessarily comparable with those obtained at much lower temperatures. The results are shown in the usual manner in Fig. 7, the units of the activity being the percentage conversion at 500° per 100 cm.^{2} surface. Especially striking is the very abrupt

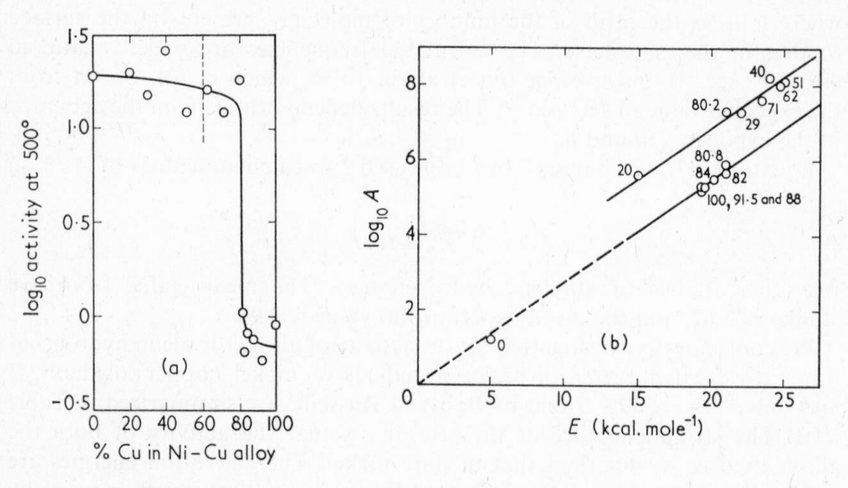

FIG. 7. Ethylene hydrogenation over nickel–copper foils.[49]
(a) Activity as a function of composition.
(b) Compensation effect: the composition (%Cu) to each point corresponds is indicated.

decrease in activity between 80.2 and 80.8 per cent copper (Fig. 7a), but while this is above the normal critical composition, it is not impossible that thermal excitation will create additional *d*-band holes, and hence will raise the critical copper concentration. Fig. 7(b) shows that, except for pure nickel, the more active alloys owe their activity to an enhanced pre-exponential factor, following the general rule.

Less extensive studies of olefin hydrogenation over nickel–copper alloys have been carried out using styrene and cinnamic acid. Styrene has been hydrogenated in methanol solution between 20 and 80° over nickel–copper foils,[62] and the activity fell linearly with increasing copper content, becoming zero at about 56 per cent copper. A similar result is shown by cinnamic acid over kieselguhr-supported alloys,[63] although the results obtained with

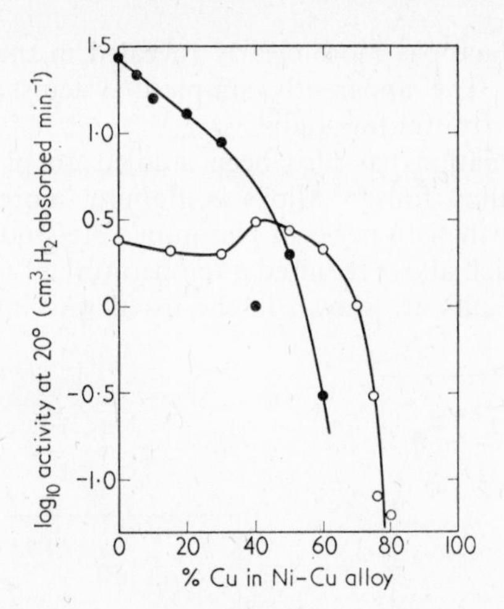

FIG. 8. The hydrogenation of cinnamic acid at 20° over nickel–copper alloys: the rate of hydrogen uptake as a function of composition.[63]

○ Unsupported alloy powders.

● Alloys supported on kieselguhr.

unsupported alloy powders are somewhat different (see Fig. 8). Hall and Emmett[44] have concluded that "the nickel–copper alloy system is a particularly poor one to be used for the correlation of activity data to unmeasured properties of the solid state." This stricture would seem to apply especially to the hydrogenation of ethylene, and there is a *prima facie* case for believing

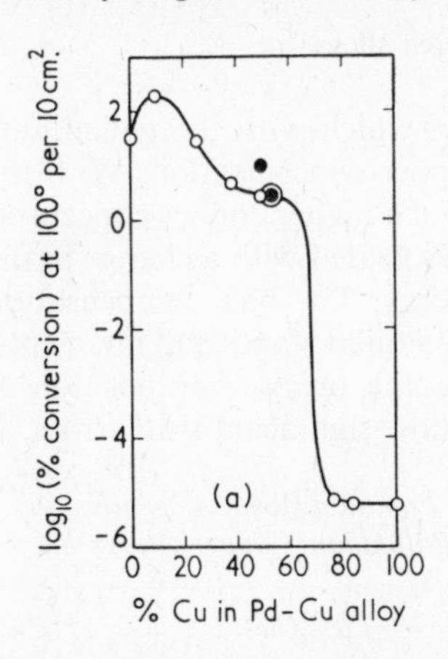

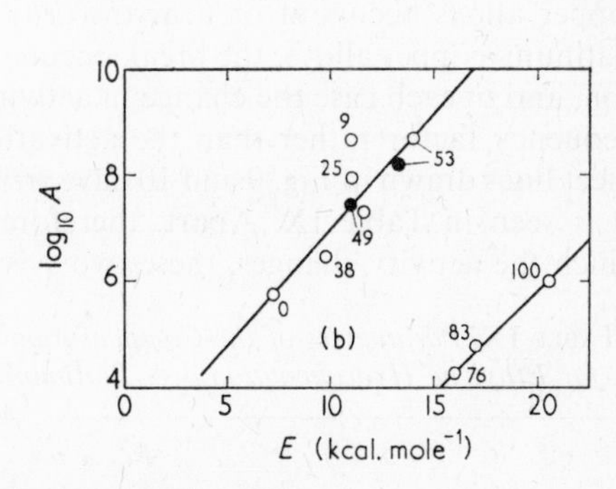

FIG. 9. Ethylene hydrogenation over palladium–copper foils.[64]

(a) Activity as a function of composition.

(b) Compensation effect: the composition (%Cu) to which each point corresponds is indicated.

○ Disordered alloys. ● Ordered alloys.

that the electronic factor is more clearly revealed in the reactions of more complex molecules. The apparently simplest systems are, therefore, not necessarily the most fruitful for study.

Ethylene hydrogenation has also been studied on platinum–copper and palladium–copper alloy foils.[64] Alloys containing more than 47 per cent palladium and more than 16 per cent platinum were studied between 70 and 130°, while copper-rich alloys required a temperature of 650° to give measurable activity: the results are shown in the usual way in Figs. 9 and 10. In

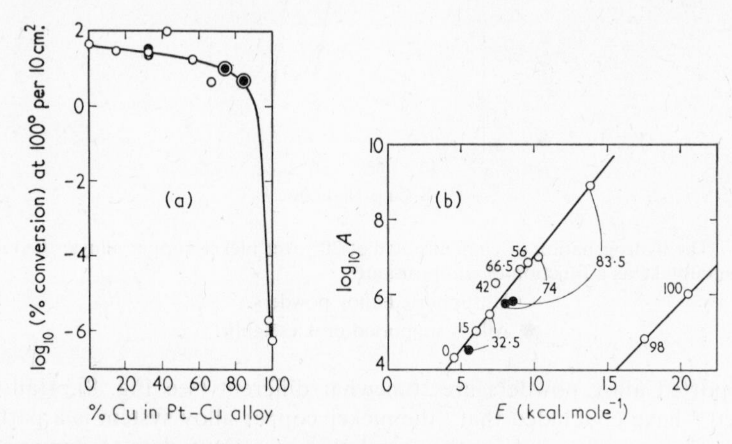

Fig. 10. Ethylene hydrogenation over platinum–copper soils.[64]
(a) Activity as a function of composition.
(b) Compensation effect: the composition (%Cu) to which each point corresponds is indicated.
○ Disordered alloys. ● Ordered alloys.

each system there is a sharp change in activity, which with the palladium–copper alloys occurs at or near the critical copper concentration. With the platinum–copper alloys, the break occurs at a much higher copper concentration, and in each case the change in activity is associated with a change in the frequency factor rather than the activation energy. The best compensation effect lines drawn in Fig. 9 and 10 have strikingly similar slopes and intercepts, as is seen in Table IX. Apart, therefore, from the precise composition at which the activity changes, these two systems show significant similarities.

Table IX. *Parameters of the Compensation Effect Equation* ($\log_{10} A = mE + c$) *for Ethylene Hydrogenation over Platinum– and Palladium–Copper Alloys*[64]

	Pt—Cu		*Pd—Cu*	
	m	*c*	*m*	*c*
Line I	0.51	1.85	0.50	1.9
Line II	0.38	−1.8	0.40	—2.0

Ethylene has been hydrogenated over palladium–silver alloys[65] between 0 and 100°, with results which are shown in Table X. They show a marked resemblance to those referred to in Chapter 8 for *para*-hydrogen conversion over palladium–gold alloys: the activation energy is constant up to 50 per cent silver, whereafter it increases, the log$A$ term remaining constant (as in Figs. 8 and 9). Measurements of the rate of adsorption of hydrogen by these alloys show a quite remarkable similarity (see also Table X), the activation energies being almost identical for both reactions for each alloy. The maximum rate for both reactions occurs at about 35 per cent silver, close to the composition at which the volume absorbed at equilibrium is also a maximum. Pretreatment by hydrogen lowers the activity of palladium to one-half its usual value, but slightly increases the activity of alloys containing between 20 and 50 per cent silver. No measurements could be made on alloys containing more than 60 per cent silver. It is not suggested that the parallelism between the two reactions has mechanistic implications, but rather it is noted that the same electronic factors can influence similarly the rates of two quite different processes.

TABLE X. *The Hydrogenation of Ethylene over, and the Absorption of Hydrogen by, Palladium–Silver Alloys*[65]

% Ag in alloy	Hydrogenation			Absorption		
	log$r$* at 100°	E(kcal.mole^{-1})	log$A$*	log$r$† at 100°	E(kcal. mole^{-1})	log$A$†
0	−1.02	5.5	2.20	0.03	5.8	3.43
20	−1.30	5.1	1.69	−0.24	5.1	2.75
30	−1.11	5.4	2.06	0.04	4.9	2.92
40	−1.05	5.3	2.06	0.02	5.3	3.09
50	−1.55	5.0	1.49	−0.47	5.2	2.58
60	−2.70	8.0	2.00	−1.70	8.0	3.00

*, A and r in min.$^{-1}$; †, A and r in cm. min.$^{-1}$.

TABLE XI. *Ethylene Hydrogenation over Copper–Silver Alloy Wires*[41]

Atomic % Ag	Mean crystallite diameter (mm.)	Activity at 700° per 100 cm.^{2}	E(kcal. mole^{-1})	$\log_{10} A$
0	0.13	14.8	19.5	6.68
3	0.13	12.1	17.1	5.91
37	0.01	25.7	15.9	5.90
59	0.01	29.5	15.7	5.90
84	0.03	10.8	15.8	5.49
92	0.03	13.2	16.6	5.81
97	0.02	18.3	19.1	6.66
100	0.05	20.9	27.1	8.97

Finally ethylene hydrogenation has been studied over copper–silver alloy wires in a flow-system between 550 and 700°.[41] The results, which are given in Table XI, are of less interest than the foregoing, in that in this system no radical change takes place in the electronic structure of the catalyst. The highest activity is shown by those wires having the smallest crystallite size, and this is apparently associated with a lower activation energy. The points for these two wires lie away from the best compensation effect line.

11.5 The Mechanisms of Olefin Hydrogenation and Related Processes[26, 32, 33]

11.51 Introduction

We have not yet inquired into the nature of the processes intervening between the chemisorption of the reactants and the appearance of the desorbed product. That the mechanism is not always simply the simultaneous addition of two adsorbed hydrogen atoms to the associatively adsorbed olefin is made abundantly evident by two kinds of observation. (i) During olefin hydrogenation, processes other than addition occur at the same time where conditions permit, notably double-bond migration and *cis–trans* isomerization. (ii) When reactions are carried out with deuterium in place of hydrogen, the dideuterated paraffin is rarely the sole product.

It has long been known that, during the hydrogenation of unsaturated glycerides, migration of the double bonds and isomerization of the *cis*-isomers occurs very readily.[66] It is neither possible nor desirable to review this work, since the complexity of the systems and the analytical difficulties have made it impossible to derive quantitative results.[67] Valuable results have, however, been obtained with much simpler systems, and these will be discussed in due course.

The history of the application of isotopic tracers, particularly deuterium, to this system closely parallels that of its application to the exchange of saturated hydrocarbons (Chapter 9). In the first phase (roughly from 1934 to 1948) the existence of an exchange reaction, which in the case of ethylene may be written as

$$C_2H_4 + D_2 \rightarrow C_2H_3D + HD, \qquad \text{(i)}$$

was established by detecting a decrease in the deuterium content of the "hydrogen." Subsequently the application of mass-spectrometry has enabled the appearance of deuterium in the olefin to be followed, and the distribution of the various deuterated paraffins to be determined. It has become apparent[32] that the reactions leading to the formation of hydrogen deuteride and of deuterated olefin do not necessarily proceed at equal rates and hence that equation (i) is not accurate; it is, therefore, convenient to refer to the former as the *hydrogen exchange reaction* and the latter as the *olefin exchange reaction*. It has further very frequently appeared that saturated hydrocarbons containing more and less than the expected number of deuterium atoms do not entirely arise from the subsequent reaction of respectively deuterium with deuterated olefin and olefin with hydrogen deuteride and hydrogen. These species must, therefore, result from the occurrence of some kind of *redistribution reaction* on the surface.

A further word concerning the terminology to be used is necessary. The process of saturating the olefinic double bond, as witnessed by the appearance of the product in the gas or liquid phase, will be referred to as hydrogenation, regardless of the isotopic nature of the reaction partners. Terms such as deuteration and deuterogenation (the latter of very doubtful derivation) will be avoided because of their ambiguity. The terms "hydrogen" and olefin will be used except where specification of their isotopic nature is called for.

The analysis of mixtures of deuterated olefins and deuterated paraffins by mass-spectrometry is more difficult than that of the latter alone. Two methods may be used. (i) The mass-spectrum of the olefin mixture may first be determined by the use of electrons insufficiently energetic to ionize the paraffin, followed by the use of more energetic electrons to obtain the total mass–spectrum;[37, 68] alternatively (ii) partial or complete separation of the components may be achieved by chemical means.[50, 52, 69, 70] Gas–liquid chromatography is a most promising means of effecting this separation. When the separate mass-spectra for each chemical species are measured or derived, calculations to obtain the isotopic composition follow the lines indicated in Chapter 9.

Instead of trying to infer the most probable reaction mechanism by consideration of the available (and sometimes discordant) results, the reverse procedure will be adopted of setting down a selection of possible elementary steps, in the hope of showing that these allow of a qualitative interpretation of the observations. Subsequently, this interpretation will be made as quantitative as possible, when the experimental results are considered in detail.

11.52 Reaction Mechanisms

It will be remembered that we proposed to assume that the olefin before suffering reaction was associatively adsorbed (Section 11.11). The *precise* mode of adsorption of the "hydrogen" is immaterial to a first consideration of detailed reaction mechanisms, although questions such as whether both reactants occupy the same kind of site must ultimately be answered.[71] It will, of course, affect the overall kinetics, and this is why it is important that for the gleaning of the greatest amount of information these should be established simultaneously with the internal kinetics.

Adopting the principle of economy of hypothesis, we will try to set down the minimum number of steps to account for the observations. Starting with the generalized olefin $R_aHC{=}CHR_b$ we may write

$$R_aHC{=}CHR_b + 2* \rightleftharpoons R_a\underset{*}{HC}{-}\underset{*}{CHR_b} \qquad (j, k)$$

and

$$D_2 + 2* \rightleftharpoons 2\,\underset{*}{D}. \qquad (1)$$

Two kinds of further process may now be envisaged. (i) One deuterium atom adds to the adsorbed olefin creating an adsorbed alkyl radical, which is the half-hydrogenated state first suggested by Horiuti and Polanyi,[72] and since widely employed by numerous authors. (ii) The two deuterium atoms may add simultaneously (or effectively so) liberating the dideutero-paraffin to the gas phase: this is termed the *direct addition mechanism*, and although there is good evidence for its occurrence, it only rarely achieves prominence. These processes may then be written

$$R_aH\underset{*}{C}—\underset{*}{C}HR_b + \underset{*}{D} \rightarrow R_aH\underset{*}{C}—CHDR_b + 2* \qquad \text{(m)}$$

$$\rightarrow R_aDHC—\underset{*}{C}HR_b + 2* \qquad \text{(m')}$$

and

$$R_aH\underset{*}{C}—\underset{*}{C}HR_b + 2\underset{*}{D} \rightarrow R_aDHC—CHDR_b + 4*. \qquad \text{(n)}$$

They have also been written as

$$R_aH\underset{*}{C}—\underset{*}{C}HR_b + \overset{D_2}{\vdots} \rightarrow R_aH\underset{*}{C}—CHDR_b + \underset{*}{D} \qquad \text{(o)}$$

$$\rightarrow R_aHDC—\underset{*}{C}HR_b + \underset{*}{D}. \qquad \text{(o')}$$

and indeed according to Twigg[73] this is the only mechanism by which deuterium gains access to a nickel surface. Where R_a and R_b are not the same, the radicals formed in (m) and (o) will be recognizably different from those formed in (m′) and (o′).

The further reaction of the radicals may first be considered by reference to the ethyl radical $\underset{*}{C}H_2—CH_2D$ formed from ethylene. We have the following possibilities. (i) The reverse of steps (m), (m′), (o) and (o′) may occur: ignoring possible zero-point energy effects, the radical has twice the chance of losing a hydrogen atom as of losing a deuterium atom.

$$\underset{*}{C}H_2—CH_2D + 2* \rightarrow \underset{*}{H} + H_2\underset{*}{C}—\underset{*}{C}HD \qquad \text{(p)}$$

$$\rightarrow \underset{*}{D} + H_2\underset{*}{C}—\underset{*}{C}H_2 \qquad \text{(p')}$$

$$\underset{*}{C}H_2—CH_2D + \underset{*}{D} \rightarrow H_2\underset{*}{C}—\underset{*}{C}HD + \overset{HD}{\vdots} \qquad \text{(q)}$$

$$\rightarrow H_2\underset{*}{C}—\underset{*}{C}H_2 + \overset{D_2}{\vdots}\,. \qquad \text{(q')}$$

Desorption of the olefin formed in steps (p) and (q) will account for the appearance of deuterated olefin in the gas phase.

The second possibility is that (*ii*) the radicals may disproportionate, in either of two ways:

$$2\,\underset{*}{\mathrm{CH_2}}\text{—}\mathrm{CH_2D} \rightarrow \mathrm{H_2}\underset{*}{\mathrm{C}}\text{—}\underset{*}{\mathrm{CH_2}} + \underset{\vdots}{\mathrm{H_2DC\text{—}CH_2D}} \qquad \text{(r)}$$

$$\rightarrow \mathrm{H_2}\underset{*}{\mathrm{C}}\text{—}\underset{*}{\mathrm{CHD}} + \underset{\vdots}{\mathrm{H_3C\text{—}CH_2D}}\,. \qquad \text{(r')}$$

In step (r′) an ethane molecule is formed with one less than the proper number of deuterium atoms, but this is counterbalanced by the formation of adsorbed ethylene-d_1, which must eventually be converted (on average) to ethane-d_3.

A third possibility (iii) is that the ethyl radical may react with a deuterium atom or molecule to form ethane:

$$\underset{*}{\mathrm{CH_2}}\text{—}\mathrm{CH_2D} + \underset{*}{\mathrm{D}} \rightarrow \underset{\vdots}{\mathrm{H_2DC\text{—}CH_2D}} + 2* \qquad \text{(s)}$$

$$\underset{*}{\mathrm{CH_2}}\text{—}\mathrm{CH_2D} + \underset{\vdots}{\mathrm{D_2}} \rightarrow \underset{\vdots}{\mathrm{H_2DC\text{—}CH_2D}} + \underset{*}{\mathrm{D}}. \qquad \text{(t)}$$

Now many of the foregoing processes have their exact counterparts in the exchange reactions of saturated hydrocarbons, the chief difference between the two systems being in the steady-state concentration of hydrocarbon species. In hydrocarbon exchange it is usually low because saturated hydrocarbons are only weakly adsorbed, whereas in olefin hydrogenation it is usually large because of the stronger adsorption of olefins. Reactions (r) and (r′) are therefore improbable in the former system. The fourth possible mode of reaction of adsorbed ethyl radicals also applies only to olefin hydrogenation since it depends on the adjacent adsorption of hydrocarbon species. It is (iv) a simple atom interchange:

$$\underset{*}{\mathrm{CH_2}}\text{—}\mathrm{CH_2D} + \mathrm{H_2}\underset{*}{\mathrm{C}}\text{—}\underset{*}{\mathrm{CH_2}} \rightarrow \mathrm{H_2}\underset{*}{\mathrm{C}}\text{—}\underset{*}{\mathrm{CHD}} + \underset{*}{\mathrm{CH_2}}\text{—}\mathrm{CH_3} \qquad \text{(u)}$$

$$\rightarrow \mathrm{H_2}\underset{*}{\mathrm{C}}\text{—}\underset{*}{\mathrm{CH_2}} + \underset{*}{\mathrm{CH_2}}\text{—}\mathrm{CH_2D}. \qquad \text{(u')}$$

There is evidence (to be discussed in the next sub-section) that this is a relatively rapid process; hence if the ratio of ethyl radicals to ethylene molecules is small, the ethyl radicals in the early stages of the reaction will be predominantly ethyl-d_0.

Processes analogous to the above may also, of course, occur with higher olefins: however, the situation grows progressively more complex. Thus for example, when in the generalized olefin we have $R_a = CH_3$ and $R_b = H$, two initiating steps are possible (written here with atomic deuterium):

$$\mathrm{CH_3}\text{—}\underset{*}{\mathrm{CH}}\text{—}\underset{*}{\mathrm{CH_2}} + \underset{*}{\mathrm{D}} \rightarrow \mathrm{CH_3}\text{—}\mathrm{CHD}\text{—}\underset{*}{\mathrm{CH_2}} + 2* \qquad \text{(v)}$$

$$\rightarrow \mathrm{CH_3}\text{—}\underset{*}{\mathrm{CH}}\text{—}\mathrm{CH_2D} + 2*. \qquad \text{(v')}$$

With any unsymmetrically substituted olefin, therefore, different radicals are initially possible, although they will doubtless be rapidly brought into equilibrium. The relevance of the nature of the first-formed radicals becomes clear when it is realized that the 1-adsorbed, 2-deuteropropyl radical has a one-half chance of losing a deuterium atom, whereas the 1-deutero, 2-adsorbed propyl radical has only a one-sixth chance. The difference is even greater with the radicals formed from isobutane.

Several other kinds of process become possible with the n-butenes. In the first place, the position of the double-bond may migrate:

$$\begin{array}{ccccc} \text{1-butene} & & & & \text{2-butene} \\ \Downarrow\Uparrow & & & & \Downarrow\Uparrow \\ CH_3\text{—}CH_2\text{–}\underset{*}{CH}\text{–}\underset{*}{CH_2} & \underset{-H}{\overset{+\overset{*}{H}}{\rightleftharpoons}} & CH_3\text{–}CH_2\text{–}\underset{*}{CH}\text{–}CH_3 & \underset{+\underset{*}{H}}{\overset{-H}{\rightleftharpoons}} & CH_3\text{–}\underset{*}{CH}\text{–}\underset{*}{CH}\text{–}CH_3. \end{array} \qquad (w)$$

As indicated, this process may be observed without the use of isotopic tracers, and indeed its occurrence has long been experienced in the hydrogenation of unsaturated fatty acids and their glycerides.[66] Academic studies of this system are presently confined chiefly to the butenes and cyclohexene. Because of the free rotation about the central carbon–carbon bond in the half-hydrogenated state written above, it is possible for the adsorbed 2-butene to exist in either the *cis* or the *trans* structure, and hence the 2-butene formed from 1-butene is expected to have the equilibrium ratio of *cis* to *trans* isomers. The phenomenon of *cis–trans* isomerization is also well known in the hydrogenation of unsaturated fatty acids.[66] While the 2-adsorbed butyl radical alone may be formed from 2-butene, the half-hydrogenated state formed from 1-butene may be either the 1-adsorbed butyl or the 2-absorbed butyl radical; however, loss of hydrogen from the former can only re-form 1-butene.

It is evident that much valuable information may be obtained from the simultaneous study of the exchange, double-bond migration and *cis–trans* isomerization of the butenes. Because every time a 2-adsorbed butyl radical loses a hydrogen or deuterium atom, it forms the *cis* amd *trans* isomers in equilibrium proportions, the rate of formation of (say) *cis*-2-butene from *trans*-2-butene relative to the rate of formation of deuterobutenes indicates how much faster the interchange reactions (u) and (u′) are than the exchange processes. By the interchange reactions, *one* butyl-d_1 radical could lead to the equilibration of a large number of adsorbed butene molecules, whereas at most one butene-d_1 molecule would appear. Ethylene and propylene do not, of course, bear the trace of having been adsorbed as radicals in the way the butenes do, although it is in principle possible to study the isomerization processes with isotopically labelled ethylene or propylene, for example, starting with *cis*-ethylene-d_2 or *cis*-propylene-d_1:

$$\begin{array}{ccc} CH_3 & & D \\ & \diagdown \quad \diagup & \\ & C = C & \\ & \diagup \quad \diagdown & \\ H & & H \end{array}$$

To obtain the most complete information concerning the mechanism of the hydrogenation of any olefin, it is therefore necessary to determine the following. (i) The overall kinetics (with either hydrogen or deuterium) both by initial rates and by analysis of the variation of rate with time, over a range of temperature. (ii) The activation energy (preferably with both hydrogen and deuterium). (iii) The variation in the composition of the products (deuterated paraffins and olefins, and hydrogen isotopes) with time and the dependence of their initial rates of formation on the partial pressures of reactants, hence obtaining the orders of the hydrogen and olefin exchange reactions. (iv) The dependence of the initial rates of product formation on temperature, hence finding the separate activation energies for the exchange processes. (v) The kinetics of the exchange processes over a range of temperatures. It is hardly necessary to add that no one investigation has yet covered all these points.

Having listed possible elementary steps in the total process, we must now inquire into their quantitative interrelation. One part of the problem is to explain the initial distribution of deuterated paraffins, that is, that arising from isotopically pure reactants: a second part is to relate this to the initial distribution of deuterated olefins, and when this is done the extent of the hydrogen exchange reaction follows automatically, since mass balance must be preserved. With regard to the first part, an early attempt[68] to interpret the distributions of deuterated paraffins formed from *cis*-2-butene and ethylene in terms of binomial distributions was not markedly successful: in particular, this treatment seriously underestimated the more completely deuterated species. A semi-quantitative treatment[50] has been more successful; this is based on the observation that the yields of deuterated paraffins often decrease logarithmically with increasing deuterium content, that is,

$$\frac{\text{yield of } C_nH_{2n+2-x}D_x}{\text{yield of } C_nH_{2n+3-x}D_{x-1}} = \sigma.$$

This observation has been interpreted as follows. Any adsorbed olefin which following an exchange step such as (p), (q) or (r′) contains one deuterium atom must necessarily be converted by one of the initiating steps, (m) or (o), into an alkyl-d_2 radical. Now if addition occurs predominantly through mechanism (r), each alkyl radical will have roughly the same chance of desorbing as a paraffin-d_x or of remaining on the surface, suffering further exchange, and ultimately appearing as a paraffin-d_{x+1}. Thus σ may be expected to have a value of one-half: factors which may cause variation from this are (i) the unequal occurrence of the exchange reactions, (ii) addition by other mechanisms, and (iii) zero-point energy effects. The application of this approach will be developed in the next sub-section.

Other more general schemes have been given by Kemball,[37] Horiuti and co-workers[74–76] and Keii.[77] Kemball's treatment considers only adsorbed ethylene molecules and ethyl radicals, and does not specify the origin of the hydrogen and deuterium atoms which are added to these species: these may come from either adsorbed atoms or other ethyl radicals or gaseous molecules. Each conceivable process is then assigned a probability, as follows.

Ethylene (adsorbed)	→ ethyl	$p(1 + p)^{-1}$
	→ ethylene (gaseous)	$(1 + p)^{-1}$
Ethylene + H	→ ethyl	$(1 + q)^{-1}$
Ethylene + D	→ ethyl	$q(1 + q)^{-1}$
Ethyl − H, D	→ ethylene	$r(1 + r)^{-1}$
Ethyl + H, D	→ ethane	$(1 + r)^{-1}$
Ethyl + H	→ ethane	$(1 + s)^{-1}$
Ethyl + D	→ ethane	$s(1 + s)^{-1}$

These probabilities are independent of the isotopic content of the hydrocarbon entity. There are six possible ethylenes and twelve possible ethyl radicals (including of course positional isomers), and by means of a generating equation it is possible to construct eighteen simultaneous equations which may be solved for any set of values of the parameters p, q and r. The distribution of ethyl radicals is then converted into an ethane distribution by use of the parameter s. This procedure yields more information than is attainable experimentally. Thus the fraction of ethylene-d_0 returned to the gas phase is given, as are also the separate fractions of the positional isomers of ethane-d_2, etc. The refinement of mass-spectrometric analysis may, therefore, lead to a more complete test of this approach.

Before concluding this theoretical section, it is necessary to mention one further kind of approach which can assist in determining the details of hydrogenation mechanisms. If the olefin is associatively chemisorbed and if both the hydrogen atoms are always added to the same side of the molecule (not necessarily in one step), then the original configuration of the adsorbed state will be retained, and in the case of tetrasubstituted olefins optically-different products may arise. Thus, for example, *cis*-addition of hydrogen to the olefin *trans*-$C_2A_2B_2$ will yield the racemic (DL) product, while *cis*-addition to *cis*-$C_2A_2B_2$ will yield the *meso* (internally compensated) product. The same phenomenon is observable in substituted cyclic olefins: for example, *cis*-addition of hydrogen to 1, 2-dimethylcyclohexene gives *cis*-1,2-dimethylcyclohexane, which is the *meso*-form. *Cis*-addition of hydrogen to 9,10-octalin would result in the formation of *cis*-decalin.

Having set down the basic framework, we now turn to a consideration of the experimental results in the light of the foregoing concepts.

11.53 Experimental Results

In this sub-section, the results of all reactions studied on nickel catalysts will first be discussed, followed subsequently by the results on platinum and other metal catalysts.

It will be recalled that the earliest isotopic tracer experiments on these systems were performed by estimating the degree of dilution of the deuterium employed, that is, by following what we have termed the hydrogen exchange reaction: hydrogen is released from the hydrocarbon entities either through step (q) or steps (p) and (l). Both hydrogen and hydrogen deuteride may be formed. Table XII records the activation energies for hydrogen exchange (E_e) obtained over nickel wire catalysts; activation energies for addition (E_h; see also Tables III–V) are quoted for comparison. E_e is always significantly

TABLE XII. *Activation Energies for Hydrogen Exchange* (E_e) *and Hydrogenation* (E_h) *in kcal. mole*$^{-1}$ *over Nickel Wire Catalysts*

Molecule	E_e	E_h	*Ref.*
Ethylene	18.6 (70–100°)	~14 (70–100°)	38
	4 (~200°)	~0 (~200°)	38
Ethylene	17.2 (55–120°)	8.2 (55–120°)	34
Propylene	13.7 (55–120°)	6.0 (55–120°)	34
1-Butene	9.0 (76–126°)	2.5 (76–126°)	47
2-Butene	10.0 (55–120°)	3.3 (55–120°)	34
Isobutene	10.0 (55–120°)	3.3 (55–120°)	34

greater than E_h. Above about 100°, both activation energies in the reaction of ethylene decrease with rising temperature, although the difference remains constant at between 4 and 5 kcal. mole^{-1}.[38] This difference decreases with increasing size of the olefin.[34]

Activation energies of the various processes in which the n-butenes participate are given in Table XIII: measurements of the distribution of deuterated

TABLE XIII. *Activation Energies (kcal. mole*$^{-1}$*) for the Reactions of n-Butenes over Nickel Wire Catalysts*

E_m = activation energy for double-bond migration
E_{ct} = activation energy for *cis–trans* isomerization
E_e = activation energy for hydrogen exchange
E'_e = activation energy for olefin exchange

Molecule	E_h	E_e	E'_e	E_m	E_{ct}	*Temp. range*	*Ref.*
1-Butene	2.5	9.0	—	5.9†	—	76–126°	47
1-Butene	2.0	—	7.1	5.0* 7.8†	—	60–135°	14, 78
2-Butene	3.3	10.0	—	—	—	55–120°	34
cis-2-Butene	3.5	—	8.0	—	5.3*†	75–130°	14, 78
trans-2-Butene	3.5	—	8.0	—	4.8*†	75–130°	14, 78

* Using H_2; † using D_2.

butanes will be considered later. The activation energies determined by different workers agree to within the experimental uncertainty, which is usually between ±0.5 and ±1.0 kcal. mole^{-1}. There are only two significant points of difference between the work of Twigg[47] and that of Taylor and his associates.[14, 33, 78] The first concerns the ratio of the rate of double-bond migration to that of hydrogenation at about 60°, which was found to be about unity by Taylor[14] and about 2.5 by Twigg.[47] Minor differences between their surfaces may have been responsible. The second point stems from the different meanings of the word "exchange." Thus it was found[14] that the ratio of the rates of *olefin* exchange and double-bond migration was about unity over the temperature range investigated, while the ratio of the rates of *hydrogen* exchange and double-bond migration was only about 0.2.[47] There is no disagreement when it is realized that the two exchange processes are separate and not related: further it is implied that in the early stages of the reaction each molecule isomerized also acquires a deuterium atom.

Cis-trans isomerization of 2-butene is about five times faster than hydrogenation and about ten times faster than exchange over nickel wire at 75°; it is significant that, while for this process it is immaterial whether hydrogen or deuterium is used, the rate of migration depends on the isotope used. The pressure dependences for hydrogenation, for both kinds of exchange and for migration are the same,[14, 38, 78] and with 1-butene the rate expression is

$$r \propto P_{B}^{0.5} P_{H_2}^{0.5}.$$

This implies that hydrogen is dissociatively adsorbed, probably on sites not available to butene, and that butene is only weakly adsorbed because of steric repulsions between the aklyl groups (see also Ref. 75).

The various proposed mechanisms have been thoroughly reviewed by Taylor,[33] but the following interpretation seems to be the most economical possible. Olefin desorption (process (k)) cannot be rate-determining for olefin exchange and double-bond migration since (i) there is an isotope effect and (ii) *cis–trans* isomerization is faster. Therefore the addition of a hydrogen or a deuterium atom (steps (m) and (m′)) is probably the slow step in these processes. The hydrogen transfer process (steps (u) and (u′) as written for ethylene) is probably the slow step in isomerization, no isotope effect being found because even when deuterium initiates the process it will be mainly hydrogen atoms which are transferred, at least in the early stages of the reaction. In agreement with the observed kinetics, the slow step in hydrogenation is probably the addition of a hydrogen or a deuterium atom to a butyl radical (step (s) as written for ethylene).

The reaction of olefins with deuterium over nickel catalysts above room temperature is characterized by substantial olefin and hydrogen exchange.[76] The former predominates, and its course has been followed in the reaction of ethylene[69] and 1-butene[14, 33] over nickel wire. Some results for ethylene are shown in Fig. 11. The partial pressure of ethylene-d_1 passes through a maximum after about 25 per cent reaction, ethylene-d_2 after about 40 per cent, ethylene-d_3 after about 65 per cent, and ethylene-d_4 after about 80 per cent reaction. Similar results were found for 1-butene.[14, 33] The manner in which the partial pressures of the ethanes change with increasing conversion,

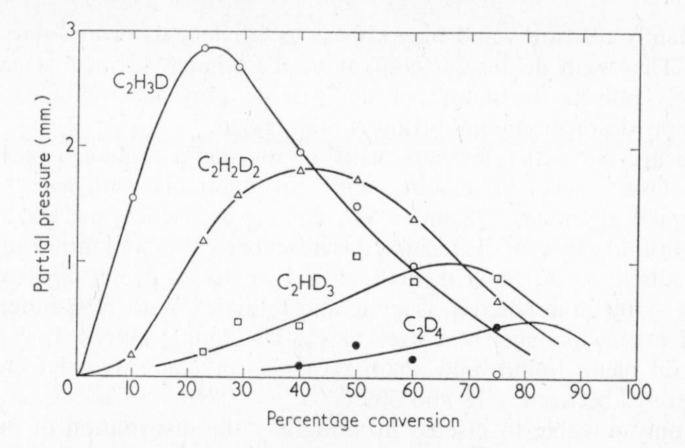

FIG. 11. The reaction of ethylene with deuterium over nickel wire at 90°: partial pressures of deuterated ethylenes as a function of conversion.[69]

under the same conditions, is shown in Fig. 12. The striking feature of these results is that ethane-d_0 and ethane-d_1 are the chief initial products, the former ceasing to be produced after 30 per cent reaction. The relative rates of formation of ethanes-d_0 to -d_2 decrease with increasing conversion, while those of ethanes-d_3 to -d_6 increase: ethane-d_6 is only apparent after 70 per

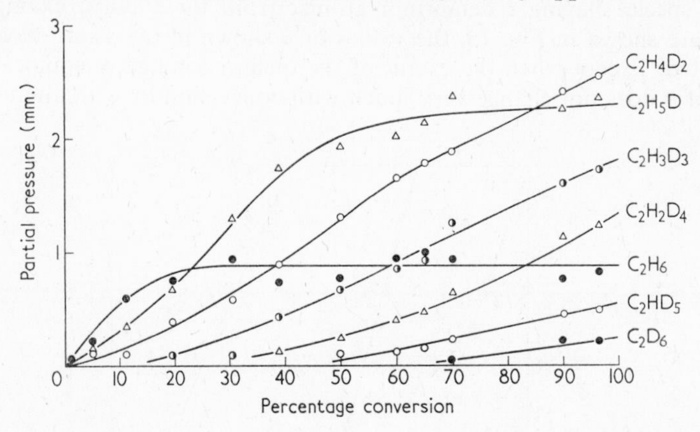

FIG. 12. The reaction of ethylene with deuterium over nickel wire at 90°: partial pressures of deuterated ethanes as a function of conversion.[69]

cent reaction. Similar results have been found with 1-butene.[14, 33] The explanation is briefly as follows. The hydrogen transfer reaction (u) is rapid,[79] and each deuterium atom initially in an ethyl radical soon is in an adsorbed ethylene which has a high chance of desorbing; the ethyl radicals in the early stages of reaction are then predominantly ethyl-d_0, and when they recombine by step (r) ethane-d_0 is the chief product. The desorbed ethylene-d_1

subsequently readsorbs and may appear as ethylene-d_2 or as some deutero-ethane. The mean deuterium content of the ethanes formed at each stage accurately reflects the nature of the gaseous ethylenes, showing that the adsorption–desorption equilibrium is maintained.

There are few other measurements of the olefin exchange reactions to report. Over nickel–kieselguhr, with an equimolar ethylene-deuterium mixture, it is absent at —78 and —50°, slight at 0° and very marked at 110°;[70] with a ten-fold excess of deuterium, it is absent at —50°, and rather surprisingly also absent at 50°.[68] With a three-fold excess of deuterium over nickel films at —100°, the reaction is quite substantial.[37] With *cis*-2-butene and a ten-fold excess of deuterium over nickel–kieselguhr, butene-d_1 is the only exchanged olefin found, and again rather surprisingly it is detected at all temperatures between —78 and 50°.[68]

It is only possible to discuss meaningfully the distribution of deuterium in the saturated hydrocarbons either when the extent of both exchange reactions is small, viz. when the undeuterated olefin and deuterium are the major reactants throughout most if not all the reaction, or when attention is confined to the initial distribution. Determinations fulfilling these conditions have been made with ethylene over films[37] and supported catalysts,[68, 70] and with *cis*-2-butene and 1-hexene over the latter:[68, 80] some of them are presented in Table XIV. In every case, within certain limitations to be discussed below, the plot of log n_i against i is linear, where n_i is the percentage of the species having i deuterium atoms: from these plots, examples of which are shown in Fig. 13, the values of σ shown in the Table have been calculated. Except when the extent of the olefin exchange is significant, the value of σ does not change very much with conversion or with alteration of

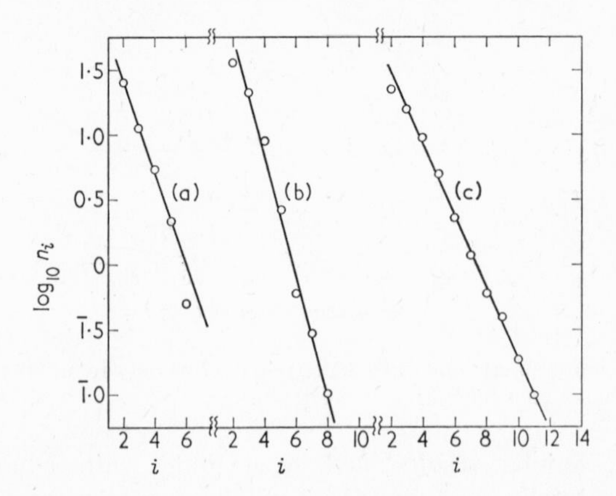

FIG. 13. Distributions of deuterated hydrocarbons plotted semi-logarithmically.
(a) Ethanes from the ethylene + deuterium reaction over a nickel film at —100° (initial distribution).[37]
(b) Butanes from the *cis*-butene-2 + deuterium reaction over nickel–kieselguhr at —78°.[68]
(c) Hexanes from the hexene-1 + deuterium reaction over nickel–silica at 105°.[80]

TABLE XIV. *Percentage Distributions of Deuterated Paraffins from the Reaction of Olefins with Deuterium over Nickel Catalysts*

Olefin	D_2/*olefin*	*Catalyst*	*Temp.* (°C)	*Conversion* (%)	*Percentage composition* d_0	d_1	d_2	d_3	d_4	d_5	d_6	d_7	d_8	d_9	d_{10}	d_{11}	d_{12}	*Olefin exchange*	*Final H content of deuterium* (%)	σ	*Ref.*
Ethylene	3	film	−100	0	21.2	34.0	25.8	10.9	5.4	2.2	0.5	—	—	—	—	—	—	—	—	0.43	37
Ethylene	3	film	−100	100	17.9	26.8	23.2	14.0	9.6	5.9	2.6	—	—	—	—	—	—	significant	0.7	0.62	37
Ethylene	1	Ni–k	−78	55	10.7	32.0	32.0	13.2	6.3	4.0	1.8	—	—	—	—	—	—	absent	0	0.52	70
Ethylene	10	Ni–k	−50	59	21.2	23.8	28.0	14.2	8.0	4.4	0.0	—	—	—	—	—	—	—	—	0.54	68
Ethylene	10	Ni–k	−50	100	17.8	25.6	27.4	16.1	7.8	3.6	1.5	—	—	—	—	—	—	small	0.5	0.48	68
Ethylene	1	Ni–k	0	55	0.0	34.5	24.4	17.8	10.7	7.4	5.2	—	—	—	—	—	—	small	0	0.67	70
cis-2-Butene	10	Ni–k	−78	97	7.3	21.8	36.8	22.1	9.0	2.8	0.6	0.3	0.1	0.1	0.1	—	—	small	0	0.33	68
cis-2-Butene	10	Ni–k	−48	33	11.0	22.1	33.8	17.2	10.3	5.6	0.0	0.0	0.0	0.0	0.0	—	—	—	—	0.47	68
cis-2-Butene	10	Ni–k	−48	99	7.5	20.2	33.5	21.3	11.0	4.0	2.0	1.0	0.0	0.0	0.0	—	—	small	2.0	0.49	68
cis-2-Butene	10	Ni–k	0	98	5.1	17.4	25.6	22.3	15.3	9.2	5.1	2.0	1.0	0.0	0.0	—	—	small	4.9	0.51	68
cis-2-Butene	10	Ni–k	50	96	2.0	9.4	21.8	21.8	19.8	14.6	9.4	5.2	2.0	1.0	0.0	—	—	small	10.2	0.57	68
1-Hexene	3.5	Ni–SiO$_2$	105	100	4.9	15.2	23.2	22.0	15.7	9.3	4.9	2.3	1.2	0.6	0.4	0.2	0.1*	—	22	0.54	80
1-Hexene	18	Ni–SiO$_2$	104	100	1.4	6.1	16.3	21.3	21.0	16.8	8.0	4.5	2.2	1.1	0.9	0.4	0.0*	—	5.7	0.55	80
1-Hexene	73	Ni–SiO$_2$	105	100	1.8	2.8	9.4	15.7	19.6	21.4	12.1	8.7	3.8	2.5	1.4	0.7	0.0*	—	1.8	0.57	80

* Hexane-d_{13} and -d_{14} not detected.
k : kieselguhr.

the deuterium/olefin ratio. Values of σ tend to the smaller at the very lowest temperatures, and generally the observed values are close to the theoretical value of 0.5 at and above $-50°$. The average of all the values of σ quoted in the Table is 0.52. The semi-logarithmic plot is not always linear from the dideutero-species onwards. With *cis*-2-butene, especially at 0 and 50°, and with 1-hexene at the higher deuterium/olefin ratios, the first few points lie below the best line. It is to be noted in these cases, because of the more extensive occurrence of hydrogen exchange, that the mean deuterium number of the hydrocarbons is substantially greater than two, and that the d_2-species is not even always the predominating one. This must mean that here there is a sufficient concentration of deuterium atoms on the surface for the radicals to be extensively exchanged and that the radicals themselves are so far separated from each other that their usual modes of reaction are not feasible. There is a general tendency, particularly noticeable in the series of results for *cis*-2-butene, for the yield of species containing two or less deuterium atoms to decrease with rising temperature, and for the yields of species containing four or more deuterium atoms to increase.

The behaviour of isobutene is surprisingly and inexplicably different from that of 2-butene[68] (see also Ref. 81). The products of its reaction with deuterium over nickel–kieselguhr at $-78°$ are: $C_4H_8D_2$, 97 per cent; $C_4H_7D_3$, 2.4 per cent $C_4H_6D_4$, 0.5 per cent. At $-46°$ these yields are respectively 85 per cent, 8.5 per cent and 1.6 per cent. Only traces of more highly deuterated species are formed in either case. The first stage of the interpretation is straightforward. The 1-adsorbed t-butyl-2-d_1 radical must have a much higher probability of formation than the 2-adsorbed t-butyl-1-d_1 radical: reversal of its formation can only remake adsorbed butene, and its only other mode of reaction is to acquire a second deuterium atom and appear as butane-1,2-d_2. It is not clear whether the readier attack at the 2-position is due to electronic effects within the molecule, or to the greater thermochemical ease of formation of the tertiary C—D bond.

Before concluding this discussion of the reaction of olefins with deuterium over nickel catalysts, it is necessary to refer again to Kemball's work[37] using evaporated films. In this paper the author quotes a theoretical distribution calculated, after the manner described in the last sub-section, with the following values of the parameters:

$$p = 3; q = 2; r = 12; s = 1.$$

This distribution does not give a linear semi-logarithmic plot. Although the detailed agreement with the observations is not very precise, the importance of this approach is that it shows the exchange and hydrogenation processes to be interrelated, and not as is sometimes[68, 76] suggested independent. The results obtained over an iron film at $-100°$ with a three-fold excess of deuterium may be mentioned at this point, since they are closely similar to those found with nickel. The extents of hydrogen and olefin exchange are almost identical in the two cases, and from the initial distribution of deutero-ethanes (Table XV) a value of 0.43, identical with the corresponding value for nickel, can be calculated. It is worth noting in passing that over both iron and nickel the yields of the deutero-ethylenes also decline logarithmically with increasing number of deuterium atoms, and values of σ' of 0.15 and 0.25 respectively may be derived.

TABLE XV. *Initial Distribution of Deuteroethanes from the Reaction of Ethylene with Deuterium over an Iron Film at −100°* [37]

d_0	d_1	d_2	d_3	d_4	d_5	d_6
40.8	27.2	19.7	7.2	3.0	1.5	0.6

We turn now to consider results obtained with other metals; a selection of these is recorded in Table XVI. The extents of the exchange reactions, particularly olefin exchange, are markedly less on platinum than on nickel. Thus, for example, they are quite insignificant on platinum–pumice catalysts both with ethylene at 0°[50] and with propylene at 18°,[52, 82] although with propylene over palladium–pumice at 50°[83] olefin exchange is more substantial. In these systems the rate of hydrogen exchange relative to that of addition increases with increasing deuterium pressure and temperature. The deuterium content of the olefin at about 50 per cent conversion increases as the square root of the deuterium pressure over palladium-pumice, but tends to be suppressed by increasing deuterium pressure over platinum–pumice catalysts. Over a rhodium film[37] at −104°, olefin exchange is less than over nickel films, but is nevertheless quite marked, and ethylene-d_1 accounts for 34 per cent of the products initially returned to the gas phase; σ' for the deuteroethylenes is 0.24, and 5 per cent HD is formed in the reaction. Olefin exchange over a tungsten film at −100° is very small indeed, and only ethylene-d_1 is detectable, and that in minor amounts.

In cases where both exchange reactions are small, the distribution of deuterated paraffins naturally remains approximately constant throughout reactions: the first two results over platinum–pumice catalysts in Table XVI provide an example. The results obtained with ethylene and with propylene over these catalysts under roughly corresponding conditions show a satisfactory measure of agreement. In addition to the results shown in this Table, the reaction of ethylene with deuterium has also been studied over the following catalysts: platinized-platinum foil, platinum on silica, on alumina and on silica–alumina.[50] From the results of this study, together with measurements made at temperatures other than those shown in the Table, the following generalizations emerge concerning the olefin–deuterium system over supported platinum catalysts. Of the deuterated paraffins, the yields of the d_0-species and of those containing three or more deuterium atoms generally increase with rising temperature, while the d_2-species nearly always decreases and the d_1-species shows variable behaviour. The results found with platinum on silica–alumina do not accord with these trends, and this together with other minor differences was taken as evidence for an effect of the nature of

TABLE XVI. *Percentage Distributions of Deuterated Paraffins from the Reaction of Olefins with Deuterium over Metal Catalysts*

Metal	*Form*	*Olefin*	D_2/*Olefin*	*Temp.* (°C)	*Conversion* (%)	*Percentage composition* d_0	d_1	d_2	d_3	d_4	d_5	d_6	d_7	d_8	σ	*D.A.* (%)	*Ref.*
Rh	film	C_2H_4	3	−104	0	15.0	25.7	28.3	13.2	8.9	6.4	2.5	—	—	0.56	0	37
Rh	film	C_2H_4	3	−104	100	11.5	27.2	29.1	13.7	9.1	6.8	2.6	—	—	0.57	0	37
Pd	on SiO_2	C_2H_4	*	−78	88	0.0	33.2	39.5	11.4	6.5	6.4	3.0	—	—	0.64	22	70
Pd	on C	C_2H_4	**	−78	100	0.0	36.6	38.5	12.0	6.1	4.3	2.5	—	—	0.60	18	70
Pd	on p	C_3H_6	1	50	45	35.9	27.5	17.5	8.9	4.4	2.2	2.1	1.0	0.5	0.56	0	83
Pd	on p	C_3H_6	1	50	100	37.0	25.9	13.7	9.2	5.9	4.1	2.5	1.2	0.5	0.60	0	83
Pd	on p	C_3H_6	5.5	50	60	30.2	25.2	17.9	11.2	6.1	3.7	2.6	2.1	1.2	0.60	0	83
Pt	on p	C_2H_4	1	0	52	11.1	33.4	31.8	10.3	6.3	4.7	2.3	—	—	0.56	10	50
Pt	on p	C_2H_4	1	0	100	13.2	31.7	29.0	10.8	7.5	5.7	2.3	—	—	0.55	5	50
Pt	on p	C_2H_4	10	0	60	10.4	25.3	37.8	12.8	7.0	4.3	2.4	—	—	0.70	16	50
Pt	on p	C_2H_4	0.13	0	47	18.3	32.4	20.9	11.7	7.5	5.3	3.9	—	—	0.58	5	50
Pt	on p	C_3H_6	1.2	18	100	13.5	26.7	24.2	14.8	8.6	5.5	3.7	2.2	0.7	0.61	0	52
Pt	on p	C_3H_6	8.4	18	100	2.1	21.8	37.6	18.8	8.8	4.5	2.7	2.2	1.4	0.57	10	52
Pt	on p	C_3H_6	40	18	100	1.4	19.6	44.9	18.4	7.5	3.7	1.8	1.5	1.0	0.52	14	52
Pt	on p	C_3H_6	0.1	18	100	32.3	32.4	19.5	8.9	3.6	2.0	1.2	0.4	0.0	0.46	0	52
W	film	C_2H_4	3	−100	0	3.3	15.8	75.1	4.9	0.7	0.2	0.0	—	—	0.21	53	37
W	film	C_2H_4	3	−100	100	4.8	15.5	70.5	6.7	1.6	0.5	0.1	—	—	0.28	49	37

* Experiment performed at 500 lb. in.$^{-2}$; ** at 400 lb. in.$^{-2}$; D.A. = direct addition; p = pumice.

the support on the properties of the metal. The yields of the more heavily deuterated species increase with increasing deuterium/olefin ratio, and vice versa.

Values of σ for deuterated ethanes formed over platinum catalysts are close to the expected value above 0° (0.53 $\pm$ 0.03): at this temperature and with approximately equimolar reactant mixtures, values ranged between 0.43 and 0.59. Substantially larger ($\sim$0.7) values were sometimes found at low deuterium/olefin ratios and a very low value of 0.23 was found with a 126-fold excess of deuterium over ethylene, using platinum–alumina at 0°.[50] Now it will be recalled that σ is expected to be 0.5 if mechanism (r) is the only mode of reaction of alkyl radicals. Values greater than this may arise if processes (p) and (q) and their congeners occur, and smaller values if either olefin desorption or steps (s) and (t) occur: these latter reactions are probably responsible for the low value of σ mentioned above and also for that found over tungsten films at low temperature.[37]

Inspection of many of the semi-logarithmic plots for the deuterated paraffins formed over palladium, platinum and especially tungsten shows a yield of the d_2-species greater in some measure than expected. This has been taken to indicate the occurrence of the direct addition mechanism. Although several pieces of work[52, 73, 84] have ruled this out as the *sole* contributing mechanism in certain systems, its occurrence over tungsten and to smaller extents over other metals has never been disproved. The contribution of direct addition tends to fall with rising temperature (except, significantly, with platinum on silica–alumina), and to rise with increasing deuterium/olefin ratio.

No study of the gas-phase reactions of butenes over metals of the platinum group has yet been reported. 1-Butene isomerizes rapidly during hydrogenation in ethanol over Pd–$BaSO_4$[85] and optically active 3-phenyl-1-butene is racemized under similar conditions.[86]

It is now necessary to attempt to relate the parameters describing the interaction of olefins with deuterium to other physical and catalytic properties of the metals concerned. The contribution of direct addition is probably inversely related to the value of σ, and the following short discussion will, therefore, be confined to considering values of σ: these increase with increasing activity for ethylene hydrogenation, with percentage *d*-character, and therefore decrease with increasing heat of hydrogen adsorption on the metal. Perhaps most significant is the correlation between σ and the parameters describing the exchange of ethane with deuterium.[83, 87] Although it is not very satisfactory to have to use results from such diverse systems, there is nonetheless a smooth change of σ with the mean deuterium content of exchanged ethanes, the mean values of σ obtained with supported metals appearing to lie slightly above the line for evaporated films. A correlation also exists between the deuterium content of propanes exchanged over supported platinum and palladium and mean values of σ.

Considerable attention has recently been paid to the hydrogenation of cyclic olefins. In their reaction with deuterium over metal films, cyclopentene, cyclohexene and cycloheptene[88] show similar behaviour to ethylene.[37] Unfortunately the fast rates shown by these molecules precluded intermediate analysis, except on sintered iron films: here, however, it was seen that very substantial olefin exchange occurred, and the variations of the yields of deuterated olefins and of deuterated cycloparaffins with time were much like those reported for ethylene[69] and 1-butene[14] (see Figs. 11 and 12). In all cases the deuterium number of the final products rose with increasing temperature, and the distributions broadened. New maxima appeared, and at 60 or 90° these were at cyclopentane-d_9, cyclohexane-d_{10} and cycloheptane-d_{10} and -d_{11}: deuterium numbers were then between seven and eight. The products formed over sintered iron films showed lower deuterium numbers than those formed over unsintered films.

It is evident that with these molecules over iron films substantial exchange of the adsorbed radicals with deuterium occurs. This also seems to be true as well for nickel and platinum films: with palladium the distribution and deuterium number are insensitive to temperature, while tungsten shows its characteristically sharp distribution. 4-Methyl- and 4-methylmethylenecyclohexane behave similarly to the unsubstituted olefins, although the latter shows quite a sharp distribution at 0°. Norbornylene yields mainly the dideuterated product and no species with more than four deuterium atoms.

As noted earlier, studies of the hydrogenation of substituted olefins yield information of stereochemical interest.[17] Work carried out before 1942 showed [28] that in a variety of cases products of the kind expected from *cis*-addition constituted between 70 and 100 per cent of the total. Recent studies[89–91] of the hydrogenation of a wide variety of substituted cyclohexenes and of some methylenecyclohexanes have shown that *cis*-products account for some 50 to 80 per cent of the total products, the *cis/trans* ratio being a function of hydrogen pressure, and the nature of the catalyst, but independent of temperature. This ratio for any olefin is highest for products formed over Adams platinum, lower for Raney nickel and lower still for supported palladium. This last catalyst showed a particularly strong tendency to isomerize the reacting olefins, especially 2-methyl-1-methylenecyclohexane. The occurrence of the *trans*-isomers may be interpreted in the same way as the racemization of (+)3-methylhexane during its exchange over metal catalysts (see Chapter 9), although other forms of explanation are possible:[90] it provides still further evidence for the existence of adsorbed radicals during the hydrogenation of olefins.

11.54 Theoretical Approaches

The principal task of theoretical investigations is to attempt to arbitrate between conflicting mechanisms. Almost all such investigations have been concerned with reactions proceeding over nickel catalysts, for here the differences of opinion have been most severe. The chief point at issue is whether in the hydrogenation of ethylene over nickel catalysts the independent adsorption of hydrogen or deuterium is possible or not, that is, whether the mechanism is of the Langmuir–Hinshelwood or the Rideal–Eley type. Twigg, following the Rideal school of thought, has argued[73] that the independent adsorption of hydrogen does not occur, and that mechanism (o) is its sole mode of entry to the reactive layer. Most other workers, especially the Horiuti school,[74–77, 82, 92] have assumed that its independent adsorption does occur. The resolution of this difficult issue clearly requires the assistance of the fullest possible experimental evidence and has, therefore, been postponed until now.

Of the various kinds of theoretical approach, the Power Rate Law (to which reference has been made in Section 11.4) has not been applied to this problem, and it is doubtful whether such an application would be rewarding. The other theoretical techniques described or referred to in the last sub-section are more limited in scope. There remains the Absolute Rate Theory.[33, 93, 94]

If the mechanism of the hydrogenation of ethylene over nickel is of the Rideal–Eley type, there should be no decrease in rate at high ethylene pressures.[33] Here the experimental evidence is sparse and conflicting (Section 11.3), and so recourse has been made to information concerning the exchange reactions. Surprisingly enough, the kinetics of neither of the exchange reactions has been established with certainty, and, to make matters worse, even in the latest theoretical treatment both are treated equivalently. In this treatment, Laidler assumes first that following the independent adsorption of the reactants steps (m) and (s) occur: it then follows by application of the Absolute Rate Theory that if the coverage by hydrogen is very low, the rate will be proportional to hydrogen pressure, and will pass through quite a sharp maximum with increasing ethylene pressure. On the alternative assumption that ethane is formed by mechanism (r), the order in hydrogen is still first, but the rate maximum as the ethylene pressure is raised is extremely flat, and the order in ethylene may pardonably be interpreted as zero. The absolute magnitudes of the rates on these alternative assumptions are not significantly different, and mean values of these calculated rates agree satisfactorily with those observed, as is seen in Table XVII.

Laidler has further concluded that insuperable difficulties arise if the rate of "the" exchange reaction is taken to be first order in deuterium pressure. On the basis of the observed activation energies, either the rate of exchange should be 10^{-5} of the hydrogenation rate if the frequency factors are the same (which they cannot be) or the frequency factor for exchange is 10^5 times that for hydrogenation, for which there is no apparent reason. This

TABLE XVII. *Absolute Rates of Ethylene Hydrogenation over Nickel Catalysts*[33]

Temp. (°*C*)	P_{H_2}(*mm.*)	*Surface area* (*cm.*^{2})	*E*(*kcal. mole*$^{-1}$) *obs.*	*Rate* $\times 10^{-16}$ (*mol cm.*$^{-2}$ *sec.*$^{-1}$)		*Ref.*
				obs.	*calc.*	
120	14	0.47	4.7	2.6	14.3	95
117	72.5	1.88	6.0	2.1	16.3	43
156	29.9	2.51	3.2	142	320	38

difficulty does not arise if the exchange rate is dependent on the square-root of the deuterium pressure, which is not inconsistent with the observations. On the assumption that the exchange reaction involves step (p) followed by olefin desorption, application of the Absolute Rate Theory shows that the activation energy for exchange should exceed that for hydrogenation by the heat of adsorption per atom of hydrogen under the relevant conditions. A calculated exchange rate is not in good agreement with that observed, which is hardly surprising when it is appreciated that two different processes are being compared.

11.6 Exchange Reactions between Olefins in the Absence of "Hydrogen"

Because of its supposed relevance to the mechanism of olefin hydrogenation, several studies have been made of the rates of exchange between deuterated and non-deuterated olefins in the absence of hydrogen or deuterium. In the earliest experiments, no exchange was found between ethylene and ethylene-d_4 over a nickel wire at 76°, in times much longer than those required to effect hydrogenation.[96] The failure to observe exchange in this system was at least partly due to the small surface area used, for exchange between ethylene-d_4 and propylene and butenes[97] was subsequently detected using nickel powder at 45°. Exchange between ethylene and deuterated 1-butene and 2-butene has also been found using Raney nickel and palladium–charcoal catalysts at 110°.[98] Ethylene exchanges with ethylene-d_4 over nickel wire and nickel–kieselguhr at room temperature, and *trans*-ethylene-d_2 also isomerizes under these conditions.[84]

In a thorough study of the latter system,[99] complete equilibration was found over a nickel film at 23° in less than an hour, showing that hydrogen remaining from the reduction of the catalyst was not responsible for the exchange. Over nickel wire, the kinetics of exchange and isomerization are similar. The activation energy for isomerization is 13.5 kcal. mole^{-1} between 35 and 105°, falling to 6.7 kcal. mole^{-1} between 170 and 195°: the activation energy for exchange is not more than 1.5 kcal. mole^{-1} greater, and this is attributed to an isotope effect. The order rises from 0.3 at 53° to 1.0 at 170°. The reaction is thought to be initiated by hydrogen and deuterium atoms released in the dissociative adsorption of some of the ethylene. These will react with associatively adsorbed ethylene to give ethyl radicals which will then exchange through the hydrogen transfer mechanism (u). It is clear that the conditions on the surface during these reactions differ considerably from those obtained during the hydrogenation of olefins, and that the information obtained is of doubtful relevance to the problems of hydrogenation mechanisms.

11.7 The Hydrogenation of Alicyclic Compounds

11.71 Kinetics and Mechanisms

Cyclopropane and its derivatives have properties intermediate between those of olefins and saturated hydrocarbons; they may be hydrogenated catalytically, but less readily than olefins. Cyclobutanes show much weaker olefinic properties, and their reaction with hydrogen, which occurs only under more drastic conditions than those required for cyclopropanes, should properly be called hydrogenolysis. The intermediate properties of cyclopropanes give them an important place in studies of the mechanisms of catalytic hydrogenation.

We may start by surveying the observed kinetics of cyclopropane hydrogenation: no product other than propane is ever detected. Over iron catalysts containing various quantities of K_2O, the initial rate law between 100 and 212° is [100]

$$r \propto P_{C_3H_6} P_{H_2}^{-1}.$$

When the K_2O content is not more than 0.05 per cent the activation energy is 13.5 kcal. mole^{-1}, and it increases somewhat irregularly, and the activity decreases, with increasing K_2O content. Over nickel on silica–alumina, the activation energy between 56 and 100° is 15.2 kcal. mole^{-1}, and the initial rate law at 75° is [101]

$$r \propto P_{C_3H_6}^{0.3} P_{H_2}^{-1}.$$

The isosteric heat of adsorption of cyclopropane on this catalyst is 8 kcal. mole^{-1} between 0 and 32°, and it was inferred that the slow step is the interaction of chemisorbed cyclopropane with an adsorbed hydrogen atom. Over nickel–pumice, the activation energy is 10.6 kcal. mole^{-1} between 130 and 200°, and the initial rate law at 170° is[102]

$$r \propto P_{C_3H_6} P_{H_2}^{0}.$$

A number of measurements on the kinetics of this reaction have been made on pumice-supported metals of the platinum group:[102–105] the observed activation energies are shown in Table XVIII: all except one of the values lie in the range 9.0 $\pm$ 1.0 kcal. mole^{-1}. Orders of reactions have been thoroughly studied over these catalysts;[105] to obtain reproducible orders it is necessary to adopt standard procedures for catalyst reduction. Orders in cyclopropane between about 0.2 and 1.0 have been found: over each catalyst, the order tends to rise with temperature and with increasing fixed hydrogen pressure to a limiting value of unity. With increasing hydrogen pressure, rates rise to a maximum value and thereafter either remain constant (zero order) or decrease (negative order). The orders observed using hydrogen pressures above that which gives the maximum rate rise from about -0.8 at 0° to a limiting value of zero with increasing temperature over all catalysts. These results are in the main adequately interpreted in terms of a Langmuir–Hinshelwood mechanism, where the slow step is the interaction of adsorbed cyclopropane with adsorbed hydrogen atoms, the latter being the more strongly adsorbed at all temperatures.

TABLE XVIII. *Activation Energies (kcal. mole⁻¹) for the Hydrogenation of Cyclopropane over Pumice-supported Noble Group VIII Metals*

Metal	*Temp. range (°C)*	*E*	*Ref.*
Rh	49–124	10.0	105
	0–200	9.5*	104
Pd	72–203	8.1	102
	95–215	10.0	105
Ir	55–177	9.8	104
	0–60	11.5	105
	15–100	8.4*	104
Pt	50–201	8.9	102
	−18–52	8.0	103
	16–126	8.4	105

*Obtained using deuterium.

Nevertheless cyclopropane is quite strongly chemisorbed in the region of room temperature, although the mode of adsorption is at present uncertain. There would appear to be three possibilities:

$$C_3H_6 + 2* \rightarrow \underset{*}{CH} \overset{CH_2}{\diagup \diagdown} CH_2 + \underset{*}{H} \quad (x)$$

$$C_3H_6 + 2* \rightarrow \underset{*}{CH_2} \overset{CH_2}{\diagup \quad \diagdown} \underset{*}{CH_2} \quad (y)$$

$$C_3H_6 + * \rightarrow \underset{*}{C_3H_6}. \quad (z)$$

Mechanisms (x) and (y) have been ruled out on kinetic grounds, (x) because the kinetics are not consistent with dissociative adsorption of cyclopropane, and (y) because the 1,3-diadsorbed propyl radical should be as strongly adsorbed as, say, propylene. There remains mechanism (z) which represents the chemisorption of cyclopropane by π-bond formation between the partially delocalized electrons in the centre of the ring with the unfilled *d*-orbitals of the metal. That this is the most likely mechanism is reinforced by the finding[105] that methylcyclopropane is more strongly adsorbed than the parent molecule, due to the electron-releasing influence of the methyl group. On steric grounds, it would be expected to be less strongly adsorbed than cyclopropane. Further consideration of the mechanism will be given in the next sub-section.

With alkyl-substituted cyclopropanes, the ring may break on hydrogenation to yield different products. Thus methylcyclopropane may break in the 1,2 position, yielding n-butane, or in the 2,3 position, yielding isobutane:

$$\begin{array}{c} {}_3CH_2 \\ | \diagdown \\ | \quad CH{-}CH_3 \\ | \diagup^{1} \\ CH_2 \\ {}_2 \end{array} \quad \begin{array}{l} \xrightarrow{1,\,2\text{ breaking}} \text{n-butane} \\ \\ \xrightarrow{2,\,3\text{ breaking}} \text{isobutane} \end{array}$$

A survey of the literature[105, 106] shows that the ring opens predominantly by breaking of the bond opposite to the carbon atom carrying the greatest number of substituent groups. Thus with 1-substituted and 1,1-disubstituted cyclopropanes, ring opening is predominantly in the 2,3 position. This is partly a steric and partly an electronic effect: steric hindrance at carbon atom 1 in the adsorbed state favours attack by a hydrogen atom at position 2 or 3, but the electrons constituting the carbon–carbon bonds may then either move towards the alkyl group (1,2 or 1,3 opening) or at right angles to it (2,3 opening). The former movement will be against the electron-repelling alkyl group(s) and is therefore more difficult.

A detailed study of the hydrogenation of methylcyclopropane over platinum–pumice has shown that at room temperature the products are 95 per cent isobutane and 5 per cent n-butane. The proportion of the latter rises exponentially with temperature, becoming about 30 per cent at 250°: the activation energy for 1,2 ring-opening is, therefore, greater (10.1 kcal. $mole^{-1}$) than that for 2,3 opening (8.4 kcal. $mole^{-1}$), as expected from the above argument. The rate of this reaction is at all temperatures about the same as that for cyclopropane, showing that the stronger adsorption of methylcyclopropane, previously noted, compensates for any steric repulsion between the methyl group and the surface. It would be instructive to compare the reactivities of *cis*- and *trans*-1,2-dimethylcyclopropane.

11.72 The Interaction of Cyclopropane with Deuterium

The reaction of cyclopropane with deuterium has been examined over pumice-supported rhodium, palladium, iridium and platinum.[103, 104] Under all conditions there is a massive hydrogen exchange reaction, which necessitates the use of a large excess of deuterium to dilute the hydrogen so released. Some deuterated cyclopropanes are also formed, more especially at lower temperatures, but the deuterium content of the cyclopropane is never greater than about 2 per cent. Rates of exchange and addition are comparable over a rhodium film at −78°.[107] Initial distributions of deuterated propanes are independent of the D_2/C_3H_6 ratio used, and bear marked resemblances to those found in the exchange of propane over the corresponding metal: propane-d_8 is frequently the major product. Selected distributions are given in Table XIX. Distributions are independent of temperature with palladium and rhodium, slightly dependent with iridium and markedly dependent with platinum.

TABLE XIX. *Initial Propane Distributions from the Cyclopropane–Deuterium Reaction over Pumice-supported Metals*[104]

Metal	*Temp.* (°C)	*Percentage composition*								ΣA	δ_A	ΣB	δ_B	*D.A.*
		d_1	d_2	d_3	d_4	d_5	d_6	d_7	d_8					
Pd	50	1.2	4.3	3.3	5.1	2.4	1.3	17.2	65.2	83.8	96.9	14.1	47.5	2.1
Rh	200	0.6	6.0	2.4	4.9	4.3	4.7	12.3	64.8	76.8	97.9	18.5	55.0	4.7
Ir	15	1.2	3.4	1.8	5.9	1.8	2.9	10.6	72.4	83.6	98.3	14.6	50.0	1.8
Pt	50	2.0	15.5	16.5	20.4	13.8	10.8	10.4	10.6	23.5	91.0	70.7	47.5	5.8
Pt	200	1.3	7.8	6.7	10.6	7.0	7.5	18.5	44.6	64.3	95.5	32.7	50.0	3.0

D.A.= direct addition.

These distributions are empirically described in a manner similar to that applied to the propane distributions obtained from propane exchange. Part A consists chiefly of propane-d_7 and propane-d_8, with some propane-d_6, and these together constitute about 80 per cent of the products (except over platinum): their distribution is reproduced by random drawing of eight atoms from a pool containing 97 to 98 deuterium (δ_A) and 2–3 per cent hydrogen. Part B takes in the remaining propanes, except that it is necessary to postulate a small percentage of direct addition (D.A.) forming additional propane-d_2. The quantity $\Sigma A(\Sigma A + \Sigma B)^{-1}$ falls with increasing temperature over iridium, but rises markedly over platinum ($\sim$10 per cent at 0°; 50–60 per cent at 200°). Over this metal, δ_A rises from 90 to 95.5 per cent in the same temperature range: δ_B is in all cases close to 50 per cent.

The similarity between these results and those for propane exchange over the same catalysts (see Chapter 9) is unmistakable: it is believed that the mechanisms are identical in the two cases, apart from the initiating steps which because of the different rates of the two reactions must be the rate-limiting steps in each case. The initiating step for cyclopropane hydrogenation must, therefore, be written

$$\underset{*}{C_3H_6} + \underset{*}{D} \rightarrow \underset{*}{CH_2}CH_2CH_2D + * \qquad \text{(aa)}$$

and must be succeeded by the familiar repeated second-point adsorption mechanism. The extensive hydrogen exchange indicates that the propyl radicals are surrounded by an ample source of deuterium atoms and hence are widely separated, their concentration being comparable with that existing during propane exchange. The occurrence of some cyclopropane exchange may mean that some adsorption according to mechanism (x) does take place: this would be described as:

$$C_3H_6 + 2* \rightarrow \underset{*}{CH}\overset{CH_2}{\triangle}CH_2 + \underset{*}{H} \qquad \text{(x)}$$

$$D_2 + 2* \rightarrow 2\underset{*}{D} \qquad \text{(1)}$$

$$\underset{*}{H} + \underset{*}{D} \rightarrow HD \qquad \text{(1')}$$

$$\underset{*}{CH}\overset{CH_2}{\triangle}CH_2 + \underset{*}{D} \rightarrow C_3H_5D. \qquad \text{(x')}$$

The activity order for metals in the reaction of cyclopropane with both hydrogen and deuterium is

$$Rh > Ir > Pt > Pd > Ni.$$

This is the order of decreasing *d*-character of the metal–metal bonds, except that palladium falls below platinum rather than above it. Other cases of the low activity of palladium have been met already. The order of decreasing multiple exchange as measured by the magnitude of δ_A is[104]

$$\mathrm{Rh} \doteqdot \mathrm{Ir} > \mathrm{Pd} > \mathrm{Pt}.$$

11.73 The Hydrogenation of Unsaturated Alicyclic Compounds

Alkenylcyclopropanes are of interest in that on hydrogenation they yield saturated products in which the ring has been broken adjacent to rather than opposite the point of substitution.[106, 108] Thus some ring fission must occur simultaneously with and not after the saturation of the double-bond. Methylenecyclopropane, which is much more strongly adsorbed than butenes, yields at room temperature n-butane and methylcyclopropane, but little isobutane:[108] at higher temperatures, all the butenes are formed in considerable quantities. Vinyl-, isopropenyl- and isopropylidenecyclopropane show similar behaviour. The explanation for this unexpected ring-opening must be in the case of methylenecyclopropane as follows:

$$\text{(H}_2\text{C)}_2\text{C}{=}\text{CH}_2 + 2* \rightarrow \text{H}_2\text{C}{-}\overset{*}{\text{C}}{-}\overset{*}{\text{C}}\text{H}_2 \ (\text{ring through CH}_2) \tag{ab}$$

$$\text{H}_2\text{C}{-}\underset{*}{\text{C}}{-}\underset{*}{\text{C}}\text{H}_2 + \underset{*}{\text{H}} \rightarrow \text{H}_2\text{C}{-}\underset{*}{\text{C}}{-}\text{CH}_3 + 2* \tag{ac}$$

$$\text{H}_2\text{C}{-}\underset{*}{\text{C}}{-}\text{CH}_3 + \underset{*}{\text{H}} \rightarrow \text{H}_2\text{C}{-}\text{CH}{-}\text{CH}_3 + 2* \tag{ad}$$

$$\rightarrow \underset{*}{\text{H}_2\text{C}}\ \ \underset{*}{\text{C}}\text{H}{-}\text{CH}_3 \ (\text{both linked through CH}_2). \tag{ae}$$

The 1,3-diadsorbed butyl radical formed in step (ae) may then acquire two further hydrogen atoms and appear as n-butane. The abnormal ring opening follows if it is assumed that attack by hydrogen atoms occurs preferentially at carbon atoms already attached to the surface. Spiropentane behaves as an alkenylcyclopropane, yielding on hydrogenation ethylcyclopropane and n-pentane: phenylcyclopropane yields n-propylbenzene and n-propylcyclohexane.

References

1. O. Beeck, *Discuss. Faraday Soc.* **8,** 118 (1950).
2. G. I. Jenkins and E. K. Rideal, *J. Chem. Soc.* 2490, 2496 (1955).
3 S. J. Stephens, *J. Phys. Chem.* **63,** 512 (1959).
4. B. M. W. Trapnell, *Trans. Faraday Soc.* **48,** 160 (1952).
5. P. W. Selwood, *J. Amer. Chem. Soc.* **79,** 3346 (1957); Proc. 2nd International Congress on Catalysis (Editions Technip, Paris, 1961), **2,** 1795.
6. R. P. Eischens and W. A. Pliskin, *Adv. Catalysis* **10,** 1 (1958).
7. L. H. Little, N. Sheppard and D. J. C. Yates, *Proc. Roy. Soc.* **A259,** 242 (1960).
8. A. K. Galwey and C. Kemball, *Trans. Faraday Soc.* **55,** 1959 (1959).
9. H. L. Pickering and H. C. Eckstrom, *J. Phys. Chem.* **63,** 512 (1959).
10. B. M. W. Trapnell, "Chemisorption", (Butterworths, London, 1955).
11. D. D. Eley, "Catalysis and the Chemical Bond" (University of Notre Dame Press, Notre Dame, 1954).
12. E. K. Rideal, *Trans. Faraday Soc.* **17,** 655 (1922).
13. A. Eucken, *Discuss. Faraday Soc.* **8,** 128 (1950); *Z. Elektrochem.* **54,** 108 (1950).
14. T. I. Taylor and V. H. Dibeler, *J. Phys. Colloid Chem.* **55,** 1036 (1951).
15. G. H. Twigg and E. K. Rideal, *Trans. Faraday Soc.* **36,** 533 (1940).
16. J. Sheridan, *J. Chem. Soc.* 301 (1945).
17. R. L. Burwell, *Chem. Rev.* **57,** 895 (1957).
18. R. E. Cunningham and A. T. Gwathmey, *Adv. Catalysis* **10,** 25 (1957).
19. J. B. Conant and G. B. Kistiakowsky, *Chem. Rev.* **20,** 187 (1937).
20. H. A. Skinner, "Modern Aspects of Thermochemistry" (Royal Institute of Chemistry, London, 1958).
21. R. B. Turner, *Tetrahedron* **5,** 127 (1959).
22. G. B. Kistiakowsky and A. G. Nickle, *Discuss. Faraday Soc.* **10,** 175 (1951).
23. F. F. Caserio, S. H. Parker, R. Piccolini and J. D. Roberts, *J. Amer. Chem. Soc.* **80,** 5507 (1958).
24. P. D. Gardner, R. L. Brandon and N. J. Nix, *Chem. and Ind.* 1363 (1958).
25. J. G. Traynham and J. R. Olechowski, *J. Amer. Chem. Soc.* **81,** 571 (1959).
26. D. D. Eley, In "Catalysis", edited by P. H. Emmett (Reinhold, New York, 1955), **3,** 49.
27. B. B. Corson, In "Catalysis", edited by P. H. Emmett (Reinhold, New York, 1955), **3,** 79.
28. K. N. Campbell and B. K. Campbell, *Chem. Rev.* **31,** 77 (1942).
29. H. E. Hoelscher, W. G. Poynter and E. Weger, *Chem. Rev.* **54,** 575 (1954).
30. D. D. Eley, *Adv. Catalysis* **1,** 157 (1948).
31. D. D. Eley, *Quart. Rev.* **3,** 209 (1949).
32. G. C. Bond, *Quart. Rev.* **8,** 279 (1954).
33. T. I. Taylor, In "Catalysis", edited by P. H. Emmett (Reinhold, New York, 1957), **5,** 257; K. J. Laidler, **1,** 168, 219 (1954).
34. G. H. Twigg, *Trans. Faraday Soc.* **35,** 934 (1940).
35. O. Toyama, *Rev. Phys. Chem., Japan* **14,** 86 (1940).
36. T. G. Foss and H. Eyring, *J. Phys. Chem.* **62,** 103 (1958).
37. C. Kemball, *J. Chem. Soc.* 735 (1956).
38. E. K. Rideal and G. H. Twigg, *Proc. Roy. Soc.* **A171,** 55 (1939).
39. T. Tucholski and E. K. Rideal, *J. Chem. Soc.* 1701 (1935).
40. E. K. Rideal, *J. Chem. Soc.* **121,** 309 (1922).
41. G. Rienacker and E. A. Bommer, *Z. anorg. Chem.* **236,** 263 (1938).
42. O. Toyama, *Proc. Imp. Acad. (Tokyo)* **11,** 319 (1935); *Rev. Phys. Chem., Japan* **11,** 152 (1937).
43. O. Toyama, *Rev. Phys. Chem., Japan* **12,** 115 (1938).
44. W. K. Hall and P. H. Emmett, *J. Phys. Chem.* **63,** 1102 (1959).
45. G. C. A. Schuit and L. L. van Reijen, *Adv. Catalysis* **10,** 242 (1958).
46. L. A. Wanninger and J. M. Smith, *Chem. Weekblad* **56,** 273 (1960).
47. G. H. Twigg, *Proc. Roy. Soc.* **A178,** 106 (1941).

48. R. N. Pease, *J. Amer. Chem. Soc.* **45,** 1196, 2297 (1923); R. N. Pease and C. A. Harris, *J. Amer. Chem. Soc.* **57,** 1147 (1935).
49. G. Reinacker and E. A. Bommer, *Z. anorg. Chem.* **242,** 302 (1939).
50. G. C. Bond, *Trans. Faraday Soc.* **52,** 1235 (1956).
51. A. Farkas and L. Farkas, *J. Amer. Chem. Soc.* **60,** 22 (1938).
52. G. C. Bond and J. Turkevich, *Trans. Faraday Soc.* **49,** 281 (1953).
53. R. F. Kayser and H. E. Hoelscher, *Chem. Eng. Progr. Symp.*, ser. 10, **50,** 109 (1954).
54. J. Newham, Ph.D. thesis. Hull (1959).
55. E. B. Maxted and C. H. Moon, *J. Chem. Soc.*, 1190 (1935).
56. H. zur Strassen, *Z. phys. Chem.* (*Leipzig*) **A169,** 81 (1934).
57. U. Grassi, *Nuovo cim.* **11,** 47 (1916).
58. E. K. Rideal, *Proc. Cambridge Phil. Soc.* **35,** 130 (1939).
59. G. C. A. Schuit, *Discuss. Faraday Soc.* **8,** 205 (1950).
60. L. L. van Reijen and G. C. A. Schuit, *Bull. Soc. Chim. belges* **67,** 489 (1958).
61. R. J. Best and W. W. Russell, *J. Amer. Chem. Soc.* **76,** 838 (1954).
62. P. W. Reynolds, *J. Chem. Soc.*, 265 (1950).
63. G. Rienacker and R. Burmann, *J. prakt. Chem.* **158,** 95 (1941).
64. G. Rienacker, E. Muller and R. Burmann, *Z. anorg. Chem.* **251,** 55 (1943).
65. M. Kowaka, *J. Jap. Inst. Metals* **23,** 655 (1959).
66. R. O. Feuge, In "Catalysis", edited by P. H. Emmett (Reinhold, New York, 1954), **3,** 413; J. W. E. Coenen, Proc. 2nd International Congress on Catalysis (Editions Technip, Paris, 1961), **2,** 2705.
67. J. H. Baxendale and E. Warhurst, *Trans. Faraday Soc.* **36,** 1181 (1940); N. Dinh-Nguyen and R. Rhyage, *J. Res. Inst. Catalysis, Hokkaido Univ.* **8,** 73 (1960); *Acta Chem., Scand.* **13,** 1032 (1959).
68. C. D. Wagner, J. N. Wilson, J. W. Otvos and D. P. Stevenson, *J. Chem. Phys.* **20,** 338, 1331 (1952); *Ind. Eng. Chem.* **45,** 1480 (1953).
69. J. Turkevich, F. Bonner, D. O. Schissler and A. P. Irsa, *Discuss. Faraday Soc.* **8,** 352 (1950); J. Turkevich, D. O. Schissler and A. P. Irsa, *J. Phys. Colloid Chem.* **55,** 1078 (1951).
70. D. O. Schissler, S. O. Thompson and J. Turkevich, *Adv. Catalysis* **9,** 37 (1957).
71. P. W. Selwood, *J. Amer. Chem. Soc.* **79,** 3346 (1957).
72. M. Polanyi and J. Hortiuti, *Trans. Faraday Soc.* **30,** 1164 (1934).
73. G. H. Twigg, *Discuss. Faraday Soc.* **8,** 152 (1950).
74. J. Horiuti, *J. Res. Inst. Catalysis, Hokkaido Univ.* **6,** 250 (1958); **7,** 163 (1959); J. Horiuti and I. Matsuzaki, **6,** 187 (1958); K. Miyahara and Y. Yatsurugi **6,** 197 (1958).
75. J. Horiuti, Proc. 2nd International Congress on Catalysis (Editions Technip, Paris, 1961), **1,** 1191.
76. I. Matsuzaki, Proc. 2nd International Congress on Catalysis (Editions Technip, Paris, 1961), **1,** 1121.
77. T. Keii, *J. Res. Inst. Catalysis, Hokkaido Univ.* **3,** 36 (1953); *J. Chem. Phys.* **22,** 144 (1954).
78. T. I. Taylor and A. R. Weiss, unpublished work; see Ref. 33.
79. T. B. Flanagan and B. S. Rabinovitch, *J. Phys. Chem.* **61,** 664 (1957).
80. R. L. Burwell and R. H. Tuxworth, *J. Phys. Chem.* **60,** 1043 (1956).
81. C. Kemball, *Proc. Chem. Soc.* 264 (1960).
82. T. Keii, *J. Chem. Phys.* **23,** 210 (1955).
83. J. Addy and G. C. Bond, *Trans. Faraday Soc.* **53,** 377 (1957).
84. J. E. Douglas and B. S. Rabinovitch, *J. Amer. Chem. Soc.* **74,** 2486 (1952).
85. W. G. Young, R. L. Meier, J. Vinograd, H. Bollinger, L. Kaplan and S. L. Lindin, *J. Amer. Chem. Soc.* **69,** 2046 (1947).
86. D. J. Cram, *J. Amer. Chem. Soc.* **74,** 5518 (1952).
87. G. C. Bond, *J. Oil Colour Chemists' Assoc.* **40,** 895 (1957).
88. J. Erkelens, A. K. Galwey and C. Kemball, *Proc. Roy. Soc.* **A260,** 273 (1961).
89. S. Siegel and M. Dunkel, *Adv. Catalysis* **9,** 15 (1957).

90. S. Siegel and G. V. Smith, *J. Amer. Chem. Soc.* **82,** 6082, 6087 (1960).
91. J.-F. Sauvage, R. M. Baker and A. S. Hussey, *J. Amer. Chem. Soc.* **82,** 6090 (1960).
92. T. Keii, *J. Chem. Phys.* **25,** 364 (1956).
93. K. J. Laidler, *Discuss. Faraday Soc.* **8,** 47 (1950).
94. H. Eyring, C. B. Colburn and B. J. Zwolinski, *Discuss. Faraday Soc.* **8,** 39 (1950).
95. A. Farkas, L. Farkas and E. K. Rideal, *Proc. Roy. Soc.* **A146,** 630 (1934).
96. G. K. T. Conn and G. H. Twigg, *Proc. Roy. Soc.* **A171,** 70 (1939).
97. M. Koidzumi, *J. Chem. Soc. Japan* **63,** 1512, 1715 (1942); **64,** 23 (1943).
98. J. Aman, A. Farkas and L. Farkas, *J. Amer. Chem. Soc.* **70,** 727 (1948).
99. T. B. Flanagan and B. S. Rabinovitch, *J. Phys. Chem.* **60,** 724, 730 (1956).
100. K. E. Hayes and H. S. Taylor, *Z. phys. Chem.* (*Frankfurt*), **15,** 127 (1958).
101. J. E. Benson and T. Kwan, *J. Phys. Chem.* **60,** 1601 (1956).
102. G. C. Bond and J. Sheridan, *Trans. Faraday Soc.* **48,** 713 (1952).
103. G. C. Bond and J. Turkevich, *Trans. Faraday Soc.* **50,** 1335 (1954).
104. J. Addy and G. C. Bond, *Trans. Faraday Soc.* **53,** 368, 383, 388 (1957).
105. G. C. Bond and J. Newham, *Trans. Faraday Soc.* **56,** 1501 (1960).
106. E. F. Ullman, *J. Amer. Chem. Soc.* **81,** 5386 (1959).
107. J. R. Anderson and C. Kemball, *Proc. Roy. Soc.* **A226,** 472 (1954).
108. G. C. Bond and J. Newham, *Trans. Faraday Soc.* **56,** 1851 (1960).

Chapter 12

The Hydrogenation of Acetylenic Compounds and Diolefins

12.1 Introduction

The hydrogenation of acetylenic compounds has commanded relatively little attention in comparison with the enormous body of work on the hydrogenation of olefins. Part of the reason for this is undoubtedly the greater complexity of the reaction: but the system is nonetheless of great interest, and it is relevant in this context to state again the paradox of catalytic studies, namely, that it is not always the simplest systems which yield the most fruitful information.

Little direct information is available concerning the chemisorption of acetylene, and nothing is known of its state under reaction conditions. Over active nickel catalysts, acetylene undergoes some self-hydrogenation yielding ethylene, but the extent of this process is much less than with ethylene.[1] Adsorbed ethyl radicals have been detected by infra-red spectroscopy on nickel–silica catalysts following the adsorption of acetylene,[2] and the associatively adsorbed state has been observed on palladium–alumina.[3] Nickel wires[4] and films[5] are substantially poisoned by acetylene, part of the poisoning over films being reversible in the presence of hydrogen.[6] Curiously enough, supported nickel (and other metal) catalysts are generally quite immune to this kind of poisoning. The heat of adsorption of acetylene on a nickel film is 66–67 kcal. mole^{-1} at zero coverage, and is independent of coverage until 5×10^{18} molecules are adsorbed.[7] This may be taken to imply that adsorbed acetylene is immobile at room temperature. The zero-coverage value for ethylene over nickel is 58 kcal. mole^{-1}, and this falls quite rapidly with increasing coverage.

Acetylene and its homologues are highly endothermic compounds, and their heats of hydrogenation are correspondingly greater than those for olefins. In Table I are presented values for the heats of hydrogenation of acetylene and its two methyl derivatives to the corresponding olefins. The first column of figures gives the heats at 25° calculated from the heats of formation,[8] the second the calorimetric values at 82° [9] and the third the calorimetric heats of hydrogenation at 82° for the olefins formed, for comparison. Heats of complete hydrogenation of a number of other acetylenic compounds have also been determined:[10] values range between 87 kcal. mole^{-1} for acetylene dicarboxylic acid to 64 kcal. mole^{-1} for diphenylacetylene. Heats of complete hydrogenation of other acetylenic compounds have also been computed from their known heats of formation.[10, 11] With mono-substituted acetylenes, increasing the length of the alkyl chain causes a decrease in the heat of hydrogenation, the effect terminating when there are three or more carbon atoms in the chain ($-\Delta H_h$ for 1-pentyne and 1-hexyne, 69.5 kcal. mole^{-1}). Values for dialkyl-substituted acetylenes lie between 65 and 66 kcal. mole^{-1}.

TABLE I. *Heats of Hydrogenation (kcal. mole^{-1}) of Acetylenic Compounds and Olefins*[8, 9]

Acetylenic compound	$-\Delta H_h$(*calc.*)	$-\Delta H_h$(*obs.*)	*Olefin*	$-\Delta H_h$(*obs.*)
Acetylene	41.7	42.3	Ethylene	32.6
Methylacetylene	39.4	39.6	Propylene	29.9
Dimethylacetylene	36.7	37.0	*cis*-Butene-2	28.6
Dimethylacetylene	37.4	38.0	*trans*-Butene-2	27.6

The above results may be taken to show that the first π-bond in acetylene and its immediate homologues is 5–7 kcal. mole^{-1} weaker than the second.[8] Now we shall assume, following the precedent of the last Chapter, that *under reaction conditions* acetylenic compounds are associatively adsorbed, by opening of the first π-bond and the formation of two carbon–metal bonds.[3] The structure adsorbed of acetylene is, therefore, ethylene-like:

```
H       H
 \     /
  C = C
 /     \
*       *
```

Other things being equal (which they are probably not), we may expect the heat of adsorption of an acetylene to exceed that of the corresponding olefin by some 6 kcal. mole^{-1}. The fact that this difference is just that observed over evaporated nickel films at low coverage can only be a coincidence, since here the associative structures are almost certainly not being formed. Nevertheless, all the kinetic investigations of the hydrogenation of acetylenic compounds indicate that the reactant is in some measure more strongly adsorbed than the olefinic product. Added olefin almost always behaves as an inert diluent, at least until most of the acetylene has reacted.

The stronger adsorption of the acetylene than the corresponding olefin is of crucial importance in determining the nature of the products formed. In the most favourable cases, the olefin is forced to vacate the surface as soon as it is formed, and the olefin is, therefore, produced selectively. In almost all cases, the rate of formation of olefin exceeds that of the corresponding saturated compound in the early stages of the reaction. This fact is made daily use of in preparative organic chemistry, and has been the basis of the commercial synthesis of ethylene.[12] The preferential adsorption of acetylene also enables it to be removed selectively by hydrogenation from gas streams containing it in only very minor concentrations. The selectivity of acetylene removal and olefin formation will be treated in more detail in Section 12.4.

The geometry of the associatively adsorbed state of acetylene has been considered by several workers.[13–15] Assuming normal bond lengths and angles, and 2.0 Å for the carbon–nickel distance and 2.1 for the carbon–platinum and –palladium distances, optimum metal–metal distances are readily calculated. These are for nickel, 3.33 Å, and for platinum and palladium, 3.43 Å.[14] It has, therefore, been widely assumed that, whereas olefins are adsorbed with least strain on the shorter interatomic spacings, acetylene and its derivatives are preferentially adsorbed on the spacings which are longer by a factor of $\sqrt{2}$. These distances are, for nickel, 3.5 Å, and for palladium and platinum, 3.9 Å. This conclusion has several repercussions. (i) Acetylenes are adsorbed with greater strain on platinum and palladium than on nickel, and for this reason alone the former metals should show a higher activity in hydrogenation. It is, of course, difficult if not impossible to distinguish this geometric effect from the concurrent electronic effects. (ii) There being none of the longer spacings in the (111) plane of the face-centred cubic metals, acetylene is not expected to be adsorbed on this face. This concept has also been used to interpret the negligible activity of the close-packed hexagonal metals osmium and ruthenium in acetylene hydrogenation.[16] It has, however, recently been claimed that ruthenium–charcoal catalysts readily effect the hydrogenation of acetylenic compounds such as diphenylacetylene.[17]

Associatively adsorbed acetylene can pack more tightly on the (100) and (110) planes of face-centred cubic metals than can ethylene, and Fig. 1 shows a possible manner of arrangement on the (100) face of palladium. Stacking in vertical columns on (110) faces, as proposed by Sheridan,[14] appears impossible because of massive overlapping, although a staggered arrangement (as with bricks in a wall) seems feasible.[15] Associative adsorption of acetylene or a derivative automatically forces the *cis*-configuration to be taken up, and hence on the simplest view the *cis*-olefin should result, although it is often the less stable isomer (Section 12.6).

The residual unsaturation in the chemisorbed state accounts for the widespread occurrence of polymerization during the hydrogenation of acetylenes.[18]

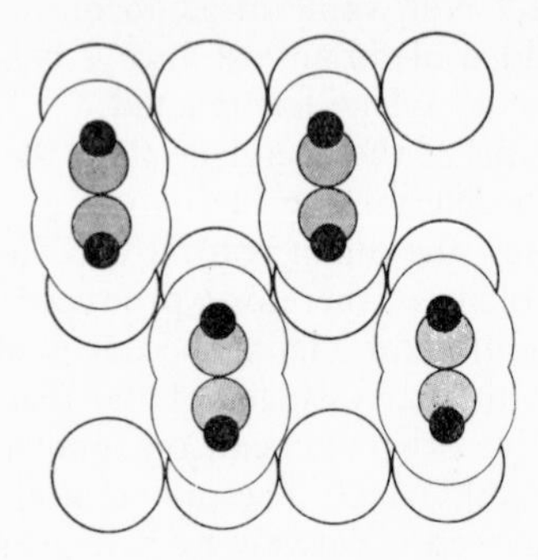

FIG. 1. A possible method of packing acetylene molecules on the (110) face of palladium.

The adsorbed vinyl radical which is the half-hydrogenated state of acetylene may exist in either a normal or a free-radical form, viz.

$$\underset{*}{HC}{=}\underset{*}{CH} + \underset{*}{H} \longrightarrow \underset{\text{normal}}{\underset{*}{HC}{=}CH_2} \text{ or } \underset{\text{free-radical}}{\underset{*}{H\dot{C}}{-}\underset{*}{CH_2}}, \qquad \text{(a)}$$

depending simply on whether a carbon–metal bond or the π-bond is broken following attack by a hydrogen atom. The free-radical form may then initiate a vinyl polymerization process in which adsorbed acetylene molecules act as the monomer units.[18] The process will be discussed more fully in Section 12.3.

12.2 THE KINETICS OF THE HYDROGENATION OF ACETYLENE[8]

In this Section we shall be solely concerned with the kinetics of the hydrogenation of acetylene over pure metals, as derived from the dependence of initial rates of pressure fall on partial pressures and temperature in static systems. The dependence of the rates of formation of the several products on these and other variables, and results for alloys, will be treated in subsequent sections. Most of the available results are shown in Tables II and III.

Complex kinetic behaviour has been found in the hydrogenation of acetylene over nickel catalysts.[21, 22] The shapes of pressure-time curves have been found to depend on the reactant ratio, on the order of addition of the reactants and on the pretreatment given to the catalyst. With hydrogen/acetylene ratios of less than about two, pressure–time curves are always first order with respect to hydrogen, but with higher values of this ratio they are usually of zero order until most of the acetylene has been removed. Another type of curve, showing a marked change in rate after about half the acetylene has been removed, is sometimes found under these conditions, but the reasons for this are not properly understood. A distinct change in the dependence of the initial rate on hydrogen pressure occurs at the hydrogen pressure $P^0_{H_2}$,

TABLE II. *The Kinetics of the Hydrogenation of Acetylene over Iron, Cobalt, Nickel and Copper Catalysts*

$$\text{Rate} \propto P^{x}_{H_2} P^{y}_{C_2H_2}$$

Metal	*Form*	*Temp. (°C)*	*x*	*y*	*Temp. range (°C)*	*E(kcal. mole⁻¹)*	*Ref.*
Fe	on pumice	136	1.4	~0	20–200	15.3	19
Fe	on pumice	~150	1	—	145–225	7.1	20
Fe	powder	~135	1	—	108–162	8.7	20
Co	on pumice	~130	1	—	107–157	4.1	20
Co	powder	~135	1	—	111–156	9.0	20
Ni	on pumice	79	1	0	0–126	12.1	14, 18
Ni	on pumice	86	*	−0.14, 0	68–152	10.3	21
Ni	on pumice	—	*	—	53–160	6.4–10.5	22
Ni	kieselguhr	~70	*	0	60–80	9.2–12.8	22
Ni	powders	~140	*	0	73–150	6.4–11.4	22
Ni	powder	30	1	−0.5	16–57	14.0	23
Cu	on pumice	~150	*	0.3	150–195	~19	20
Cu	powder	—	*	—	121–175	21	20

*See text

TABLE III. *The Kinetics of the Hydrogenation of Acetylene over Rhodium, Palladium, Iridium and Platinum Catalysts*

$$\text{Rate} \propto P^{x}_{H_2} P^{y}_{C_2H_2}$$

Metal	*Form*	*Temp. (°C)*	*x*	*y*	*Temp. range (°C)*	*E(kcal. mole⁻¹)*	*Ref.*
Rh	on pumice	85	~1	~0	17–110	15.5	16
Rh	on Al_2O_3	130	~1	—	132–162	10.6	24
Rh	on Al_2O_3	130	1.4	~0	115–165	9.0	15
Pd	on pumice	49	~1	~−0.5	0–120	11.9	19
Pd	on Al_2O_3	20	1.4	—	—	—	24
Pd	on Al_2O_3	0	1.0	−0.5	0–30	10.9	15
Pd	on Al_2O_3	30	1	neg.	30–74	12	25
Pd	on SiO_2	114	1	0	114–160	17.0	26
Ir	on pumice	175	~1	0	—	—	16
Ir	on Al_2O_3	130	~1	−0.3	—	—	15
Pt	on pumice	73	~1.2	−0.7	0–120	12	27
Pt	on Al_2O_3	105	1.5	—	77–161	17.6	24
Pt	on Al_2O_3	110	1.5	−1.7	—	—	15

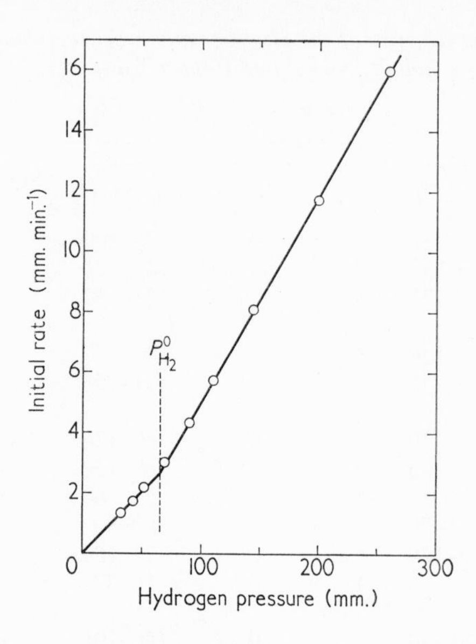

FIG. 2. The dependence of initial rate of pressure fall on hydrogen pressure over nickel–pumice catalyst at 93°: initial $P_{C_2H_2}$, 30.5 mm.[21]

where the change in curve type takes place (Fig. 2), so that at constant acetylene pressure the rate expression is

$$r = k_A P_{H_2} + k_B(P_{H_2} - P^0_{H_2}). \tag{1}$$

The ratio of k_B/k_A increases markedly with increasing temperature, and for nickel–pumice catalysts values of E_A lie between 6.4 and 10.5 (see Table II) and of E_B between 16.0 and 24.2 kcal. mole^{-1}. The ratio E_B/E_A varies much less than the separate values from one sample to another, the mean value being 2.34 $\pm$ 0.15. A convincing compensation effect operates (see Fig. 3), the equation for which is

$$\log_{10} A_i = -1.6 + 0.58\, E_i. \tag{2}$$

Similar results were found for nickel–kieselguhr, which is much more active than other forms of nickel catalysts: here the mean value of E_B/E_A is 2.40 $\pm$ 0.27, and the equation for the compensation effect is

$$\log_{10} A_i = 1.0 + 0.65\, E_i. \tag{3}$$

Discussion of a possible interpretation is postponed until some results obtained with alloy systems are presented (Section 12.5). Orders in acetylene are zero or sometimes slightly negative. Neither iron nor cobalt catalysts show these complex kinetics.

Supported and unsupported copper catalysts show kinetic phenomena analogous to those shown by nickel, but here the ratio of k_B/k_A *decreases*

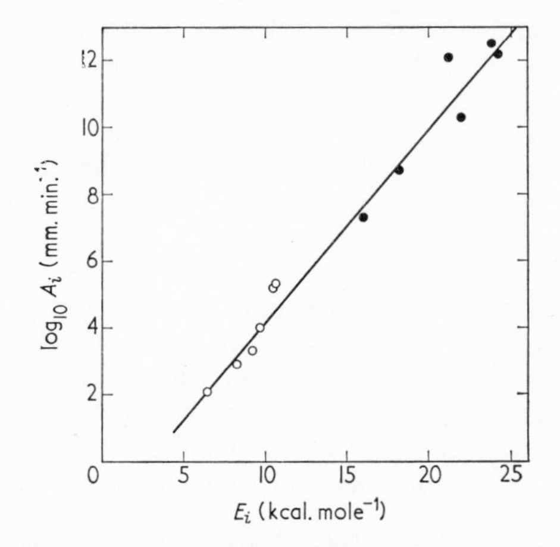

FIG. 3. The compensation effect for the hydrogenation of acetylene over nickel–pumice catalysts: ○, E_A . . . log A_B; ●, E_B . . . log A_B.[21, 22]

with increasing temperature, values of E_A being 19 ± 2 kcal. mole^{-1} and of E_B 4 ± 1 kcal. mole^{-1}. A compensation effect again operates.

Orders of reaction and activation energies for acetylene hydrogenation over the platinum group metals are recorded in Table III. Orders in hydrogen lie between 1.0 and 1.5, and it seems more than a coincidence that it was also with platinum that hydrogen orders greater than unity were found in ethylene hydrogenation (Chapter 11). Orders in acetylene are either zero or negative. More complex kinetics are encountered with a palladium–silica catalyst above 160°, but these have not been fully interpreted.[26] Pressure–time curves over palladium and platinum catalysts are generally of zero order when the hydrogen to acetylene ratio exceeds about two, and first order in hydrogen when less than two (as with nickel), although over both rhodium and iridium catalysts they are respectively second and first order in hydrogen.[15, 16, 24]

It appears that on all the metals studied (with the possible exception of copper) both reactants are adsorbed in competition, acetylene being much more strongly adsorbed than hydrogen, although relatively less so over palladium and platinum. The adsorption coefficient for acetylene has been estimated to be about one hundred times the value for hydrogen over nickel powder at 30°.[23] It is instructive to find that the differences between the various metals are of the same type in both the hydrogenation of acetylene and of ethylene, although activation energies tend to be higher in the former system. The kinetics of the hydrogenation of methylacetylene have been studied:[27] orders of reaction are similar to those found with acetylene, but activation energies are somewhat larger.

12.3 CATALYSED POLYMERIZATION OF ACETYLENE[8, 14, 18]

A unique feature of the hydrogenation of acetylene is the observation that hydrocarbons containing more than two carbon atoms are frequently found in the products, and that they sometimes constitute the major part of the products. They are formed at temperatures substantially less than that at which acetylene polymerizes by itself, even in the presence of a catalyst. A study of this process divides itself into two parts: (i) the chemical nature of the products, and (ii) the dependence of total and individual yields on variables such as the nature of the catalyst, temperature, and partial pressures of reactants.

The nature and distribution of the polymers in the products of acetylene hydrogenation have been investigated, using nickel on zinc chloride,[28] nickel–pumice[14] and nickel–alumina[29] as catalysts. The approximate distribution in terms of the number of carbon atoms in the polymer molecules formed over nickel–pumice in a flow system between 200 and 250° is shown in Table IV. Molecules containing even numbers of carbon atoms predominate, C_4 and C_6

TABLE IV. *Percentage Distribution of Polymers formed in the Hydrogenation of Acetylene over Nickel–Pumice at 200 to 250°* [14]

Number of carbon atoms	4	5	6	7	8	9–14	15–30	31–∞
Approximate yield (%)	25	2	25	2	5	7	17	17

molecules being formed in equal amounts. Evidence concerning the types of carbon skeletons present was obtained from infra-red spectroscopy: thus the C_6 fraction was shown to be largely n-hexane and 3-methylpentane, while other skeletons positively identified were n-pentane, 2-methylbutane and 3-methylhexane. Vassiliev, using similar conditions, concluded[29] that aliphatic hydrocarbons formed the bulk of the polymer product, but in addition he was able by the use of Raman spectroscopy to infer the presence of cyclohexene, cyclohexane and some of their methyl derivatives, as well as aromatics (such as benzene and methylbenzenes) whose presence Sheridan had suspected.[14] Butadiene was shown to be a constituent of the C_4 fraction. Use of the more active zinc chloride as support[28] probably led to greater isomerization of the initially formed products, and mono- and diolefins having the carbon skeletons of 2- and 3-methylpentanes, 2,3-dimethylbutane, 3-ethylhexane and 2-, 3- and 4-methylheptanes were detected.

The C_4 fractions of the polymers formed in the hydrogenation of acetylene over some alumina–supported Group VIII metals have recently been analysed by gas–liquid chromatography,[15] with the results shown in Table V. The butenes are formed in nothing like their equilibrium proportions, and 1-butene is the major product except over iridium, which is characterized by a high yield of butane and a low yield of *trans*-2-butene. The values quoted for the products over the rhodium catalyst total only 91.3 per cent, the remainder being isobutene, which was not detected elsewhere.

Over most pumice-supported metal catalysts, the yields of polymers from acetylene[14, 16] and methylacetylene[27] are only slightly dependent on temperature and partial pressures of reactants. The chief exception is nickel,

TABLE V. *Percentage Composition of the C_4 Products from Acetylene Hydrogenation over Alumina-supported Group VIII Metals (initial H_2/C_2H_2, ~1)*[15]

Metal	*Temp. (°C)*	*Butadiene*	*1-Butene*	*Cis-2-butene*	*Trans-2-butene*	*Butane*
Pd	17.6	Trace	59.3	13.5	23.3	3.9
Rh	130	0.0	42.5	34.3	7.3	7.2
Pt	135	8.3	46.5	20.3	22.1	2.8
Ir	130	0.0	35.4	17.9	1.5	45.2

where 35 per cent of acetylene removed at 0° appears as polymers, and 69 per cent at 126°; from these and other results, together with the overall activation energy (Table II), *E*(polymerization) was calculated to be 14.5 kcal. mole^{-1} at 0° and 12.9 at 126°, and *E*(C_2 production) to be 10.9 kcal. mole^{-1} independent of temperature. With methylacetylene over nickel–pumice, the polymer yield rises from 10 per cent at 50° to 20 per cent at 110°, the activation energies for polymerization and C_3 production being respectively 13.8 and 15.0 kcal. mole^{-1}. Table VI gives a selection of typical values of C_2 and C_3 hydrocarbon yields from acetylene and methylacetylene respectively, when equimolar quantities of reactants are used. In each case, the extent of the

TABLE VI. *Yields of Monomeric Hydrocarbons from the Hydrogenation of Acetylenes over Metal–Pumice Catalysts*[14, 16, 27]

				Acetylene				
Metal	Fe	Co	Ni	Cu	Rh	Pd	Ir	Pt
Temp. (°C)	135	200	83	200	85	24	175	163
C_2 yield (%)	71	50	41	~40	~75	75	85	70

	Methylacetylene		
Metal	Ni	Pd	Pt
Temp. (°C)	91	135	75
C_3 yield (%)	87	93	94

polymerization is greatest in the first row Transition metals, and this is perhaps more likely to be the result of a geometric factor than an electronic one. The low C_2 yield over copper is not in this case due to the formation of cuprene, which is a solid polymeric material formed from copper and acetylene alone. The production of monomeric hydrocarbons can apparently be made quantitative if sufficient excess of hydrogen is used.[9] Under comparable conditions, the C_3 yield from the methylacetylene is considerably higher than the C_2 yield from acetylene. There is no information whatsoever available concerning the dependence of the nature of the products or their distribution on temperature, partial pressures, or nature of the catalytic metal. It is also unfortunate that the only comprehensive analyses available are on products prepared at quite high temperatures (>200°) where at least some isomerization and cracking is to be expected. Nevertheless, sufficient information is to hand to render further consideration of this interesting reaction profitable.

As noted in Section 12.1, it has been suggested[14] that the origin of the polymerization lies in the possibility of the half-hydrogenated state existing in a free-radical form. The entity may perhaps remain adsorbed across the longer ($\sqrt{2}a$) interatomic spacing in a somewhat strained condition or may, after passing through the normal form, be adsorbed across the shorter spacing. Regardless of this, it may then attack one end of an adjacent chemisorbed acetylene molecule, viz.

$$\underset{*}{H_2C}—\underset{*}{\dot{C}H} + \underset{*}{HC}{=}\underset{*}{CH} \longrightarrow \underset{*}{H_2C}—\underset{*}{CH}—\underset{*}{CH}—\underset{*}{\dot{C}H}, \qquad (b)$$

and reiteration of this will lead to the formation of an adsorbed n-polymer chain. While such a C_4-radical may not be unduly strained, increase in the chain length by this simple mechanism must ultimately lead to breaking of some carbon–metal bonds, either by hydrogenation or desorption. The formation of n-carbon skeletons containing an integral number of pairs of carbon atoms is, therefore, readily explained, and it is understandable how with methylacetylene the insertion of a methyl group into the molecule will gravely inhibit polymerization, through steric effects. The explanation of the occurrence of branched polymers is more difficult, although 3-methypentane could arise as follows. Interaction of a vinyl free-radical with a normal vinyl radical could lead to a s-butyl free radical, as

$$\underset{*}{H_2C}—\underset{*}{\dot{C}H} + \underset{*}{HC}{=}CH_2 \longrightarrow \underset{*}{H_2C}—\underset{*}{CH}—CH{=}CH_2 \longrightarrow$$

$$\underset{*}{H_2C}—\underset{*}{CH}—\dot{C}H—\underset{*}{CH_2}. \qquad (c)$$

Addition of a further C_2 unit in the usual way gives the skeleton of 3-methylpentane. Other mechanisms have been proposed.[14] Since it is uncertain what other skeletons are primary products, it is not fruitful to consider this aspect of the mechanism further.

Possible termination steps must be briefly considered. The first part of process (c) is clearly a possibility, and indeed desorption of the 3,4-diadsorbed 1-butene radical leads to the observed butadiene. Other conceivable fates for the free-radical forms are (i) interaction with adsorbed hydrogen atoms, (ii) mutual recombination, (iii) mutual disproportionation or (iv) ejection of a hydrogen atom (e.g. the reverse of step (a)). To what extent the ultimate process of breaking carbon–metal bonds precedes termination of the chain-reaction is a matter for speculation.

For those metals which show identical kinetics for both simple hydrogenation and polymerization, the same rate-limiting step must be common to both processes, and this can only be the formation of the vinyl radical. Over nickel,[14] increasing the hydrogen:acetylene ratio increases the C_2 hydrocarbon yield and the activation energy for polymerization is greater than for addition. A possible interpretation is that in this case the general process

$$\text{vinyl} \xrightarrow{+H} \text{ethylene} \tag{d}$$

is rate-limiting for hydrogenation, while step (b) is rate-limiting for polymerization.

Polymeric products are only rarely encountered in the hydrogenation of higher acetylenes. 1-Heptyne has been reported to form dimers and trimers during hydrogenation over copper at 200° and phenylacetylene to form diphenylbutane and other polymers under similar conditions.[30]

12.4 Selectivity

The hydrogenation of acetylenic compounds is the first type of reaction we have encountered in which the reactant is converted to the main ultimate product in two distinguishable phases. The general theoretical framework was presented in Section 7.24. We may begin by considering how the mechanistic and thermodynamic selectivity factors (respectively S_m and S_t, both defined in Chapter 7) may operate in the present instance.

Now the salient experimental observations are as follows. (i) When acetylene is hydrogenated in a static system, the ethylene:ethane ratio (and hence S_m) generally remains constant until most of the acetylene has been removed. (ii) S_m is a function of the nature and state of the catalyst, the temperature and the partial pressures of reactants. (iii) When the partial pressure of acetylene has fallen to a sufficiently low value, the further hydrogenation of the gaseous ethylene commences, the rate of this second stage being sometimes much greater than that of the first stage. An illustration of this situation is shown in Fig. 4.

Before describing in detail the results upon which these generalizations are based, it would be as well to derive some preliminary conclusions. From (i) it follows that ethane is truly an initial product, and that it is formed from acetylene without the intervention of gaseous ethylene. The fact that hydrogenation of the latter does not usually start until the acetylene pressure has fallen to a low value (observations (i) and (iii)) shows (a) that acetylene is more strongly chemisorbed than ethylene, to an extent determined by the value of S_t, and (b) that both reactions occur on the same crystal faces and on the same kind of sites. A thorough understanding of the problem will, therefore, require the evaluation of S_m and S_t under a wide variety of conditions.

Some typical values of S_m shown by supported metals are contained in Table VII. Omitting from further consideration the few results available for

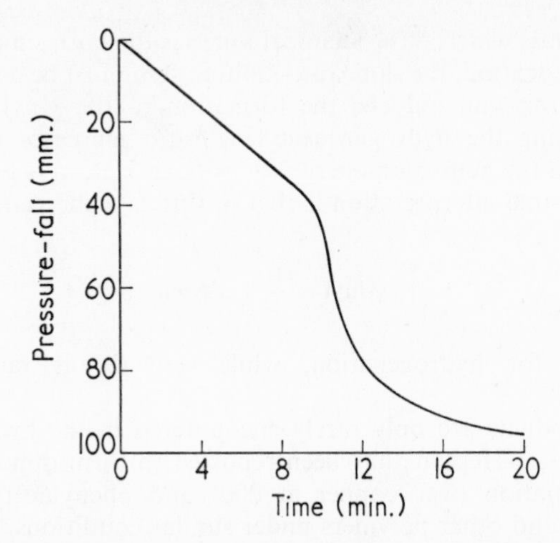

FIG. 4. Pressure-fall against time curve for acetylene hydrogenation over palladium-alumina at 20°: initial pressures, $P_{C_2H_2}$ = 50 mm.; P_{H_2} = 150 mm.[15]

TABLE VII. *Values of the Mechanistic Selectivity* (S_m) *shown by Supported Metals*

Metal	*Support*	*Initial* $P_{H_2}/P_{C_2H_2}$	*Temp.* (°*C*)	S_m	*Ref.*
		Acetylene			
Fe	pumice	1	156	0.91	19
Co	pumice	1	197	0.90	19
Ni	pumice	1	80	0.83	14, 18
Cu	pumice	1	200	0.91	19
Rh	pumice	1	85	0.86	16
Rh	Al_2O_3	2	133	0.92	24
Rh	Al_2O_3	2	150	0.90	15
Pd	pumice	2	36	0.92	19
Pd	Al_2O_3	2	22	0.95	24
Pd	Al_2O_3	2	0	0.97	15
Pd	SiO_2	3.75	181	0.97	26
Ir	pumice	1	175	0.30	18
Ir	Al_2O_3	2	130	0.55	15
Pt	pumice	1	163	0.82	30
Pt	Al_2O_3	2	105	0.86	24
Pt	Al_2O_3	2	110	0.90	15
		Methylacetylene			
Ni	pumice	1	91	0.93	27
Pd	pumice	1	80	0.97	27
Pt	pumice	1	75	0.89	27

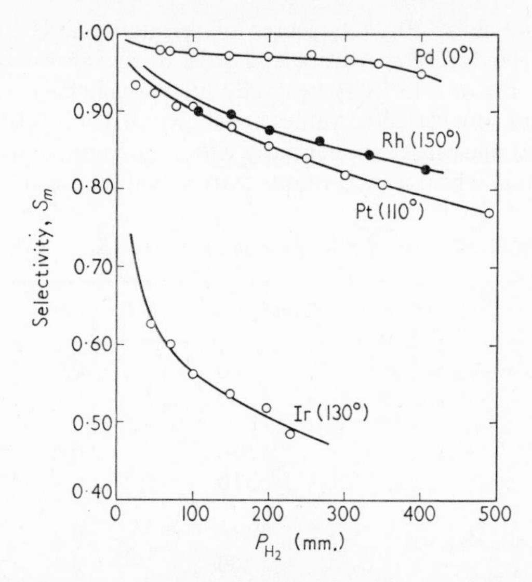

FIG. 5. The dependence of mechanistic selectivity (S_m) on hydrogen pressure over alumina-supported rhodium, palladium iridium and platinum catalysts; initial $P_{C_2H_2}$, 50 mm.[15]

iron, cobalt and copper catalysts,[19] S_m falls in the sequence

$$Pd > Rh, Pt > Ni \gg Ir.$$

There is no ready explanation of the low selectivity shown by iridium. S_m is of course a function of the ratio of the partial pressures of the reactants, and some results for the dependence of S_m on hydrogen pressure at constant acetylene pressure are shown in Fig. 5. The dependence may be adequately represented by the relation

$$1 - S_m = kP^x_{H_2}. \tag{4}$$

TABLE VIII. *Dependence of S_m on Temperature*

Catalyst	*Initial $P_{H_2}/P_{C_2H_2}$*	*Temp. (°C)*	S_m	*Ref.*
Ni–pumice	1	0	0.71	14
		125	0.91	
$Rh–Al_2O_3$	4.5	18	0.57	15
		116	0.82	
$Ir–Al_2O_3$	4	110	0.45	15
		160	0.65	
$Pt–Al_2O_3$	2	40	0.68	15
		100	0.80	

Over nickel–pumice at 80°, the degree of selectivity falls linearly with increasing hydrogen: acetylene ratio, and so x in the above equation is here unity.[18] The degree of selectivity generally increases linearly with rising temperature[14, 15] and some selected values are shown in Table VIII. The exponent x in equation (4) increases exponentially with rising temperature, except over rhodium–alumina, where it is constant: extreme values are given in Table IX.[15]

TABLE IX. *Values of x in the Equation:* $1 - S_m = kP_{H_2}^x$

Catalyst	*Temperature (°C)*	x
$Pd–Al_2O_3$	0	0.2
	30	0.6
$Ir–Al_2O_3$	50	0.05
	180	0.3
$Pt–Al_2O_3$	50	0.2
	100	0.5

The following interpretation of the dependence of S_m on hydrogen pressure has been advanced.[24] Addition of a hydrogen atom to the free-radical form of the vinyl radical necessarily leads to chemisorbed ethylene, but its addition to the normal form leads either to chemisorbed or to gaseous ethylene depending on whether the π-bond or the carbon–metal bond is broken. The full situation is contained in the scheme

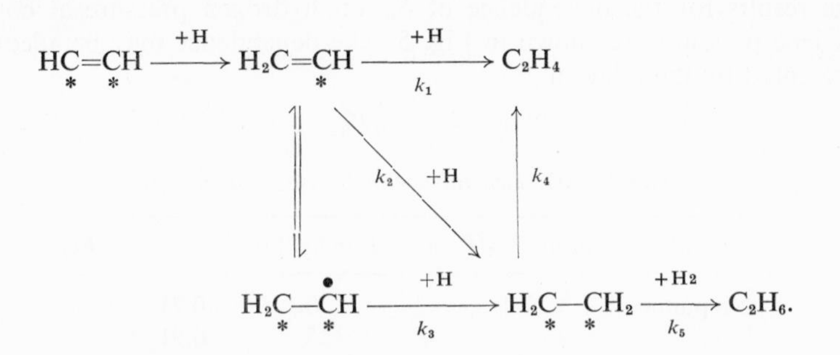

Whence if f_n is the fraction of free radicals in the normal form,

$$r_{C_2H_4} = [H]\left\{k_1 f_n + \frac{k_4 B}{k_4 + k_5 P_{H_2}}\right\} \tag{5}$$

and

$$r_{C_2H_6} = \frac{k_5 P_{H_2}[H]B}{k_4 + k_5 P_{H_2}}, \tag{6}$$

where

$$B = \{k_2 f_n + k_3(1 - f_n)\}. \tag{7}$$

The expression for the degree of selectivity as a function of hydrogen pressure now becomes

$$1 - S_m = \frac{r_{C_2H_6}}{r_{C_2H_4} + r_{C_2H_6}} = \frac{k_5 P_{H_2} B}{k_4(B + k_1 f_n) + k_5 P_{H_2}(B + k_1 f_n)} \qquad (8)$$

to which equation (4) can be regarded as an approximation. The increase of selectivity with rising temperature tallies with the general observation that the activation energy for acetylene hydrogenation is greater than for ethylene hydrogenation. The increase of x with temperature is a consequence of the unknown temperature dependences of the several rate constants and of f_n.

Selectivity increases with acetylene pressure at constant hydrogen pressure, and in some cases is determined solely by the hydrogen to acetylene ratio.[15]

The foregoing observations on the relative degrees of selectivity shown by various metals are qualitatively supported by numerous investigations of the hydrogenation of other acetylenic compounds in the liquid phase.[8, 32, 33] Palladium and platinum "blacks" are non-selective, but colloidal palladium, Raney nickel and especially Raney iron show high selectivity. Thus, for example vinylacetylene can be reduced to butadiene by palladium[34] and 3-methylbutenyne to isoprene by Raney iron.[35]

We now consider the experimental evidence on the thermodynamic selectivity S_t: this can be expressed in terms of the minimum ethylene: acetylene ratio necessary to secure the entry of the former into the reactive layer to the extent where its hydrogenation becomes detectable. Estimation of this ratio requires full analyses to be carried out, but in cases where the second stage of the reaction is faster than the first (see Fig. 4), its value may be inferred with reasonable certainty by measuring the pressure fall at which the rate starts to increase. S_t is probably highest over supported rhodium (C_2H_4/C_2H_2 ratio $\sim$50)[24] and is also high over nickel (ratio $\sim$20):[14, 18] it is distinctly lower over supported palladium, platinum and iridium (ratio $\sim$5).[15, 19, 24, 31] Now from equations (30) and (31) in Chapter 7 we may calculate the differences between the free energies of adsorption of acetylene and ethylene, $\delta\Delta G_a$ which these figures imply, assuming that the hydrogenation of the latter is detectable if it occupies 10 per cent of the surface: where this reaction is faster than that in the first stage, this condition will result approximately in a doubling of the rate of pressure fall. The value of $\delta\Delta G_a$ is about 3.7 kcal. mole^{-1} for an acetylene:ethylene ratio of 50 at 30°; at 130° it is 4.9 and at 230° 6.1 kcal. mole^{-1}. For an acetylene:ethylene ratio of 10 at 30°, is 3.3 kcal. mole^{-1}. Thus at moderate temperatures, quite small differences between the free energies of adsorption can lead to high thermodynamic selectivity. Assuming that the pressure fall $-\Delta P_a$ at which acceleration starts in the case of the noble Group VIII metals gives an approximate measure of the critical acetylene:ethylene ratio, decreasing thermodynamic selectivity with rising temperature has been observed.[24] This is in contrast to mechanistic selectivity which generally increases with rising temperature. Calculation shows that if $\delta\Delta G_a$ is 3.6 kcal. mole^{-1} and θ_A/θ_B is 9, then the critical value of P_A/P_B is 50 at 30°, and 10 at 130°.

The pressure fall at which acceleration starts decreases linearly with increasing hydrogen pressure at constant temperature and acetylene pressure over palladium and platinum catalysts, the ratio of hydrogen plus ethylene to acetylene at this time being constant.[15] This means that hydrogen is acting equivalently to ethylene in serving to secure the entry of ethylene to the surface. This in turn may imply that ethylene is adsorbed under these conditions through the process

$$C_2H_4 + \underset{*}{H} \longrightarrow \underset{*}{C_2H_5}. \qquad \text{(e)}$$

There is no strict correlation between S_m and S_t for the various metals and indeed it is not to be expected. Only in the case of iridium are the two selectivity factors consistently low.

Added olefin rarely affects the rate or the product distribution in the first stage, although $-\Delta P_a$ decreases linearly with increasing pressure of added ethylene over palladium and palladium–silver catalysts:[15, 24] this decrease is the greater the greater the fixed hydrogen pressure and so it appears once again that hydrogen may act in place of ethylene. Over rhodium catalysts, however, $-\Delta P_a$ is largely independent of the pressures of hydrogen and added ethylene, confirming high thermodynamic selectivity for this metal.

It is evident that the main selectivity phenomena encountered in the hydrogenation of acetylenes are explicable in terms of the weaker adsorption of the corresponding olefins. The basis for investigating thermodynamic selectivity is broadened when the simultaneous hydrogenation of highly unsaturated hydrocarbons is considered.[36] It has been concluded from such studies that over nickel–pumice at 90°, acetylene occupies 55 per cent of the surface and methylacetylene 45 per cent of the surface when the two are hydrogenated together. Now this means that the former is the more strongly adsorbed, although $\delta\Delta G_a$ is only about 0.15 kcal. mole^{-1}. It is worth enquiring whether there is any relationship between the heat of associative adsorption of an acetylene and its heat of hydrogenation to the olefin, since the processes are quite analogous. From Table I we see that for acetylene and methylacetylene, $\delta\Delta H_h$ is about 2.5 kcal. mole^{-1} as compared with a value of 0.15 kcal. mole^{-1} for $\delta\Delta G_a$ obtained above. On comparing ethylene and acetylene, we find from Table I that $\delta\Delta H_h$ is about 10 kcal. mole^{-1} while $\delta\Delta G_a$ is very roughly 4 kcal. mole^{-1}. On the basis of this small sample it seems that $\delta\Delta H_h$ is qualitatively greater than $\delta\Delta G_a$, but a quantitative relation may not hold unless the same or very similar chemical types are compared.

Numerous attempts have been made to employ selective poisons to improve selectivity in the hydrogenation of acetylenic compounds, but the mechanism of their action is not well understood. From the foregoing considerations it seems unlikely that a poison can affect the mechanistic selectivity; more probably it inhibits the adsorption and hence the hydrogenation of the olefin, and, therefore, causes high thermodynamic selectivity. To be effective the poison must be less strongly adsorbed than the acetylene and more strongly adsorbed than the olefin. A notable example is the Lindlar catalyst which employs plumbic acetate and an organic nitrogen base such as pyridine or quinoline. What is uncertain is how far the poisoning action is related to the consequent change in the electronic properties of the metal and how far it results from simple steric blocking of surface sites.

A recent study[15] of the poisoning of palladium–alumina by mercury vapour has shown that activity for ethylene hydrogenation is lost much more rapidly than that for acetylene hydrogenation. Ultimately a catalyst can be produced which hydrogenates ethylene only negligibly slowly, while maintaining fair activity towards acetylene. This selective poisoning cannot, therefore, be due to complete blocking of the surface by the poison, and it seems more probable in this case that when most of the sites are covered by mercury there are left aggregates of vacant sites large enough to allow the hydrogenation of acetylene but insufficiently large to allow the hydrogenation of ethylene, because of its slightly larger size. Other supported metals, investigated less thoroughly, show similar phenomena.

12.5 The Activity of Metals and Alloys

The relative activities of metals and alloys in the hydrogenation of acetylene have been much less widely studied than for olefins. Metallic films of iron and tungsten are inactive for this reaction at 23°, and nickel films although mildly active are at least a hundred times less active than in ethylene hydrogenation. The activity sequence for evaporated films is[5, 6]

$$\text{Pd} > \text{Rh, Pt} > \text{Ni} \gg \text{Fe, W},$$

and the activation energy is in all cases between 6 and 7 kcal. mole^{-1}. Similar qualitative activity sequences have been established for supported metals: thus for pumice-supported metals the order is[16, 20]

$$\text{Pd} > \text{Pt} > \text{Ni, Rh} > \text{Co} > \text{Fe} > \text{Cu} > \text{Ir} > \text{Ru, Os}.$$

The low activity of iridium has, however, not been confirmed, for with alumina-supported metals the order is[15, 24]

$$\text{Pd} > \text{Pt} > \text{Rh, Ir}.$$

The activities and Arrhenius parameters of some of the first row Transition metals have been studied in some detail[20]. Iron, cobalt, nickel and copper powders were prepared by *in situ* reduction of the oxides under closely controlled conditions, and the rates referred to unit surface area. Activation energies (measured within the temperature range of 70 to 175°) and specific pre-exponential factors are given in Table X, and the specific activities at

Table X. *Arrhenius Parameters for the Hydrogenation of Acetylene over Metal Powders*[20]

Metal	Fe	Co	Ni	Cu
E_A(kcal. mole^{-1})	8.7	9.0	8.2	21.0
log A_A(min.$^{-1}$ m.$^{-2}$)	1.95	3.50	5.4	9.63

TABLE XI. *Values of k_A for the Hydrogenation of Acetylene at 100°* [20]

Metal	Fe	Co	Ni	Cu
$10^2 k_A$ for powders (min.$^{-1}$ m.$^{-2}$)	0.28	1.9	60	0.18
$10^2 k_A$ for pumice-supported metals (min.$^{-1}$ g.$^{-1}$)	0.40	3.4	47	0.21

100° are compared with the non-specific values derived for the pumice-supported metals in Table XI. The *d*-metal powders show a constant activation energy (8.6 ± 0.4 kcal. mole^{-1}), and so here as with the hydrogenation of ethylene on films the differing activities are associated with differing values of log$A$. The low activity of copper is, however, chiefly due to its high activation energy, not entirely compensated by the high pre-exponential factor. All the foregoing observations are, of course, based simply on measurements of rates of pressure fall, and make no allowance for variation in the nature of the products.

No comparable measurements are available for the noble Group VIII metals. The general similarity between the activity sequences for metals in different forms is, however, heartening, although they differ from that found in olefin hydrogenation in two important ways. First, palladium and sometimes platinum show a higher activity than rhodium and iridium, both of which have higher percentage *d*-characters. Second, palladium, which here always has the highest activity, often shows in other hydrogenation and exchange reactions an activity lower than predicted from its *d*-character. The inactivity of the body-centred cubic iron and tungsten is at least partly ascribable to geometric effects. The interpretation cannot be taken further at present.

The activity of unsupported nickel–copper and nickel–cobalt alloy powders in acetylene hydrogenation has also been examined.[20] The rate expression (1) holds for all the alloys, although of course the second term is absent with pure iron and cobalt (Section 12.2). Table XII gives the activation energies E_A and

TABLE XII. *Arrhenius Parameters for the Hydrogenation of Acetylene over Nickel–Copper and Nickel–Cobalt Alloys*[20]

	Nickel–copper alloys					
% Nickel in alloy	100	79	61	47.5	21	0
E_A(kcal. mole^{-1})	8.2	15.1	20.1	21.3	25.2	21.0
logA_A(min.$^{-1}$ m.$^{-2}$)	5.4	8.2	11.1	11.8	12.8	9.6
	Nickel–cobalt alloys					
% Nickel in alloy	100	83	64	42	23	0
E_A(kcal. mole^{-1})	8.2	19.2	21.0	12.5	16.0	9.0
logA_A(min.$^{-1}$ m.$^{-2}$)	5.4	9.8	10.7	6.5	7.2	3.5

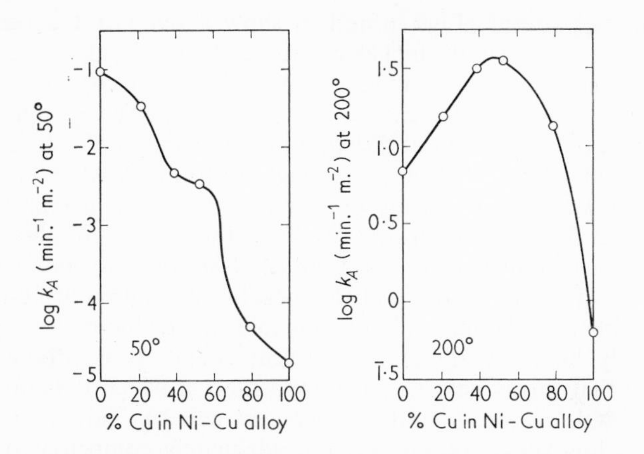

FIG. 6. The dependence of activity (expressed as logk_A) at 50 and 200° on composition of nickel–copper alloys.[20]

the specific pre-exponential factors A_A, while Figs. 6 and 7 show the dependence of log A_A at 50° and 200° (obtained by extrapolation from these results) on composition. In the nickel–copper series, the activation energy rapidly increases with increasing copper content to an approximately constant value, and there is a parallel increase in log$A$. In the resulting compensation effect (for which the equation is: log$A_i = 1.8 + 0.44\ E_i$) only copper fails to conform; this behaviour is reminiscent of that of copper alloy foils in ethylene hydrogenation (see Chapter 11). There is no sharp change in the activation energy at the composition where the *d*-band is expected to be filled. In the nickel–cobalt series, the activation energies are always greater than for either of the pure metals, although they change somewhat irregularly with composition. A compensation effect (for which the equation is: log$A_i = -2.0 + 0.60\ E_i$) holds, although here nickel does not conform.

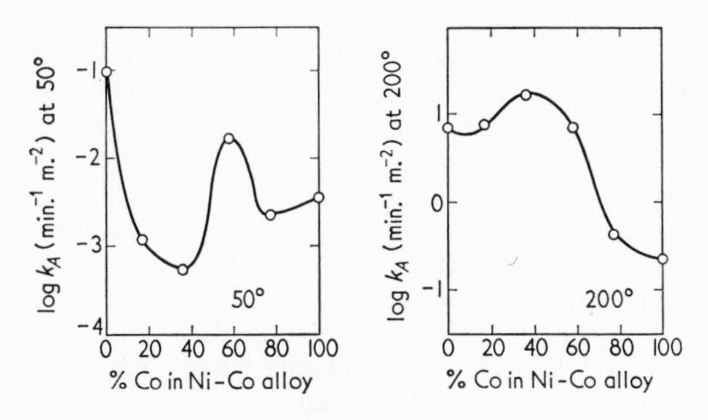

FIG. 7. The dependence of activity (expressed as logk_A) at 50 and 200° on composition of nickel–cobalt alloys.[20]

The activity patterns (Figs. 6 and 7) show a significant dependence on temperature, especially in the nickel–copper series: this is, of course, caused by variations in the activation energies. At 50° in the nickel–copper system, there is at first a fairly smooth decrease in activity with increasing copper content, followed by a more substantial decrease in the region of 60 per cent copper, i.e. at the point where the *d*-band is thought to be filled. At 200° the activity at first *increases* with increasing copper content and a maximum activity exists at about 50 per cent copper: results of this form were obtained in the hydrogenation of ethylene over similar catalysts by Best and Russell (see Chapter 11). At 50° the activity of the nickel–cobalt alloys at first decreases with increasing cobalt content, but this is followed by increasing activity and a particularly high activity at 58 per cent cobalt. It is probably only a coincidence that this is near to the composition at which the alloy contains exactly one hole in the *d*-band (54 per cent cobalt). This high activity is caused by a low activation energy, not adequately compensated by a low pre-exponential factor. The position of the maximum shifts towards nickel with rising temperature, and at 200° the alloy containing 36 per cent cobalt is more active than pure nickel. Further discussion of these and other activity patterns will be given in Chapter 21.

Observations made on other catalysts containing more than one metal[19, 24] will not be discussed, since their physical state has not been adequately characterized.

12.6 The Stereochemistry of the Hydrogenation of Acetylenic Compounds, and the Exchange of Acetylene with Deuterium

12.61 Stereochemistry[8, 32, 33]

It has already been noted (Section 12.1) that the associative adsorption of acetylenic compounds implies their taking up a *cis*-configuration, which may be retained in the corresponding vinyl radical and in the olefin ultimately formed, although in most instances the *cis*-isomer is the more unstable. Most of the results which bear on this problem have been obtained by work done in the liquid phase.[32, 33] The hydrogenation of a wide variety of disubstituted acetylenes leads to the preponderant formation of *cis*-olefins.[37] The early view[32] that these are the *sole* products, and that *trans*-isomers are formed only by isomerization, is probably erroneous, since isolation techniques cannot readily detect small proportions of *trans*-isomers. More recent work has shown that 5–20 per cent of *trans*-isomers are among the genuine initial products. Thus, for example, the hydrogenation of methyl stearolate ($C_8H_{17}C{\equiv}CC_7H_{14}COOCH_3$) over Raney nickel gives predominantly methyl octadecenoate, of which 6 per cent is the *trans*-isomer.[38] Over the Lindlar catalyst, 5 per cent of the *trans*-isomers is formed, but this is reduced to 1 to 2 per cent by larger quantities of quinoline.[39] The 2-octene formed by the hydrogenation of 2-octyne over nickel–kieselguhr at moderate temperatures and pressures is 20 per cent *trans*,[40] and the olefinic diol resulting from the reduction of butyne-1,3-diol over Raney nickel at 20° is 21 per cent *trans*.[41] A discussion of reaction mechanisms will be given at the end of the next sub-section.

12.62 The Exchange of Acetylene with Deuterium

The exchange reactions of acetylene have been relatively little studied. An early investigation[42] showed that over platinum foil at 20° the hydrogen exchange reaction proceeded very much more slowly than in the case of ethylene. Attempts to synthesize *cis*-dideuteroethylene by the reaction of acetylene with deuterium over palladium[1, 43] or nickel[1] catalysts have been unsuccessful, due to the simultaneous production of other deuterated ethylenes in substantial quantities. This indicates the occurrence of a re-distribution reaction similar to that encountered with olefins (see Chapter 11). A somewhat more detailed study[1] of the reaction over nickel–kieselguhr showed that *cis*- and *trans*-dideuteroethylene were formed in approximately equal amounts (20 to 25 per cent each) at room temperature, but lowering the temperature to −80° increased the yield of the *cis*-isomer to 50 per cent without affecting the yield of the *trans*-isomer. Small amounts of acetylene-d_1 were detected at room temperature. The use of equilibrated and non-equilibrated mixtures of hydrogen and deuterium gave rise to closely similar products, showing that the addition occurs atomically rather than molecularly.

The equivalent reaction of hydrogen and deuterated acetylene (96 per cent C_2D_2 + 4 per cent C_2HD) has been studied over nickel–pumice.[44] Some results for the dependence of the yields of deuteroethylenes on variation of the partial pressures of reactants at constant temperature are given in Table XIII;

TABLE XIII. *Percentage Yields of Deuteroethylenes from the Reaction of Hydrogen with Acetylene–d_2 over Nickel–pumice at 97°; Analyses Performed after 40 per cent Conversion*[44]

P_{H_2} (*mm.*)	$P_{C_2D_2}$ (*mm.*)	*Percentage composition* C_2D_4	C_2HD_3	$C_2H_2D_2$	C_2H_3D	C_2H_4	*Deuterium number*
38	36	1.5	19.4	60.8	16.3	2.0	2.06
68	36	1.8	16.7	59.1	20.2	2.2	2.00
94	36	1.3	16.8	61.1	19.1	1.7	2.01
180	36	0.9	13.2	65.5	19.1	1.2	1.97
38	73	1.9	21.0	61.8	14.2	1.2	2.12
38	146	2.3	22.3	59.0	14.9	1.4	2.13

the deuterium numbers have been corrected for the isotopic impurity of the acetylene. Ethylene-d_2 is by far the most abundant product in all cases, and its yield increases with increasing hydrogen pressure. The deuterium number decreases with increasing hydrogen pressure and decreasing acetylene pressure. Now a deuterium number greater than two means that there are on average more than two deuterium atoms in each ethylene molecule formed, the excess necessarily having come from acetylene-d_2 with the resultant formation of acetylene-d_1: this was detected in the expected amount. There is, therefore, an *acetylene exchange reaction*, but as opposed to olefin exchange during hydrogenation it is only of very minor importance. Deuterium numbers of less than two must indicate a net hydrogen exchange reaction, but this is only significant at quite high hydrogen:acetylene ratios. Infra-red analysis of the ethylene-d_2 fraction showed about 65 per cent of the *cis*-isomer, 31 per cent of the *trans*-, and 4 per cent of the asymmetric isomer, with little dependence on reactant ratio.

The temperature-dependence of the product distribution was determined between 40 and 97° using an approximately five-fold excess of hydrogen: the results are shown in Table XIV. In confirmation of the earlier work, the yield

TABLE XIV. *Temperature Dependence of Products from the Reaction of Hydrogen with Acetylene–d_2 after 80 per cent Conversion, using a Five-fold Excess of Hydrogen*[44]

Temp.	Composition of ethylenes (%)					Deuterium	Composition of ethylene–d_2 (%)		
(°C)	C_2D_4	C_2HD_3	$C_2H_2D_2$	C_2H_3D	C_2H_4	number	cis	trans	asym
40.7	1.3	7.8	70.2	17.8	2.9	1.91	77.5	20.6	1.9
58.0	1.8	10.1	65.6	19.5	3.0	1.92	75.0	22.3	2.7
80.7	1.6	15.9	61.7	18.8	2.0	2.00	67.7	28.2	4.1
97.7	1.9	17.3	59.1	19.4	2.3	2.01	64.2	30.7	5.1

of the ethylene-d_2 is seen to rise with decreasing temperature, although it is apparently more extensively formed than over nickel–kieselguhr:[1] the yield of ethylene-d_3 falls concomitantly. Of the isomers of ethylene-d_2, the *cis*-isomer yield increases, while those of the *trans*- and asymetric isomers fall, with decreasing temperature.

These results have been interpreted with fair success by a simplied form of the general theory proposed by Kemball for the hydrogenation and exchange of ethylene over metal films (see Chapter 11). Only two disposable parameters were required: these are, (i) the chance of any vinyl radical gaining a hydrogen or deuterium atom and forming ethylene (chance p) or of losing an atom and reforming acetylene (chance $1-p$), and (ii) the chance of any adsorbed acetylene or vinyl radical gaining a hydrogen atom (chance s) or a deuterium atom (chance $1-s$). The experimental distributions were closely reproducible, including the relative proportions of the symmetrical and asymmetrical ethylene-d_2, and s and p were shown to change with conditions in the expected manner.

It is finally necessary to try to understand the mechanism of the formation of *trans*-ethylenic compounds in the hydrogenation of disubstituted acetylenes. For the formation of *trans*-isomers it is necessary to disrupt the planar configuration of the adsorbed "normal" vinyl radical: this disruption of course occurs in the formation of the free-radical form of the vinyl radical, which must be represented as, for example,

D H
$\dot{C}$—C
D
* *

Addition of a further hydrogen atom must lead to adsorbed *cis*- and *trans*-ethylene-d_2 in equal proportions, and hence to equal proportions in the gas phase if the stereochemistry is preserved in the act of desorption. It is relevant to note that the yield of *trans*-ethylene-d_2 increases by a factor of 1.25 between 40 and 97° and that the yield of polymers over the same kind of catalyst increases by a factor of 1.35 over the same temperature interval.[14] This strongly suggests that the same intermediate is involved in both processes and hence that the vinyl free-radical leads to equal amounts of *cis*- and *trans*-ethylene-d_2 and to polymers, which together account for some 75 per cent of the total products at about 100°. The dependence of the degree of stereospecificity on molecular structure is insufficiently understood to make further discussion profitable.

12.7 Exchange Between Acetylene in the Absence of Hydrogen

Exchange between acetylene and acetylene-d_2 occurs rapidly over nickel–kieselguhr at room temperature, and measurably at −80°, but no detailed study was carried out.[1] The same reaction occurs readily over nickel–pumice at about 60°, and this system has been thoroughly studied using infra-red spectroscopy.[45] The usual first-order course kinetics were observed, equilibrium being attained in two hours at 120°. The equilibrium constant defined as

$$K = \frac{[C_2HD]^2}{[C_2H_2]\,[C_2D_2]} \tag{9}$$

was 3.2, in fair agreement with a value of 3.6 calculated by the methods of statistical mechanics. The order with respect to total pressure of equimolar reactant mixtures was 0.65 at 70°, and the activation energy was 10 kcal. mole^{-1} between 40 and 100°.

Acetylene-d_2 also reacts with methylacetylene under similar conditions, and the reaction

$$CH_3{-}C{\equiv}CH + C_2D_2 \longrightarrow CH_3{-}C{\equiv}CD + C_2HD \tag{f}$$

takes place. Subsequently of course the acetylene-d_1 reacts to form acetylene and acetylene-d_2. The order of this reaction was found to be 0.47 with respect to total pressure, and an activation energy of 12.7 kcal. mole^{-1} was estimated.

The mechanism by which these reactions occur is uncertain. In view of the highly reproducible rates and the absence of polymer formation, it was concluded[45] that the conventional processes of dissociation and recombination did not occur. Only the exchange of acetylenic hydrogen atoms is possible, and the difference between the strengths of acetylenic and aliphatic carbon–hydrogen bonds is probably not sufficient to explain the difference in reactivity. Instead it was suggested that the driving force in the reaction was the relatively high polarity of the acetylenic carbon–hydrogen bond, and that a kind of Rideal–Eley mechanism based on the interaction of chemisorbed and physically adsorbed acetylene might operate:

```
 +→
 D—C≡C—D                         D···C≡C—D
                 ——→              :     :
H—C=C—H                      H—C=C···H
  *  *                          *  *
                                   /
            D   C≡C—D            ↙
            |   |
       H—C=C    H
          *  *
```

(g)

The observed orders are consistent with such a mechanism, and the lower order found with the higher boiling methylacetylene is especially suggestive. The higher activation energy shown when methylacetylene is one of the reactants may have its origin in the steric consequences of the methyl group.

12.8 The Hydrogenation of Diolefins

12.81 The Hydrogenation of Allene

The hydrogenation of diolefins is considered here, rather than in the previous Chapter, since it is potentially a two-stage reaction, and hence the phenomenon of selectivity may be shown, as with acetylenic compounds. Indeed, in allene (1,2-propadiene) the adjacent position of the formal double bonds leads to such strain that the molecule has some of the characteristics of an acetylene. Thus, for example, its heat of hydrogenation to propylene (41.4 kcal. mole^{-1}) is only about 1 kcal. mole^{-1} less than the heat of hydrogenation of methylacetylene to propylene[46] and some 10 kcal. larger than for an isolated double bond.

The kinetics of the hydrogenation of allene have been studied using pumice-supported nickel, palladium and platinum catalysts.[47] In each case the orders of reaction were first with respect to hydrogen and approximately zero with respect to allene, indicating strong adsorption of the latter. Propylene was invariably formed faster than propane, and the S_m values observed are given in Table XV, together with the apparent activation energies. Over nickel and platinum catalysts, the hydrogenation of propylene started when the allene pressure had fallen below about 20 mm., and in the case of platinum this latter reaction was faster than the first stage, which showed zero-order course kinetics. Although C_3 hydrocarbons always form the bulk of the products, some 10 per cent of the allene removed over nickel

TABLE XV. *Kinetic Features of the Hydrogenation of Allene over Pumice-supported Metals*[47]

Metal	*Initial* $P_{H_2}/P_{C_3H_4}$	*Temp.* °*C.*	S_m	*E(kcal. mole*$^{-1}$)	*Temp. range* (°*C*)
Ni	1	73	0.93	12.8	0–114
Pd	1	116	1.0	12.3	89–197
Pt	1	89	0.80	17.1	48–173

and platinum appears as polymers, and some 20 per cent over palladium, although in each case the polymer yield is quite strongly dependent on the instantaneous allene pressure.

These results bear a striking similarity to those for methylacetylene: the selectivity order of the metals is the same (compare Table VI) and even the activation energies are approximately the same. In order to account for the selective formation of propylene and the formation of polymers, the following reaction scheme must be constructed.

Allene ⟶ $H_2C{=}\underset{*}{C}{-}\underset{*}{C}H_2$

+H (upper branch):
$H_2C{=}\underset{*}{C}{-}CH_3 \xrightarrow{+H} C_3H_6$
↕
$H_2\underset{*}{C}{-}\underset{*}{\dot{C}}{-}CH_3 \xrightarrow{+H} H_2\underset{*}{C}{-}\underset{*}{C}H{-}CH_3 \xrightarrow{+H_2} C_3H_8$
($H_2C{=}\underset{*}{C}{-}CH_3 \xrightarrow{+H} H_2\underset{*}{C}{-}\underset{*}{C}H{-}CH_3$)

+H (lower branch):
$H_2C{=}CH{-}\underset{*}{C}H_2 \xrightarrow{+H} C_3H_6$
↕
$H_2\dot{C}{-}\underset{*}{C}H{-}\underset{*}{C}H_2 \xrightarrow{+H} H_3C{-}\underset{*}{C}H{-}\underset{*}{C}H_2 \xrightarrow{+H_2} C_3H_8$

Once again, as in the case of acetylene, the selectivity depends in some measure on the fraction of allyl radicals existing in a free-radical form. The dependence of polymer yield on allene pressure suggests that, perhaps for steric reasons, the free allyl radicals react more readily with physically adsorbed allene molecules than with other chemisorbed species. 2-Methylpentane has been detected in the products obtained over an unspecified catalyst.[46] It is interesting to note that the radical $CH_2{=}\underset{*}{C}{-}CH_3$ or its free-radical equivalent is equally one of the half-hydrogenated states for both methylacetylene and allene, so that the thermodynamically feasible[48] conversion of the latter to the former could occur through the sequence

$$CH_2{=}\underset{*}{C}{-}\underset{*}{C}H_2 \xrightarrow{+H} CH_2{=}\underset{*}{C}{-}CH_3 \xrightarrow{-H} \underset{*}{HC}{=}\underset{*}{C}{-}CH_3 \rightarrow \text{methylacetylene.}$$

That this conversion is not observed in practice[47] is adequately explained by the difficulty of desorbing adsorbed methylacetylene.

It is evident that allene is more strongly chemisorbed than propylene[36, 47] and indeed it is competitively adsorbed with both acetylene and methylacetylene.[36] This lends weight to the view previously expressed that the strength of adsorption is determined by the heat of hydrogenation to the next less unsaturated form, and hence that the adsorption, at least over supported metals, is associative in nature. Allene also shows the high activation energy typical of strongly adsorbed molecules.

12.82 The Hydrogenation of other Diolefins[49]

Over alumina-supported rhodium, palladium, iridium and platinum, butadiene is hydrogenated to a mixture of the butenes and butane, and the selectivity shown by each metal is much the same as for the hydrogenation of acetylene and of allene. 1-Butene is the principal olefinic product, but the 2-butenes are also formed in amounts which vary widely between the metals.[50]

The hydrogenation of butadiene has also been studied[51] in 95 per cent ethanol, using platinum and palladium suspensions, palladium on $BaSO_4$, and Raney nickel as catalysts: the principal results are contained in Table XVI. The last two catalysts have a notable tendency to favour isomerization, and with the supported palladium the butene composition corresponds closely to the equilibrium composition.

The hydrogenation of cyclopentadiene[52] and of 1,3-[53–55] and 1,4-cyclohexadiene[54, 56] has been investigated, and some activation energies are reported.[54, 55] The reaction of cyclopentadiene and of 1,4-cyclohexadiene with deuterium over evaporated iron films has also been briefly studied[57], but the mechanisms are not thoroughly established.

TABLE XVI. *The Products of the Hydrogenation of Butadiene in 95 per cent Ethanol*[51]

Catalyst	*Temp. (°C)*	S_m	*Percentage composition of butenes*		
			1-Butene	*Trans-2-butene*	*Cis-2-butene*
Pt	−12	0.61	72.1	18.4	9.5
Pd	−12	0.94	48.5	40.1	11.4
$Pd–BaSO_4$	−8	0.40	6.0	75.0	19.0
Raney Ni	28	0.34	21.5	61.0	17.5
Equilibrium proportions at 25°:			3.0	75.1	21.9

The liquid-phase hydrogenation of several substituted butadienes has been investigated in order to assess the relative extents of 1,2 and 1,4 addition. The results for isoprene (2-methylbutadiene)[58] and 2,5-dimethyl-2,4-hexadiene[59] are recorded in Tables XVII and XVIII respectively. In all cases, 1,2 addition predominates over 1,4 addition, especially with the latter

TABLE XVII. *Products of the Liquid-phase Hydrogenation of Isoprene after the Consumption of 1 Mole of Hydrogen*[58]

Carbon skeleton of product	Percentage composition of products		
	Pt black	Pd black	Raney Ni
C=C(C)—C—C	35	31	41
C—C(C)—C=C	10	25	16
C—C(C)=C—C	20	42	41
C—C(C)—C—C	35	2	2
Selectivity, S_m	0.65	0.98	0.98

TABLE XVIII. *Products of the Liquid-phase Hydrogenation of 2,5-Dimethyl-2,4-hexadiene after the Consumption of 1 Mole of Hydrogen*[59]

Carbon skeleton of product	Percentage composition of products		
	Pt black	Pd black	Raney Ni
(C)₂C=C—C—C(C)₂	70	87	90
(C)₂C—C=C—C(C)₂	15	6	9
(C)₂C—C—C—C(C)₂	15	7	1
Selectivity, S_m	0.84	0.93	0.99

molecule. Comparing these results with those for butadiene, it appears that the extent of 1,4 addition decreases with increasing molecular complexity. Raney nickel and palladium black always show the highest selectivities, and it is interesting that these catalysts also show high selectivity in the hydrogenation of substituted acetylenes. Other diolefins which have been the object of similar studies include 2,3-dimethyl-butadiene[58] and 1,5- and substituted 1,5- and 2,5-hexadienes.[60]

References

1. J. E. Douglas and B. S. Rabinovitch, *J. Amer. Chem. Soc.* **74,** 2486 (1952).
2. R. P. Eischens and W. A. Pliskin, *Adv. Catalysis* **10,** 1 (1958).
3. L. H. Little, N. Sheppard and D. J. C. Yates, *Proc. Roy. Soc.* **A259,** 242 (1960).
4. A. Farkas, L. Farkas and E. K. Rideal, *Proc. Roy. Soc.* **A146,** 630 (1934).
5. O. Beeck, *Discuss. Faraday Soc.* **8,** 118 (1950).
6. A. Wheeler, private communication: see also Ref. 8.
7. J. N. Wilson, private communication.
8. G. C. Bond, In "Catalysis", edited by P. H. Emmett (Reinhold, New York, 1954), **3,** 109.
9. J. B. Conn, G. B. Kistiakowsky and E. A. Smith, *J. Amer. Chem. Soc.* **61,** 1868 (1939).
10. T. L. Flitcroft, H. A. Skinner and M. C. Whiting, *Trans. Faraday Soc.* **53,** 784 (1957); T. L. Flitcroft and H. A. Skinner, *Trans. Faraday Soc.* **54,** 47 (1958).
11. E. J. Prosen, F. W. Maron and F. D. Rossini, *J. Res. Nat. Bur. Stand.* **46,** 106 (1951).
12. B.I.O.S. Report No. 30. H.M.S.O., London (1951).
13. E. F. G. Herington, *Trans. Faraday Soc.* **37,** 361 (1941).
14. J. Sheridan, *J. Chem. Soc.* 133, 301 (1945).
15. G. C. Bond and P. B. Wells, Proc. 2nd International Congress on Catalysis (Editions Technip, Paris, 1961), **1,** 1135, 1139. And unpublished work.
16. J. Sheridan and W. D. Reid, *J. Chem. Soc.* 2962 (1952).
17. L. M. Berkowitz and P. N. Rylander, *J. Org. Chem.* **24,** 708 (1959).
18. J. Sheridan, *J. Chem. Soc.* 373 (1944).
19. J. Sheridan, *J. Chem. Soc.* 470 (1944).
20. G. C. Bond and R. S. Mann, *J. Chem. Soc.* 3566 (1959).
21. G. C. Bond, *J. Chem. Soc.* 2705 (1958).
22. G. C. Bond and R. S. Mann, *J. Chem. Soc.* 4738 (1958).
23. F. de Pauw and J. C. Jungers, *Bull. Soc. chim. belges* **57,** 618 (1948).
24. G. C. Bond, D. A. Dowden and N. Mackenzie, *Trans. Faraday Soc.* **54,** 1537 (1958).
25. K. Tamaru, *Bull. Chem. Soc. Japan* **23,** 64 (1950).
26. A. Grignon-Dumoulin and C. Thonon, *Rev. Inst. franç. Pétrole* **14,** 214 (1959).
27. G. C. Bond and J. Sheridan, *Trans. Faraday Soc.* **48,** 651 (1952).
28. A. D. Petrov and L. I. Antsus, *Zhur. fiz. Khim.* **14,** 1308 (1940).
29. G. A. Vassiliev, *Bull. Soc. chim., France* **15,** 381 (1948).
30. P. Sabatier and J. B. Senderens, *Compt. rend.* **135,** 87, 88 (1902).
31. J. Sheridan, *J. Chem. Soc.* 305 (1945).
32. K. N. Campbell and B. K. Campbell, *Chem. Rev.* **31,** 77 (1942).
33. R. L. Burwell, *Chem. Rev.* **57,** 895 (1957).
34. Z. Hurukawa, *J. Electrochem. Assoc. Japan* **7,** 346 (1939).
35. A. F. Thompson and S. B. Wyatt, *J. Amer. Chem. Soc.* **62,** 2555 (1940).
36. G. C. Bond and J. Sheridan, *Trans. Faraday Soc.* **48,** 664 (1952).
37. W. M. Hamilton and R. L. Burwell, Proc. 2nd International Congress on Catalysis (Editions Technip, Paris, 1961), **1,** 987.
38. N. A. Khan, *J. Amer. Chem. Soc.* **74,** 3018 (1952).
39. B. W. Baker, R. P. Linstead and B. C. L. Weedon, *J. Chem. Soc.* 2217 (1955).
40. A. L. Henne and K. W. Greenlee, *J. Amer. Chem. Soc.* **65,** 2020 (1943).
41. R. Romanet, *Compt. rend.* **236,** 1044, 1176, 1677 (1953).

42. A. Farkas and L. Farkas, *J. Amer. Chem. Soc.* **61,** 3396 (1939).
43. R. L. Arnett and B. L. Crawford, *J. Phys. Chem.* **18,** 118 (1950).
44. G. C. Bond, *J. Chem. Soc.* 4288 (1958).
45. G. C. Bond, J. Sheridan and D. H. Whiffen, *Trans. Faraday Soc.* **48,** 715 (1952).
46. G. B. Kistiakowsky, J. R. Ruhoff, H. A. Smith and W. E. Vaughan, *J. Amer. Chem. Soc.* **58,** 146 (1936).
47. G. C. Bond and J. Sheridan, *Trans. Faraday Soc.* **48,** 658 (1952).
48. D. A. Frank-Kamenetskii and V. G. Markovich, *Acta Physicochim. U.R.S.S.* **17,** 308 (1942).
49. B. B. Corson, In "Catalysis", edited by P. H. Emmett (Reinhold, New York, 1954), **3,** 79.
50. G. C. Bond and J. M. Winterbottom, unpublished work.
51. W. G. Young, R. L. Meier, J. Vinograd, H. Bollinger, L. Kaplan and S. L. Linden, *J. Amer. Chem. Soc.* **69,** 2046 (1947).
52. L. Kh. Freĭdlin and B. D. Polkovnik, *Izvest. Akad. Nauk. S.S.S.R., Otdel. Khim. Nauk* 541 (1957); 1106 (1959).
53. L. Kh. Freĭdlin, B. D. Polkovnik and Yu. P. Egorov, *Izvest. Akad. Nauk. S.S.S.R., Otdel. Khim. Nauk*, 910 (1959).
54. H. A. Smith and H. T. Meriwether, *J. Amer. Chem. Soc.* **71,** 413 (1949).
55. E. de Ruiter and J. C. Jungers, *Bull. Soc. chim. belges* **58,** 210 (1949).
56. V. M. Gryaznov, V. D. Yagodovskii, A. M. Bogomol'nyi and K. Dyu-ok, *Doklady Akad. Nauk S.S.S.R.* **121,** 1416 (1958).
57. J. Erkelens, A. K. Galwey and C. Kemball, *Proc. Roy. Soc.* **A260,** 273 (1961).
58. S. V. Lebed'ev and A. O. Yabubchik, *J. Chem. Soc.* 823, 2190 (1928); G. Dupont and C. Paquot, *Compt. red.* **205,** 805 (1937).
59. B. A. Kazanskii and N. I. Popova, *Izvest. Akad. Nauk S.S.S.R., Otdel. Khim. Nauk* 442 (1952).
60. B. A. Kazanskii, I. V. Gostunskaya and A. I. Leonova, *Doklady Akad. Nauk S.S.S.R.* **126,** 1264 (1954).

Chapter 13

The Hydrogenation of Aromatic and Heterocyclic Compounds

13.1 Introduction

13.11 The Chemisorption of Benzene

The chemisorption of aromatic compounds has been much less thoroughly studied than the chemisorption of olefins, and almost all the experimental work has been done only with benzene. Evidence concerning the adsorbed state of this molecule comes from a few direct measurements on the process of adsorption and from inferences drawn from kinetic studies of the reactions it undergoes. It seems generally agreed that aromatic compounds lose their energy of resonance on adsorption. This interprets the relatively low heat of adsorption of benzene (~30 kcal. mole^{-1} on nickel powder and ~12 kcal. mole^{-1} on copper powder at zero coverage[1]) and also the difference between the heats of adsorption of thiophen and ethyl sulphide on platinum[2]. It is also supported by the comparison of the activation energy for benzene hydrogenation with the endothermicity of the conversion of benzene to a cyclic diene.[3] The relative magnetization of supported nickel falls when benzene is chemisorbed upon it at 150°, to an extent which suggests that it is held by at least six bonds to the surface.[4] Essentially the same conclusion has been reached from measurements of the change in resistance of thin nickel films following the adsorption of benzene at −183°.[5]

While these observations would tend to discount the possibility that benzene is only chemisorbed dissociatively, that is, as a phenyl radical and a hydrogen atom, they do not distinguish with absolute certainty between the alternative possible processes of associative adsorption, viz.

$$C_6H_6 + 2* \rightarrow \quad \text{(ring with two *)} \qquad \text{(a)}$$

and

$$C_6H_6 + 6* \rightarrow \quad \text{(ring with six *)}, \qquad \text{(b)}$$

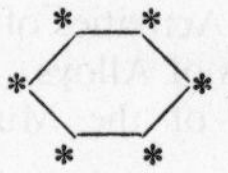

in both of which the resonance energy would be largely lost. There are, however, other considerations which are relevant. (i) There is evidence that some hydrogen is liberated when benzene is chemisorbed on nickel, iron and platinum films at room temperature:[6] this suggests some adsorption as phenyl radicals, and is supported by observations on the kinetics of the exchange of benzene with deuterium.[7] (ii) The formation of the hexa-adsorbed species in process (b) has certain important geometric implications which do not seem to have received attention. The (111) plane of face-centred cubic metals and the corresponding plane of close-packed hexagonal metals both possess an hexagonal array of conveniently spaced atoms, the spacing in the (110) plane of body-centred cubic metals being only slightly less convenient.[8] However, the absorbed species must have the structure of cyclohexane, and hence must be considerably strained if it is to make simultaneous six-point adsorption. The adsorption of benzene in this manner is shown pictorially in Fig. 1. (iii) Since cyclohexene and not benzene is the primary product in the dehydrogenation of cyclohexane,[9] application of the principle of microscopic reversibility would suggest that structure (a) rather than (b) is that which exists *during the hydrogenation of benzene*.

We are up against the familiar difficulty of trying to decide the nature of the adsorbed species existing under reaction conditions largely on the basis of experiments performed in the absence of hydrogen. Deductions made from kinetic measurements at most tell us something about the relative strengths of adsorption of the reactants, and (apart from detailed isotopic tracer studies) little about the structure of adsorbed species. Orders of reaction in benzene for hydrogenation and exchange reactions vary between zero and 0.4 (see Section 13.2) and hence, benzene must be quite strongly

FIG. 1. A possible arrangement of chemisorbed benzene molecules on the (111) face of platinum.

adsorbed, although the presence of benzene does not effectively retard *para*-hydrogen conversion,[10–12] and hence it cannot pack tightly on the surface. Figure 1 illustrates how vacant sites may be left between adsorbed molecules. Such kinetic arguments, however, cannot establish the nature of the chemisorbed species existing during reaction, because random and immobile adsorption according to process (b) is bound to leave numerous uncovered sites, some of which will be in pairs, while steric interference between the species formed in process (a) will also result in sites available only to hydrogen.

We may provisionally conclude that under reaction conditions benzene is partly adsorbed as phenyl radicals and partly as the di-adsorbed state (a), which has received wide support.[7, 13, 14] Structure (b) may exist in the absence of hydrogen, but its participation in reactions has not been conclusively proved. The technique of infra-red spectroscopy has not yet been applied to this problem, but it should afford valuable help in determining the nature of the adsorbed species.

Explicit attention has not been given to the idea that benzene may be chemisorbed through donor bonds formed between the π-electrons of the ring and the unfilled *d*-levels of the metal. A bond of this sort was mentioned as a possibility for the chemisorption of olefins, and the complexes formed between aromatic compounds and silver ions may be recalled in this connection. Such bonds would have less stringent directional requirements than conventional covalent bonds.

13.12 *The Thermochemistry and Thermodynamics of the Hydrogenation of Aromatic Compounds*

The thermochemistry of the hydrogenation of aromatic compounds is dominated by the substantial resonance energies possessed by these compounds. It is unanimously found that the only isolatable product from the hydrogenation of benzene is cyclohexane. From the heats of complete hydrogenation of benzene and possible intermediates[15] given in Table I it appears that the formation of 1,3-cyclohexadiene is endothermic by 5.6 kcal.

TABLE I. *Heats of Complete Hydrogenation of Benzene and Possible Intermediates at 82°* [15]

Compound	$-\Delta H_h$(*kcal. mole*$^{-1}$)
Benzene	49.80
1,3-Cyclohexadiene	55.37
Cyclohexene	28.59

mole^{-1} at 82°: now the heat of hydrogenation of the hypothetical non-resonating cyclohexatriene may be estimated as three times the value for *cis*-2-butene, viz. 85.7 kcal. mole^{-1}, and the formation of cyclohexadiene from benzene is endothermic because the heat of hydrogenation of benzene is less than the "expected" value by the resonance energy of 36 kcal. mole^{-1}. The value for 1,3-cyclohexadiene is less than twice the value for either cyclohexene or *cis*-2-butene by 1.8 kcal. mole^{-1}, indicating that its resonance energy is negligible. Since the formation of cyclohexene from benzene is exothermic, its absence from the products of the hydrogenation must either be due to its greater reactivity or be a consequence of the mechanism.

The thermodynamics of the equilibria have been studied by Janz.[16] Values of ΔG for the formation of products from benzene and hydrogen at 25° are: for 1,3-cyclohexadiene, +13.2 kcal. mole^{-1}; for cyclohexene, —4.7 kcal. mole^{-1}; for cyclohexane, —23.4 kcal. mole^{-1}. However, ΔG for the complete process increases rapidly with rising temperature, becoming zero at 287°, where K_p has of course a value of unity. The hydrogenation is found to stop measurably short of completion, and hence the kinetics are complicated by a significant back reaction, at the temperatures above about 200°. Much higher temperatures (~600°) are needed before back reactions become important with non-resonating hydrocarbons. Thus, for example, ΔG for the hydrogenation of cyclopentadiene is —10.9 kcal. mole^{-1} at 340°, and for cycloheptatriene it is —11.9 kcal. mole^{-1}.[17]

The substitution of alkyl groups leads to a very slight decrease in the heat of hydrogenation. Values of $-\Delta H$ at 82° are: for ethylbenzene, 48.92; for *o*-xylene, 47.25 kcal. mole^{-1}.[15] Because of the isomeric complexity of the intermediates their thermochemistry has not received attention.

Few direct thermochemical measurements have been made on hetero-aromatic compounds. The heat of hydrogenation of furan at 82° is 36.63 kcal. mole^{-1}, giving it a resonance energy of about 20 kcal. mole^{-1}. Pauling[18] lists empirical resonance energies for numerous resonating systems: the values for naphthalene, anthracene and phenanthrene are respectively 75, 105 and 110 kcal. mole^{-1}, and pyridine is assigned a value of 43 kcal. mole^{-1}.

13.2 Kinetics and Mechanisms of the Hydrogenation and Exchange of Benzene

13.21 The Kinetics and Mechanism of the Hydrogenation of Benzene

Only comparatively few worthwhile studies of the kinetics of benzene hydrogenation have been reported. We may exclude from further consideration at this point (i) those studies made with liquid benzene or benzene solutions,[19] by reason of the difficulty of ensuring the absence of diffusion limitation and (ii) those studies whose sole purpose it was to assess the effect on this rate of varying the nature of the catalyst.[20]

The more important results are summarized in Table II. It is generally observed that in vapour-phase reactions the rate is independent of benzene pressure and proportional to hydrogen pressure, although sometimes[21, 22] the exponent of the hydrogen pressure increases with temperature, tending to or attaining a value of unity at a temperature dependent on the catalyst used. The interpretation of these results must be that on most catalysts (nickel-kieselguhr being a possible exception) benzene is strongly chemisorbed, with

Table II. *Kinetics of the Vapour Phase Hydrogenation of Benzene*

$$r \propto P^{x}_{C_6H_6}\, P^{y}_{H_2}$$

Metal	*Form*	*x*	*y*	*Temp.* (°C)	*E(kcal. mole^{-1})*	*logA*	*Temp. range* (°C)	*Ref.*
Ni	on kieselguhr	0.3	0.4	70	11.0	—	70–190	21
		0.4	—	180				
		—	0.9	210				
Ni	powder	—	0.25	48	10.6	—	40–80	22
Ru	on Al_2O_3	0	1	40	11.9	8.18*	23–45	23
Rh	on Al_2O_3	—	—	—	11.9	8.34*	24–47	23
Pd	film	0.2	0.8	?	8.9	20.5†	20–80	7
Pt	film	—	—	—	9	23†	0– −44	7
Pt	on Al_2O_3	—	—	—	12.3	7.25*	83–112	23
Pt	foil	0	1	17	7	—	17–96	12
Pt	powder	0	0.4	42	6.8	—	34–61	22
		—	0.7	66				
		—	1.0	87				

* *A*, in sec.$^{-1}$; † *A*, in mol. (10 mg.)$^{-1}$ sec.$^{-1}$.

the hydrogen only weakly chemisorbed or reacting from the van der Waals layer when its order is unity. The lower temperature-dependent orders suggest that atomic hydrogen, adsorbed with moderate strength, is the reactive species at least on certain catalysts, and it is interesting to note that the limiting order of unity is found with platinum[22] at a lower temperature (87°) than is found with nickel[21] ($>$210°).

There is no unanimous view on the detailed reaction mechanism, and this is partly attributable to uncertainty concerning the state of chemisorbed benzene. It is not even certain whether all the hydrogen atoms are added during one period of residence on the surface. Studies of the stereochemistry of the hydrogenation of xylenes (to be described in Section 13.42) seem to show that the cyclohexene may vacate the surface, only to be re-adsorbed and rapidly reduced. At the moment it is most probable that at least the first four hydrogen atoms are added in quick succession, and to the same side of the ring.[14] Selwood's views[4] on the mechanism of this process are so much at variance with those of other workers that a comparative discussion is of little use.

13.22 The Kinetics and Mechanism of the Exchange of Benzene with Deuterium

The early work on the exchange reaction between benzene and deuterium was performed by following the release of hydrogen deuteride to the gas phase.[19] As has been stressed in earlier Chapters, this method has severe limitations, and the fullest information on the progress of the reaction is only achieved when the appearance of deuterium in the unchanged reactant hydrocarbon and in the products is followed, most satisfactorily by mass-spectrometry. Only one such detailed investigation has yet been reported.[7]

The early studies on what we may again term the *hydrogen exchange reaction* showed that this reaction always proceeds in some measure faster than hydrogenation, although it has the higher activation energy. Thus, for example, hydrogen exchange occurs over copper powder between 100 and 140° with an activation energy of 14 kcal. mole^{-1}, although hydrogenation is undetectable even at 210°.[22] Kinetic parameters for the exchange of benzene vapour are summarized in Table III. Although orders in benzene are similar to those found for hydrogenation, the orders in hydrogen are very distinctly lower. *Para*-hydrogen conversion and hydrogen–deuterium equilibration proceed rapidly and at about the same rates during benzene hydrogenation, rates being between 30 and 300 times the rate of exchange.[12, 22] It seems that although benzene is strongly adsorbed, there are still sites which are accessible to hydrogen but which for steric reasons are not accessible to benzene (see Fig. 1).

There is very good evidence[7] that the hydrogenation and exchange reactions proceed by independent mechanisms: for example, the exchange reaction is inhibited by the cyclohexane produced, whereas hydrogenation is not. Mass-spectrometric analysis shows that rather more than one deuterium atom is

TABLE III. *Kinetics of the Exchange of Benzene with Deuterium*

$r \propto P^{x}_{C_6H_6} P^{y}_{H_2}$

Metal	*Form*	*x*	*y*	*Temp.* (°C)	*E*(*kcal. mole*$^{-1}$)	*log A**	*Temp. range* (°C)	*Ref.*
Ni	powder	—	−0.15	40	15	—	40–80	22
Cu	powder	—	0	100	14	—	100–140	22
Pd	film	0.1	−0.5	?	13	24.6	0–58	7
Pt	film	—	—	—	18	32	0– −44	7
Pt	foil	0.4	0	17	9	—	17–96	12
Pt	powder	0.3	−0.05	51	7.3	—	34–61	22
		—	0.25	80				
Ag	film	—	—	—	6	17	293–373	7

* *A*, in mol. (10 mg.)$^{-1}$ sec.$^{-1}$.

introduced into a benzene molecule in each act of exchange: some typical values of *M*, the mean number of deuterium atoms introduced, are shown in Table IV. Typical analyses of the individual benzenes are shown in Table V.

TABLE IV. *Mean Numbers of Deuterium Atoms Introduced into Benzene During Exchange over Metal Films*[7]

Metal	*Temp.* (°C)	*M*
Pd	0	1.8
	58.0	2.7
Pt	−43.5	1.5
	−22.5	1.4
Ag	293	1.2
	373	1.4

TABLE V. *Analyses of Deuterated Benzenes Formed by Exchange over Metal Films*[7]

Metal	*Temp.* (°C)	*Percentage composition*					
		C_6H_5D	$C_6H_4D_2$	$C_6H_3D_3$	$C_6H_2D_4$	C_6HD_5	C_6D_6
Pd	29.5	61.8	17.7	7.1	3.8	3.5	6.1
Pt	−43.5	77.6	13.0	2.8	2.3	2.0	2.3
Ag	373	71.2	17.0	3.5	2.1	2.5	3.7

The distributions are characterized by a minimum at C_6HD_5, and the interpretation of this observation requires the coexistence of two separate mechanisms. By analogy with ethane exchange the following mechanism has been supposed.

$$D_2 + 2* \rightarrow 2\underset{*}{D} \qquad \text{(c)}$$

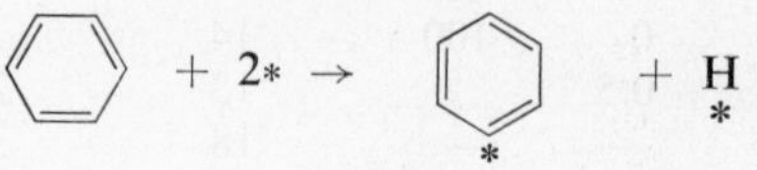

$$+ 2* \rightarrow \underset{*}{} + \underset{*}{H} \qquad \text{(d)}$$

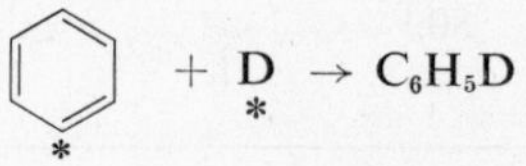

$$\underset{*}{} + \underset{*}{D} \rightarrow C_6H_5D \qquad \text{(e)}$$

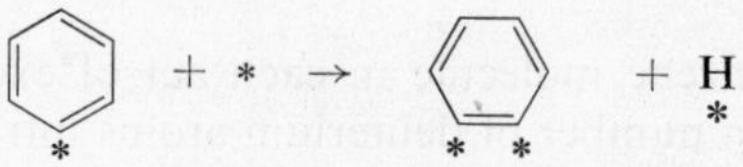

$$\underset{*}{} + * \rightarrow \underset{*\ *}{} + \underset{*}{H} \qquad \text{(f)}$$

$$\underset{*\ *}{} + \underset{*}{D} \rightarrow \underset{*}{}D + 2* \qquad \text{(g)}$$

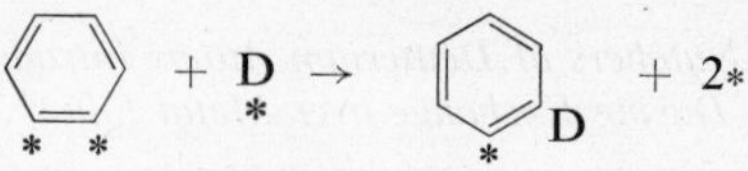

A parameter $\mathscr{P}$ is defined as k_f/k_e and the observed distribution over palladium is reproduced if it is assumed that 79.6 per cent of the exchange proceeds with a $\mathscr{P}$-value of 0.30 and the remainder with a $\mathscr{P}$-value of 14.8. The major deuterated cyclohexane is cyclohexane-d_6 confirming the view that the hydrogenation proceeds through the addition of deuterium atoms or molecules to benzene chemisorbed as in process (a) or (b). This process differs from the hydrogenation of olefins, in that no redistribution reaction is observed. There are two possible reasons for this: the transfer of a hydrogen atom from one half-hydrogenated state to another may be difficult for steric reasons, or more probably, since the deuterium atoms are all added to one side of the ring, the hydrogen atoms are inaccessible.[14] This would be in harmony with the known behaviour of cyclohexane in exchange reactions.

Very rapid exchange also occurred over tungsten films at $-25°$, over nickel films at $-45°$ and over iron films at $0°$. Addition of deuterium to benzene took place rapidly over tungsten at $-25°$, and at a measurable rate over iron at $0°$. No addition took place over silver films even at the highest temperature used (373°), although exchange occurred at a readily measurable rate at this temperature: this is in harmony with the observations on copper powder, referred to above.

13.3 THE ACTIVITY OF METALS AND ALLOYS

13.31 The Effect of Degree of Dispersion on Activity

Much experimental work has been performed in which the effect of the nature of the catalyst on the rate of benzene hydrogenation has been studied: on occasions the Arrhenius parameters have also been evaluated.[20] This information, however, adds only indirectly to our understanding of the reaction mechanisms. It is convenient first to consider briefly the effect of the degree of dispersion of the metal on the activity of supported catalysts. This is a field in which Russian workers have been especially active: their findings are ably summarized in a recent review,[24] where the original references are listed.

With series of nickel crystallites having diameters between 50 and 100 Å, the rate has been found to increase continuously with decreasing crystallite size; this may be partly ascribable to the accompanying decrease in the activation energy, from 10.5 to 3.1 kcal. mole^{-1}. Nickel crystallites supported on charcoal or alumina show a maximum activity at a diameter of 40 Å. There is other evidence for optimum size of crystallite. Palladium and platinum supported on charcoal show a sharp break in their activity per unit weight when the metal content falls below 0.1 per cent, and this is possible support for Kobozev's hypothesis of *active ensembles*. This hypothesis supposes that on each elementary part of the support's surface (not clearly defined) a certain minimum and small number of metal atoms must be present in aggregation before activity results: it is thus conceptually similar to Balandin's "multiplet hypothesis," but is less susceptible to experimental verification and has not been generally accepted among Western scientists.

In the following sub-section, consideration will only be given to experiments designed to compare the activity of metals in the same physical state.

13.32 The Relative Activities of Pure Metals

Measurements of the rate of benzene hydrogenation over pure metals in a variety of physical forms lead to certain general conclusions concerning their relative activities. (i) The noble Group VIII metals are usually the most active, although tungsten films are enormously active, while palladium often[7, 23] has an anomalously low activity. This may be ascribed to the poisoning action of dissolved hydrogen, but it is worth recalling that palladium is invariably the most active metal for hydrogenating acetylenic compounds (see Chapter 12). (ii) Cobalt and nickel are somewhat less active, there being a divergence of opinion on which is the more active of the two. The position is complicated by (a) changes in their activity with time of use,[25] (b) comparison being usually made on a weight rather than an area basis (cobalt powders generally have larger specific areas than nickel powders[26, 27]), and (c) the possibility that cobalt exists in two allotropic modifications (see Chapter 2). The fact that close-packed hexagonal cobalt formed by reduction of the oxide below 500° is found[28] to be more active than the face-centred cubic modification which results at higher temperatures is most probably due to its being less sintered, and hence possessing a higher specific surface area. The possibility that the two modifications do not expose their hexagonal faces to equal extents cannot, however, be ruled out. (iii) Chemically formed iron is rarely active (see, however, Ref. 29) although evaporated iron films have moderate activity.[7, 30] Copper catalysts have minimal[27, 31] or zero activity, and silver is also inactive. The few meaningful activity sequences and the even fewer quantitative results are given in Table VI.

TABLE VI. *The Relative Activities of Metals for Benzene Hydrogenation*

Form	*Decreasing activity⟶*							*Ref.*
Film	W >	Pt >	Ni >	Fe >	Pd			7
On Al_2O_3	Rh >	Ru >	Pt >	Pd				23
log*k* at 47°	0	−0.16	−1.01	—				
On SiO_2	Pt >	Rh >	Ru >	Pd >	Co >	Ni >	Fe	
log*k* at 100°	+0.4	0	−0.1	−0.2	−1.1	−1.2	−2.3	29

It is interesting to try to establish with which of the Arrhenius parameters the differences in the activities of metals in the same physical state are related. The available information is contained in Table II, and it is clear that for both metal films and alumina-supported metals the activation energy is constant, and that it is the pre-exponential factor which changes with activity. Benzene hydrogenation therefore shows a Type IV "no compensation" effect (see Chapter 7). Table III reveals the striking conclusion that benzene exchange on the other hand shows a normal Type I compensation effect.

13.33 The Activities of Alloys

The activities of nickel–copper alloy powders prepared by reduction of the mixed oxides in hydrogen have been investigated several times.[27, 32, 33] The results obtained by Hall and Emmett[33] are shown in Fig. 2, where the log of the specific activity at 162° (in units based on conversion under standard conditions) is plotted against alloy composition. The activity at first increases with increasing copper content, and passes through a maximum at 25 per cent copper, subsequently falling smoothly to zero for pure copper. The results found by Rienäcker and Unger[27] for closely similar catalysts operated at 190° are also shown in Fig. 2, and the agreement, except at the copper-rich end, is very satisfactory. Earlier measurements on non-specific activities of these catalysts[32] showed a *minimum* activity at 30 per cent copper, but this was probably due to the commonly found decrease in specific area with increasing copper content. Skeletal alloys also show a sharp drop in activity with rising copper content, and a minimum activity at 40 per cent copper.

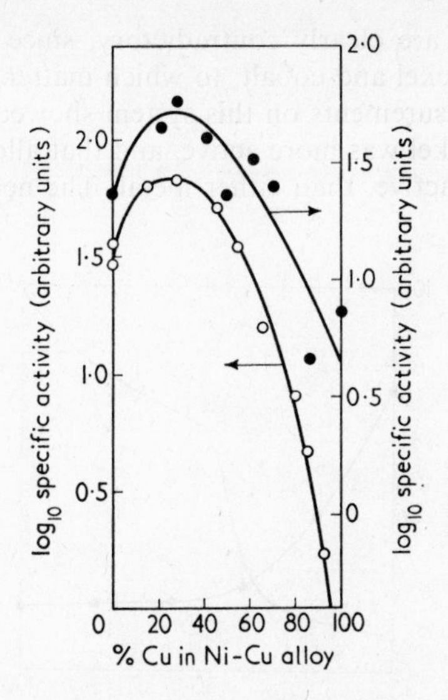

FIG. 2. The activity of nickel–copper alloy powders for benzene hydrogenation.
○ At 162°: (Hall and Emmett[33]).
● At 190°: (Rienacker and Unger[27]).

Only one complete series of activation energies has been obtained,[33] and these are plotted in the form of a compensation effect in Fig. 3. Calculations based on the results quoted in Ref. 32 give activation for alloy powders containing 28, 54 and 72 per cent copper of 18 to 22 kcal. mole^{-1}.

The activities of nickel–cobalt alloy powders have also been studied,[27, 28, 32] and the two more complete sets of results are shown, for what they are worth,

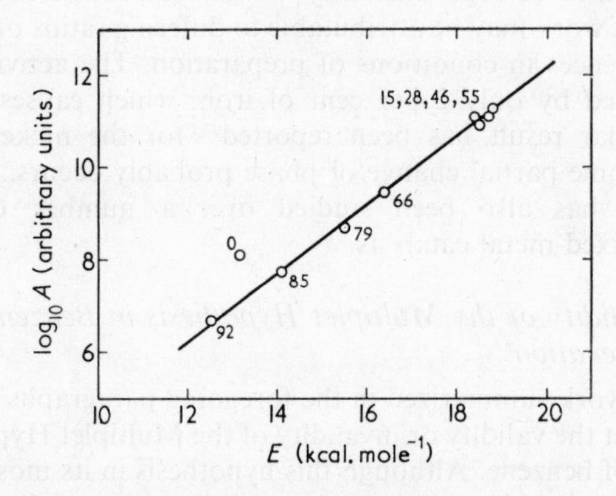

FIG. 3. Compensation effect for benzene hydrogenation over nickel–copper alloy powders.[33] The %Cu to which each point refers is noted on the graph.

in Fig. 4. The results are clearly contradictory, since they disagree on the relative activities of nickel and cobalt, to which matter reference has already been made. Early measurements on this system showed[32] that the alloy containing 30 per cent nickel was more active, and that alloys containing 55 and 80 per cent were less active, than either metal. The need for further experimental work is clear.

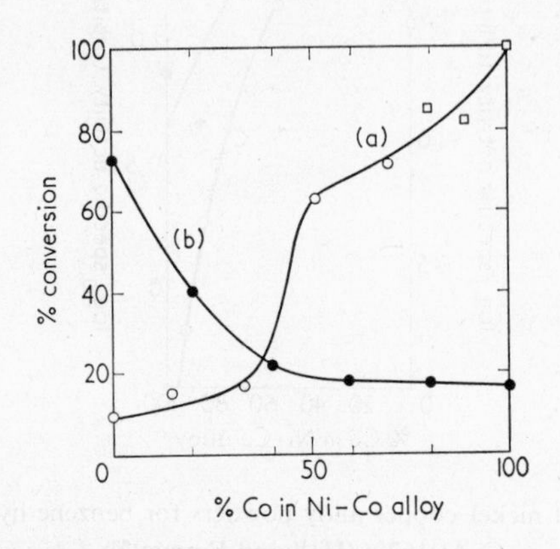

FIG. 4. The activity of nickel–cobalt alloys for benzene hydrogenation.
(a) Non-specific conversion at 140°:[28] squares for close-packed hexagonal phases, circles for face-centred cubic phases.
(b) Specific conversion at 190°.[27]

Cobalt–iron alloy powders containing less than 75 per cent cobalt are generally found to have a body-centred cubic structure, and to be inactive:[28,32] however, an alloy of unknown structure containing only 40 per cent cobalt has been reported to be active.[26] Alloys containing between 10 and 25 per cent cobalt have been shown to be a mixture of face- and body-centred cubic forms, and the lack of reproducibility[28, 32] and of consistency between the various pieces of work may be attributable to differing ratios of the two forms caused by differences in conditions of preparation. The activity of cobalt is severely depressed by only 2 per cent of iron, which causes no change in phase.[28] A similar result has been reported[27] for the nickel–iron systems although here some partial change of phase probably occurs.

The reaction has also been studied over a number of imperfectly characterized mixed-metal catalysts.[34]

13.34 The Validity of the Multiplet Hypothesis in Benzene Hydrogenation[8]

Much of the work summarized in the foregoing paragraphs was motivated by a desire to test the validity or invalidity of the Multiplet Hypothesis for the hydrogenation of benzene. Although this hypothesis in its most general form has been applied to a wide variety of systems,[8] we are here only concerned with Balandin's view[35] that for the successful dehydrogenation of cyclohexane, and hence also for the reverse process, an hexagonal array of six suitably spaced atoms is required. If the Multiplet Hypothesis is valid, activity should only be determined by geometric and not by electronic factors, and metals and alloys having either a face-centred cubic or a close-packed hexagonal structure should be more active than those having a body-centred cubic structure.

It may be said at once that the experimental evidence is highly discordant. Thus, while chemically formed iron is nearly always inactive, evaporated films of iron and tungsten, both having the normal body-centred cubic structure, are highly active. Furthermore, copper and silver, which are face-centred cubic metals, are inactive or of low activity. Therefore, at best the Multiplet Hypothesis as applied to benzene hydrogenation must be regarded as a necessary but not a sufficient condition. Even if we exclude copper and silver, since they are not Transition metals, we are left with the task of reconciling the low activities of body-centred cubic metals and alloys formed by chemical means with the high activity of evaporated iron and tungsten films. This cannot be done without further research.

13.4 The Hydrogenation of Alkyl-substituted Benzenes

13.41 The Effect of Substitution on the Rate of Hydrogenation

Divergent results have been reported for the effect of alkyl-substitution on the rate of hydrogenation of benzene derivatives. Since all the work has been done in the liquid phase, some of the discrepancies may be attributable to varying degrees of diffusion limitation. Thus, for example, the hydrogenation of a wide variety of alkylbenzenes has been said to proceed at about the same rate over nickel–alumina,[36] indicating that perhaps the rate of diffusion of hydrogen through the liquid phase was the slow step in all cases. On the other hand, over colloidal and Adams platinum[37] and over Raney nickel[38] at 170°, the rates for mono-substituted alkylbenzenes have been found to decrease with increasing molecular weight. As Fig. 5 shows, the rates for

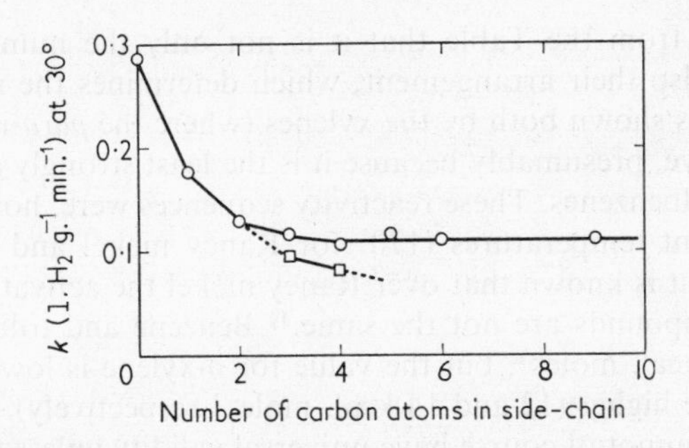

FIG. 5. The effect of alkyl-substitution on the rates of hydrogenation of benzene derivatives over Adams Pt at 30°.[39]

○ n-Alkyl substituents; □ s-alkyl substituents.

mono-substituted n-alkylbenzenes attain a limiting minimum value when the side-chain contains four or more carbon atoms.[39]

Information is also available on the effect of the *number* of substituted alkyl-groups on rates of hydrogenation.[24, 38, 40] The results of three not quite consistent sets of results[38, 41, 42] are given in Table VII, where rates relative to that of benzene are compared with those predicted on the basis of the proposed[42] relation:

$$r_n = r_0\, 2^{-n}\,. \qquad (1)$$

Here r_0 is the rate of benzene hydrogenation and r_n is the rate for a benzene derivative containing n substituents. A closely similar expression is claimed[40] to reproduce the relative rates of hydrogenation of alkylbenzenes over a rhodium–alumina catalyst.

TABLE VII. *Relative Rates of Hydrogenation of Polyalkyl-substituted Benzenes*

Compound	*On Raney Ni*[38]	*On Adams Pt*[41]	*On Ni–Al_2O_3*[42]	*Predicted by equation (1)*
Benzene	100	100	100	100
Toluene	77	62	50	50
o-Xylene	16	32	24	25
m-Xylene	21	49	23	25
p-Xylene	26	65	31	25
1,2,3-Trimethylbenzene	—	14	—	12.5
1,2,4-Trimethylbenzene	—	29	—	12.5
1,3,5-Trimethylbenzene	—	58	10	12.5
1,2,3,4-Tetramethylbenzene	—	10	—	6.2
1,2,4,5-Tetramethylbenzene	—	18	3.8	6.2
Pentamethylbenzene	—	3.5	0.5	3.1
Hexamethylbenzene	—	0.2	0	1.5

It is evident from the Table that it is not only the number of the substituents, but also their arrangement, which determines the reactivity of the molecule: this is shown both by the xylenes (where the *para*-isomer is always the most reactive, presumably because it is the least strongly adsorbed[43]) and by the trimethylbenzenes. These reactivity sequences were, however, obtained at quite different temperatures (170° for Raney nickel and 30° for Adams platinum), and it is known that over Raney nickel the activation energies for the several compounds are not the same.[44] Benzene and toluene both show values of 10.5 kcal. mole^{-1}, but the value for *o*-xylene is lower (6.2) and for *m*- and *p*-xylene higher (12 and 14 kcal. mole^{-1} respectively). The theoretical expression (1) cannot of course have universal validity unless the temperature coefficients for the hydrogenation of all the reactants are the same.

The effect of chain length on rates of hydrogenation is reminiscent of that found for the vapour-phase hydrogenation of the lower olefins (see Chapter

11). Factors which might in principle lead to decreased rates for alkylbenzenes are (i) a lower concentration in the adsorbed layer due to steric effects, and (ii) an increase in the strength of adsorption of the reactant through the electron-releasing effects of the alkyl groups. Either factor could reasonably interpret the results shown in Fig. 5.

13.42 The Stereochemistry of the Hydrogenation of Alkylbenzenes

Dialkyl-substituted cyclohexanes can exist in two isomeric forms, that is, a *cis*-form where both groups are on the same side of the ring, and a *trans*-form in which they are on opposite sides of the ring. In 1,2- and 1,4- derivatives, the *trans*-configuration is the more stable, whereas in 1,3- derivatives the reverse is true.

In the general case, the hydrogenation of polyalkylbenzenes leads to complex mixtures of isomers, and only the products formed from the isomeric xylenes have been estimated with any accuracy. Even so, much of the older work on them is now suspect. All three xylenes appear to yield on hydrogenation at room temperature products having predominantly the *cis*-configuration, but in the case of *o*- and *p*-xylene increasing the temperature raises the proportion of the *trans*-isomers. Indeed above 150° these may be the major ones, due probably to the catalytic epimerization of the initially formed *cis*-isomers.[45] The precise *cis*/*trans* ratio found will, therefore, depend on the activity of the catalyst and the duration of the experiment. Since the *cis*-form of 1,3-dimethylcyclohexane is the more stable, the yield of the *trans*-isomer does not rise with temperature.

A recent very careful study of this problem[46] has shown that the yields of *cis*-isomer over Adams platinum at room temperature are respectively: from *o*-xylene, 96 per cent; from *p*-xylene, 74 per cent; and from *m*-xylene, 86 per cent, which is *less* than the equilibrium proportion. In this case at least, the *trans*-isomer cannot have been formed from the *cis*-isomer, but must have arisen directly from the xylene. These results closely parallel those obtained with substituted cyclohexenes, and it appears that the same intermediates must be involved in both reactions. This is evidence against the simultaneous hydrogenation of all three double bonds in aromatic compounds.

13.5 The Hydrogenation of other Substituted Benzenes

13.51 Phenols

If the hydrogenation of phenol is carried out under sufficiently vigorous conditions, hydrogenolysis to benzene (subsequently hydrogenated to cyclohexane) and water, as well as the expected formation of cyclohexanol, may result. It is also well-established that cyclohexanone is an intermediate product, formed perhaps by enolization of the unstable 1-hydroxycyclohexene:

$$C_6H_5\text{—OH} \xrightarrow{+2H_2} C_6H_9\text{—OH} \longrightarrow C_6H_{10}\text{=O} \qquad \text{(h)}$$

Careful analysis of the course of the hydrogenation of phenol over Raney nickel, and separate work on the hydrogenation of cyclohexanone,

$$\text{C}_6\text{H}_{10}{=}\text{O} \xrightarrow{+\text{H}_2} \text{C}_6\text{H}_{11}\text{—OH} \qquad \text{(i)}$$

has shown[47] (a) that between 113 and 174°, $E_{(h)}$ is 8.5 and $E_{(i)}$ is 6.5 kcal. mole^{-1}; (b) that $k_{(i)}/k_{(h)}$ is 1.95 at 174° and 3.0 at 113°, and hence that the maximum yield of cyclohexanone increases with rising temperature; (c) that cyclohexanol is also formed directly from phenol without the detectable intervention of cyclohexanone. Full analysis of the system is complicated by the slow reaction between phenol and cyclohexanol, viz.

$$\text{C}_6\text{H}_5\text{—OH} + 2\ \text{C}_6\text{H}_{11}\text{—OH} \longrightarrow 3\ \text{C}_6\text{H}_{10}{=}\text{O} \qquad \text{(j)}$$

The phenoxide ion ($C_6H_5O^-$) is more readily hydrogenated than phenol itself.

The rates of hydrogenation of the cresols decrease in the sequence, *para* > *meta* > *ortho*: this is the same as the order for the xylenes (Table VII), and the same explanation is likely to hold in both cases. All the cresols yield *trans*-methyl-cyclohexanols. Over Raney nickel between 100 and 200°, the cresols, thymol, resorcinol and hydroquinone are hydrogenated with activation energies of between 9 and 17 kcal. mole^{-1}.[44]

13.52 *Aromatic Ethers*

Under conditions necessary to cause hydrogenation of the aromatic nucleus, the hydrogenolysis of the ether group is frequently an important side reaction. This process occurs more easily than the corresponding process with phenols: either the oxygen–aryl or the oxygen–alkyl bond may be broken, more usually the former. For example, the products of the hydrogenation of *o*-dimethoxybenzene by nickel at 140–200° and 50 atm. pressure are: 1,2-cyclohexanediol, 70 per cent; cyclohexanol, 20 per cent; cyclohexane, 10 per cent.[48] The extent of hydrogenolysis increases with temperature, and is greater for di- and trimethoxybenzenes than with anisole. It is markedly less over rhodium–alumina than over Adams platinum (6–18 per cent as against 40–60 per cent).[49] The rates of hydrogenation of methoxybenzenes over platinum are somewhat less than those of the methylbenzenes, but an exactly equivalent effect of number and arrangement of substituents is found. Activation energies for anisole and the dimethoxybenzenes are between 4.4 and 6.4 kcal. mole^{-1} over platinum and between 5.1 and 8.7 kcal. mole^{-1} over rhodium.[49]

13.53 *Aromatic Acids and Esters*

Benzoic acids and esters are quite readily hydrogenated to the corresponding cyclohexane compounds. Benzoic acid is hydrogenated over platinum at the same rate and with the same activation energy as phenylacetic acid,[24] in contrast to their vastly different rates of esterification. This is further evidence for the loss of resonance energy on chemisorption.

The rates of hydrogenation of a large number of methylbenzoic acids have been measured over Adams platinum.[50] As with methylbenzenes and methoxybenzenes, rates decrease with increasing numbers of substituents, but their position is very relevant: thus, for example, 4-methylbenzoic acid is hydrogenated at 30° about three times as rapidly as 2-methylbenzoic acid.

13.54 Aromatic Amines

Important side reactions accompany the hydrogenation of aniline over nickel at elevated temperatures. In addition to cyclohexylamine, the products include diphenylamine, dicyclohexylamine, phenylcyclohexylamine, cyclohexane, benzene and ammonia. The formation of dicyclohexylamine is detected even under quite mild conditions.[51] It is apparently formed by the condensation of cyclohexylamine with aniline to give phenylcyclohexylamine, which is subsequently hydrogenated. In the hydrogenation of aniline and alkylanilines over colloidal platinum in acid solutions, the yields of the mono- and diamines have been shown[52] to be a function of temperature and of the concentrations of the aniline and hydrochloric acid. The anilinium ion is hydrogenated by Adams platinum in glacial acetic acid with an activation energy of 7.5 kcal. mole^{-1}.[53]

13.6 The Hydrogenation of Polynuclear Aromatic Compounds [24]

13.61 Compounds Containing two Unfused Benzene Rings

From the hydrogenation of compounds containing two separated benzene rings, it is usually possible to isolate the intermediate phenylcyclohexyl compound in fair yield. Moreover, the rates and kintetics for both compounds are similar.[54] Information relating to these points is contained in Table VIII.

Table VIII. *Rates of, and Yields of Intermediates from, Hydrogenation of Compounds containing Two Unfused Benzene Rings, using Adams Platinum at 30°* [54]

Reactant	$k \times 10^4$*	*Intermediate*	
		Percentage yield at half-conversion	$k \times 10^4$*
Biphenyl	541	65	614
Diphenylmethane	629	95–100	665
1,1-Diphenylethane	474	95–100	366
Diphenylacetic acid	182	90–100	191

* l. H_2 g.$^{-1}$ min.$^{-1}$.

The intermediate is sometimes formed quantitatively, especially under relatively mild reaction conditions, while more drastic conditions usually favours complete reduction. With 2- or 3-substituted biphenyls reduction occurs preferentially in the substituent-bearing ring, although the reverse is true for 4-substituted compounds.[55] This is yet another of the minor unsolved problems of heterogeneous catalysis.

The hydrogenation of substituted biphenyls, in so far as it has been studied, appears to follow closely the rules which apply to benzene derivatives.

13.62 Compounds Containing Fused Aromatic Ring Systems

The hydrogenation of naphthalene proceeds in two distinct stages:

$$\text{naphthalene} \xrightarrow{+2H_2} \text{tetralin} \xrightarrow{+3H_2} \text{decalin} \qquad \text{(k)}$$

While there is only one possible isomer of tetralin, there are seven possible conformers of decalin, since there are four different conformations of the *cis*-isomer and three of the *trans*-. *Cis*-decalin, however, has been shown to consist of two chair forms of cyclohexane fused by equitorial–axial bonds (Fig. 6a), while *trans*-decalin has two chair-form rings fused by purely equatorial bonds (Fig. 6(b)). The energy difference between the two forms is only about 2.4 kcal. mole^{-1}, so that isomerization of the initially formed isomer is to be expected except under the mildest reaction conditions. Catalytic hydrogenation of tetralin over Adams platinum at room temperature

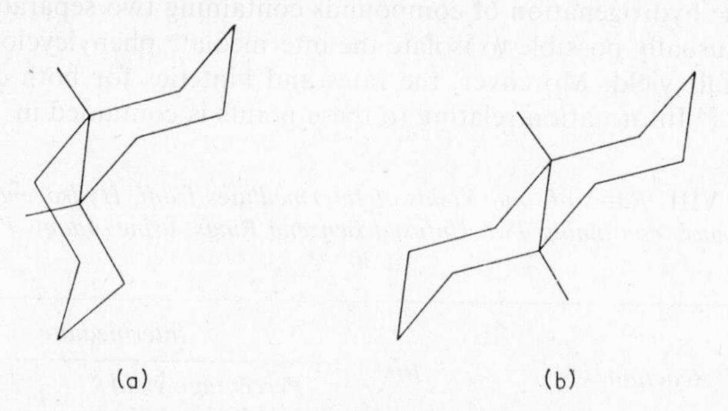

FIG. 6. Configurational isomers of decalin.
(a) The *cis*-isomer; (b) the *trans*-isomer.

and high pressure yields pure *cis*-decalin, although under similar conditions naphthalene yields only 77 per cent of the *cis*-isomer: a higher yield is reported over platinum black. With nickel catalysts there is a tendency for the reduction to stop at tetralin, more vigorous conditions being required to form decalin. Over nickel–alumina, the second stage proceeds more than six times more slowly than the first, whose rate is itself some three times greater than that for benzene under the same conditions.

Catalytic hydrogenation of 2-methylnaphthalene leads to 6-methyltetralin, so the unsubstituted ring is preferentially reduced. The hydrogenation of 2-naphthol by nickel at high pressures forms 6-hydroxytetralin in neutral or acidic ethanol, and 2-hydroxytetralin in alkaline ethanol. 2-Naphthyl ethers behave similarly, save that cleavage to tetralin and methanol occurs under alkaline conditions.

In the hydrogenation of anthracene, four moles of hydrogen are added quite readily, and the next three with more difficulty:

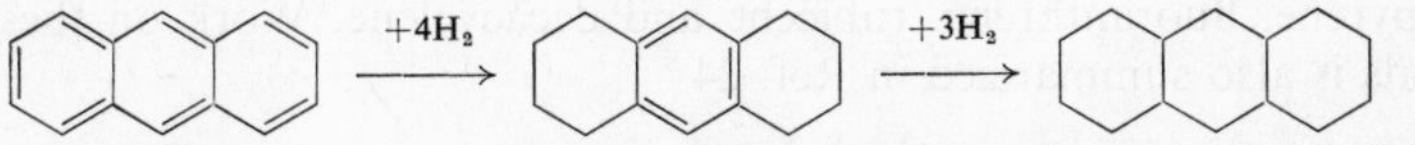

$$\text{anthracene} \xrightarrow{+4H_2} \text{octahydroanthracene} \xrightarrow{+3H_2} \text{perhydroanthracene} \quad (l)$$

The actual course of the reaction is more complex, as a thorough study using copper as catalyst has shown.[56] The first product is 9,10-dihydroanthracene, and this is then reduced to the hexa-, octa- and perhydro-compounds:

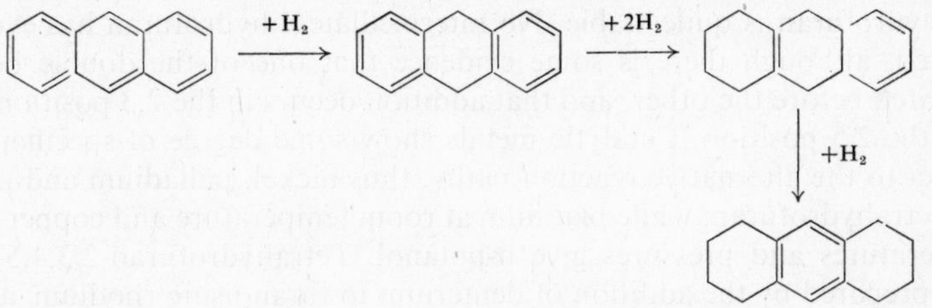

$$\xrightarrow{+H_2} \quad \xrightarrow{+2H_2} \quad \xrightarrow{+H_2} \quad (m)$$

Each successive stage requires progressively more vigorous conditions (higher temperatures and pressures, and longer times) for its execution. The stereochemistry of perhydroanthracene is complex, but the observed product usually consists of only two isomers. Both anthracene and the 9,10-dihydro-compound are reduced over nickel–alumina some three times faster than benzene, although the rate of hydrogenation of the octahydro-compound is very much slower.

The primary attack of hydrogen on phenanthrene also occurs at the 9,10 positions, the octahydro- and perhydro-compounds being formed subsequently:

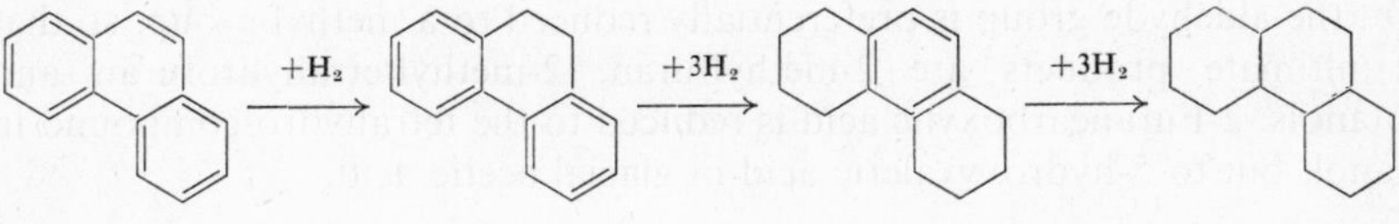

$$\xrightarrow{+H_2} \quad \xrightarrow{+3H_2} \quad \xrightarrow{+3H_2} \quad (n)$$

Again each of the successive stages demands progressively more vigorous conditions. The stereochemistry of perhydrophenanthrene is also complex, since due to the presence of four asymmetric centres there are six possible isomers. An exhaustive study by Linstead and his associates of the stereochemical course of the hydrogenation of phenanthrene and its derivatives (summarized in Ref. 24) has shown that the *cis-syn-cis* isomer is the exclusive product in almost every case, this being interpreted as due to the addition of hydrogen to the same side of the molecule regardless of the number of times it is adsorbed before being fully hydrogenated. It is beyond the scope of this book to go into further details.

A large number of more complex fused aromatic ring systems have also been hydrogenated catalytically: these include pyrene, chrysene, perylene, benzpyrene, fluoranthrene, rubicene and decacyclene. Work on these compounds is also summarized in Ref. 24.

13.7 The Hydrogenation of Heterocyclic Systems [24]

13.71 *Furan and its Derivatives*

Furan undergoes catalytic hydrogenation under a variety of conditions. The products are tetrahydrofuran (two moles of hydrogen being consumed) and n-butanol (requiring three moles of hydrogen). These reactions seem to be simultaneous rather than consecutive, since under the reaction conditions tetrahydrofuran is quite stable. No intermediate dihydrofuran has ever been isolated, although there is some evidence that one of the double bonds is saturated before the other, and that addition occurs in the 2,3 position rather than the 2,5 position. Catalytic metals show some degree of specificity with respect to the alternative reaction paths: thus nickel, palladium and osmium give tetrahydrofuran, while platinum at room temperature and copper at high temperatures and pressures give n-butanol. Tetrahydrofuran-2,3,4,5-d_4 has been prepared by the addition of deuterium to furan using rhodium–alumina as catalyst.[57]

There is a considerable commercial interest in the hydrogenation of 2-furfuraldehyde, from which a number of products may be isolated, depending on the conditions employed. With copper or platinum, the first and rapid process is the reduction of the aldehyde group:

$$\text{C}_4\text{H}_3\text{O—CHO} \xrightarrow{+H_2} \text{C}_4\text{H}_3\text{O—CH}_2\text{OH} \qquad \text{(o)}$$

The furfuryl alcohol may then either be further reduced to 2-hydroxymethyltetrahydrofuran or with ring cleavage to a mixture of 1,2- and 1,5-pentanediols. With iron, cobalt and nickel catalysts, and with copper at 200°, the aldehyde group is preferentially reduced to a methyl group, so that the ultimate products are 2-methylfuran, 2-methyltetrahydrofuran and pentanols. 2-Furancarboxylic acid is reduced to the tetrahydro-compound in ethanol, but to 5-hydroxyvaleric acid in glacial acetic acid.

The Arrhenius parameters for the hydrogenation of a number of furan derivatives over Adams platinum in acetic acid have been measured,[58, 59] and the results are shown in Fig. 7 as a compensation effect.

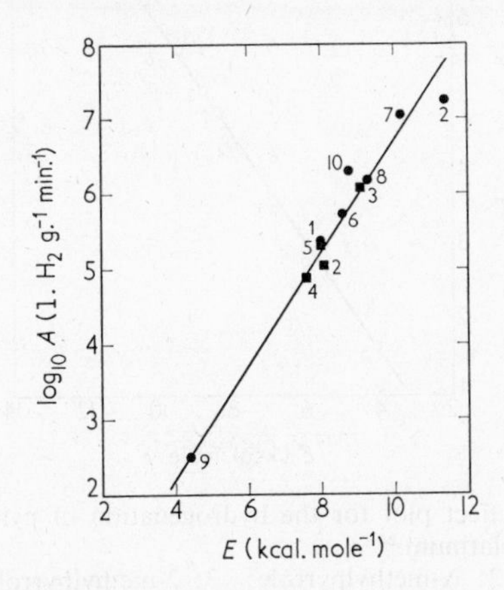

FIG. 7. Compensation effect plot for the hydrogenation of furan and its derivatives over Adams platinum in acetic acid.

1: Furan; 2: 2-furancarboxylic acid; 3: 2-furanacetic acid; 4: 3-furancarboxylic acid; 5: 3-furanacetic acid; 6: 2-methylfuran; 7: 2,5-dimethylfuran; 8: 2-hydroxymethylfuran; 9: 2-furfuraldehyde; 10: dibenzofuran.

■, ref. 58; ●, ref. 59.

13.72 *Molecules Containing Nitrogen as the Hetero-atom*[24]

The hydrogenation of pyrrole leads to pyrrolidine, together with various other products formed by hydrogenolysis: their yield naturally increases with increasing temperature. Palladium and platinum catalysts work satisfactorily, especially if care is taken to purify the reactant. Nickel catalysts tend to favour hydrogenolysis, probably because of the higher temperatures needed for them to function. The substitution of alkyl groups increases the rate of hydrogenation over Adams platinum: thus, although the velocity constants (in l. H_2 g.$^{-1}$ min.$^{-1}$) at 30° for pyrrole and its 2- and 3-methyl derivatives are about the same (~0.03), *N*-methylpyrrole is more reactive (k ~ 0.05) and the 2,3-, 2,4 and 3,4- dimethyl derivatives even more so (k ~ 0.05 to 0.08). 2,5-Dimethylpyrrole is exceptionally reactive (k ~ 0.23). Arrhenius parameters have been derived for these compounds, and are plotted in the form of a compensation effect in Fig. 8.

Pyridine and its derivatives are hydrogenated somewhat less readily than benzenes. 2-Methylpyridine is reduced more slowly than pyridine itself over Adams platinum, and the rate decreases further as the methyl group is removed to positions more remote from the nitrogen atom. Arrhenius parameters have also been derived for these systems, and are shown in Fig. 8.

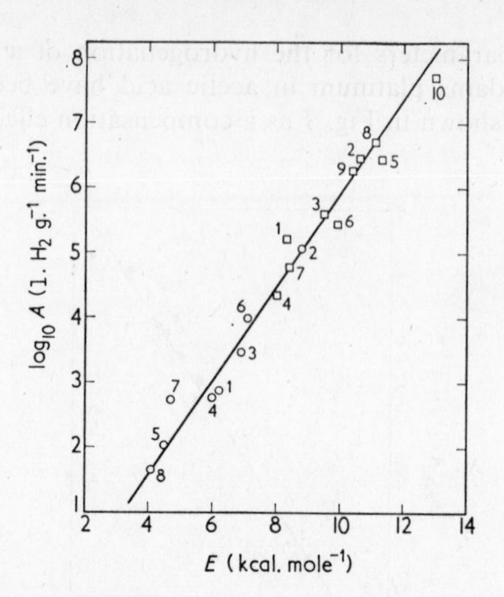

FIG. 8. Compensation effect plot for the hydrogenation of pyrrole, pyridine and their derivatives over Adams platinum.[24]

Circles: 1: pyrrole; 2: *N*-methylpyrrole; 3: 2-methylpyrrole; 4: 3-methylpyrrole; 5: 2,3-dimethylpyrrole; 6: 2,4-dimethylpyrrole; 7: 2,5-dimethylpyrrole; 8: 3,4-dimethylpyrrole.

Squares: 1: pyridine; 2: 2-methylpyridine; 3: 3-methylpyridine; 4: 4-methylpyridine; 5: 2,3-dimethylpyridine; 6: 2,4-dimethylpyridine; 7: 2,5-dimethylpyridine; 8: 2,6-dimethylpyridine; 9: 2,3,6-trimethylpyridine; 10: 2,4,6-trimethylpyridine.

Quinoline is reduced first to the tetra-, then to the decahydro-compound:

$$\text{Quinoline (positions 1–8)} \xrightarrow{+2H_2} \text{tetrahydroquinoline} \xrightarrow{+3H_2} \text{decahydroquinoline} \qquad (p)$$

The *trans*-isomer generally predominates. The substitution of methyl groups has little effect on the rate of hydrogenation over Adams platinum, save for the 4-position, where methyl substitution greatly decreases the rate. Methyl substitution in one ring favours reduction of the other, roughly in proportion to the number of groups substituted. Thus, for example, the only tetrahydro-compound formed from 2,3,4-trimethylquinoline is

CH_3, CH_3, N, CH_3 (5,6,7,8-tetrahydro-2,3,4-trimethylquinoline structure)

A very large number of more complex heterocyclic compounds have been subjected to catalytic hydrogenation; Ref. 24 summarizes work in this field.

REFERENCES

1. Y.-F. Yu, J. J. Chessick and A. C. Zettlemoyer, *J. Phys. Chem.* **63,** 1626 (1959).
2. E. B. Maxted and M. Josephs, *J. Chem. Soc.* 2635 (1956).
3. H. A. Smith and H. T. Meriwether, *J. Amer. Chem. Soc.* **71,** 413 (1949).
4. P. W. Selwood, *J. Amer. Chem. Soc.* **79,** 4637 (1957).
5. E. Suhrmann, G. Wedler and G. Kruger, *Z. Elektrochem.* **63,** 155 (1959).
6. R. Suhrmann, *Adv. Catalysis* **9,** 88 (1957).
7. J. R. Anderson and C. Kemball, *Adv. Catalysis* **9,** 51 (1957).
8. B. M. W. Trapnell, *Adv. Catalysis* **3,** 1 (1951).
9. M. Y. Kagan and S. D. Friedman, *Doklady Akad. Nauk S.S.S.R.* **68,** 697 (1949).
10. D. D. Eley and M. Polanyi, *Trans. Faraday Soc.* **32,** 1388 (1936).
11. C. Horrex, R. K. Greenhalgh and M. Polanyi, *Trans. Faraday Soc.* **35,** 511 (1939).
12. A. Farkas and L. Farkas, *Trans. Faraday Soc.* **33,** 827 (1937).
13. D. D. Eley, *Quart. Rev.* **3,** 1 (1949).
14. R. L. Burwell, *Adv. Catalysis* **9,** 87 (1957).
15. J. B. Conant and G. B. Kistiakowsky, *Chem. Rev.* **20,** 181 (1937).
16. G. J. Janz, *J. Chem. Phys.* **22,** 751 (1954).
17. H. S. Taylor, *J. Amer. Chem. Soc.* **60,** 627 (1938).
18. L. Pauling, "Nature of the Chemical Bond" (Cornell U.P., Ithaca, 1948).
19. J. Horiuti, G. Ogden and M. Polanyi, *Trans. Faraday Soc.* **30,** 663 (1934); J. Horiuti and M. Polyanyi, *Ibid.* **30,** 1164 (1934); F. Hartog, J. H. Tebben and P. Zwietering, Proc. 2nd International Congress on Catalysis (Editions Technip, Paris, 1961), **1,** 1229.
20. See for example V. Nikolajenko, V. Danes and M. Ralek, Proc. 2nd International Congress on Catalysis (Editions Technip, Paris, 1961), **2,** 2135.
21. J. Nicolai, R. Martin and J. C. Jungers, *Bull. Soc. Chim. belges* **57,** 555 (1948).
22. R. K. Greenhalgh and M. Polanyi, *Trans. Faraday Soc.* **35,** 520 (1939).
23. A. Amano and G. Parravano, *Adv. Catalysis* **9,** 716 (1957).
24. H. A. Smith, In "Catalysis", edited by P. H. Emmett (Reinhold, New York, 1957), **5,** 175.
25. F. Lihl and P. Zemsch, *Z. Elektrochem.* **56,** 979 (1952); **57,** 58 (1953).
26. P. H. Emmett and N. Skau, *J. Amer. Chem. Soc.* **65,** 1029 (1943).
27. G. Rienacker and S. Unger, *Z. anorg. Chem.* **274,** 47 (1953).
28. F. Lihl, H. Wagner and P. Zemsch, *Z. Elektrochem.* **56,** 612, 619 (1952).
29. G. C. A. Schuit and L. L. van Reijen, *Adv. Catalysis* **10,** 242 (1958).
30. O. Beeck and A. W. Ritchie, *Discuss. Faraday Soc.* **8,** 159 (1950).
31. P. W. Reynolds, *J. Chem. Soc.* 265 (1950).
32. J. H. Long, J. C. W. Frazer and E. Ott, *J. Amer. Chem. Soc.* **56,** 1101 (1934).
33. W. K. Hall and P. H. Emmett, *J. Phys. Chem.* **62,** 816 (1958).
34. A. A. Alchudzhan and M. A. Mantikyan, *Zhur. fiz. Khim.* **33,** 780 (1959); A. A. Alchudzhan and M. A. Indzhikyan, *Ibid.* **33,** 1467 (1959); A. A. Alchudzhan and E. T. Kristoturyan, *Izvest. Akad. Nauk Armian. S.S.S.R., Khim Nauk* **12,** 305 (1959).
35. A. A. Balandin, *Adv. Catalysis* **10,** 96 (1958).
36. M. K. Dyakova and A. V. Lozovoy, *Zhur. obschei Khim.* **9,** 26, 895 (1939).
37. R. Adams and J. R. Marshall, *J. Amer. Chem. Soc.* **50,** 1970 (1928); A. F. Nikolaeva and P. V. Puchkov, *Izvest. Akad. Nauk. S.S.S.R.* 913 (1938).
38. J.-P. Wauquier and J. C. Jungers, *Bull. Soc. Chim. France*, 1280 (1957).
39. H. A. Smith and E. F. H. Pennekamp, *J. Amer. Chem. Soc.* **67,** 276 (1945).
40. G. Gilman and G. Cohn, *Adv. Catalysis* **9,** 733 (1957).
41. H. A. Smith and E. F. H. Pennekamp, *J. Amer. Chem. Soc.* **67,** 279 (1945).
42. M. K. Dyakova and A. V. Lozovoy, *Zhur. obschei Khim.* **7,** 2964 (1937); **8,** 105 (1938); **10,** 1 (1940).
43. H. A. Smith and C. P. Rader, Proc. 2nd International Congress on Catalysis (Editions Technip, Paris, 1961), **1,** 1213.
44. E. de Ruiter and J. C. Jungers, *Bull. Soc. Chim. belges* **58,** 210 (1949).

45. R. L. Burwell, *Chem. Rev.* **57,** 895 (1957).
46. S. Siegel and M. Dunkel, *Adv. Catalysis* **9,** 15 (1957).
47. F. Coussemant and J. C. Jungers, *Bull. Soc. Chim. belges* **59,** 295 (1950); *J. Chim. phys.* **47,** 139 (1950).
48. R. Amatatsu, *J. Chem. Soc. Japan* **52,** 585 (1931).
49. H. A. Smith and R. G. Thomson, *Adv. Catalysis* **9,** 727 (1957).
50. H. A. Smith and J. A. Stanfield, *J. Amer. Chem. Soc.* **71,** 81 (1949).
51. G. Debus and J. C. Jungers, *Bull. Soc. Chim. belges* **62,** 172 (1933).
52. A. Skita and W. Berendt, *Ber.* **52B,** 1519 (1919).
53. H. A. Smith and W. C. Bedoit, *J. Phys. Colloid Chem.* **55,** 1085 (1951).
54. H. A. Smith, D. M. Alderman, C. D. Shacklett and C. M. Walsh, *J. Amer. Chem. Soc.* **71,** 3772 (1949).
55. D. M. Musser and H. Adkins, *J. Amer. Chem. Soc.* **60,** 664 (1938).
56. K. Sugino and K. Outi, *J. Chem. Soc. Japan* **62,** 401 (1941).
57. E. R. Bissel and M. Finger, *J. Org. Chem.* **24,** 1259 (1959).
58. H. A. Smith, J. B. Conley and W. H. King, *J. Amer. Chem. Soc.* **73,** 4633 (1951).
59. H. A. Smith and J. F. Fuzek, *J. Amer. Chem. Soc.* **71,** 415 (1949).

Chapter 14

The Hydrogenation of Other Unsaturated Groups

14.1 The Hydrogenation and Hydrogenolysis of Ketones

14.11 The Kinetics of the Reactions

There are two possible products of the interaction of hydrogen with a ketone: (i) hydrogen addition across the carbon–oxygen double bond leads to the corresponding secondary alcohol, and (ii) hydrogenolysis of the hydroxyl group leads to the formation of the corresponding hydrocarbon and water. Depending on the temperature, the ketone in question and particularly on the nature of the catalyst, either type of product may be formed exclusively, or both may be formed together. In the latter case, it seems generally agreed that the two products are formed simultaneously through different reaction paths, and that the alcohol is not an intermediate in the formation of the hydrocarbon.

Over Raney nickel and Raney copper, acetone and other non-cyclic ketones yield the secondary alcohol selectively.[1–4] Colloidal or supported platinum when promoted with an iron salt behaves similarly.[4–7] However, over unpromoted platinum–charcoal and platinized-platinum foil[8, 9] acetone is reduced quantitatively or almost so to propane. Over evaporated films of a number of metals the hydrogenation of acetone gives 2-propanol as the chief product, and propane formation becomes less marked as reactions proceed, and increases with rising temperatures. The activity order for propane formation at 60 to 100° is

$$Pt > W > Ni > Fe > Pd \simeq Au,$$

no propane being detected over the last two metals.[10] It was suggested that the decreasing rate of propane formation is due to the existence of a limited number of sites which were active in hydrogenolysis and which are rapidly poisoned. The differences in the behaviour of the other types of catalyst are not thoroughly understood.

Cyclopentanone tends to give rise to larger amounts of hydrocarbons over metal films than does acetone.[11] Thus, while cyclopentanol is the major product of the hydrogenation at low temperatures over rhodium, nickel and tungsten films, hydrogenolysis occurs to a comparable extent over platinum and palladium films. The product of hydrogenolysis over platinum, palladium and rhodium is cyclopentane, but cyclopentene is also formed over tungsten. The Arrhenius parameters for these processes are given in Table I (i). The activity order for the hydrogenolysis of cyclopentanone is

$$Pt > Pd > Rh > W > Ni,$$

this sequence being significantly different from that for acetone. More hydrocarbon is formed from cyclohexanone than from cyclopentanone under comparable conditions.

Table I also summarizes most of the available kinetic information on the hydrogenation of ketones. The Arrhenius parameters for the hydrogenations over evaporated metal films are derived from rate constants, although over all metals above 0° the reverse reaction (the dehydrogenation of 2-propanol or cyclopentanol) becomes important, and the rate constants are then those which obtain in the early part of the reactions. The formation of 2-propanol follows a first-order rate law, although over nickel films at 0° the order in acetone is zero and in hydrogen also zero above 12 mm.: the hydrogen order is positive at lower pressures, and 2-propanol inhibits the reaction.[10] These results are in general harmony with those found using other catalysts (Table I, ii), although the hydrogen pressure at which the order in hydrogen becomes zero varies very widely from one catalyst to another. The interpretation is briefly as follows. Both acetone and 2-propanol are equally and strongly adsorbed, probably because of the existence of the common intermediate radical $(CH_3)_2\underset{*}{C}—OH$. As the reaction proceeds, acetone is displaced from the surface in proportion to the amount of 2-propanol formed, and hence a first-order rate law is observed. Hydrogen is adsorbed atomically on sites which for steric reasons are not available to acetone, and which become saturated with hydrogen at a pressure determined by the affinity of the catalyst for hydrogen. Further discussion of mechanisms will be given in the next sub-section.

Table I also gives a measure of the relative activities of metals in the form of films: the activity sequences are the same for both ketones, the sequence being

$$Rh \simeq Pt > Ni > Fe \simeq W > Pd > Au.$$

This, apart from the familiar low activity of palladium, is approximately the order of decreasing percentage *d*-character of the metals. There is no very obvious compensation effect for this reaction.

Activation energies for the hydrogenation of acetone and butanone over metal powders[12] are also included in Table I (ii). Unfortunately it is impossible on the basis of the results presented to derive an activity sequence or values of the pre-exponential factor. However, it appears that activities follow the order expected from the activation energies, and that, for example, copper is highly active while silver is not.

The relative reactivities of a number of open-chain ketones in hydrogenation to alcohols over Raney nickel have been measured[3] and the results are

TABLE I. *The Kinetics of the Hydrogenation of Ketones*
(i) *Over evaporated metal films*

Metal	*Ketone*	*Product*	*E(kcal. mole⁻¹)*	*log A*	*Temp. range (°C)*	*Relative activity*‡	*Ref.*
Pt	Acetone	2-Propanol	5.0	20.5*	−46–−22	4.76	10
Ni	Acetone	2-Propanol	8.8	22.8*	−45–24	3.90	10
Fe	Acetone	2-Propanol	12.5	23.3*	0–98	2.94	10
W	Acetone	2-Propanol	9.1	21.1*	0–88	2.94	10
Pd	Acetone	2-Propanol	5.8	18.0*	25–116	2.18	10
Au	Acetone	2-Propanol	5.7	~16.0*	130–203	~1.38	10
Ni	Cyclopentanone	Cyclopentanol	11.0	21.2†	0–27	3.78	11
W	Cyclopentanone	Cyclopentanol	10.6	18.7†	11–87	2.82	11
Pd	Cyclopentanone	Cyclopentanol	4.6	14.8†	0–80	2.63	11
Pd	Cyclopentanone	Cyclopentane	4.6	14.6†	0–58	—	11
Rh	Cyclopentanone	Cyclopentane	3.2	13.2†	0–162	—	11
W	Cyclopentanone	Cyclopentane	4.8	13.1†	11–136	—	11
W	Cyclopentanone	Cyclopentene	10.1	16.7†	11–136	—	11

* A in mol. (10 mg.)$^{-1}$ sec.$^{-1}$.
† A in mol. cm.$^{-2}$ sec.$^{-1}$.
‡ For acetone, $10^3/T$°K, where T is the temperature at which the rate is 1% (10 mg.)$^{-1}$ min.$^{-1}$.
‡ For cyclopentanone, $10^3/T$°K, where T is the temperature at which the rate is 1% (1000 cm.^{2})$^{-1}$ min.$^{-1}$.

TABLE I—*continued*

(ii) *Over other types of catalyst:* $r \propto P_{H_2}^{x} P_{K}^{y}$.

Metal	*Form*	*Ketone*	*Product*	*Phase*	*E(kcal. mole⁻¹)*	*Temp. range (°C)*	*x*	*y*	*Ref.*
Fe	powder	Acetone	2-Propanol	Vapour	14.1	?	—	—	12
Fe	powder	Butanone	2-Butanol	Vapour	14.1	?	—	—	12
Co	powder	Acetone	2-Propanol	Vapour	18.0	?	—	—	12
Co	powder	Butanone	2-Butanol	Vapour	16.6	?	—	—	12
Ni	powder	Acetone	2-Propanol	Vapour	7.2	?	—	—	12
Ni	Raney	Acetone	2-Propanol	Liquid	9.0	60–150	0*	0	2
Ni	Raney	Acetone	2-Propanol	Liquid	9.†	100–160	low	low	3
Ni	Raney	Acetone	2-Propanol	Liquid	8	25–46	0.5	—	1
Ni	powder	Butanone	2-Butanol	Vapour	8.3	?	—	—	12
Cu	powder	Acetone	2-Propanol	Vapour	6.7	?	—	—	12
Cu	Raney	Acetone	2-Propanol	Liquid	8.5–11.9†	100–175	—	—	3
Cu	powder	Butanone	2-Butanol	Vapour	8.0	?	—	—	12
Ag	powder	Acetone	2-Propanol	Vapour	16.9	?	—	—	12

* At greater than 35 atm.
† At 50 atm.

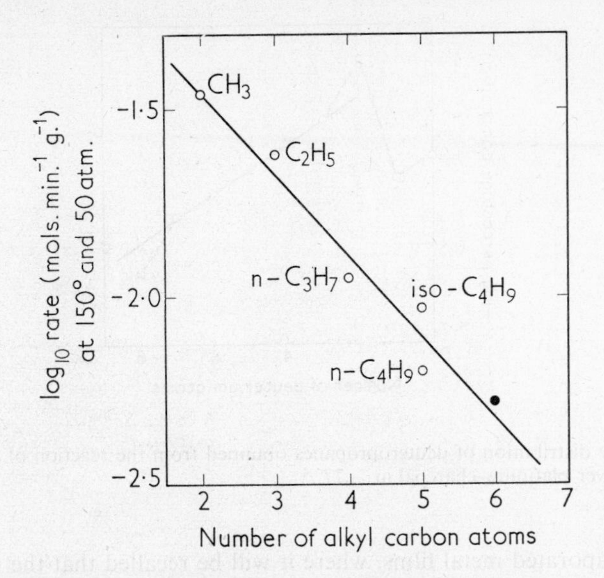

FIG. 1. The relative reactivities of a series of ketones in hydrogenation over Raney nickel at 150° and 50 atm. pressure.[3]
○ Methyl alkyl ketones, CH_3COR: the nature of R is indicated by each point.
● Di-n-propylketone.

shown in Fig. 1. The reactivity declines approximately in proportion to the total number of alkyl-carbon atoms, with minor differences between skeletal isomers.

Ruthenium supported on charcoal has been shown to be especially active in the hydrogenation of ketones:[13] compounds such as acetone, butanone, acetonylacetone and ethyl acetoacetate are reduced in its presence at room temperature and atmospheric pressure. With unsaturated ketones (e.g. mesityl oxide), the carbonyl group is reduced in preference to the olefinic double bond.

14.12 The Interaction of Ketones with Deuterium

Early experiments on the interaction of acetone with deuterium catalysed by platinized platinum foil showed that hydrogen deuteride was formed only above 0°.[8] The absence of exchange at lower temperatures led to the expectation that pure propane-2,2-d_2 could be obtained under these conditions, but in fact a redistribution reaction occurs, and propanes up to propane-d_8 are formed.[6, 9] The distribution of deuteropropanes formed over platinum–charcoal at −77° is shown in Fig. 2: it is reminiscent of the distributions obtained from olefins and deuterium (see Chapter 11) and suggests that some elementary processes may be common to both reactions. Under the conditions of these experiments, the exchange of propane and of acetone with deuterium was negligible.

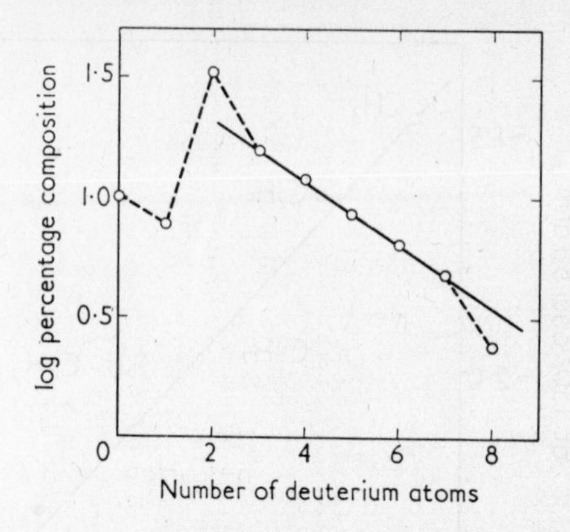

FIG. 2. The distribution of deuteropropanes obtained from the reaction of acetone with deuterium over platinum–charcoal at −77°.[6]

Over evaporated metal films, where it will be recalled that the major product from acetone is 2-propanol, exchange of acetone occurs readily, and, over the metals least active for hydrogenation (Pd, Au, Ag), very much more rapidly than addition.[14] Table II gives the Arrhenius parameters and relative activities of metals for acetone exchange (based on the rates of removal of acetone-d_0). The activities declining in the order of presentation in the Table. Initial distributions of deuteroacetones, and values of *M*, the mean number of deuterium atoms introduced, are shown in Table III: neither changes significantly with temperature.

TABLE II. *The Arrhenius Parameters for the Exchange of Acetone with Deuterium over Evaporated Metal Films*[14]

Metal	*E(kcal. mole⁻¹)*	*log A**	*Temp. range (°C)*	*Relative activity†*
Rh	—	—	—	5.78
Pd	10.1	21.3	−43–0	4.10
Ni	7.3	18.7	−44–0	4.00
Pt	3.4	15.2	−44–−22	3.95
W	10.0	18.7	0–94	2.98
Fe	9.9	18.1	0–38	2.71
Au	13.9	20.6	76–167	2.38
Ag	14.6	19.3	211–286	1.83

* *A* in mol. cm.$^{-2}$ sec.$^{-1}$ (except for Au and Ag, where apparent film areas are used).
† $10^3/T$°K, where *T* is the temperature at which the rate is 1% (1000 cm.^{2})$^{-1}$ min.$^{-1}$ (except for Au and Ag).

TABLE III. *Initial Distributions of Deuteroacetones from the Exchange of Acetone with Deuterium over Evaporated Metal Films*[14]

Metal	*Temp.* (°C)	*Percentage composition*						*M*
		d_1	d_2	d_3	d_4	d_5	d_6	
Fe	22.5	94.2	3.6	2.2	0.0	0.0	0.0	1.08
W	69.5	92.2	6.2	1.3	0.4	0.1	0.0	1.11
Ag	230.8	90.5	8.5	1.1	0.0	0.0	0.0	1.11
Au	120.6	76.1	11.2	5.6	2.5	2.1	2.5	1.51
Pt	−35.5	64.6	16.1	17.6	0.7	0.5	0.5	1.58
Pd	−34.5	65.3	16.8	11.6	2.8	1.8	1.8	1.64
Ni	−23.0	52.8	11.2	17.5	6.7	4.6	7.1	2.20

The interpretation of these distributions and the mechanisms by which the exchange occurs are not thoroughly understood. In principle it has been envisaged that one or both of the methyl groups in adsorbed acetone may undergo either stepwise or multiple exchange (or, of course, both simultaneously) as postulated for saturated hydrocarbons (see Chapter 9). The preponderance of acetone-d_1 suggests that stepwise exchange on one methyl group is the single most important process, and it can be formulated as

$$\underset{\qquad *\quad *}{H_3C{-}\overset{CH_3}{\overset{|}{C}}{-}O} \xrightarrow{-H} \underset{*\quad *\quad *}{H_2C{-}\overset{CH_3}{\overset{|}{C}}{-}O} \xrightarrow{+D} \underset{\qquad\quad *\quad *}{H_2DC{-}\overset{CH_3}{\overset{|}{C}}{-}O}. \qquad (a)$$

Repetition of this unit step probably accounts in large measure for the nature of the exchange products over iron, tungsten and silver. With the other metals, the distributions suggest that multiple exchange involving, in varying degrees, both methyl groups is an important contributor. The exact mechanism is uncertain but the radical

$$\underset{***\quad *\quad *}{C{-}\overset{CH_3}{\overset{|}{C}}{-}O}$$

has been suggested[14] as the intermediate. The desorption of adsorbed acetone is probably the rate-limiting step. Over tungsten films, the rate of exchange is independent of acetone pressure, but varies in a complex manner with deuterium pressure.

It is well established that the addition of deuterium to acetone is the straightforward addition of deuterium atoms across the double-bond.[4, 6, 14] The rate of this process is slower than that for hydrogenation by a factor of from 2.1 to 3.6, due to zero-point energy effects. The slow step, which is probably also the slow step in the exchange of 2-propanol, is likely to be

$$\begin{array}{c} CH_3 \\ | \\ H_3C\text{—}\underset{*}{C}\text{—}OD + \underset{*}{D} \longrightarrow (H_3C)_2\,CD\text{—}OD. \end{array} \qquad (b)$$

The activity sequence for the exchange of cyclopentanone is[11]

$$Rh \simeq Pt > Ni > W,$$

which is similar to that for acetone exchange. Arrhenius parameters were obtainable only over tungsten films, the values being: E, 10.0 kcal. mole^{-1}; log$A$, 18.9 (A in mol. cm.$^{-2}$ sec.$^{-1}$). Deuterocyclopentanone distributions were obtained over nickel, tungsten and palladium films: the last metal gave a very rapid exchange of four hydrogen atoms, probably those α to the keto-group, followed by a slower exchange of the remainder. Some details of the results for the other metals are shown in Table IV: no molecules containing

TABLE IV. *Initial Distributions of Deuterocyclopentanones from the Exchange of Cyclopentanone with Deuterium over Evaporated Metal Films*

Metal	*Temp.* (°C)	*Percentage composition*				*M*
		d_1	d_2	d_3	d_4	
Ni	0	89.8	8.4	1.5	0.3	1.12
W	11.3	89.8	8.5	1.4	0.3	1.12

more than four deuterium atoms were detected. Although the value of M over tungsten is the same as that found with acetone, the value over nickel is here much smaller.

It is now possible to present a general mechanism for the interaction of ketones with deuterium. It is generally agreed that at temperatures less than about 150° ketones react in the keto- rather than the enol-form,[4, 6, 14] and the following elementary processes, therefore, probably describe the hydrogenation and hydrogenolysis of acetone:

$$D_2 + 2* \longrightarrow 2\underset{*}{D} \qquad (c)$$

$$(CH_3)_2CO + 2* \longrightarrow (CH_3)_2\underset{*}{C}\text{—}\underset{*}{O} \qquad (d)$$

$$(CH_3)_2\underset{*}{C}\text{—}\underset{*}{O} + \underset{*}{D} \longrightarrow (CH_3)_2\underset{*}{C}\text{—}OD + 2* \qquad (e)$$

$$(CH_3)_2\underset{*}{C}\text{—}OD + \underset{*}{D} \longrightarrow (CH_3)_2CD\text{—}OD + 2* \qquad (b)$$

$$(CH_3)_2\underset{*}{C}\text{—}OD \longrightarrow H_2C{=}\underset{*}{C}\text{—}CH_3 + HDO \qquad (f)$$

$$H_2C{=}\underset{*}{C}\text{—}CH_3 + \underset{*}{D} \longrightarrow H_2\underset{*}{C}\text{—}\underset{*}{CD}\text{—}CH_3 \qquad (g)$$

Subsequent processes will then be identical with those occurring during the reaction of olefins with deuterium, in agreement with the observation (see Fig. 2) that propane distributions from acetone and deuterium closely resemble those from olefin–deuterium reactions. The mechanism for acetone exchange has been discussed above. The mechanisms for the reactions of other ketones such as cyclopentanone can be formulated similarly.

It remains to try to assess the role of the electronic factor in the reactions of ketones. It has been claimed[10, 14] on somewhat slender evidence that activity in both exchange and hydrogenation follows the order of percentage *d*-character, and hence that these reactions have some relation with the hydrogenation of olefins. This correlation is not, however, firmly established. The following generalizations may, however, be made on the basis of Tables I and II. Platinum and rhodium are most active in hydrogenation, while palladium is least active, presumably because of poisoning by dissolved hydrogen. Tungsten and iron have about the same activity, less than nickel, the low activity of iron perhaps being due to the difficulty of preparing clean films. Rhodium is very active in exchange, but nickel, platinum and (curiously) palladium have similar but lower activities. Iron and tungsten are again the least active metals.

14.2 The Hydrogenation of Aldehydes

The hydrogenation of aldehydes has been less thoroughly studied than the hydrogenation of ketones: there is, however, evidence that as with ketones addition proceeds predominantly through the keto-form at temperatures less than about 150°, and through the enol-form at higher temperatures. This has been established for acetaldehyde and n-butanal over nickel and platinum catalysts by estimation of the C—D and O—D bonds in the resulting alcohols by Raman spectroscopy.[4] The same result has been obtained by investigating the hydrogenation of an optically active aldehyde and the dehydrogenation of an optically active alcohol over Raney nickel.[15] Now configuration will be retained if the reactions proceed without enolization, while racemization will take place if the enol-form is involved. It was found that in the hydrogenation of (+) 2-methyl-1-butanal, 30 per cent racemization occurred at 150° and 100 per cent at 250°. A similar trend was shown in the dehydrogenation of (—) 2-methyl-1-butanal. The aldehyde was shown to be effectively racemized at 190° by the hydrogen remaining on the catalyst from its reduction.

Only one kinetic study of the hydrogenation of aldehydes seems yet to have been made.[16] The vapour-phase hydrogenation of acetaldehyde, propanal and butanal has been examined in a flow-system at superatmospheric pressures, using nickel–kieselguhr as catalyst. Conversions were kept low, and the influence of products hence not studied. The rate law for all three aldehydes was

$$r \propto P_{H_2}^{-0.5}\ P_{A}^{0.1} \exp(-7800/RT).$$

There was, however, an increase of rate with molecular weight, due to an increase in the pre-exponential factor (Table V). These results were interpreted as follows. The rate-controlling step is the adsorption of the enol-form of the aldehyde on a pair of sites not covered by hydrogen: this accounts satisfactorily for the observed kinetics. The increase in rate with molecular weight is ascribed to the increasing reactivity of the enol-form, since the electron-releasing properties of R in the structure R—CH=CH—OH increase in the sequence $H < CH_3 < C_2H_5$. The temperature ranges used are, in general, sufficiently high to be in the range where other workers have concluded that enol-forms are involved; it would, however, be of interest to examine the hydrogenation of aldehydes at lower temperatures.

TABLE V. *Kinetic Parameters for the Hydrogenation of Aldehydes over Nickel–Kieselguhr*[16]

	CH_3CHO	C_2H_5CHO	n-C_3H_7CHO
Temp. range (°C)	120–140	150–175	160–180
E(kcal. mole^{-1}) (± 0.1)	7.9	7.8	7.7
log$A$ (arbitrary units)	4.94	5.17	5.31
Relative rates (180°, 20 lb. in.$^{-2}$)	1.00	1.54	1.91

Under more drastic conditions, hydrogenolysis also occurs, sometimes accompanied by loss of carbon atoms as well. Thus, for example, the reaction between benzaldehyde and hydrogen over nickel at 210° results in the formation not only of toluene and water, but also of benzene and carbon monoxide, later reduced to methane: this latter is indeed the major reaction over copper at 350°.[17] Over nickel–kieselguhr at 250°, heptanal and hydrogen yield, besides heptanol, hexane and carbon monoxide: no heptane is detected.[18] The mechanism of these reactions is obscure.

Ruthenium on charcoal shows the same high activity in the hydrogenation of aldehydes as it does with ketones: unsaturated aldehydes (2-ethyl-2-hexenal and furfural) can be reduced to unsaturated alcohols in high yields.[13] It is especially effective for converting reducing sugars to polyhydric alcohols, although for this reaction higher temperatures and pressures are required. Disaccharides such as sucrose and lactose are hydrolysed as well, so that the products are respectively mannitol and sorbitol, and dulcitol and sorbitol. Maltose, on the other hand, cannot be hydrolysed, and is only with difficulty reduced to maltitol.

14.3 The Hydrogenation of Carboxylic Acids

The carboxyl group (—COOH) is notoriously difficult to reduce catalytically. Thus, for example, the reduction of acetic acid in the presence of Adams platinum requires a temperature of 200° and a pressure of 290 atmospheres:[19] the isolated products are ethanol (43 per cent) and ethyl acetate (30 per cent), the latter resulting from the reaction of ethanol with unreacted acetic acid. The recent observation[19] that metallic rhenium catalyses this reaction under much milder conditions is, therefore, of interest.

Rhenium was formed by the reduction of the heptoxide by hydrogen, the process being nucleated by a trace of colloidal platinum. The form of the reduced metal and the rate of the reduction to the metal varies with the solvent used. Acetic acid was reduced at 150° and 160 atm. to 77 per cent ethanol and 23 per cent ethyl acetate or in aqueous solution cleanly to ethanol. Many other mono- and dibasic acids were studied and found to yield the corresponding products in similar amounts. Formic acid, however, required more drastic conditions (240° and 240 atm.), and the products were methane, water and "polymethylene." Only di- and trichloracetic and trimethyl-acetic acids could not be reduced.

14.4 The Hydrogenation of the Nitro-group

14.41 The Nature of the Products

Nitro-groups attached to aliphatic or aromatic systems are readily reduced by hydrogen in the presence of nickel or platinum catalysts, at quite moderate temperatures and pressures. Relatively little work has been done with other metals. The reaction is highly exothermic, and the temperature may rise considerably during the reaction unless adequate precautions are taken. In general, aromatic nitro-compounds are cleanly reduced to the corresponding amine, which can be recovered in high yield. Dinitro- and trinitro-compounds usually yield only the corresponding di- and triamines, although with platinum black *m*-dinitrobenzene yields *m*-nitroaniline as well as *m*-phenylenediamine.[21] Reduction of the aromatic ring is a much slower process, and formation of alicyclic amines requires more vigorous conditions.

The situation is somewhat different with aliphatic nitro-compounds, especially where the molecule contains other functional groups. In certain circumstances, the nitro-group is first reduced to an oxime, presumably through the sequence

$$\text{-CH}_2\text{—NO}_2 \xrightarrow{+\text{H}_2} \text{-CH}_2\text{—N(OH)}_2 \longrightarrow \text{-CH=N—OH} + \text{H}_2\text{O}. \qquad \text{(h)}$$

The oxime subsequently reacts with a further two moles of hydrogen:

$$\text{-CH=N—OH} \xrightarrow{+2\text{H}_2} \text{-CH}_2\text{—NH}_2 + \text{H}_2\text{O}. \qquad \text{(i)}$$

The oxime can undergo other reactions. Thus, for example, the reduction of dinitroneopentane in ethanol over Raney nickel at 60° gives 5 per cent of dimethylmalonamide by rearrangement of the dioxime:

$$\text{(CH}_3\text{)}_2\text{C(CH=NOH)}_2 \longrightarrow \text{(CH}_3\text{)}_2\text{C(CONH}_2\text{)}_2 \qquad \text{(j)}$$

The expected diaminoneopentane is formed in 67 per cent yield.[22] Furthermore the hydrogenation of γ-nitroketones of the general formula

$$\begin{array}{l}\text{R—CH—CH}_2\text{—CO—R}'\\ \quad\;\;|\\ \quad\text{CH}_2\text{—NO}_2\end{array}$$

over platinum black yields, in addition to the expected aminoketones, the substituted pyrrolidines

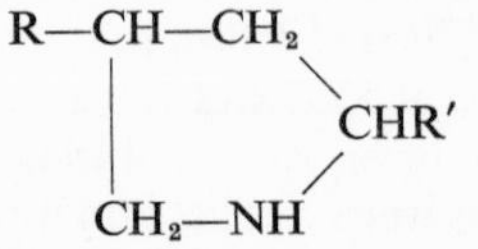

$$\begin{array}{l} R\text{—}CH\text{—}CH_2 \\ \quad | \qquad\quad \diagdown \\ \quad | \qquad\qquad CHR' \\ \quad | \qquad\quad \diagup \\ CH_2\text{—}NH \end{array}$$

presumably through reaction of the intermediate oxime with the keto-group.[23] Aliphatic nitro-compounds react slowly with amines to yield complex products even at room temperature, so that the use of active catalysts and low temperatures is necessary if high yields of amines are to be obtained.

The catalytic reduction of conjugated nitro-olefins is non-specific: for example, 2-nitro-1-butene on hydrogenation over Adams platinum in acetic acid yields the oxime, s-butylamine and what is described as "a deep red polymeric oil," but no nitrobutane.[24] The mechanism of the polymerization, which frequently accompanies the hydrogenation of nitro-olefins, is not understood. Non-conjugated nitro-olefins (such as 4-nitro-5-phenylcyclohexene), however, may be reduced over Raney nickel first to the cyclohexenylamine, and subsequently to the cyclohexylamine.

The substitution of a phenyl group into a nitro-olefin exerts a notable influence. Thus, 1-phenyl-2-nitro-1-propene and 1-phenyl-2-nitro-1-butene on hydrogenation over palladium–charcoal at 200–500 lb. in.$^{-2}$ and near room temperature in a variety of solvents yield 5–17 per cent of ketone, 30–63 per cent of nitroparaffin and 11–42 per cent of oxime.[20]

$$\underset{\displaystyle NO_2}{H_3C\text{—}\underset{|}{C}}{=}CH\text{—}C_6H_5 \longrightarrow H_3C\text{—}CO\text{—}CH_2\text{—}C_6H_5 \qquad (k)$$

$$\longrightarrow H_3C\text{—}\underset{\underset{\displaystyle NO_2}{|}}{CH}\text{—}CH_2\text{—}C_6H_5 \qquad (l)$$

$$\longrightarrow H_3C\text{—}\underset{\underset{\displaystyle NOH}{\|}}{C}\text{—}CH_2\text{—}C_6H_5 \qquad (m)$$

The presence of the phenyl group, therefore, permits the partially selective hydrogenation of the double bond. Over Adams platinum, however, dimeric and polymeric products are also formed.[20]

14.42 The Kinetics of the Hydrogenation of Nitro-compounds

The kinetics of the hydrogenation of both aliphatic and aromatic nitro-compounds have been studied in fair detail over Raney nickel and Adams platinum: these two catalysts show significantly different kinetics and some discussion of these is therefore worthwhile.

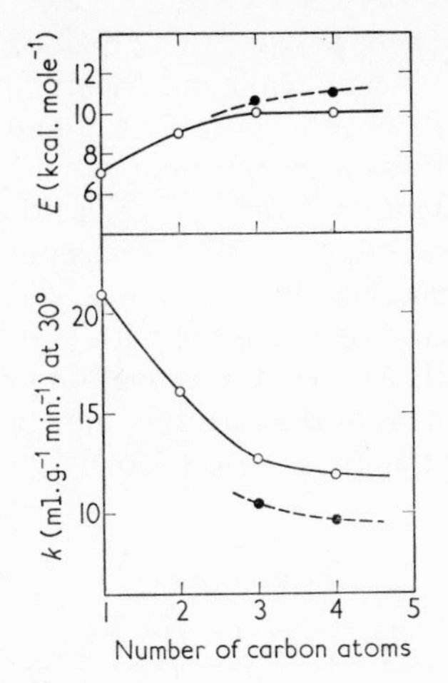

FIG. 3. Rates and activation energies for the hydrogenation of aliphatic nitro-compounds over Raney nickel.[20]

○ NO_2-group on primary carbon atom.

● NO_2-group on seconadry carbon atom.

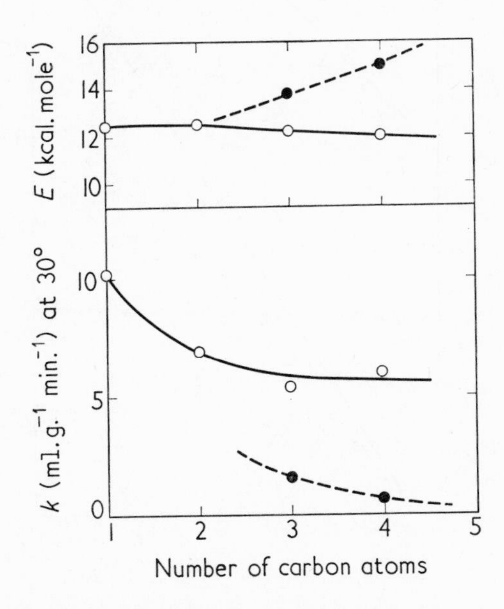

FIG. 4. Rates and activation energies for the hydrogenation of aliphatic nitro-compounds over Adams platinum.[20]

○ NO_2-group on primary carbon atom.

● NO_2-group on secondary carbon atom.

Rates and activation energies have been obtained for the hydrogenation of the lower members of the aliphatic nitro-paraffin series over both these catalysts[20] and the results are shown in Figs. 3 and 4. It will be seen that in each case the rates for the primary nitro-compounds decrease with increasing molecular weight, and tend to a limiting value: the rates for the secondary nitro-compounds are less than for the corresponding primary ones. With nickel, the activation energies for the primary compounds increase to a limiting value of 10 kcal. mole^{-1}, while with platinum they are essentially constant at 12–12.5 kcal. mole^{-1}: the activation energies for the secondary compounds are higher than for the corresponding primary compounds. From this it might be thought that the rate is solely governed by the activation

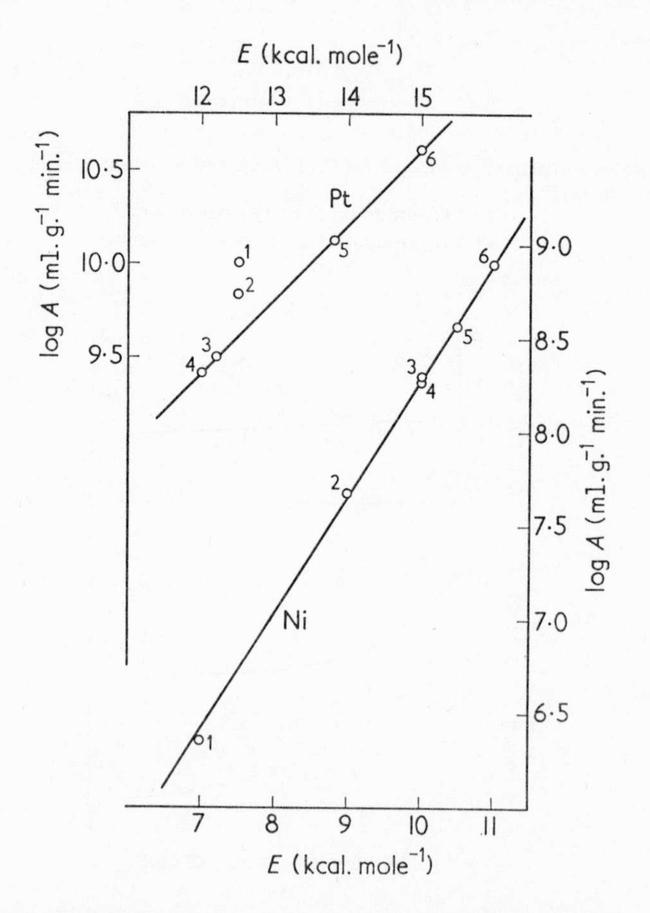

FIG. 5. Compensation effect for the hydrogenation of aliphatic nitro-compounds over Adams platinum (upper line) and over Raney nickel (lower line).[20]

1, nitromethane; 2, nitroethane; 3, 1-nitropropane; 4, 1-nitrobutane; 5, 2-nitropropane; 6, 2-nitrobutane.

energy, but calculation of the pre-exponential factors shows there to be a wide variation in their values. However, as Fig. 5 shows, there is a normal compensation effect between E and $\log A$, except for the hydrogenation of nitromethane and nitroethane over platinum, where E is constant and the rate is determined by the A-factor.

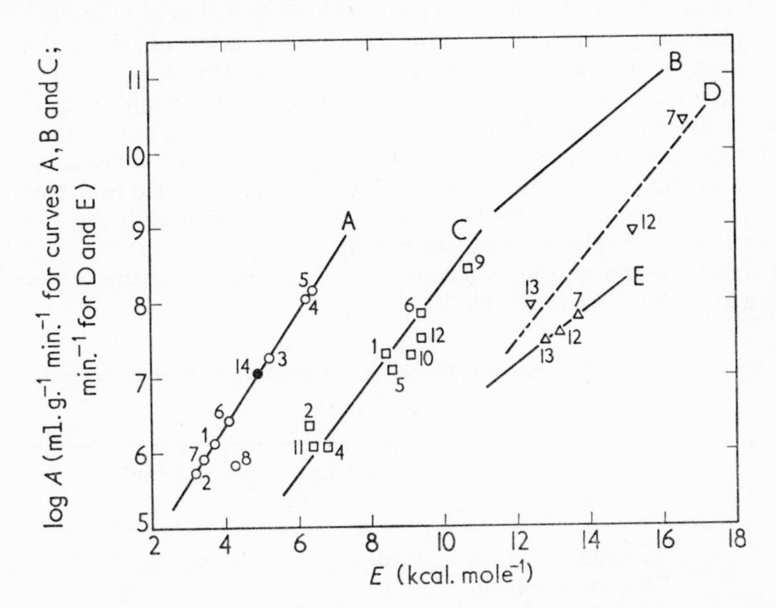

FIG. 6. Compensation effects for the hydrogenation of aromatic nitro-compounds.[20]
Curve A: aromatic nitro-compounds over Adams platinum.
Curve B: aliphatic nitro-compounds over Adams platinum (from Fig. 5, for comparison).
Curve C: aromatic nitro-compounds over Raney nickel (the line is that shown in Fig. 5 for aliphatic compounds).
Curves D and E: aromatic nitro-compounds over colloidal palladium and rhodium.
1, Nitrobenzene; 2, *o*-nitrophenol; 3, *p*-dinitrobenzene; 4, *m*-dinitrobenzene; 5, trinitrotoluene; 6, *o*-nitrotoluene; 7, *p*-nitrotoluene; 8, nitromesitylene; 9, *o*-nitroanisole; 10, *m*-nitrophenol; 11, *o*-dinitrobenzene; 12, *p*-nitrophenol; 13, *p*-nitroaniline; 14, 2-nitro-1-butene.

Over Adams platinum and other noble metal catalysts, aromatic nitro-compounds are reduced faster and with a lower activation energy than are aliphatic nitro-compounds: the nitro-group is reduced very much faster than the aromatic ring.[20, 25] Over Raney nickel, on the other hand, the aromatic compounds show rates and activation energies which are comparable with those for the aliphatic compounds. This is made clear in Fig. 6, where the results are plotted as compensation effects: here the line drawn through the points which pertain to Raney nickel is that shown in the previous Fig. for the aliphatic compounds. Several points are omitted from this series for the sake of clarity: thus *o*-, *m*- and *p*-nitrotoluene, and *p*-dinitrobenzene all show an activation energy of 9.2 to 9.6 kcal. mole^{-1} and a log$A$ of 7.60 to 7.95.[20] Figure 6 also contains a few results from the hydrogenation of *p*-substituted nitrobenzenes over colloidal rhodium and palladium:[26] here the rates were reported in terms of a compound rate constant and so the absolute values of log$A$ are not comparable with those for the other metals.

It will be noted in Fig. 6 that the rate of hydrogenation of nitromesitylene over platinum is unexpectedly low. The interpretation of this is that the nitro-group is sterically hindered by the adjacent methyl groups, so that it is not in the plane of the ring, and is, therefore, not fully conjugated with it: this is confirmed by the Raman spectrum of this molecule. The nitro-group in this molecule behaves more as if it were attached to an aliphatic system, and hence the rate is lower. 2-nitro-1-Butene is hydrogenated over platinum at a rate and with an activation energy which places it with the aromatic rather than the aliphatic series (see Fig. 6).

Further relevant information comes from the observed orders of reaction, which are summarized in Table VI.

TABLE VI. *Orders of Reaction for the Hydrogenation of Nitro-compounds*[20]

$$r \propto C_N^x \, P_{H_2}^y$$

Type	Platinum		Nickel	
	x	*y*	*x*	*y*
Aromatic	0	1	0	1
Conjugated olefinic	0	1	—	—
Aliphatic	1	0	0	1

Some caution is necessary when trying to interpret them, particularly since it has been shown that at least for palladium and rhodium the order in the nitro-compound varies with the nature of the solvent and the weight of catalyst used.[26] However, accepting the values in the Table at their face value we would conclude that, except in the case of aliphatic compounds over platinum, the nitro-compound is strongly adsorbed and the hydrogen only weakly adsorbed. This view is confirmed by the finding that the exchange of acetic acid[27] and of methanol[28] with deuterium over Adams platinum is inhibited by aromatic nitro-compounds, but not by aliphatic nitro-compounds. It would, therefore, appear that the low reactivity of the latter over platinum is due to their low concentration in the adsorbed state. The fact that both aliphatic and aromatic nitro-compounds behave similarly over nickel but not over platinum is not readily understood: one possible explanation is that over nickel the primary point of attachment of the molecule is at the nitro-group, whereas over platinum it is on the hydrocarbon part. This might explain why aromatic and olefinic compounds react faster than aliphatic ones over this last metal.

References

1. T. Freund and H. M. Hulburt, *J. Phys. Chem.* **61,** 909 (1957).
2. E. de Ruiter and J. C. Jungers, *Bull. Soc. chim. belges* **58,** 210 (1949).
3. C. van Mechelen and J. C. Jungers, *Bull. Soc. chim. belges* **59,** 597 (1950).
4. L. C. Anderson and N. W. MacNaughton, *J. Amer. Chem. Soc.* **64,** 1456 (1942).
5. E. B. Maxted and S. Akhtar, *J. Chem. Soc.* 3130 (1959).
6. L. Friedman and J. Turkevich, *J. Amer. Chem. Soc.* **74,** 1669 (1952).
7. M. Faillebin, *Ann. Chim. (France)* **4,** 156, 410 (1925).
8. A. Farkas and L. Farkas, *J. Amer. Chem. Soc.* **61,** 1336 (1939).
9. L. N. Kauder and T. I. Taylor, *Science* **113,** 238 (1951).
10. C. Kemball and C. T. H. Stoddart, *J. Colloid Sci.* **11,** 532 (1956).
11. C. Kemball and C. T. H. Stoddart, *Proc. Roy. Soc.* **A246,** 521 (1958).
12. P. Fuderer-Luetić and I. Brihta, *Croat. Chem. Acta* **31,** 75 (1959).
13. G. Gilman and G. Cohn, *Adv. Catalysis* **9,** 733 (1957).
14. C. Kemball and C. T. H. Stoddart, *Proc. Roy. Soc.* **A241,** 208 (1957).
15. E. J. Badin and E. Pascu, *J. Amer. Chem. Soc.* **66,** 1963 (1944).
16. C. C. Oldenburg and H. F. Rase, *J. Amer. Inst. Chem. Eng.* **3,** 462 (1957).
17. P. Sabatier and J. B. Senderens, *Compt. rend.* **137,** 301 (1903); P. Sabatier and B. Kubota, *Compt. rend.* **172,** 173 (1921).
18. T.-J. Suen and S. Fan, *J. Amer. Chem. Soc.* **64,** 1460 (1942).
19. H. S. Broadbent, G. C. Campbell, W. J. Bartley and J. H. Johnson, *J. Org. Chem.* **24,** 1847 (1959).
20. H. A. Smith and W. C. Bedoit, In "Catalysis", edited by P. H. Emmett (Reinhold, New York 1954), **3,** 149.
21. V. Vesely and E. Rein, *Arkiv Kem.* **1,** 55 (1927); A. A. Strel'tsova and N. D. Zelinskii, *Izvest. Akad. Nauk S.S.S.R.*, 401 (1941).
22. J. Rockett and F. C. Whitmore, *J. Amer. Chem. Soc.* **71,** 3249 (1949).
23. E. P. Kohler and N. L. Drake, *J. Amer. Chem. Soc.* **45,** 2144 (1923).
24. H. A. Smith and W. C. Bedoit, *J. Phys. Colloid Chem.* **55,** 1085 (1951).
25. P. N. Rylander and G. Cohn, Proc. 2nd International Congress on Catalysis (Editions Technip, Paris, 1961), **1,** 997.
26. H.-C. Yao and P. H. Emmett, *J. Amer. Chem. Soc.* **81,** 4125 (1959).
27. L. E. Lyne, B. Wyatt and H. A. Smith, *J. Amer. Chem. Soc.* **74,** 1808 (1952).
28. E. L. McDaniel and H. A. Smith, *Adv. Catalysis* **9,** 76 (1957).

Chapter 15

The Hydrogenation of the Oxides of Carbon, and the Fischer–Tropsch Synthesis

15.1 The Reactions of Hydrogen with the Oxides of Carbon[1]

In most of the hydrogenation reactions considered so far, the molecules suffering reduction have been converted to products containing the same number of carbon atoms: the only exception has been the polymerization of acetylene and related compounds during their reduction. We come now to consider a system in which under certain conditions polymerization occurs extremely readily. This is principally the hydrogen–carbon monoxide system, and the polymerization process is termed the Fischer–Tropsch synthesis in honour of its discoverers.

The more obvious products to expect from the catalytic reaction of hydrogen with carbon monoxide and with carbon dioxide are methanol and methane, and possibly formaldehyde. Methanol is efficiently synthesized over oxide catalysts, and methane is commonly formed to some extent over metals, but with the appropriate catalysts (to be described in the next Section) a wide variety of other classes of organic compounds of higher molecular weight (saturated and olefinic hydrocarbons, alcohols, aldehydes, ketones, acids and esters) is also formed. The remainder of this Section is devoted to a brief consideration of the thermodynamics of some of these processes.

Stoichiometric equations for the formation of, for example, saturated hydrocarbons, olefins and alcohols may be written as follows. For saturated hydrocarbons, either

$$(2n + 1)H_2 + nCO \rightarrow C_nH_{2n+2} + nH_2O \qquad \text{(a)}$$

or

$$(n + 1)H_2 + 2nCO \rightarrow C_nH_{2n+2} + nCO_2. \qquad \text{(b)}$$

For olefins, either

$$2nH_2 + nCO \rightarrow C_nH_{2n} + nH_2O \qquad (c)$$

or

$$nH_2 + 2nCO \rightarrow C_nH_{2n} + nCO_2. \qquad (d)$$

For alcohols, either

$$2nH_2 + nCO \rightarrow C_nH_{2n+1}OH + (n - 1)H_2O \qquad (e)$$

or

$$(n + 1)H_2 + (2n - 1)CO \rightarrow C_nH_{2n+1}OH + (n - 1)CO_2. \qquad (f)$$

Equations for the formation of other compounds may be similarly constructed. These processes are all calculated to be highly exothermic, as are also those leading to the formation of alicyclic, aromatic and acetylenic hydrocarbons, and many other organic compounds. The heats of reaction ($-\Delta H$) in kcal. mole^{-1} per carbon atom at 200° for reactions forming water are for example: for methane, ~51; for n-hexane, ~39; for 1-hexene, ~34; for benzene, ~29; and for acetylene, ~5. Typical values of this quantity for alcohols at 18° are: for methanol, 24; for 1-propanol, 33.

The standard free energy changes for these processes are generally negative at moderate temperatures, confirming that they are thermodynamically feasible. For compounds containing not more than six carbon atoms, this statement holds good for saturated hydrocarbons formed by reaction (a) below about 400°, for olefinic, aromatic and alicyclic hydrocarbons formed by reaction (c) or its congeners below about 350°, and for alcohols (excepting methanol) formed by reaction (e) below about 300°. For compounds of higher molecular weight, these temperatures are slightly lower. In reactions (b), (d) and (f), where carbon dioxide is formed instead of water, the standard free energy changes are more negative, and hence product formation is more favourable, than in the reactions forming water.

The formation of high molecular weight compounds through the hydrogenation of carbon dioxide is also thermodynamically possible at moderate temperatures. The reaction of water with carbon monoxide, according for example to the equation

$$(n + 1)H_2O + (3n + 1)CO \rightarrow C_nH_{2n+2} + (2n + 1)CO_2, \qquad (g)$$

is more exothermic than process (b), and the standard free energy change is more negative. Thus, in this case the formation of saturated hydrocarbons containing six carbon atoms is feasible up to about 480°. The formation of other classes of compounds is similarly more favoured from the reaction of water with carbon monoxide than from the reaction of hydrogen with carbon monoxide.

The hydrocarbons which are formed in practice are chiefly n-paraffins and 1-olefins, and these are not usually the most stable thermodynamically. This clearly shows that they are true initial products of the synthesis, and that they are denied the chance of equilibrating under reaction conditions.

15.2 The Chemisorption of the Reactants

It is scarcely necessary to add anything to what has already been said in Chapters 5 and 8 concerning the chemisorption of hydrogen by metals. In the temperature range of 150 to 300°, where the Fischer–Tropsch synthesis proceeds, hydrogen will certainly be in the Type A atomic form if adsorbed independently, although with iron catalysts there is a possibility of some Type B (sub-surface) adsorption.

It will be recalled that evidence was presented in Chapter 5 to show that carbon monoxide can be adsorbed on Transition metals either as a linear complex (i) or as a bridge structure (ii).

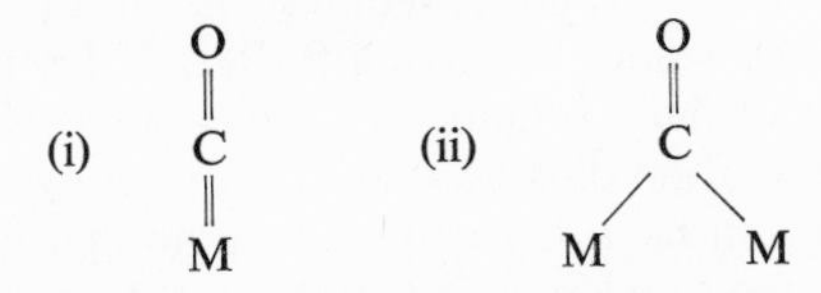

Both of these forms would be expected to exhibit negative surface potentials, and these are indeed observed (see Chapter 5). The chemisorption of carbon monoxide on nickel films at −183° results in an increase in electrical resistance of the films, again pointing to withdrawal of electrons towards the adsorbed molecules.[2] The existence of both of these forms has also been inferred by infra-red spectroscopy.[3] Measurements of (i) the ratio of the "monolayer" capacities of hydrogen and carbon monoxide (see Chapter 5), (ii) heats and (iii) kinetics of adsorption of carbon monoxide (see Chapters 5 and 6 for Refs.) and (iv) the infra-red spectrum of chemisorbed carbon monoxide[2] strongly suggest the possibility that both forms can co-exist. The most complete information comes from the last approach. With silica-supported palladium, and with a nickel film, the band attributed to the linear form appears only at higher coverages,[3, 4] while that due to the bridge form is evident at all coverages: it is, therefore, concluded that the linear form is the more weakly adsorbed. With platinum on silica, or on potassium bromide, or as a film, the linear form is present to at least 85 per cent at all coverages, although the bridge form is more favoured when the platinum is supported on alumina.[3, 4] Only the linear form is apparent on supported iron.[3]

The surface potentials of carbon monoxide on the metals of Group IB are positive (see Chapter 5), although with copper films at −183° the electrical resistance is increased by its chemisorption. The suggestion that carbon monoxide may be held on these metals by charge-transfer bonding has already been noted.

From the point of view of the Fischer–Tropsch synthesis, studies of the simultaneous chemisorption of both hydrogen and carbon monoxide are of interest. The experimental results fall into two groups: (i) those obtained by admitting hydrogen to a partial or complete monolayer of pre-sorbed carbon monoxide, and (ii) those in which the reverse procedure is employed. When hydrogen is admitted to a complete presorbed monolayer of carbon monoxide on cobalt[5] and nickel[6, 7] at temperatures of about 50°, some additional chemisorption is detected, although no change is observed in the infra-red spectrum of carbon monoxide chemisorbed on iron under these conditions.[3] Volumetric[7] and calorimetric[8, 9] observations made when the reverse order is used offer some further indication of complex formation, but its nature cannot be inferred. It seems likely that temperatures substantially greater than 50° are necessary for the formation of the species which initiates the synthesis. Evidence has been presented[10] to show that hydrogen added at −195° to a nickel film covered with carbon monoxide is held as atoms carrying about one half an electronic charge: the atoms are, however, located well above the surface and appear to be sandwiched between the adsorbed carbon monoxide molecules in a structure reminiscent of that of cobalt hydrocarbonyl. The interested reader is referred to Ref. 11 for further information on the chemisorption of the reactants on Fischer–Tropsch catalysts.

As it is known that carbon dioxide also reacts with hydrogen to form high molecular-weight substances, it is pertinent to note that fast and irreversible chemisorption of carbon dioxide occurs on tungsten, molybdenum, iron and nickel films, but not on films of the noble Group VIII metals.[12]

15.3 Catalysts for the Fischer–Tropsch Synthesis[13–15]

There are only four metals which show a significant activity in the Fischer–Tropsch synthesis: these are iron, cobalt, nickel and ruthenium, nickel being somewhat less efficient than the other three. Between 215 and 315°, osmium and the other noble Group VIII metals (excepting platinum) give small amounts of low molecular-weight hydrocarbons at atmospheric pressure, and at higher pressures rhodium and osmium give considerable yields of material which, unlike that formed over ruthenium, contains oxygenated products. Here we shall only consider the four most important metals.

Ruthenium is the only one of these four metals which is used in the pure state, that is, unpromoted and unsupported. Iron requires promotion but not supporting, while cobalt and nickel are normally used with both promoters and supports, although unpromoted cobalt is quite highly active. Some further consideration of the role of these additives is given below.

It is now necessary to examine whether the metallic phases will be thermodynamically stable under synthesis conditions. Calculations show[1] that neither cobalt nor nickel can be oxidized by water or carbon dioxide at the temperatures usually used, but that iron could be oxidized at 250° if the P_{H_2O}/P_{H_2} ratio exceeds about 0.03 or if the P_{CO_2}/P_{CO} ratio exceeds about two. These calculations of course refer to the formation of the bulk oxides, and it is likely that surface oxidation could occur more readily. In practice it is found that iron catalysts oxidize only slowly during the synthesis.

Although the carbides of iron, cobalt and nickel are thermodynamically unstable with respect to the elements, processes of the type

$$3M + 2CO \rightarrow M_3C + CO_2 \qquad \text{(h)}$$

have a negative standard free energy change, and proceed readily under synthesis conditions. The following unit steps are probably involved in the formation of bulk carbide: (i) reduction of adsorbed carbon monoxide to surface carbide; (ii) dissolution of carbon to form a solid solution; and (iii) formation of microcrystalline carbide phases from super-saturated solid solutions. Because of their instability the carbides ultimately decompose to the elements. The carbides of cobalt (Co_2C) and nickel (Ni_3C) are inactive for the Fischer–Tropsch synthesis, although dissolved carbon does not completely destroy the activity of the metals. It is likely that the maximum operating temperature for cobalt catalysts ($\sim$225°) is dictated by the rate of carbide formation.

On the other hand, the carbides of iron are excellent Fischer–Tropsch catalysts. Three of these are well defined: they are cementite (Fe_3C), Hägg carbide (χ–Fe_2C) and ϵ–Fe_2C.

The carbides can be hydrogenated at temperatures of the order of 250° according, for example, to the equation

$$n\mathrm{Fe_2C} + (n + 1)\mathrm{H_2} \rightarrow \mathrm{C}_n\mathrm{H}_{2n+2} + 2n\mathrm{Fe}, \qquad \text{(i)}$$

the products being chiefly methane and ethane. This finding, and the fact the formation of higher hydrocarbons by this mechanism has a positive free energy change, indicates the carbon in *bulk* carbides cannot be the intermediate in Fischer–Tropsch synthesis. The role of surface carbide will be further considered below.

The excellent activity of the iron carbides has stimulated much research on the possible use of other interstitial compounds of iron, and notable success has been obtained with iron nitrides. Several nitride phases have been characterized, the highest obtainable nitrogen concentration corresponding to the formula Fe_2N. Their preparation requires the *in situ* nitriding of reduced iron or an iron carbide by ammonia at about 400°. During operation in the synthesis they slowly lose nitrogen, forming first a carbonitride and ultimately a carbide.

We return now to the question of the promotion and supporting of iron, cobalt and nickel catalysts. This matter has already received some attention in Chapter 3, where the following conclusions were arrived at. The role of a *support* is to ensure that the surface of the metal is freely available to the reactants, and that its tendency to sinter is minimized. *Promoters* are somewhat arbitrarily divided into two classes. (i) Structural promoters, usually irreducible metal oxides, which also stabilize the metallic phase against loss of area by sintering during operation: their role is thus supplementary to that of the support. (ii) Electronic promoters which, by entering into a solid solution with the metal, affect the metal's electronic properties and hence its behaviour in catalysis. Very often sufficient information is not available to decide in which category a particular promoter should be placed, and it is more than likely that some promoters serve both purposes.

For the Fischer–Tropsch synthesis, cobalt and nickel are invariably supported, usually on kieselguhr, the metal/support ratio varying between unity and one-half. Unpromoted cobalt–kieselguhr is active, but rapidly loses its ability to form high molecular-weight paraffins from the reactants. The preparation of efficient cobalt and nickel catalysts depends on the addition of judiciously (but in the early stages of the work, empirically) chosen promoters. Promotion in some cases results in a reduced initial activity, but this is usually compensated by a longer life and the formation of more desirable products. Among the promoters which have been used are ThO_2, MgO, Al_2O_3, MnO, U_3O_8, Cr_2O_3 and Ce_2O_3: of these, the first three are primarily structural promoters, although MgO also acts as a "binder," imparting added mechanical strength to the catalyst granules. Combinations of two or more promoters have also been tried. Structural promoters tend to raise the temperature required to effect the initial reduction of the catalyst to the metallic state, and other readily reducible oxides, such as copper oxide, have been incorporated in order to nucleate the formation of the metallic phase: however, the presence of copper in the reduced catalyst results in a shortening of the catalyst's life and its use has been discontinued. Although supported and promoted nickel were thoroughly examined in the early phases of the study of the synthesis (1930–35), it is much inferior to cobalt, which is commonly used in combination with ThO_2 and MgO: the proportions of Co : ThO_2 : MgO : kieselguhr are generally about 100 : 5 : 10 : 200.

We return finally to the question of iron catalysts. Although these do not require supporting, they require promotion, and as with catalysts for ammonia synthesis, both structural and electronic (alkaline) promoters are necessary. In addition to those structural promoters listed above, the oxides of calcium, silicon and vanadium have also been used. Catalysts may be prepared by co-precipitation from a solution of the mixed nitrates, followed by reduction, and here, as with cobalt and nickel, a trace of copper oxide facilitates the reduction, although copper does not harmfully affect the life of iron catalysts. Alternatively, iron catalysts may be prepared by fusion of the mixed oxides, again followed by reduction. The structural promoter (either one or more of the irreducible oxides already mentioned) is usually present in a concentration of about 3 per cent, and the alkaline promoter, about 1 per cent. This latter is generally potassium oxide, the other alkali metal oxides (with the possible exception of rubidium) being less effective.

15.4 The General Kinetics of the Fischer-Tropsch Synthesis

15.41 Introduction

Accurate and meaningful kinetic measurements on the Fischer–Tropsch synthesis are hard to obtain. All the work so far reported has been done using flow systems. The operation of such a system as a "differential reactor", where the conversion is small and hence the composition of the feed-gas may be regarded as constant, is rendered difficult by the magnitude of the analytical problems, although here the techniques of gas chromatography may be expected to be of assistance. The interpretation of results obtained from an "integral reactor", where the conversion is large, is a formidable problem in a system of such complexity. The *conversion* is properly expressed in terms of the fraction of the entering hydrogen and carbon monoxide which is consumed,

x, and the *yield of products* in terms of the moles of product formed per moles of hydrogen and carbon monoxide removed. More frequently, however, the conversion is simply quoted as the "apparent contraction," and the yield of products as the number of grams of solid and liquid products per cubic metre of reactant gas. The differential rate per unit volume of catalyst, r, is defined as

$$r = \frac{dx}{d(S^{-1})}, \tag{1}$$

where S is the space velocity (volumes of gas passing per volume of catalyst per unit time). The product xS is then referred to as the "space–time yield".

Although conventional kinetic information is scarce, there is a vast corpus of information on the dependence of conversion and the nature of the products on the type of catalyst used, the temperature, pressure and other operating variables. This information is referred to in the heading of this Section as "general kinetics" for want of a better term. The following subsections will describe the general kinetics observed with the four principal metal catalysts, together with such conventional kinetics as are known. Before entering into detail, however, a brief summary may be helpful.

With all catalysts and under all conditions, the predominant products are hydrocarbons. Ruthenium is unique in that at high pressures it catalyses the formation of straight-chain paraffins of very high molecular weight. Under certain conditions the other metals also form substantial amounts of "heavy wax," that is to say, hydrocarbons boiling above about 450°. Hydrocarbons are preponderantly straight-chain, the degree of branching being slight, and quaternary carbon atoms are always absent. The yields of oxygenated products vary very much with the operating conditions, generally increasing with increasing pressure and decreasing temperature. However, the *desired* products are normally those hydrocarbons containing between about five and eighteen carbon atoms (boiling below 320°), that is, those which are equivalent to gasoline and diesel fuel. The term "selectivity" is very often used to denote the extent to which catalysts produce these hydrocarbons, but the term is somewhat lacking in rigour and cannot fully replace the detailed analysis of the products.

Since the literature on the Fischer–Tropsch synthesis has been very fully reviewed on several occasions,[11, 13, 16–19] only leading and very recent references will be given in this Chapter: the reader is referred to these reviews for more detailed information.

15.42 Iron Catalysts

The original discovery of the synthesis reaction by Fischer and Tropsch in 1923 was made using alkalized iron at 100–150 atm. and 400–450°.[20] The product obtained under these conditions was substantially oxygenated and contained little hydrocarbon, but the yield of the latter was increased by reducing the pressure to 7 atm., although the yield also fell. The development of the more active promoted cobalt and nickel catalysts in the following years resulted in attention being concentrated on operation at atmospheric pressure, which while suitable for these metals is not the most favourable for iron: this performs most satisfactorily between 7 and 30 atm., and for this reason the development of iron catalysts was somewhat delayed.

Some 55 per cent of the products obtained by operating a fused doubly promoted iron catalyst at about 200° and 20 atm. pressure are oxygenated ($\sim$45 per cent alcohols and $\sim$10 per cent aldehydes, ketones, esters and acids): very high molecular weight alcohols are formed, and some 18 per cent of the alcohol fraction contains more than 22 carbon atoms. Of the 45 per cent of hydrocarbons, about 35 per cent is olefinic and the remainder saturated. With increasing temperature, the mean molecular weight of the hydrocarbons decreases due to the onset of hydrogenolysis, although the olefin content is not much affected. The yield of alcohols also falls with rising temperature, again because of hydrogenolysis. Thus, for example, with precipitated iron catalysts (which yield smaller amounts of oxygenated products than fused catalysts), the "heavy wax" yield falls from about 70 per cent at 215° to 10 per cent at 275°, and simultaneously the yield of hydrocarbons containing five or less carbon atoms rises from about 2 per cent to 42 per cent. Activation energies of about 20 kcal. mole^{-1} have several times been reported.

Increasing the operating pressure from 1 to 20 atm. causes the rate of synthesis to rise almost in proportion, and at the same time the "heavy wax" yield increases, chiefly at the expense of low molecular-weight hydrocarbons; raising the pressure beyond about 40 atm. lowers the mean molecular weight presumably because high pressures also favour hydrogenolysis. The H_2/CO ratio in the feed gas is usually unity, and raising this to two causes very substantial hydrogenolysis. The variation of conversion with space velocity is expressible by the empirical equation

$$-\log(1 - x) = k/S. \tag{2}$$

Considerable interest attaches to the molecular-weight distribution of the products, because of its relevance to reaction mechanisms. The information is most complete for hydrocarbon fractions. Very frequently the yields of the first three hydrocarbons vary in the sequence $C_3 > C_1 > C_2$, and above C_3 the yields decrease monotonically. In this region the molar yield of hydrocarbons declines logarithmically with increasing carbon number, that is,

$$Y_{n+1}/Y_n = \alpha, \tag{3}$$

where Y_n is the molar yield of the hydrocarbon having n carbon atoms, etc. However, while semilog plots for a number of iron catalysts show constant values of α (0.67 $\pm$ 0.02) when n lies between 1 and 9 or 10, all show a break at this point, and thereafter α has values of about 0.9. An example of this kind of behaviour is shown in Fig. 1. A partial interpretation of the logarithmic decrease of yield with increasing carbon number will be presented when

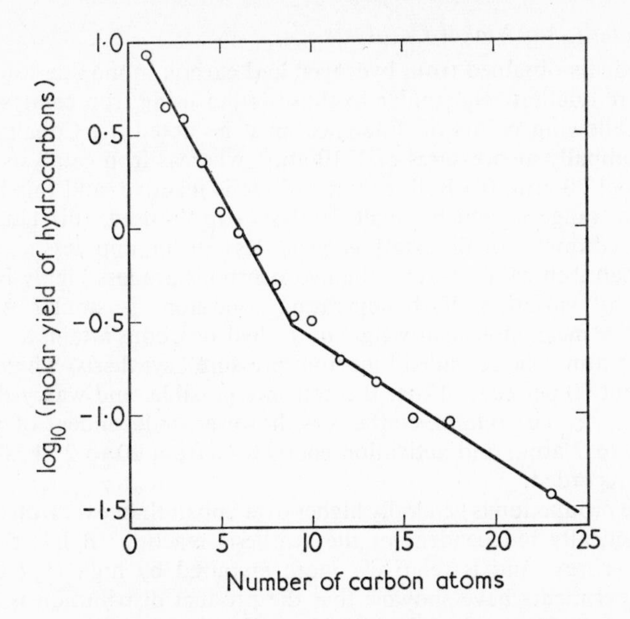

FIG. 1. Semi-logarithmic plot of the molar yield distribution of hydrocarbons from the Fischer-Tropsch synthesis over iron (entry 1 of Table 84, reference 13).

the mechanism is discussed. So far as can be ascertained, the yield of the other chemical classes declines similarly with increasing carbon number.

The hydrocarbons of each carbon number contain far more than the equilibrium amount of the straight-chain isomer. The results of a typical analysis of C_4 to C_7 paraffins[21] are given in Table I.

TABLE I. *Structural Analysis of Paraffins from the Fischer–Tropsch Synthesis over an Iron Catalyst*[21]

n	*Straight chain*	*2-methyl-*	*3-methyl-*	*2,3-dimethyl-*	*2,4-dimethyl-*
4	89.6	10.4	—	—	—
5	80.3	19.7	—	—	—
6	73.7	14.1	8.9	3.3	—
7	70.0	10.4	17.6	1.0	1.0

Iron carbide catalysts (either Fe_2C or Fe_3C) are more active than reduced iron, although the product distribution is not much different. Nitrided iron catalysts are more active still, and if the atomic N/Fe ratio exceeds 0.44, a better selectivity results, in the sense that the yield of diesel oil is increased and that of "heavy wax" is reduced, usually to zero.[16, 22, 23]

15.43 Cobalt and Nickel Catalysts

The products obtained from hydrogen and carbon monoxide using cobalt catalysts are qualitatively similar to those found using iron catalysts. However, the following points of difference must be noted. (i) Cobalt catalysts operate optimally at pressures of 1–10 atm., whereas iron catalysts perform best at about 20 atm. (ii) Bulk cobalt carbide is inactive, and this limits the temperature range in which cobalt catalysts can be used. (iii) Under comparable conditions cobalt catalysts yield less olefin and less oxygenated material than iron catalysts, and the hydrocarbons are less highly branched. The effect of variation of the operating conditions is similar with both catalysts. The mean molecular weight of the hydrocarbons attains a maximum at about 15 atm. (the so-called "medium pressure" synthesis) where conversion is about 90 per cent of that theoretically possible, and wax yields reach some 70 g.m.$^{-3}$. The rate of synthesis is, however, independent of pressure, at least up to 7 atm., and activation energies of from 20 to 27 kcal. mole^{-1} have been recorded.

Methane production is generally higher over cobalt than over iron catalysts, and is kinetically independent of the synthesis reaction: it has the higher activation energy, and is relatively more favoured by high H_2/CO ratios. Careful experiments have shown[24] that the product distribution is constant along the catalyst bed except for a tendency for the olefins' concentration to fall. The molar yields of hydrocarbons and alcohols containing more than two carbon atoms again decline exponentially, but here the values of α are usually constant, sometimes up to twenty carbon atoms. Values of α are generally close to 0.75, although for a pelleted catalyst operating at atmospheric pressure a value of 0.85 has been found.[25] Isomer analysis (Table II) shows a much lower degree of chain-branching than is usually found with iron catalysts.

TABLE II. *Structural Analysis of Paraffins from the Fischer–Tropsch Synthesis over a Cobalt Catalyst at Atmospheric Pressure*[25]

n	*Straight chain*	*2-methyl-*	*3-methyl-*	*2,3-dimethyl-*	*2,4-dimethyl-*
5	94.9	5.1	—	—	—
6	89.6	5.8	4.6	0.04	—
7	87.7	4.6	7.7	0	0

Nickel catalysts fail to give the same degree of satisfaction as iron and cobalt, because of their propensity to cause hydrogenolysis, and although this can be minimized by operating at as low a temperature as possible, this entails a loss of conversion efficiency.

15.44 Ruthenium Catalysts

As already noted, ruthenium is notable for yielding very high molecular-weight waxes with a low oxygen content, and for not requiring either promoter or support. Ruthenium prepared by reduction of the dioxide can operate at 195° and 100 atm., giving constant activity and reproducible products, for at least six months, and formation of the volatile carbonyl $Ru(CO)_4$ though thermodynamically feasible does not seem to occur. The conversion increases rapidly with rising temperatures and with increased pressure, as is shown in Table III.[26] The mean molecular weight of the products appears

TABLE III. *Percentage Conversion of Carbon Monoxide and Hydrogen over Ruthenium as a Function of Temperature and Pressure*[26]

Temperature (°C)	140	160	180	200
Conversion (% at 100 atm.)	25	45	70	85
Conversion (% at 1000 atm.)	55	85	95	97

also to increase with pressure. The highest-melting wax fraction formed at 1000 atm. is reported[26] to have a melting point of 132–134°, an average molecular weight of 23,000 and a viscosity at 150° of 35,600 centistokes. No discussion of the mechanism of the synthesis over ruthenium has been given, neither has any explanation been offered for its difference from the other metals.

The efficient production of primary alcohols by the hydrogenation of carbon monoxide over ruthenium suspended in water or an alcohol has been claimed.

15.5 The Mechanism of the Fischer–Tropsch Synthesis

15.51 The Incorporation of other Molecules in the Synthesis

Since, as was noted at the beginning of the last Section, meaningful kinetics of the synthesis are hard to come by, the formulation of the mechanism is necessarily based on (i) the interpretation of the molecular-weight distribution, and (ii) experiments, now to be described, on the incorporation of foreign molecules in the reaction. The latter give much useful information on the species which initiate chain growth, while the form of the molar yield distribution elucidates the growth and termination processes.

In experiments designed to study incorporation, the gas to be added is blended with the synthesis gas in a concentration of from 0.5 per cent to 50 per cent, and this is then passed over the catalyst. The added gas may emerge unchanged, oxidized, reduced or incorporated into the synthesis products. If incorporated, it may have become so because it (or some species derived from it) has initiated chain growth, or because it has become "built in" with the growing chain, or of course both. Quite the most sensitive method of establishing whether or not incorporation takes place is to use radioactively labelled substances, and to observe the occurrence or otherwise of radioactivity in the products.[27] By studying the manner in which the activity is distributed amongst the products, it is possible to assess to what extents incorporation by initiation and by "build-in" occur. By labelling molecules in different positions, it is sometimes possible to tell from which point in the molecule chain growth takes place. Unfortunately, it will not be possible to describe this elegant experimental work in great detail, and attention must largely be confined to the conclusions derived from it.

The thermodynamics of the incorporation of saturated hydrocarbons are somewhat unfavourable,[1] and contradictory results have been reported with methane.[11] However, the use of high concentrations of $^{14}CH_4$ has failed to show any incorporation over iron or cobalt catalysts at atmospheric pressure.[28] On the other hand, it is calculated that olefins can be incorporated at almost any olefin/carbon monoxide ratio, and positive results with olefins have often been found.[11, 24, 29, 30] It has recently been shown that when synthesis gas containing about 1 per cent of radioactive ethylene is passed over iron catalysts, some 12 per cent of the polymer chains are initiated by the ethylene at atmospheric pressure, and some 6 per cent at 7 atm.[29]

Primary alcohols are very efficient chain initiators,[29] especially over iron catalysts. At about 225° and atmospheric pressure, radioactive ethanol and 1-propanol are incorporated to the extents of about 30 per cent and 50 per cent respectively; propanal gives similar results to 1-propanol, suggesting that it is hydrogenated to the common initiating species on the surface. Analysis of the C_4 hydrocarbons formed in the presence of propanol shows that the activity appears chiefly in the n-butane and n-butenes, and to a substantially smaller extent in the branched isomers. This suggests that chain growth occurs predominantly at the end of carbon chains. Methanol is a less efficient initiator than ethanol by a factor of about five, although it and formaldehyde are also "built in." Radioactive ketene also acts as a chain initiator, and becomes "built in," over both iron and cobalt catalysts.[31]

There are a few other pieces of evidence on the nature of the initiating species. Primary alcohols decompose over Fischer–Tropsch catalysts to yield products similar to those formed in the synthesis,[11] although methanol does not always so react.[24] Ketene also behaves similarly.[32] It is possible that the products formed from alcohols arise from the hydrogen and carbon monoxide formed in their decomposition, as for example:

$$R{-}CH_2{-}CH_2OH \rightarrow R{-}CH_2{-}CHO + H_2 \rightarrow R{-}CH_3 + CO + H_2. \quad (j)$$

However, in view of the work described above, it is likely that the products are formed by the polymerization of species formed from the alcohol. It is significant that the activation energy for alcohol decomposition is sometimes very close to that for the Fischer–Tropsch synthesis.

It is now clear that species containing one or two carbon atoms can act as chain initiators. It has been suggested[31] that ketene decomposes to the methylene radical $\underset{**}{C}H_2$ and carbon monoxide, but the radical formed from methanol, and also from adsorbed carbon monoxide and hydrogen in the absence of other molecules, is probably $H{-}\underset{**}{C}{-}OH$. It is not clear, however, whether such diadsorbed species form bonds to one or to two adjacent metal atoms. The hypothesis[33, 34] that polymerization occurs solely by the conjunction of methylene groups formed by the reduction of surface carbide is now untenable: its shortcomings have been discussed,[11] the principal one being its failure to account for the formation of oxygenated products. By analogy, the radical formed from ethanol may be $\mathrm{H_3C{-}\underset{**}{C}{-}OH}$, although the structure $\mathrm{H_3C{-}\underset{*}{C}{=}O}$ has been proposed.[24] However, in view of the probable lability of hydrogen atoms in such species under synthesis conditions, it may be profitless to try to specify their structure with any further precision.

15.52 Chain Growth and Termination

Having discussed the possible nature of the chain initiators, it is now necessary to try to formulate the processes of chain growth and termination, and in particular to try to account for the form of the molecular weight distribution. Attention is confined to the *number* of carbon atoms in molecules, since the question of their degree of oxygenation is a complicated one. Although paraffins, olefins and alcohols appear to be primary products of the synthesis, they are probably interconverted after formation by hydrogenation, dehydrogenation, hydrogenolysis and dehydration.

We may start by formulating possible mechanisms for the growth and termination of chains, and follow this by the necessary mathematical development. It is generally assumed that growth occurs at only one end of a chain, and in harmony with observation that only "methyl-branching" occurs (see, however, Ref. 35). Chain-growth probably starts by the elimination of water between two C_1 initiators,[19, 29, 36] followed by hydrogenation, viz.

$$\mathrm{H{-}\underset{**}{C}{-}OH + H{-}\underset{**}{C}{-}OH \xrightarrow{-H_2O} H{-}\underset{**}{C}{-}\underset{**}{C}{-}OH \xrightarrow{+2H} H_3C{-}\underset{**}{C}{-}OH} \qquad \text{(k)}$$

This last species will be recognized as the form of adsorbed ethanol earlier proposed as the initiator which this molecule produces. There is evidence that this first conjunction is slower than subsequent similar steps: the relative efficiencies of methanol and ethanol as initiators, and the relative yields of products with one, two and three carbon atoms, clearly point to this. This may perhaps be interpretable in terms of the electron-releasing properties of the methyl group. It is evident that chain growth may proceed as

$$\mathrm{H_3C{-}\underset{**}{C}{-}OH + H{-}\underset{**}{C}{-}OH \xrightarrow[+2H]{H_2O} H_3C{-}CH_2{-}\underset{**}{C}{-}OH} \qquad \text{(l)}$$

although Emmett and his associates[29, 37] prefer to regard the C_2 species in process (k) as $\mathrm{H_3C{-}\underset{*}{C}H{-}OH}$, since this eases the understanding of chain branching. This can occur as follows:

$$\mathrm{R{-}\underset{*}{C}H{-}OH + H{-}\underset{**}{C}{-}OH \xrightarrow[+2H]{-H_2O} R{-}\overset{\displaystyle CH_3 \atop |}{\underset{*}{C}}{-}OH} \qquad \text{(m)}$$

so that although primary alcohol complexes can yield both primary and secondary alcohol complexes, the reverse is not true, since the secondary complexes lack a hydrogen atom at the appropriate point.[29]

It seems likely that chain growth proceeds as indicated, with the oxygen atom remaining in the terminal position. Termination may take place by desorption or hydrogenation:

$$\underset{**}{\text{R—C—OH}} \longrightarrow \text{R—CHO} + 2* \quad \text{(n)}$$

$$\xrightarrow{+2\text{H}} \text{R—CH}_2\text{OH} + 2* \quad \text{(o)}$$

or

$$\text{R—}\underset{*}{\text{CH}}\text{—OH} \longrightarrow \text{R—CHO} + \underset{*}{\text{H}} \quad \text{(p)}$$

$$\xrightarrow{+\text{H}} \text{R—CH}_2\text{OH}. \quad \text{(q)}$$

The aldehyde and alcohol may then later form olefins, paraffins, acids, etc. If olefins and paraffins are primary products, we must write for example,

$$\text{R—CH}_2\text{—}\underset{*}{\text{CH}}\text{—OH} \xrightarrow[-\text{H}_2\text{O}]{+2\text{H}} \text{R—CH}_2\text{—}\underset{*}{\text{CH}_2} \left.\begin{array}{l} \xrightarrow{-\text{H}} \text{R—CH=CH}_2 \\ \xrightarrow{+\text{H}} \text{R—CH}_2\text{—CH}_3 \end{array}\right\} \text{(r).}$$

Other termination processes may be envisaged.

On the basis of steps of this kind, several efforts have been made to interpret the molecular weight and isomer distributions. Two simple points may be made at the outset. (i) Any scheme which gives to each growing chain a finite probability of terminating and desorbing, or of continuing to grow, must necessarily lead to a logarithmic decrease of molar yield with increasing carbon number.[38] The mathematical formalism is precisely equivalent to that developed in Chapter 11 to account for the distribution of deuterated paraffins from olefin–deuterium reactions. (ii) If a "branching constant," representing the ratio of the probabilities of process (1) leading to normal and branched species, be chosen to agree with the relative yields of n- and iso-C_4 hydrocarbons, then the calculated distribution of isomers in hydrocarbons of higher molecular weight should automatically follow. The remainder of this sub-section merely embellishes these statements.

We may continue by developing this last point. If we assign to any adsorbed species a probability a of adding another carbon atom at a terminal position, and a probability b of addition at a penultimate position, then the ratio b/a may be termed the "branching constant" f. Assuming f to be independent of chain length and of previous branching, and that growth at both ends of the chain is possible, the relative yields of n- and iso-C_4 and C_5 hydrocarbons may be assessed as follows:[39]

$$\text{n-C}_4;\quad 2a/(a+1) : \text{iso-C}_4;\quad b/(a+1) :$$

$$\text{n-C}_5;\quad 2a/(a+1) : \text{iso-C}_5;\quad 2ab/(a+1) + b/(a+1).$$

The relative yields of the isomers of higher hydrocarbons may be derived analogously. By taking $f = 0.040$, the isomer yields obtained over cobalt (see Table II) can be reproduced to within the error of the analyses; this is also shown in Fig. 2, where just the percentages of the n-isomers calculated are compared with those observed. When this treatment is applied to results obtained over iron catalysts (see Table I), taking $f = 0.125$, there is a significant difference between the observed and calculated C_4 isomer yields (see also Fig. 2). This difference is eliminated if it is assumed that growth

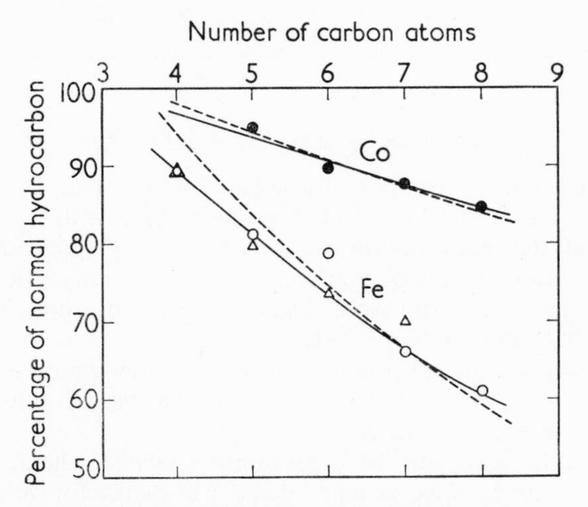

FIG. 2. The dependence of the yield of normal hydrocarbons (as a percentage of the total yield at each carbon number) on carbon number.

● Results of Friedel and Anderson[25] for a cobalt catalyst.
○ Results of Bruner[47] for an iron catalyst.
△ Results of Weitkamp *et al.*[21] for an iron catalyst.
— Lines calculated for single-end growth.[36]
--- Lines calculated for two-end growth.[39]

can only occur at one end of a chain;[36] this modification affects only slightly the isomer distributions for hydrocarbons higher than C_4.

If now rate constants are assigned to the processes of normal and branched chain growth and desorption, and if the rates of these processes for any species are related to its molar concentration by these rate constants, then application of a steady state treatment enables the carbon-number distribution and the isomer distribution to be calculated. For the carbon-number distribution, the molar yield Y_n of hydrocarbon containing n carbon atoms is given by

$$Y_n = 2Y_2F_n a^{n-2}. \tag{4}$$

The parameter F_n is the sum of the terms representing the individual isomer yields, and some values of these (based on "one-end" growth, except for C_2)

are quoted in Table IV. Terms in f^3 appear when trimethyl-compounds are possible, that is, in C_8 and higher hydrocarbons.

TABLE IV. *Values of the Isomer Distribution Terms*

n	*Straight chain*	*2-methyl-*	*3-methyl-*	*2,3-dimethyl-*	*2,4-dimethyl-*
4	1	f	—	—	—
5	1	$2f$	—	—	—
6	1	$2f$	f	f^2	—
7	1	$2f$	$2f$	$2f^2$	f^2

Expression (4) can be rearranged to

$$\log (Y_n/F_n) = n \log a + \log (2Y_2/a^2), \quad (5)$$

and the molar yield distributions for cobalt catalysts (see Table II) can be described if $a = 0.84$ and $f = 0.035$. A problem arises with the results found over iron catalysts, because of the break in the molar yield curve (see Fig. 1): when results of this type are plotted according to equation (5), it is found that agreement is obtained up to about nine or ten carbon atoms if $a \simeq 0.6$ and $f = 0.115$. Thereafter, different values of a and f are required to secure agreement, the implication being that chains containing more than about ten carbon atoms grow *more* rapidly than shorter chains. No interpretation of this effect has yet been suggested.

Emmett and his associates have developed a related scheme which, however, considers about twice as many complexes as the foregoing scheme:[29] the calculated isomer and yield distributions are, however, very similar. These authors have also considered "multiple build-in", viz. the conjunction of two species each containing more than one carbon atom. This they find does not significantly alter the pattern of the calculations. It has been observed[11] that over iron catalysts the differential rate of reactant consumption under a wide range of conditions can be expressed by the equation:

$$r = \frac{kP_{H_2}}{1 + k'(P_{H_2O}/P_{CO})}. \quad (6)$$

This can be derived from Emmett's recent scheme[29] on the assumption that (i) the water formed reacts with the C_1 complex to form CO_2 according to the process:

$$\underset{**}{\text{H—C—OH}} + H_2O \longrightarrow CO_2 + \underset{*}{4H}, \quad (s)$$

(ii) that the complex is attached to only one metal atom, and (iii) that the coverage of the surface by complexes during synthesis is high. The steady state treatment based on these premises leads, with some further approximations, to equation (6), although the treatment can only hold when water and carbon dioxide are the sole oxygenated products, that is, for low pressure synthesis.

It is evident that some differences exist between the mechanisms which operate over iron and cobalt, especially with regard to initiation processes. There has been little discussion of the mechanism over nickel and ruthenium. More detailed and accurate product analyses, particularly for oxygenated products, would be helpful, and here the application of gas chromatography may be expected to assist greatly.

15.6 The Hydrogenation of Carbon Dioxide[11]

The hydrogenation of carbon dioxide over Fischer–Tropsch catalysts usually results in the predominant formation of methane: high conversions are obtained above about 150°. Ruthenium is particularly active for this process, and alkali-promoted ruthenium gives rise to some synthesis products.[40] Since the monoxide is more strongly adsorbed than the dioxide, the latter when added to normal synthesis gas either does not react or forms only methane. It is believed that the dioxide must first be reduced to the monoxide by the water gas shift, and that the high yield of methane is due to the reaction of the monoxide with a large excess of hydrogen, a condition known to favour methane formation.

The reduction of carbon dioxide by hydrogen has been studied over a series of nickel–copper alloy powders.[41] With pure nickel, especially above about 300°, the product is mainly methane, with only a little carbon monoxide: with the alloy containing 3.7 per cent copper, between 300 and 400°, carbon monoxide is the chief product, although above 400° the yield of methane increases progressively. At 420°, the overall activity is essentially independent of alloy composition, and the yield of carbon monoxide is constant at 70 to 80 per cent for alloys containing between 11 and 100 per cent copper.

The kinetics of the water gas reaction have several times been studied over platinum surfaces at elevated temperatures (530–1200°),[42–44] with results which are largely contradictory.[45] The reaction has also been studied over tungsten at very high temperatures.[46]

References

1. R. B. Anderson, In "Catalysis", edited by P. H. Emmett (Reinhold, New York, 1956), **4**, 1.
2. R. Suhrmann and G. Wedler, *Z. Elektrochem.* **63**, 748 (1959).
3. R. P. Eischens and W. A. Pliskin, *Adv. Catalysis* **10**, 1 (1958).
4. G. J. H. Dorgelo and W. M. H. Sachtler, *Naturwiss* **20**, 576 (1959).
5. M. V. C. Sastri and T. S. Viswanathan, *J. Amer. Chem. Soc.* **77**, 3967 (1955).
6. C. W. Griffin, *J. Amer. Chem. Soc.* **59**, 2431 (1937).
7. M. McD. Baker and E. K. Rideal, *Trans. Faraday Soc.* **51**, 1597 (1955).
8. J. Bagg, F. C. Tompkins, *Trans. Faraday Soc.* **51**, 1071 (1955).
9. D. F. Klemperer and F. S. Stone, *Proc. Roy. Soc.* **A243**, 375 (1957).
10. M. M. Siddiqi and F. C. Tompkins, Proc. 2nd International Congress on Catalysis (Editions Technip, Paris, 1961), **2**, 1767.
11. R. B. Anderson, In "Catalysis", edited by P. H. Emmett (Reinhold, New York, 1956), **4**, 257.
12. A. C. Collins and B. M. W. Trapnell, *Trans. Faraday Soc.* **53**, 1476 (1957).
13. R. B. Anderson, In "Catalysis", edited by P. H. Emmett (Reinhold, New York, 1956), **4**, 29.

14. L. J. E. Hofer, In "Catalysis", edited by P. H. Emmett (Reinhold, New York, 1956), **4**, 373.
15. H. Pichler, *Brennstoff-Chem.* **19**, 226 (1938).
16. R. B. Anderson, *Adv. Catalysis* **5**, 355 (1953).
17. H. H. Storch, *Adv. Catalysis* **1**, 115 (1948); "Chemistry of Petroleum Hydrocarbons" (Reinhold, New York, 1954), **1**, 631.
18. H. Pichler, *Adv. Catalysis* **4**, 271 (1952).
19. H. H. Storch, N. Golumbic and R. B. Anderson, "The Fischer–Tropsch and Related Syntheses" (Wiley, New York, 1951).
20. F. Fischer and H. Tropsch, *Brennstoff-Chem.* **4**, 276 (1923); **5**, 201, 217 (1924).
21. A. W. Weitkamp, H. S. Seelig, N. J. Bowman and W. E. Cady, *Ind. Eng. Chem.* **45**, 343 (1953).
22. F. S. Karn, B. Seligman, J. F. Shultz and R. B. Anderson, *J. Phys. Chem.* **62**, 1039 (1958).
23. F. S. Karn, J. F. Shultz and R. B. Anderson, *J. Phys. Chem.* **64**, 446 (1960).
24. P. W. Darby and C. Kemball, *Trans. Faraday Soc.* **55**, 833 (1959).
25. R. A. Friedel and R. B. Anderson, *J. Amer. Chem. Soc.* **72**, 1212 (1950).
26. H. Pichler and H. Buffleb, *Brennstoff-Chem.* **21**, 257, 285 (1940).
27. P. H. Emmett, *Adv. Catalysis* **9**, 645 (1957).
28. J. T. Kummer, T. W. De Witt and P. H. Emmett, *J. Amer. Chem. Soc.* **70**, 3632 (1948).
29. W. K. Hall, R. J. Kokes and P. H. Emmett, *J. Amer. Chem. Soc.* **82**, 1027 (1960); **79**, 2983, 2989 (1957); J. T. Kummer, H. H. Podgurski, W. B. Spencer and P. H. Emmett, *Ibid.* **73**, 564 (1951).
30. O. A. Golovina, M. M. Sakharov, S. Z. Roginskii and E. S. Dokukina, *Zhur. fiz. Khim.* **33**, 2451 (1959).
31. G. Blyholder and P. H. Emmett, *J. Phys. Chem.* **63**, 962 (1959); **64**, 470 (1960).
32. B. R. Warner, M. J. Derrig and C. W. Montgomery, *J. Amer. Chem. Soc.* **68**, 1615 (1946).
33. S. R. Craxford and E. K. Rideal, *J. Chem. Soc.* 1604 (1939).
34. F. Fischer and H. Tropsch, *Brennstoff-Chem.* **7**, 97 (1926).
35. B. D. Blaustein, I. Wender and R. B. Anderson, *Nature* **189**, 224 (1961).
36. R. B. Anderson, R. A. Friedel and H. H. Storch, *J. Chem. Phys.* **19**, 313 (1951).
37. J. T. Kummer and P. H. Emmett, *J. Amer. Chem. Soc.* **75**, 5177 (1953).
38. E. F. G. Herington, *Chem. and Ind.* 346 (1946).
39. S. Weller and R. A. Friedel, *J. Chem. Phys.* **17**, 801 (1949); **18**, 157 (1950).
40. F. Fischer, T. Bahr and A. Meusel, *Ber.* **69B**, 183 (1936).
41. L. E. Cratty and W. W. Russell, *J. Amer. Chem. Soc.* **80**, 767 (1958).
42. C. R. Prichard and C. N. Hinshelwood, *J. Chem. Soc.* **127**, 806 (1925).
43. M. I. Temkin and E. Mikhailova, *Acta Physicochim. U.R.S.S.* **2**, 9 (1935).
44. G.-M. Schwab and K. Naikcer, *Z. Elektrochem.* **42**, 670 (1936).
45. See K. J. Laidler, In "Catalysis", edited by P. H. Emmett (Reinhold, New York, 1954), **1**, 119
46. C. N. Hinshelwood and C. R. Prichard, *J. Chem. Soc.* **127**, 1546 (1925).
47. H. B. Bruner, *Ind. Eng. Chem.* **41**, 2511 (1949).

Chapter 16

The Catalytic Synthesis and Decomposition of Ammonia and Related Reactions

16.1 Introduction

16.11 The Discovery and the Operation of Ammonia Synthesis[1–3]

The synthesis of ammonia from nitrogen and hydrogen now represents one of the most important industrial applications of catalysis; over five million tons are manufactured annually in the United States alone. The growth of this process from the status of a chemical curiosity to its present significance has occurred within the last half-century. Attempts to effect the synthesis before 1900 were uniformly unsuccessful, but at about this time appreciation of the value of "fixed" nitrogen as a fertilizer, and of the fallibility of the supply of Chile saltpetre in time of war, prompted concentrated efforts to be made towards the synthesis of ammonia from its elements, particularly in Germany.

It was at once realized that a sound knowledge of the thermodynamics of the system was essential. The work of Haber[4] and of Nernst[5] established that the synthesis according to the equation

$$N_2 + 3H_2 \rightleftharpoons 2NH_3 \qquad \text{(a)}$$

was exothermic, and that early attempts at the synthesis had failed because temperatures at which the equilibrium concentration of ammonia is very small had been used. More accurate and extensive measurements on this equilibrium were made by Larson and Dodge[6] in the early 1920's, and their results lead to $-\Delta H_f(NH_3) = 10.675$ kcal. mole^{-1} at 25°. Since the synthesis is accompanied by a decrease in the number of molecules in the system, increasing pressure causes the equilibrium (a) to move to the right, giving higher yields of ammonia: some results for this effect are shown in Fig. 1. At low

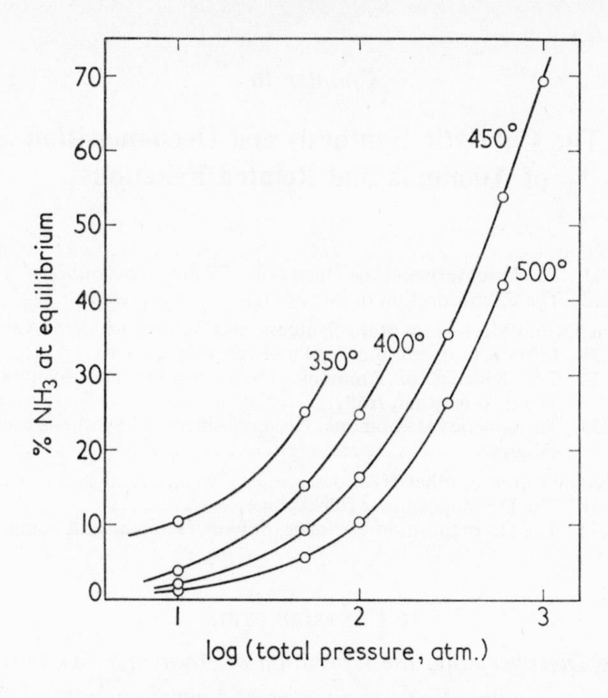

FIG. 1. The dependence of the equilibrium percentage of ammonia in the system N_2–H_2–NH_3 as a function of total pressure at various temperatures.

conversion, the equilibrium yield of ammonia is proportional to the total pressure, but this trend is not maintained at high conversions.

It is therefore evident that the synthesis of ammonia from its elements must be performed at as low a temperature and as high a pressure as possible. This requires the use of a catalyst of high activity, durability and mechanical strength. The story of the early years of empirical searching for a suitable catalyst by Haber, and by Bosch and Mittasch at the Badische Anilin und Soda Fabrik, has been told.[2, 3] A number of pure metals, especially iron, molybdenum, tungsten, manganese, uranium, osmium and ruthenium, were shown to have a promising initial activity, but all were unsuited to full-scale industrial use either because of their cost or their short life. The years of frustrating effort terminated in 1910, when it was found that iron prepared by reduction of magnetite from Gällivare in Sweden produced 3 per cent ammonia over prolonged periods when operated at 500° and 100 atm. pressure. Defining the efficiency of the synthesis as

$$\text{efficiency} = \frac{\%\ NH_3\ \text{formed}}{\text{equilibrium}\ \%\ NH_3},$$

this was an efficiency of some 30 per cent. It was soon appreciated that the activity and life of the catalyst was determined by the nature and quantities of impurities which acted as promoters, and the way was then open for the synthetic preparation of active iron catalysts by fusion of the components. Such catalysts are now almost universally used for the synthesis of ammonia.

Industrial processes employ pressures of between 200 and 1000 atm., and temperatures of about 450°: the ammonia formed is removed and the unchanged reactants are recycled. The following notes on the effect of operating conditions on the yield of ammonia obtained with a triply promoted iron catalyst ($Fe–K_2O–CaO–Al_2O_3$) are based on the review article[1] by Nielsen. (i) Because temperature affects thermodynamic and kinetic factors in opposite ways, there is for any catalyst and given pressure a temperature at which a maximum yield of ammonia is obtained: this temperature, which is approximately independent of space velocity, is about 450° for the catalyst in question. (ii) The efficiency of the reaction decreases slightly with increasing pressure, although the yield of course rises: it is uneconomical to work at above 1000 atm. (iii) The yield and efficiency decrease with increasing space velocity, but the space–time yield, which is the parameter measuring the yield of ammonia *per unit time*, increases very rapidly, as Table I shows. The maximum economic space velocity is about 50,000 $hr.^{-1}$. (iv) The maximum

TABLE I. *Variation of the Parameters of Ammonia Synthesis with Space Velocity*[1] (Triply-promoted iron, 450° and 330 atm).

Space velocity ($hr.^{-1}$)	% NH_3 *formed*	*Efficiency*	*Space–time yield* kg. NH_3 (l. cat.)$^{-1}$ $hr.^{-1}$
1,400	25.7	0.67	0.22
43,500	19.0	0.49	4.92
129,000	12.9	0.34	10.45

yield of ammonia is obtained when the $H_2 : N_2$ ratio is about 2.5; the efficiency is, however, a minimum at about this ratio.

16.12 The Chemisorption of Nitrogen[2, 7]

There is much evidence to show that nitrogen can be chemisorbed by metal surfaces in several ways (see Chapter 5 for introduction). Metals which do not adsorb nitrogen atomically to any significant extent are nevertheless capable of showing low-temperature chemisorption: thus iron,[8] cobalt,[9] and nickel[10] powders at −195° all show a weak, reversible adsorption of nitrogen to the extents respectively of about 15, 55 and 30 per cent of the BET monolayer volumes. This nitrogen is removed by pumping at room temperature, but with nickel its formation is inhibited by a very low coverage of atomic nitrogen. Some loss of magnetization results on the introduction of nitrogen to nickel–silica at −78°, although this effect is not interpreted as molecular chemisorption.[11]

The chemisorption of nitrogen by various forms of tungsten has been widely investigated,[12–20] and the existence of a weak chemisorption of nitrogen has often been inferred. Thus, for example, the flash-filament technique indicates three "levels of interaction" (including physically adsorbed nitrogen) by the temperatures at which desorption is detected,[15] while the dependence of sticking probability and surface potential on coverage at various temperatures is only reasonably interpreted by assuming the existence of Type C chemisorption.[20]

The foregoing results suggest that the weakly chemisorbed nitrogen makes only a moderate demand on the bonding capabilities of the surface metal atoms. On iron films at low temperature, the monolayer volumes of hydrogen and nitrogen are about equal,[21] and so a possible structure for Type C nitrogen is

$$\begin{array}{cc} N & = & N \\ | & & | \\ M & & M. \end{array}$$

The heat of adsorption for this structure on iron films is 10 kcal. mole^{-1}.[21]

However, this form of adsorption probably has no relevance to the synthesis or decomposition of ammonia since the nitrogen molecule is not completely dissociated. We are here interested in the Type A (atomic) chemisorption, and most of the experimental work indeed refers to this. Some of the physical properties of this state have been noted in Chapter 5 (see Tables III, VIII, XIII, XIV and XVIII). Heats of adsorption are large and comparable with the values reported for oxygen; surface potentials of about −0.5 V. have been found. With some metals, and notably for our purpose, iron, the adsorption requires a measurable activation energy. Large surface coverages cannot usually be achieved, chiefly because of the rapid decrease of heat of adsorption with coverage and the consequent rise in activation energy (see Chapter 4). Coverages as high as 50 per cent have, however, been reported for tungsten films. These observations render it likely that we should represent atomically adsorbed nitrogen as

In view of the comparatively large number of bonds which each atom makes with each metal atom in the surface, we may understand the high heats of adsorption, the low coverages achieved and the almost total inability of the metals of Groups VIII_2 and VIII_3 (possessing insufficient empty *d*-orbitals) to chemisorb nitrogen.

We are now in a position to appreciate why the early workers had their greatest success in ammonia synthesis when using as catalysts metals of Groups VIA, VIIA and VIII. The view has long been held (although recently questioned) that the adsorption of nitrogen as atoms is the slowest step in the synthesis. Of the evidence which supports this view, perhaps the most convincing is the simple fact that while a great many metals can activate hydrogen, it is only those which are capable of chemisorbing nitrogen as atoms which show any inclination to effect the ammonia synthesis. This being so, it is not surprising in view of the general principles of catalytic activity enunciated earlier that maximum activity should be found in those metals which chemisorb nitrogen as atoms *most weakly*.[2] Now as we have seen in Chapter 5 and earlier in this Section, ability to chemisorb nitrogen in this way *ceases* to all intents and purposes after Group VIII_1. Furthermore, the tendency to effect the formation of nitrogen atoms *increases* on passing from right to left across the Transition series: this is, of course, in agreement with general principles, and is shown by (i) an increase in the heats of chemisorption (on the basis of admittedly insufficient data), (ii) an increase in the tendency to form bulk nitrides, and (iii) the disappearance of the activation energy for chemisorption. We should, therefore, expect, as indeed is found, that iron, ruthenium and osmium should show the greatest activity in ammonia synthesis. It is a happy coincidence that one of these metals, namely iron, is also very abundant and, therefore, economically attractive. Some further discussion of the kinetics of chemisorption of nitrogen on this metal will be given in a later Section, when the nature of the rate-determining step in the synthesis is considered in greater detail.

Bulk nitrides of iron are formed when the metal is subjected to treatment with ammonia or (at high pressure) nitrogen between 400 and 600°, but are not formed under synthesis conditions.[2, 22] Neither are recognizable tungsten nitrides formed during the synthesis, although some nitrogen enters into solid solution after long periods: nitrided tungsten films are inactive for ammonia decomposition.[23] Hence it is concluded that dissolved nitrogen atoms play no part in ammonia synthesis or decomposition. The kinetics of ammonia decomposition over a number of metallic nitrides have been reported.[24]

16.2 The Kinetics and Mechanism of the Synthesis and Decomposition of Ammonia[2, 7, 25]

16.21 Introduction, and the Temkin–Pyzhev Treatment[2, 7, 25, 26]

Since, as discussed in Chapter 1, the presence of a catalyst does not affect the value of an equilibrium constant, the catalyst must increase the rates of the forward and backward reactions in proportion. A catalyst which shows high efficiency in ammonia decomposition must of necessity possess high activity for ammonia synthesis, and this fact has been widely applied, especially in investigations of an academic nature. The decomposition of ammonia is a far more tractable system to study than the synthesis: the former may be studied at or below atmospheric pressure, and at such a distance from equilibrium that allowance for the reverse reaction is generally unnecessary. Thus, for metals other than iron, the decomposition has been more often studied than the synthesis, but with iron, because of its immediate practical relevance, studies of the synthesis have predominated.

Other kinds of information have materially aided our understanding of the mechanism, particularly over iron: these include (i) the dependences of the activation energies for the adsorption and desorption of nitrogen as a function of coverage and (ii) the application of isotopes of both hydrogen and nitrogen, and the determination of the so-called stoichiometric number of the reaction.

The decomposition has been studied in both static and dynamic systems, and the synthesis chiefly in dynamic systems, which have the advantage of removing the ammonia from the catalyst as soon as it is formed, hence reducing the rate of nitridation of the metal.

There is little disagreement concerning the essentials of either reaction, which may be represented as:

$$NH_3 \rightleftharpoons \underset{*}{NH_3} \rightleftharpoons \underset{**}{NH} + \underset{*}{2H} \rightleftharpoons \underset{***}{N} + \underset{*}{3H} \rightleftharpoons \tfrac{1}{2}N_2 + \tfrac{3}{2}H_2. \qquad (b)$$

It is uncertain, and probably immaterial, whether the first two hydrogen atoms are lost by the adsorbed ammonia simultaneously (as shown) or not. What is important, and what has recently been the subject of controversy, is which is the rate-determining step. It has, however, recently been suggested[27] that under certain conditions the reactions may proceed as:

$$2NH_3 \rightleftharpoons \underset{*}{2NH_3} \rightleftharpoons \underset{*}{2NH_2} + \underset{*}{2H} \rightleftharpoons \underset{*\quad *}{HN{-}NH} + \underset{*}{4H} \rightleftharpoons \underset{*\quad *}{N{=}N} + \underset{*}{6H} \rightleftharpoons N_2 + 3H_2. \qquad (c)$$

with the possibility of the diadsorbed molecule also being an intermediate in the dissociation into nitrogen atoms.

Theoretical considerations of ammonia synthesis and decomposition during the past two decades have been dominated by the treatment proposed in 1940 by Temkin and Pyzhev.[26] By this time it was known that (i) the rate of ammonia formation was equal to the rate of nitrogen adsorption[28] and (ii) from work on the exchange of ammonia with deuterium (see Chapter 10) that neither the adsorption of hydrogen nor the desorption of ammonia was rate-determining. Temkin and Pyzhev, therefore, made the following reasonable assumptions.

1. The adsorption of nitrogen as atoms is rate-limiting, and nitrogen atoms are the principal nitrogen-containing species on the surface.
2. The adsorption of nitrogen is not influenced by the presence of either hydrogen or ammonia.
3. The activation energies for nitrogen adsorption and desorption (and hence the heat of adsorption) decline linearly with increasing coverage by atomic nitrogen, so that

$$r_a = k_a P_{N_2} \exp(-g\theta_N) \qquad (1)$$

and

$$r_d = k_d \exp(h\theta_N). \qquad (2)$$

In Chapter 5 it was seen that the adsorption isotherm giving this behaviour must be of the form:

$$\theta_N = f^{-1} \ln a_0 P_{N_2}, \qquad (3)$$

where f is equal to $g + h$; a_0, k_a and k_d are temperature-dependent constants. Thus, the rate of ammonia formation in the synthesis (r_s) must be given by the difference between the rates of nitrogen adsorption and desorption, viz.

$$r_s = k_a P_{N_2} \exp(-g\theta_N) - k_d \exp(h\theta_N). \tag{4}$$

Now to eliminate θ_N, it is necessary to define a new quantity $P^*_{N_2}$. Because the adsorption of nitrogen as atoms is postulated to be the slowest step in the synthesis, the adsorbed atoms are not in equilibrium with the pressure of gaseous nitrogen P_{N_2}, but rather with the nitrogen pressure which would exist in the gas phase if equilibrium were established between gaseous nitrogen and the instantaneous partial pressures of ammonia and hydrogen. This nitrogen pressure we term $P^*_{N_2}$. Thus:

$$\theta_N = f^{-1} \ln a_0 P^*_{N_2}, \tag{5}$$

and substitution of (5) into (4) gives

$$r_s = k_a P_{N_2}(a_0 P^*_{N_2})^{-\alpha} - k_d (a_0 P^*_{N_2})^{1-\alpha}, \tag{6}$$

where α is equal to g/f. If then $P^*_{N_2}$ is given by

$$P^*_{N_2} = K^{-1} \frac{P^2_{NH_3}}{P^3_{H_2}}, \tag{7}$$

where K is the constant for equilibrium (a), equation (6) becomes

$$r_s = k_1 P_{N_2} \left(\frac{P^3_{H_2}}{P^2_{NH_3}}\right)^{\alpha} - k_2 \left(\frac{P^2_{NH_3}}{P^3_{H_2}}\right)^{1-\alpha}, \tag{8}$$

where k_1 is $k_a\, a_0^{-\alpha}\, K_1$ and k_2 is $k_d\, a_0^{1-\alpha} K^{\alpha-1}$. When g is equal to h, α becomes 0.5 and so

$$r_s = k_1 \frac{P_{N_2} P^{1\cdot5}_{H_2}}{P_{NH_3}} - k_2 \frac{P_{NH_3}}{P^{1\cdot5}_{H_2}}. \tag{9}$$

The Temkin-Pyzhev treatment further enables the activation energy E for ammonia decomposition to be estimated[7, 26, 29] since

$$E = E_a + \alpha(-\Delta H_a) + (1 - \alpha)(-\Delta H), \tag{10}$$

where E_a and $-\Delta H_a$ are respectively the activation energy and the heat of adsorption of nitrogen at zero coverage, and $-\Delta H$ is the enthalpy change accompanying the synthesis.

The validity of the initial postulates and the subsequent steps is demonstrated if the rate constant k_1 for the synthesis (equation 8) can be shown to be independent of space velocity, the P_{H_2}/P_{N_2} ratio and of the total pressure, and to be unchanged if hydrogen is replaced by deuterium. The activation energy and the constant α should be similarly invariant, but it will be seen shortly that these criteria are not always met. It is, of course, necessary to ensure that the rate measurements are made under conditions where pore diffusion within the catalyst particles is not rate-limiting.

16.22 The Kinetics of Ammonia Decomposition and Synthesis on Metals other than Iron

The principal results for ammonia decomposition are given in Table II. The observed exponents of the hydrogen and ammonia pressures, respectively x and y, as defined by the expression

$$r = kP^{x}_{NH_3}\,P^{y}_{H_2} \tag{11}$$

are quoted, and when of interest the ratio $-y/x$. The effect of variation of nitrogen pressure, where investigated, is usually negligible, although occasionally[30, 31] it has been shown to exert a slight inhibiting effect. The column headed pressure (range) gives either the range of ammonia pressures, or of the sum of ammonia and hydrogen pressures, used, as appropriate. Values of the exponent y are usually determined through the effect on the initial rate of varying the pressure of added hydrogen, although sometimes the variation of rate with time in a static system seems to have been used. Where accurate values of the pressure range are not easily available, approximate mean values are given.

The order in ammonia over tungsten and molybdenum is always found to be zero by the method of initial rates: however, particularly at low ammonia pressures, the rate decreases rapidly with time, although the order in hydrogen is zero or only slightly negative (see Fig. 2). Moreover, the rate of decomposition shows a kinetic isotope effect,[32, 33] the rate for ammonia-d_3 being

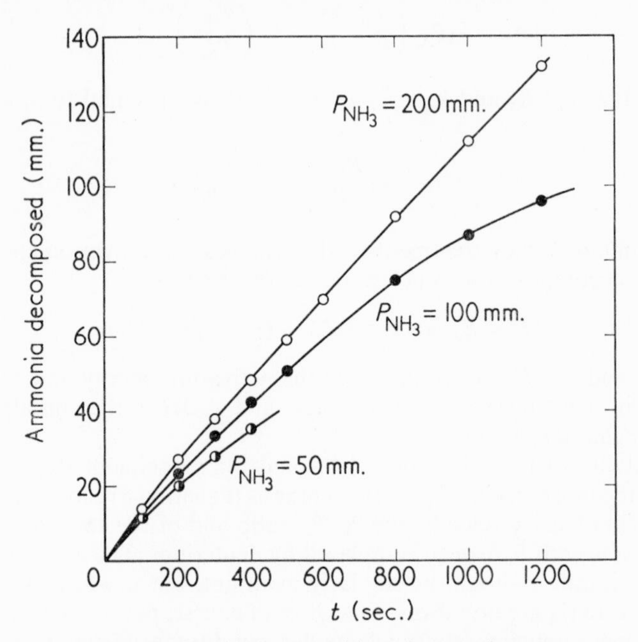

FIG. 2. Pressure-time curves for the decomposition of ammonia over a tungsten filament at 856°.[36]

TABLE II. *The Kinetics of Ammonia Decomposition on Metals other than Iron*

$$r = k\, P^{x}_{NH_3}\; P^{y}_{H_2}$$

Metal	Form	x	y	$-y/x$	Pressure (range), mm.	E(kcal. mole⁻¹)	log A*	Temp. range (°C)	Ref.
Mo	wire	0	—	—	—	53.2	—	824–955	37
Mo	wire	0	−0.5	—	~100	42.7	—	725–850	30
						31.8	—	850–1125	
Mo	powder	—	—	—	760	42.5	—	447–550	38
W	wire	0	0	—	50–200	38.7	—	631–941	36
W	wire	0	~−0.2	—	16–265	45.3	—	800–1000	30
						36.5	—	1000–1250	
W	wire	0	0	—	7	26.8	—	950–1150	39
					37	30.1	—		
W	wire	0†	—	—	150–350	35.0	—	630–750	32
W	wire	0	—	—	50–150	42.1	—	950–1180	40
W	wire	0	—	—	0.006–0.6	42.4	—	680–880	33
W	film	—	—	—	10–53	38	—	385–500	23
Re	powder	0.53	−0.89	1.68	—	32.2	—	380–440	41
Re	film	0.7	−1.4	2.00	10–53	49	27.3	455–570	23
Ru	on SiO_2	1.0	−1.75	1.75	—	59.2	—	552–736	42
Ru	on Al_2O_3	0.6	−0.91	1.52	600–800	30.5	—	340–400	43
Ru	film	1.2	−2.0	1.67	10–53	45	29.7	270–465	23
Os	powder	0	−1	—	50–300	47.6	—	290–370	31
Os	on SiO_2	1.0	−1.5	1.5	~760	~40	—	400–600	44

TABLE II (*continued*)

Metal	*Form*	*x*	*y*	$-y/x$	*Pressure (range), mm.*	*E(kal. mole*$^{-1}$*)*	*log A**	*Temp. range (°C)*	*Ref.*
Co	film	0.85	−1.42	1.67	10–53	45.0	27.4	370–480	23
Rh	on Al_2O_3	0.6	—	—	300–500	25.9–31.1‡	—	360–450	43
Rh	film	1.35	−2.45	1.82	10–53	57	30.7	420–500	23
Ni	film	0.96	−1.53	1.59	10–53	43	25.7	390–500	23
Pd	on Al_2O_3	—	—	—	300–400	27.8–32.1‡	—	510–570	43
Pt	wire	1	−1	—	100–200	140	—	933–1215	36
Pt	ribbon	1	−1	—	20–76	—	—	1050–1160	45
Pt	wire	1	−1	—	0.24–4	44	—	1100–1485	34
Pt	wire	1.4	−2.3	1.64	10–300	140	—	1100–1485	34
Pt	wire	1	0	—	~0.01	5.1	—	900–1357	35
Pt	wire	1.5	−2.2	1.47	~0.01	49.3	—	474–564	35
Pt	film	0.96	−1.63	1.70	10–53	59	27.4	520–610	23
Cu	powder	~1	~−1	—	~760	46.0	—	495–620	46

* *A* in mol. cm.$^{-2}$ sec.$^{-1}$; †, experiments with ND_3; ‡, activation energy increases with increasing P_{H_2}.

slower than that for ammonia-d_0. The interpretation must be that the desorption of nitrogen is not rate-limiting in these cases, but that the ammonia is fairly strongly adsorbed, and that the slow step is a dehydrogenation, probably of adsorbed imine radicals, which cover most of the surface. Of the activation energies quoted for these metals, nine out of thirteen fall within the limits 40 ± 5 kcal. mole^{-1}: higher and lower values probably result from errors in temperature measurement, particularly from failure to allow for cooling at the ends of heated wires, and the most accurate value is likely to be 42.4 kcal. mole^{-1} found in an investigation[33] where especial attention was paid to this problem.

Over platinum catalysts, the decomposition has sometimes been found to be first order in ammonia, and either zero or more usually minus first order in hydrogen (see Table II); this implies weak adsorption of ammonia and strong competitive adsorption of hydrogen. There is a tendency to pass over to Temkin–Pyzhev kinetics either as the pressure range is increased[34] or as the temperature is lowered.[35] The very high activation energies sometimes found[34, 36] suggest that the decomposition can proceed homogeneously if initiated by active species vacating the surface.

Other metals which have been studied usually show orders in ammonia and in hydrogen conforming to the Temkin–Pyzhev scheme, although the quotient $-y/x$ is often significantly greater than the theoretical 1.5 (see Table II). This has been attributed[23] to the effect of independently adsorbed hydrogen, which is not allowed for in their theory. Low activation energies ($\sim$30 kcal. mole^{-1}) accompany low ammonia orders ($\sim$0.6), the former increasing with the latter and also with the quotient $-y/x$ up to a value of about 60 kcal. mole^{-1}: this effect is predicted by the Temkin–Pyzhev theory,[7, 23] although sufficient information is not usually available for quantitative comparisons.

The activation energies and log$A$ terms given in Table II for ammonia decomposition over evaporated films of various metals show only an approximate compensation effect.[23] However, from these values we may compute relative activities at a typical temperature, and the figures (including one for iron) are given in Table III. The activity sequence conforms well with that derived from metals in other forms.

TABLE III. *Activities of Evaporated Metal Films for Ammonia Decomposition at 400°* [23] (k in molecules cm.$^{-2}$ sec.$^{-1}$).

Metal	Ru	Fe	Co	Ni	Rh	Re	Pt
log k	15.1	13.1	12.8	11.7	11.5	9.9	8.2

The kinetics of ammonia synthesis on metals other than iron appears only to have been studied rarely, chiefly by Temkin and Kiperman. With molybdenum,[38] tungsten[47] and ruthenium,[42] the synthesis between about 500 and 700° appears to conform to Temkin–Pyzhev kinetics. The situation with osmium[44] is, however, somewhat different: between 550 and 600°, normal kinetics were found, α having a value of 0.5 and the activation energy being 41.2 kcal. mole^{-1}; the efficiency was between 0.38 and 0.65. Between 400 and 450°, however, where the efficiency lay between 0.14 and 0.21, the value of α was zero, although the activation energy was practically unchanged. The change in orders occurring at about 500° suggests that θ_N is so small below this temperature that the exponential isotherm on which the Temkin–Pyzhev treatment is based is not valid.

16.23 The Kinetics of Ammonia Decomposition and Synthesis over Iron Catalysts

Here, experimental investigations of the synthesis far outnumber those of the decomposition: some of the kinetic results for the decomposition of ammonia on iron catalysts are given in Table IV. These results call for little comment. The Temkin–Pyzhev formulation appears generally to hold, while the activation energies show the usual spread. More interest attaches to the behaviour of singly promoted iron catalysts and to results found with iron films using reactant mixtures rich in ammonia. Both of these types of catalyst show three distinct activation energies, a low (or sometimes zero) value falling between two higher values (see Fig. 3). With singly promoted iron,[49] the precise values and indeed the temperatures at which the changes occur show variation with (i) the direction of temperature change, and (ii) the composition of the reaction mixture. In the low temperature region where a high activation energy is first observed (below about 410°), Temkin–Pyzhev kinetics have been found,[7] but in the region of low activation energy over both singly promoted iron and iron films, the signs of the pressure dependences are inverted. Thus,

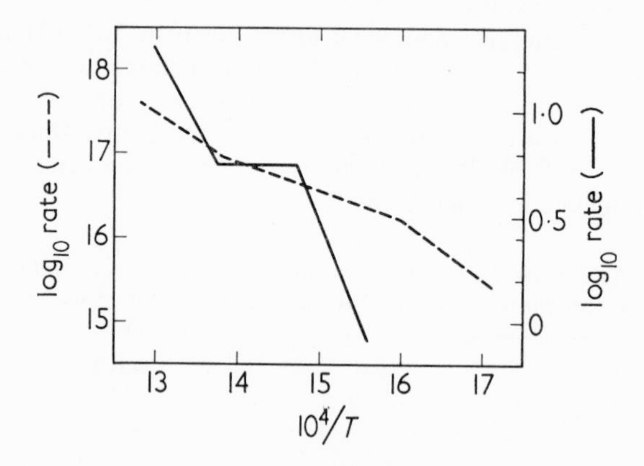

FIG. 3. Temperature dependence of the activation energy for ammonia decomposition over iron catalysts.
-------- Iron films: rate in molecules of N_2 formed per 10 mg. per minute.[22]
—— Singly promoted iron: rate in cm.^{3} ammonia (S.T.P.) decomposed per minute.[49]

TABLE IV. *Kinetics of Ammonia Decomposition on Iron Catalysts at Atmospheric Pressure or below*

Form	x	y	$-y/x$	*Pressure range (mm.)*	E*(kcal. mole*$^{-1}$*)*	$\log A$*	*Temp. range (°C)*	*Ref.*
Film	0.5	−0.7	1.4	10–53	38.8	25.8	355–470	22, 23
Gauze	0.8	−0.9	1.1	~760	—	—	—	48
On Al_2O_3	0.9	−1.5	1.7	~760	54.0	—	492–524	48
Doubly prom.	0.6	−0.85	1.4	?	45.6	—	335–430	49
Doubly prom.	—	—	—	—	59	—	400–450	7

* A in mol. cm.$^{-2}$ sec.$^{-1}$.

over the former catalyst at 420°, x is -0.9 and y is $+1.35$:[49] this, of course, implies a negative value of α. It has been suggested[7] that in the region of low activation energy nitriding of the surface takes place, with the activation energy resuming a high value when this process is finished. The inverted pressure dependences are reasonably explained on the basis of this model.[7, 22] The fact that doubly promoted iron does not show these phenomena clearly shows that the alkali plays an important role in reducing the avidity of the iron surface for nitrogen.

We return now to investigations of ammonia synthesis, which have been made, usually with doubly promoted iron, both at atmospheric and superatmospheric pressures. Obedience to the Temkin–Pyzhev scheme is established if the velocity constant derived from the appropriate[7] integration of equation (8) is independent of space velocity, efficiency and hydrogen : nitrogen ratio. It is, of course, necessary to consider only those measurements in which diffusional retardation is absent or corrected for. At atmospheric pressure, the velocity constant is sensibly constant if α is taken as 0.5,[26, 50] although sometimes[7, 51] better agreement is obtained if α is 0.6 or 0.67. Several thorough studies have been made at superatmospheric pressures.[7, 50, 52, 53] Between 33.3 and 100 atm.,[52] the velocity constant is independent of space velocity, but falls somewhat with increasing pressure and decreasing efficiency and is also somewhat dependent on nitrogen : hydrogen ratio; agreement is not improved if α is increased from 0.5 to 0.67. It has been suggested[7] that during these experiments the reactor was not behaving isothermally, for when care is taken to see that this is so,[50, 53] velocity constants are found which are independent of efficiency, and only slightly dependent on total pressure, although still a function of nitrogen : hydrogen ratio.

Some further information is available concerning the proper value of α. Experiments at 350° have shown[7] that for the synthesis the order in hydrogen is 2.0 (hydrogen pressure range, 9.4–22 atm.) and in ammonia -1.2 (ammonia pressure range, 0.2–1.1 atm.): this corresponds to a value of α of 0.67, in good agreement with that deduced from measurements made at atmospheric pressure. Nevertheless, the fact remains that rate constants become progressively less consistent as the value of α is raised above 0.5. Thus, although the Temkin–Pyzhev formulation provides a reasonably satisfying description of both ammonia synthesis and decomposition, it fails in matters of detail: the choice of the "best" value of α depends on the parameter for which agreement is sought, and the effect of variation of reactant ratio is not properly accommodated. Possible flaws in the basic assumptions will be further discussed below.

Further evidence concerning the parameter α comes from studies of the kinetics of nitrogen chemisorption on iron catalysts: reference has already been made to these studies in Section 6.23. It will be recalled that the nitrogen isotherm upon which the Temkin–Pyzhev treatment is based (equation 3) may be taken to imply a linear increase of activation energy for chemisorption, and decrease of activation energy for desorption, with increasing coverage, the slopes being respectively g and $-h$, so that α equals $g/(g + h)$. Such changes have indeed been found,[54–56] and have been briefly described in Chapter 6: unfortunately the measurements were made with singly and not doubly promoted iron catalysts, and hence the derived value of α ($\sim$0.75) is of doubtful relevance to the great majority of the studies of ammonia synthesis. However, it appears from much earlier work[29] that the kinetics of nitrogen chemisorption are similar on both kinds of technical iron catalysts, and from this work too α may be computed to be about 0.75. Thus, this kind of approach seems to offer some support for the higher values of α.

We must now briefly review the few studies of the exchange of molecular nitrogen on synthesis catalysts: the reaction is

$$^{28}(N_2) + {}^{30}(N_2) \rightleftharpoons 2\,{}^{29}(N_2). \qquad \text{(d)}$$

Historically, the occurrence of this reaction served to confirm the existence of chemisorbed nitrogen atoms on metals active in the synthesis, and its slowness that nitrogen adsorption was the probable slow step, but latterly this exchange has featured in attempts to determine the so-called "stoichiometric number" of the synthesis, and this matter will shortly be reverted to. On somewhat poorly reduced iron, both singly and doubly promoted, reaction (d) was not detected at 410°, where decomposition of ammonia was rapid: it was even only slow at 750°.[57] This exchange was yet slower over tungsten, but over both metals the rate was increased by the presence of hydrogen. Over osmium, however, the exchange rate is *inhibited* by hydrogen.[58] With more thoroughly reduced technical iron catalysts of both sorts, exchange has been detected at 500°, where its rate was found equal to the rate of nitrogen desorption.[59] The effect of degree of reduction, and especially the detrimental effect of traces of water in the hydrogen used for the purpose, has been confirmed by studies on rhenium powder,[41] although it remains uncertain whether the high activity of the more thoroughly reduced samples should not be properly ascribed to their higher hydrogen content.

Now the shortcomings of the Temkin–Pyzhev theory have caused it to be wondered whether or not the supposition that nitrogen adsorption is the slowest step in the synthesis is true. If, following Horiuti, we defined the *stoichiometric number* of the reaction as the number of times the slowest step occurs for every completion of the overall reaction, then this quantity γ will be unity if nitrogen chemisorption is the slow step, or two if anyone of the following steps is the slow step:

$$\underset{***}{N} + \underset{*}{H} \rightarrow \underset{**}{NH} + 2* \qquad \text{(e.i)}$$

$$\underset{**}{NH} + \underset{*}{H} \rightarrow \underset{*}{NH_2} + 2* \qquad \text{(e.ii)}$$

$$\underset{*}{NH_2} + \underset{*}{H} \rightarrow NH_3 + 2*\,. \qquad \text{(e.iii)}$$

The parameter γ may be determined by comparison of the rates of the exchange reaction

$$^{15}NH_3 + {}^{28}(N_2) \rightleftharpoons {}^{14}NH_3 + {}^{29}(N_2) \qquad \text{(f)}$$

and of the synthesis near equilibrium.[60, 61] The first attempts to do this[60] have been criticized,[61] on the grounds that (i) the two rates were measured on different samples of catalyst, and (ii) the exchange process (f) may not proceed via the same elementary steps as the synthesis. The first objection is overcome by the *simultaneous* measurement of the two rates, and the second by comparing the rates of the exchange reactions

$$^{30}(N_2) + {}^{14}NH_3 \rightleftharpoons {}^{29}(N_2) + {}^{15}NH_3 \qquad (g)$$

$$^{29}(N_2) + {}^{14}NH_3 \rightleftharpoons {}^{28}(N_2) + {}^{15}NH_3 \qquad (h)$$

$$^{30}(N_2) + {}^{28}(N_2) \rightleftharpoons 2\,{}^{29}(N_2) \qquad (d)$$

with the synthesis rate near equilibrium. The rates of process (f) and of the synthesis may be measured at the same time if labelled ammonia is introduced into a nitrogen–hydrogen stream, and the percentage of labelled ammonia after passage through the catalyst determined. The measurements of the rates of processes (g), (h), (d) and of the synthesis requires the use of two reactors in series and at different temperatures. Using a mixture of highly enriched nitrogen [37 per cent $^{30}(N_2)$] and hydrogen, together with some ammonia, the rates of exchange reactions (g) and (h), and the synthesis rate, were determined in the first reactor, whereafter, having removed ammonia, the rate of process (d) was measured in the second reactor, whose synthesis activity was separately determined.

The stoichiometric number is derived from these measurements in the following manner. The rate of synthesis near equilibrium is given by:

$$r_s = k_1 P_{N_2}^{a} P_{H_2}^{3a} - k_2 P_{NH_3}^{2a} \qquad (12)$$

where

$$\frac{k_1}{k_2} = \frac{{}_eP_{NH_3}^{2a}}{{}_eP_{N_2}^{a}\,{}_eP_{H_2}^{3a}} = K^a, \qquad (13)$$

the subscript e indicating equilibrium pressures. The stoichiometric number γ is the reciprocal of a. Then if Δ replaces $({}_eP_{NH_3} - P_{NH_3})$, the synthesis rate becomes

$$r_s = k_1\,{}_eP_{N_2}^{a}\,{}_eP_{H_2}^{3a}\,a\Delta \left\{\frac{1/2}{{}_eP_{N_2}} + \frac{9/2}{{}_eP_{N_3}} + \frac{2}{{}_eP_{NH_2}}\right\}. \qquad (14)$$

Since the term $k_1\,{}_eP_{N_2}^{a}\,{}_eP_{H_2}^{3a}$ gives the rate of synthesis at equilibrium, it is equal to $2n$ if n is the number of molecules reacting *in either direction* per unit time at equilibrium. Then

$$\frac{r_s}{\Delta} = k_s = an\left\{\frac{1}{{}_eP_{N_2}} + \frac{9}{{}_eP_{H_2}} + \frac{4}{{}_eP_{NH_3}}\right\}, \qquad (15)$$

where k_s is the synthesis rate constant. In an analogous manner, the rate constant for the exchange reactions (f), (g) and (h), k'_e, may be formulated as

$$k'_e = n'_e\left(\frac{2}{P_{NH_3}} + \frac{1}{P_{N_2}}\right) \tag{16}$$

and that for process (d) as

$$k''_e = n''_e P_{N_2}^{-1}, \tag{17}$$

where n'_e and n''_e are the numbers of nitrogen molecules entering into the respective exchange reactions per unit time. Thus a, and hence γ, may be directly evaluated by comparing k_s with k' or with k''_e, if n is taken to be equal to n'_e and n''_e.

The first measurements[60] of γ gave a value of about two, seeming to show that nitrogen adsorption is not the slow step, but these measurements have been criticized as noted above. More recent and careful work[61] leads to values of γ close to unity, obtained by using both kinds of exchange reaction, and using both singly and doubly promoted iron catalyst. There is, therefore, little reason to doubt that nitrogen adsorption is indeed the slowest step in the synthesis, and the deficiencies of the Temkin–Pyzhev theory must be sought elsewhere.

The next points then to investigate are whether the assumptions (i) that θ_N is not affected by hydrogen pressure, and (ii) that nitrogen atoms are the sole nitrogen-containing adsorbed species, are correct. This last assumption implies that the steps involved in hydrogenating nitrogen atoms are *very* rapid compared to the slow step: but if, for example, process (e) were not much faster than the slowest step, then θ_{NH} might be considerable.

There is now much evidence to show that neither of the foregoing assumptions is correct. It has long been known, as noted above, that the rate of exchange reaction (d) is increased by the presence of hydrogen, and it has recently been clearly shown that the rate of nitrogen chemisorption on doubly promoted iron is faster in the presence of hydrogen than in its absence.[62] Thus, the nitrogen coverage is dependent on the hydrogen pressure, and the failure of the Temkin–Pyzhev theory to account for the variation of velocity constants with variation in the nitrogen : hydrogen ratio may be traced to the incorrectness of assumption (i) above.

Now if the adsorption of nitrogen is the slow step in synthesis, the synthesis rate should be unchanged when deuterium is substituted for hydrogen. This experiment has recently been performed,[27] and indeed one wonders why it was not performed long since. Using two different kinds of doubly promoted iron, working at very low efficiencies, the kinetics of the synthesis have been studied with nitrogen : hydrogen and nitrogen : deuterium mixtures between 218 and 302°. The synthesis rate expressed as in equation (8) becomes at constant total pressure and low conversions

$$dy_a/dt = c_1 P^{\alpha}/y_A^{2\alpha}, \tag{18}$$

where y_A is the yield of ammonia and P the total pressure. Since the contact time is proportional to P/v, v being the flow rate,

$$dy_a/d(1/v) = c/y_A^{2\alpha}, \tag{19}$$

where

$$c = c_1 P^{\alpha+1}. \tag{20}$$

Thus, c_1 is proportional to k_1. In integrating equation (19) we obtain

$$y_A^{2\alpha+1} = (2\alpha + 1)\, c\, (1/v). \tag{21}$$

The validity of this expression appears when straight lines are found on plotting log y_A against log (P/v), from whose slopes values of α may be calculated. Selected values are: 0.8 with hydrogen at 302°; with deuterium, 0.7 at 302° and 0.4 at 218°. This variation of α with operating conditions has been remarked on earlier, and results from failure of the isotherm (3) to apply at low coverages: indeed α should tend to zero as the efficiency falls.[38, 44] More disturbing, however, is the fact that whereas the constant c in equation (19) should vary as $P^{1.8}$ at 302°, it is, in fact, simply proportional to P.

The concept of a heterogeneous surface is not, however, essential to the formulation of kinetics of the Temkin–Pyzhev kind. Expressing the rate of dissociative adsorption of nitrogen on a homogeneous surface as

$$r_a = k_a\, P_{N_2}(1 - \theta_N)^2, \tag{22}$$

where θ_N is determined by the equilibrium

$$\underset{***}{N} + 1.5H_2 \rightleftharpoons NH_3 \tag{i}$$

for which the equilibrium constant is K_i, it follows at once that

$$\theta_N = \frac{K_i P_{NH_3}/P_{H_2}^{1.5}}{1 + K_i P_{NH_3}/P_{H_2}^{1.5}}. \tag{23}$$

The rate of adsorption and of synthesis is then given by

$$r_s = r_a = \frac{k_a'' P_{N_2}}{(1 + K_i P_{NH_3}/P_{H_2}^{1.5})^2} \tag{24}$$

or

$$dy_a/d(1/v) = \frac{k_p}{(1 + qy_A)^2}. \tag{25}$$

The integrated form of this last equation is

$$(1 + qy_A)^3 - 1 = 3qk_p/v. \tag{26}$$

From these equations it is to be expected that k_p should be proportional to total pressure, and q inversely proportional to $P^{1/2}$. Equation (26) indeed represents the experimental results rather better than (21). Observed values of k_p are the same both for hydrogen and deuterium, and an activation energy of 20 kcal. mole^{-1} is derived; k_p is proportional to P as expected, and both k_p and q increase exponentially with temperature. The discrepancy is now that q is independent of P instead of varying as $P^{1/2}$.

It therefore becomes necessary to investigate whether a fuller treatment of the Temkin–Pyzhev method is helpful. The full form of the nitrogen isotherm is[29]

$$\theta_N = \frac{2}{f} \ln \left(\frac{1 + K_i P_{NH_3}/P_{H_2}^{1 \cdot 5}}{1 + \exp(-\frac{1}{2}f)K_i' P_{NH_3}/P_{H_2}^{1 \cdot 5}} \right), \tag{27}$$

where K_i' is the equilibrium constant of the equilibrium (i) at zero surface coverage and the other symbols have their usual significance. Now it is usually assumed that

$$K_i' P_{NH_3}/P_{H_2}^{1 \cdot 5} \gg 1 \gg \exp(-\tfrac{1}{2}f)K_i P_{NH_3}/P_{H_2}^{1 \cdot 5},$$

which when true permits equation (9) to be established: at low values of θ_N the first inequality is certainly not true, although the second may be. If, therefore, we write

$$\theta_N = \frac{2}{f} \ln [1 + K_i'' P_{NH_3}/P_{H_3}^{1 \cdot 5}], \tag{28}$$

the rate of synthesis should be

$$r_s = r_a = \frac{k_0 P_{N_2}}{(1 + K' P_{NH_3}/P_{H_2}^{1 \cdot 5})^{2\alpha}}, \tag{29}$$

where k_0 is the rate constant at zero coverage. At high efficiencies, this is equivalent to the first term in equation (8): when α is unity, equation (29) is the same as (24). It is striking that the most simple and most complex treatments can lead to the same equation.

Comparison of equations (25) and (29) shows that

$$q_H/q_D = K_{i,H}'/K_{i,D} \tag{30}$$

and this ratio may be calculated by statistical mechanics. Unfortunately it is far higher than the observed value, and too greatly dependent on temperature. The solution of all these difficulties is accomplished by a relatively small change in the basic assumptions of the theory. While retaining the postulate that nitrogen chemisorption is the slowest step, it is additionally supposed that the next step (process (e)) is also slow, so that *imine radicals are the chief adsorbed species*, their coverage being determined by the equilibrium

$$\underset{**}{NH} + H_2 \rightleftharpoons NH_3 \tag{j}$$

for which the constant is K_j. The rate equations corresponding to (8) (neglecting the second term at low conversions), (24) and (29) are readily derived and are

$$r_s = K_1' P_{N_2} \left(\frac{P_{H_2}^2}{P_{NH_3}^2} \right)^\alpha \tag{8a}$$

$$r_s = \frac{k''' P_{N_2}}{(1 + K_j P_{NH_3}/P_{H_2})^2} \tag{24a}$$

and

$$r_s = \frac{k_0' P_{N_2}}{(1 + K_j' P_{NH_3}/P_{H_2})^2} \ . \tag{29a}$$

Thus no change in the form of the kinetic analysis is demanded, but the constant c (equation 19) is now proportional to P instead of $P^{\alpha+1}$, and q is independent of P as found. The ratio q_H/q_D is now given by $K_{j,H}'/K_{j,D}'$, and may also be calculated by statistical mechanics: making reasonable assumptions concerning the partition functions of adsorbed imine radicals, the ratio is calculated to be 2.7 at 250° and 2.4 at 300°. The figures are in excellent agreement with the observed temperature-independent value of 2.7.

It has been suggested[27] that whether nitrogen atoms or imine radicals are the more populous surface species depends on the state of reduction of the catalyst. The catalysts used in the work described above are admitted by the authors to be not very thoroughly reduced, and they suggest the following schemes.

On thoroughly reduced Fe: $N_2 \longrightarrow \underset{*}{N}{=}\underset{*}{N} \longrightarrow 2\,\underset{***}{N}$.

On less thoroughly reduced Fe: $N_2 \longrightarrow \underset{*}{N}{=}\underset{*}{N} \xrightarrow{+H_2} \underset{*}{NH}{-}\underset{*}{NH} \longrightarrow 2\,\underset{**}{NH}$.

It has been claimed that equation (24) is a good description of the many results available for doubly promoted iron catalysts, while (24a) better describes results found with singly promoted iron. It would be of great interest to see the above work repeated using singly promoted iron, and very thoroughly reduced doubly promoted iron.

16.3 The Decomposition of Other Hydrides

16.31 The Decomposition of Phosphine

The decomposition of phosphine has been studied[63, 64] between 360 and 720° using filaments of molybdenum and tungsten as catalysts. The stoichiometric equation followed is:

$$4\,PH_3 \rightarrow P_4\,(\text{red}) + 6H_2, \tag{k}$$

although traces of white phosphorus have been detected in the products of the reaction over tungsten.[63] The kinetics generally suggest that phosphine is weakly chemisorbed at low pressures and strongly chemisorbed at higher pressures, since there is usually a transition from first to zero order with increasing pressure (see Table V). However, in one investigation[63] using tungsten, the order in phosphine was found to be first over an extensive range of pressure. Activation energies increase with pressure as expected (see Table V and Fig. 4). Neither tungsten nor molybdenum is attacked during reactions, but nickel rapidly disintegrates due to the formation of a phosphide.

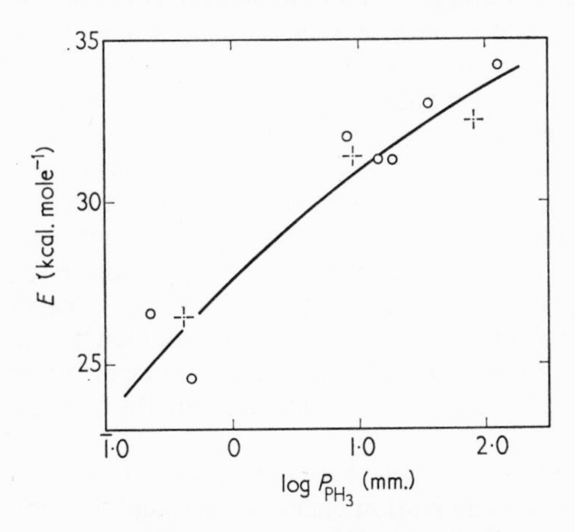

FIG. 4. The pressure dependence of the activation energy for the decomposition of phosphine over a tungsten filament:[33] ○, filament 9 cm. long; +, filament 31 cm. long.

TABLE V. *The Kinetics of the Decomposition of Phosphine over Tungsten and Molybdenum Filaments*[63, 64]

Temp. range (°C)	*Pressure* (*range*) (*mm.*)	*Order*	*E*(*kcal. mole*$^{-1}$)	*Ref.*
		Tungsten		
360–550	0.01–300	1	~25	63
610–720	0.001–0.01	1	26.5	64
610–720	0.2	$0 > x > 1$	32.0	64
610–720	1–5	0	31.3	64
		Molybdenum		
570–645	~0	1	15.1	63
570–645	0.06	$0 > x > 1$	20.8	63
570–645	0.2	0	22.3	63
420–497	~2	0	39.3	63

16.32 The Decomposition of Arsine, Stibine, Germane and Stannane

The decomposition of these hydrides in a glass vessel leads to the deposition of a film of the element upon which the hydride then decomposes catalytically. The mechanism of the catalytic process has been investigated,[65–69] as has also the chemisorptive properties of the films.[70, 71] The decomposition of the hydride of one element on a film of another element has been studied in less detail.

Stibine is the most readily decomposed of the three hydrides.[65] Between 10 and 45°, the rate is independent of hydrogen pressure, and is a function only of the stibine pressure: the order is unity at 45° and 0.75 at 10°. The activation energy is 8.8 kcal. $mole^{-1}$ at 400 mm. pressure, and decreases with decreasing pressure. Difficulty was experienced in obtaining a coherent film of arsenic, but this was overcome by depositing arsenic from the decomposition of arsine on an already-formed film of antimony. The rate of arsine decomposition is faster on antimony than on arsenic. Between 218° and 278° the rate (on arsenic) is proportional to arsine pressure and independent of hydrogen pressure: the activation energy is 23.2 kcal. $mole^{-1}$.

The decomposition of germane has been studied between 230 and 330°,[65, 66] and there is evidence for simultaneous homogeneous and heterogeneous decompositions. The former is first order in germane pressure and has an activation energy of 51.4 kcal. $mole^{-1}$; the latter is zero order in germane pressure and has an activation energy of 41.4 kcal. $mole^{-1}$. The decomposition of arsine is slower on germanium than on either arsenic or antimony, but the rate of germane decomposition is increased in the presence of a trace of arsine.

Stannane decomposes readily between 35 and 100° according to a first order rate law, with an activation energy of 9.1 kcal. $mole^{-1}$: hydrogen does not inhibit the decomposition, although a small pressure of oxygen does.[68] These observations have recently been confirmed,[69] but in addition it has been found that kinetic anomalies appear below −10°. These are shown to be due to the appearance of the grey modification of tin, which is a much poorer catalyst for stannane decomposition than white tin.

Useful information concerning the mechanisms and the nature of the rate-controlling steps comes from studying the separate and simultaneous decomposition of a hydride and a deuteride, and the decomposition of a hydride in the presence of deuterium. Similar results have been obtained with stibine, germane and stannane. (i) The rates of decomposition of the hydride and deuteride are approximately the same. (ii) No hydrogen deuteride is detected when a hydride is decomposed in the presence of deuterium. (iii) Much hydrogen deuteride is found in the products of the simultaneous decomposition of a hydride and a deuteride, but no partially deuterated hydrides are found. The following inferences can be made. (i) "Hydrogen" cannot chemisorb on either antimony or germanium surfaces, even at the highest temperatures used. (ii) "Hydrogen" is formed intermolecularly during the decomposition of a mixture of hydride and deuteride. (iii) Once a hydride molecule has been chemisorbed, it has no chance of returning to the gas phase.

On the basis of the kinetics and the foregoing observations, the rate-controlling step is assigned to be hydride chemisorption on a pair of bare sites for stibine at 45° and for arsine over the whole temperature range studied, e.g.

$$SbH_3 + 2* \rightarrow \underset{*}{SbH_2} + \underset{*}{H} \quad (1)$$

Hydrogen desorption is thought to be rate-controlling in germane decomposition because the rate of hydrogen desorption is twice the rate of decomposition.[68] It is also thought to be tending to be rate-limiting in the decomposition of stibine at 10°.

The mechanism can now be formulated, and this is done below for germane.

```
                                                       H   H
                                                       |   |
                                                    H—Ge—Ge—H
   /  H   H  \            / GeH3 H  \                  |   |    H    H
  |   |   |   |  -2H2    |   |   |   |    -H2          |   |    |    |
 2|  —Ge—Ge—  | ------> 2|  —Ge—Ge—  |  ------>      —Ge—Ge—Ge—Ge—
   \  |   |  /  +2GeH4    \  |   |  /                  |   |    |    |
```

```
    /    H   H                \                      H    H    H    H
   |     |   |                 |                     |    |    |    |
   |  H—Ge—Ge—H                |                  H—Ge—Ge—Ge—Ge—H
 2 |     |   |   H    H        |  -H2     H    H     |    |    |    |    H    H
   |     |   |   |    |        | ----->   |    |     |    |    |    |    |    |
   |   —Ge—Ge—Ge—Ge—           |         —Ge—Ge—Ge—Ge—Ge—Ge—Ge—Ge—
    \    |   |   |    |       /           |    |     |    |    |    |    |    |
```

REFERENCES

1. A. Nielsen, *Adv. Catalysis* **5,** 1 (1955).
2. W. G. Frankenburg, In "Catalysis", edited by P. H. Emmett (Reinhold, New York, 1955), **3,** 171.
3. A. Mittasch, *Adv. Catalysis* **2,** 82 (1950).
4. F. Haber, *Z. angew. Chem.* **27,** 473 (1914).
5. W. Nernst, W. Jost and G. Jellinek, *Z. Elektrochem.* **13,** 521 (1907); **14,** 373 (1908).
6. A. T. Larson and R. L. Dodge, *J. Amer. Chem. Soc.* **45,** 2918 (1924); **46,** 367 (1924).
7. C. Bokhoven, C. van Heerden, R. Westrik and P. Zwietering, In "Catalysis", edited by P. H. Emmett (Reinhold, New York, 1955), **3,** 265.
8. R. J. Kokes and P. H. Emmett, *J. Amer. Chem. Soc.* **80,** 2082 (1958).
9. R. J. Kokes and P. H. Emmett, *J. Amer. Chem. Soc.* **82,** 1037 (1960).
10. R. J. Kokes, *J. Amer. Chem. Soc.* **82,** 3018 (1960).
11. P. W. Selwood, *J. Amer. Chem. Soc.* **80,** 4198 (1958).
12. J. A. Becker and C. D. Hartman, *J. Phys. Chem.* **57,** 153 (1953).
13. J. A. Becker, *Adv. Catalysis* **7,** 159 (1955).
14. B. M. W. Trapnell, *Trans. Faraday Soc.* **48,** 160 (1952).
15. G. Ehrlich, *J. Chem. Phys.* **23,** 1543 (1955); **24,** 482 (1956); *J. Phys. Chem.* **60,** 1388 (1956).
16. G. Ehrlich and T. W. Hickmott, *J. Chem. Phys.* **26,** 219 (1957).
17. G. Ehrlich and F. G. Hudda, *J. Chem. Phys.* **32,** 942 (1960).
18. P. Kisluik, *J. Chem. Phys.* **30,** 174 (1959); **31,** 1605 (1959).
19. J. Eisinger, *J. Chem. Phys.* **28,** 165 (1958).
20. P. L. Jones and B. A. Pethica, *Proc. Roy. Soc.* **A256,** 454 (1960).
21. O. Beeck, *Adv. Catalysis* **2,** 151 (1950).
22. S. R. Logan, R. L. Moss and C. Kemball, *Trans. Faraday Soc.* **54,** 922 (1958).
23. S. R. Logan and C. Kemball, *Trans. Faraday Soc.* **56,** 144 (1960).
24. C. R. Lotz and F. Sebba, *Trans. Faraday Soc.* **53,** 1246 (1957).

25. K. J. Laidler, In "Catalysis", edited by P. H. Emmett (Reinhold, New York, 1954), **1**, 119.
26. M. I. Temkin and V. Pyzchev, *Acta Physicochim. U.S.S.R.* **12**, 327 (1940).
27. A. Ozaki, H. S. Taylor and M. Boudart, *Proc. Roy. Soc.* **A258**, 47 (1960).
28. P. H. Emmett and S. Brunauer, *J. Amer. Chem. Soc.* **56**, 35 (1934); see also Refs. 55 and 62.
29. S. Brunauer, K. S. Love and R. G. Keenan, *J. Amer. Chem. Soc.* **64**, 751 (1942).
30. C. H. Kunsman, *J. Amer. Chem. Soc.* **50**, 2100 (1928); C. H. Kunsman, E. S. Lamar and W. L. Deming, *Phil. Mag.* (ser. 7) **10**, 1015 (1930).
31. E. A. Arnold and R. E. Burk, *J. Amer. Chem. Soc.* **54**, 23 (1932).
32. H. S. Taylor and J. C. Jungers, *J. Amer. Chem. Soc.* **57**, 679 (1935).
33. R. M. Barrer, *Trans. Faraday Soc.* **32**, 490 (1936).
34. G.-M. Schwab and H. Schmidt, *Z. phys. Chem. (Leipzig)* **3B**, 337 (1929); *Z. Elektrochem.* **35**, 605 (1929).
35. L. O. Apel'baum and M. I. Temkin, *Zhur. fiz. Khim.* **33**, 2697 (1959).
36. C. N. Hinshelwood and R. E. Burk, *J. Chem. Soc.* **127**, 1105 (1925).
37. R. E. Burk, *Proc. Nat. Acad. Sci. U.S.A.* **13**, 67 (1927).
38. S. Kiperman and M. I. Temkin, *Acta Physicochim. U.S.S.R.* **21**, 267 (1946).
39. H. R. Hailes, *Trans. Faraday Soc.* **27**, 601 (1931).
40. I. Motscham, I. Perevesenov and S. Z. Roginskii, *Acta Physicochim. U.S.S.R.* **2**, 203 (1935).
41. J. P. McGeer and H. S. Taylor, *J. Amer. Chem. Soc.* **73**, 2743 (1951).
42. S. Kiperman, *Zhur. fiz. Khim.* **21**, 1435 (1947).
43. A. Amano and H. S. Taylor, *J. Amer. Chem. Soc.* **76**, 4201 (1954).
44. S. Kiperman and V. Granovskaya, *Zhur. fiz. Khim.* **25**, 557 (1951).
45. G.-M. Schwab, *Z. phys. Chem. (Leipzig)* **128**, 161 (1928).
46. J. K. Dixon, *J. Amer. Chem. Soc.* **53**, 1763 (1931).
47. S. Kiperman and M. I. Temkin, *Zhur. fiz. Khim.* **20**, 369 (1946).
48. E. Winter, *Z. phys. Chem. (Leipzig)* **13B**, 401 (1931).
49. K. S. Love and P. H. Emmett, *J. Amer. Chem. Soc.* **63**, 3297 (1941); **64**, 745 (1942).
50. A. Nielsen, thesis: summarized in ref. 7.
51. R. Brill, *J. Chem. Phys.* **19**, 1047 (1951).
52. P. H. Emmett and J. T. Kummer, *Ind. Eng. Chem.* **35**, 677 (1943).
53. I. P. Sidorov and V. D. Livshits, *Zhur. fiz. Khim.* **21**, 1177 (1947).
54. J. J. F. Scholten, P. Zwietering, J. A. Konvalinka and J. H. de Boer, *Trans. Faraday Soc.* **55**, 2166 (1959).
55. P. Zwietering and J. J. Roukens, *Trans. Faraday Soc.* **50**, 178 (1954).
56. J. J. F. Scholten and P. Zwietering, *Trans. Faraday Soc.* **53**, 1363 (1957).
57. G. G. Joris and H. S. Taylor, *J. Chem. Phys.* **7**, 893 (1939).
58. W. R. F. Guyer, G. G. Joris and H. S. Taylor, *J. Chem. Phys.* **9**, 287 (1941).
59. J. T. Kummer and P. H. Emmett, *J. Chem. Phys.* **19**, 289 (1951).
60. S. Enomoto and J. Horiuti, *J. Res. Inst. Catalysis, Hokkaido Univ.* **2**, 87 (1953); S. Enomoto, J. Horiuti and H. Hobayashi, *Ibid.* **3**, 185 (1955).
61. C. Bokhoven, M. J. Dorgelo and P. Mars, *Trans. Faraday Soc.* **55**, 315 (1959).
62. K. Tamaru, Proc. 2nd International Congress on Catalysis (Editions Technip, Paris, 1961), **1**, 325.
63. H. W. Melville and H. L. Roxburgh, *J. Chem. Soc.* 586 (1933).
64. R. M. Barrer, *Trans. Faraday Soc.* **32**, 490 (1936).
65. H. S. Taylor, *Canad. J. Chem.* **33**, 838 (1955).
66. K. Tamaru, M. J. Boudart and H. S. Taylor, *J. Phys. Chem.* **59**, 807 (1955).
67. P. J. Fensham, K. Tamaru, M. J. Boudart and H. S. Taylor, *J. Phys. Chem.* **59**, 806 (1955).
68. K. Tamaru, *J. Phys. Chem.* **60**, 610 (1956).
69. S. F. A. Kettle, *J. Chem. Soc.* 2569 (1961).
70. K. Tamaru and M. J. Boudart, *Adv. Catalysis* **9**, 699 (1957).
71. K. Tamaru, *J. Phys. Chem.* **61**, 647 (1957).

Chapter 17

Catalytic Hydrogenolysis

17.1 Introduction

The last few Chapters have been devoted to those reactions in which hydrogen is added across multiple bonds. We now consider reactions in which hydrogen interacts with single bonds according to the general formulation

$$AB + H_2 \longrightarrow AH + BH.$$

This process is described as hydrogenolysis, since it is "splitting by hydrogen." Although A is commonly carbon, and B either carbon, nitrogen oxygen or a halogen, the same term may be applied (as in Section 17.5) to the case where AB is, for example, chlorine or bromine. The reaction of hydrogen with oxygen could be regarded as the hydrogenolysis of oxygen, but is arbitrarily considered as the oxidation of hydrogen and hence is discussed in Chapter 20.

17.2 The Hydrogenolysis of Carbon–Carbon Bonds

There are several stages in the interaction of saturated hydrocarbons with metal surfaces. The initial process, both in the absence and presence of hydrogen, is undoubtedly the loss of hydrogen atoms, with the formation of radicals which may be held to the surface by multipoint adsorption.[1] Some aspects of this stage (which is the only one possible at moderate temperatures) were considered in Chapter 9. At temperatures higher than those required to effect this stage, and in particular in the presence of hydrogen, fission of carbon–carbon bonds takes place and lower molecular-weight hydrocarbons are formed. In the absence of hydrogen, hydrogen is released to the gas phase, and in the case of those metals which have the propensity, carbide formation occurs. In this Section we consider only the former case, that is, the hydrogenolysis of saturated hydrocarbons.

The catalytic hydrogenolysis of ethane has been studied over iron,[2] cobalt[3] and nickel[4, 5] catalysts, and over nickel films.[6] The reaction with propane has also been studied on nickel–kieselguhr[7] and on films of nickel, tungsten and platinum.[6] The hydrogenolysis of neopentane and neohexane has been examined using films of these metals, together with rhodium.[6] The principal kinetic features are summarized in Table I. In agreement with their

TABLE I. *The Kinetics of the Hydrogenolysis of Ethane and Propane over Metal Catalysts*

$$r \propto P_{\mathrm{hc}}^{x} P_{\mathrm{H_2}}^{y}$$

Hydro-carbon	*Metal*	*Promoter*	*x*	*y*	*Temp.* (°C)	*f*	*y*(*calc.*)	*E*(*kcal. mole*$^{-1}$)	*Temp. range* (°C)	*Ref.*
Ethane	Fe	—	1.0	−0.7	200	2	−1.0	25.6	178–222	2
Ethane	Fe	0.05% K_2O	0.9	−0.7	204	2	−0.8	25.2	177–220	2
Ethane	Fe	0.6% Li_2O	0.8	−0.4	220	2	−0.6	21.0	201–259	2
Ethane	Fe	0.6% K_2O	0.7	+0.3	250	4	+0.3	19.3	249–284	2
Ethane	Co	Cu + ThO_2	—	~−0.7	255	—	—	30	255–280	3
Ethane	Co	(on MgO)	—	~−1.3	255	—	—	~32	184–255	3
Ethane	Ni†	—	—	−2.5*	180	—	—	~43	172–184	4
Ethane	Ni†	—	0.7	−1.2*	182	0	−1.1	52	182–214	5
Propane	Ni†	—	0.9	−2.6	150	0	−2.6	34	138–172	7

* See text. † Supported on kieselguhr.

relative reactivities in exchange, the hydrogenolysis of propane occurs over nickel at significantly lower temperatures than does that of ethane,[4, 6, 7] presumably because of the lower activation energy. The activity sequence for the reaction with propane over metal films is W > Ni > Pt.

In the hydrogenolysis of ethane over nickel–kieselguhr, a hydrogen order of −1.2 is found at 182° and 214° provided hydrogen: ethane ratios greater than respectively one and two are used. If these values are not exceeded, an order of −2 or −2.5 is observed.[4, 5] Adsorbed ethylene is shown to be an intermediate in the hydrogenolysis, since ethylene reacts faster than ethane.[5] Cobalt–magnesia is some seven times more active than a cobalt Fischer–Tropsch catalyst (cobalt–copper–thoria–kieselguhr), probably because the metal is more highly dispersed in the former.[3]

Iron catalysts show varied activities and kinetics depending on their alkali contents.[2] Thus iron catalysts containing no alkali, or a little K_2O, or a larger amount of Li_2O, are active at about 200° and show positive orders in ethane and negative orders in hydrogen. However, the material containing 0.6 per cent K_2O is less active (> 250° required), and shows a *positive* order in hydrogen (see Table I). The interpretation of these results proceeds along the following lines.

Ethane on or after adsorption loses hydrogen atoms according to the process:

$$C_2H_6 \rightleftharpoons (C_2H_f)_a + \frac{6-f}{2} H_2. \tag{a}$$

The quantity f is likely to be either four, two or zero. Hydrogenolysis of the adsorbed species then takes place:

$$(C_2H_f)_a + H_2 \longrightarrow (CH_p)_a + (CH_q)_a, \tag{b}$$

and is followed by the rapid hydrogenation of the single-carbon species to gaseous methane. Now on equating the rates of the opposing processes in the equilibrium (a), we obtain

$$\alpha_1 P_{C_2H_6}(1-\theta_r) = \alpha_2 P_{H_2}{}^{[(6-f)/2]}\theta_r \tag{1}$$

and

$$\theta_r = \frac{\alpha[P_{C_2H_6}/P_{H_2}{}^{[(6-f)/2]}]}{1 + x[P_{C_2H_6}/P_{H_2}{}^{[(6-f)/2]}]}, \tag{2}$$

where θ_r is the fraction of surface covered by the adsorbed C_2H_f radicals and α is α_1/α_2. Within a restricted range of pressure, expression (2) can be written as

$$\theta_r = \alpha^x[P_{C_2H_6}/P_{H_2}{}^{[(6-f)/2]}]^x, \tag{3}$$

where x lies between zero and unity. Then if (b) is the slow step,

$$r \propto \theta_r P_{H_2} \tag{4}$$

$$\propto P^x_{C_2H_6} P_{H_2}{}^{\{1-x[(6-f)/2]\}}. \tag{5}$$

The hydrogen exponent expected can thus be calculated for any value of the ethane exponent n and the hydrogen content f of the adsorbed radical. The results are shown in Table I, and it appears that for ethane hydrogenolysis agreement between the observed and calculated hydrogen orders is obtained if f is zero over nickel, two over iron containing 0.6 per cent K_2O and four over iron containing less alkali. A similar treatment for propane gives

$$r \propto P^{x}_{C_3H_8} P_{H_2}^{\{1-x[(8-f)/2]\}} \tag{6}$$

and this leads to a calculated hydrogen order of -2.6, as found, for a propane order of 0.9.

The results throw some light on the mode of action of alkali added to iron catalysts for Fisher–Tropsch synthesis. Its action is not in promoting the formation of carbon–carbon bonds, but rather in maintaining the adsorbed intermediates in the fully saturated state required for further chain growth. The well-known failure of lithia to promote chain growth is due to the intermediate radicals becoming unsaturated ($f = 2$).

The hydrogenolysis of neopentane and neohexane has recently been examined[6] with a view to assessing the importance of 1,2-diadsorbed radicals as intermediates: such radicals could be formed from neohexane but not, of course, from neopentane. Over nickel, tungsten and rhodium films, neohexane is indeed the more reactive molecule, although over platinum films the reactivity difference is slight. Measurable rates were obtained with neohexane over rhodium films at only 105°. The nature of the products was found to vary significantly from one metal to another. Thus in the case of neohexane, the tendency for fission to occur adjacent to the quaternary carbon atom to yield ethane and isobutane was most marked over platinum, and decreased in the order: Pt $>$ W $\gg$ Ni $>$ Rh. Over rhodium the main products were methane and neopentane.

On the basis of these results and those presented in Table I it is possible to set down an approximate activity sequence for the hydrogenolysis of saturated hydrocarbons:

$$\text{Rh} > \text{W} > \text{Ni} > \text{Fe} > \text{Pt} > \text{Co}.$$

17.3 The Hydrogenolysis of Carbon-Nitrogen Bonds

Studies have been made on the hydrogenolysis of methylamine[8] and of ethylamine[9] over evaporated films of a number of metals, and of cyclohexylamine over platinum films[10] and nickel.[11] The products formed from methylamine are methane, ammonia and di- and trimethylamine, but especially over iron and tungsten films methane formation is small due to loss of carbon to the catalyst and consequent formation of metal carbide. With this exception, the processes of product formation and of reactant removal are kinetically similar over all the metals studied, and for this reason the breaking of the carbon–nitrogen bond is thought to be the common rate-determining step. With ethylamine, however, carbide formation does not occur, and ethane is generally the main hydrocarbon product. Here the rate of ammonia formation over platinum films at 123° is independent of ethylamine pressure, but the ratio of the rate of diethylamine formation to that of ethane varies as the square of the ethylamine pressure. Under these conditions the rate of hydrogenolysis is also proportional to the −0.7th power of the hydrogen pressure (−0.5 for methylamine), and hydrogen variation has no effect on the product distribution.

There appear to be two basic reactions:

$$C_2H_5NH_2 + H_2 \longrightarrow C_2H_6 + NH_3 \qquad (c)$$

and

$$2C_2H_5NH_2 \longrightarrow (C_2H_5)_2NH + NH_3. \qquad (d)$$

While the first of these is favoured over platinum (except at low temperatures and high ethylamine pressures), the second predominates over palladium, nickel and gold films. Rhodium and tungsten films catalyse both processes simultaneously, although over tungsten methyl cyanide is also an important product. Traces of methane are formed over platinum and nickel, and triethylamine is also formed especially over metals favouring process (d):

$$C_2H_5NH_2 + (C_2H_5)_2NH \longrightarrow (C_2H_5)_3N + NH_3. \qquad (e)$$

The Arrhenius parameters for reactant removal and for the formation of the several products (apart from methane) are closely similar, and mean values are quoted in Table II, together with the values derived from the rate of disappearance of methylamine. Arrhenius parameters for methane formation

TABLE II. *Arrhenius Parameters for the Hydrogenolysis of Amines over Evaporated Metal Films*[8,9]

Metal	*Temp. range (°C)*	*E(kcal. mole^{-1})*	*log A**	*log r at 200°**
		Methylamine		
W	220–280	17.0	18.3	10.4
Fe	144–204	23.1	23.3	12.6
Ni	158–226	16.9	20.2	12.4
Pd	158–226	21.5	22.8	12.8
Pt	165–236	19.9	21.8	12.6
		Ethylamine		
W	147–163	19.8	20.3	11.1
Ni	78–118	11.3	18.3	13.1
Pd	134–170	24.6	25.0	13.6
Pt	110–152	23.2	25.7	15.0
Rh	124–155	14.1	21.0	14.5
Au	199–241	10.4	17.4	12.6

* A and r in mol. cm.$^{-2}$ sec.$^{-1}$, except for Au where apparent rather than true surface areas are used.

from ethylamine are: Pt; $E = 19.9$ kcal. mole^{-1}, $\log A = 22$: Rh, $E = 13$ kcal. mole^{-1}, $\log A = 22$ (A in mol. cm.$^{-2}$ sec.$^{-1}$).

The Table shows that tungsten has a low activity in both reactions, due to a low frequency factor: in methylamine hydrogenolysis, the other metals have comparable activities, although there is a much greater spread in their activities for ethylamine hydrogenolysis. Platinum is the most active, and (significantly) gold is more active than tungsten.

The results suggested that the adsorbed amines substantially cover the surface, and the orders in hydrogen suggest that the molecules in the adsorbed state have lost one or two hydrogen atoms. Thus it is possible to write for ethylamine

$$\underset{\text{A}}{\underset{*}{C_2H_5NH}} \rightleftharpoons \underset{\text{B}}{CH_3\text{—}\underset{*}{CH}\text{—}\underset{*}{NH} + \underset{*}{H}} \rightleftharpoons \underset{\text{C}}{CH_3\text{—}\underset{*}{C}\text{=}\underset{*}{N} + 3\underset{*}{H}}. \qquad \text{(f)}$$

State A is believed to be the species which can react with a further ethylamine molecule to form diethylamine, while state B is likely to be the species in which fission to form ammonia occurs. Now because state A only occupies one site, its concentration will increase with increasing ethylamine pressure, and hence the probability of forming diethylamine also increases. At the same time, of course, the concentration of adsorbed hydrogen atoms will decrease and hence the chance of forming ethane will also decrease. This adequately interprets the results found with platinum. State C will be favoured by metals (such as tungsten) which have a high heat of adsorption of hydrogen: this adequately interprets the formation of methyl cyanide over this metal, and may also serve to explain the low frequency factor which this metal shows for hydrogenolysis.

In the hydrogenolysis of cyclohexylamine over platinum films between 100 and 150°, the principal hydrocarbon product is rather surprisingly benzene and not cyclohexane, although the latter is formed in small amounts in the early stages.[10] Subsequently, when some 70 per cent of the cyclohexylamine has reacted, the benzene starts to be converted to cyclohexane, the reaction becoming progressively more rapid as the cyclohexylamine pressure falls. Activation energies are: for cyclohexylamine removal, 17.5 kcal. mole^{-1}; for benzene production, 18.2 kcal. mole^{-1} (both similar to the values for methylamine and ethylamine hydrogenolysis over this metal); and for cyclohexane production 8.6 kcal. mole^{-1}. It is thought that, before decomposing, some of the adsorbed cyclohexylamine loses six hydrogen atoms from the ring, forming perhaps the species $C_6H_5\underset{*}{N}H$. Hydrogenolysis then leads to ammonia and benzene, and separate experiments showed that the presence of cyclohexylamine gravely inhibits the hydrogenation of benzene. Furthermore, the vapour-phase reaction of hydrogen with aniline at 100° also leads to benzene and ammonia, but not cyclohexylamine, and the similarity between the rates of reaction of aniline and of cyclohexylamine suggests the existence of common intermediates such as $C_6H_5\underset{*}{N}H$.

The dehydrogenation of cyclohexylamine over nickel in the liquid phase between 130 and 160° results in the formation of ammonia as well as hydrogen, but the products are dicyclohexylamine and phenylcyclohexylamine rather than benzene or cyclohexane:[11] the activation energy is 22 kcal. mole^{-1}. The dehydrogenation of aniline also leads to secondary amines under these conditions. The difference between these results and those obtained in the vapour phase over films is probably due to the differing concentrations of adsorbed hydrogen. It is likely to be lower in the liquid-phase system, and hence there the recombination of adsorbed species will be favoured over their hydrogenation. Cyclohexylamine is more strongly adsorbed than benzene over nickel, as over platinum films.

17.4 The Hydrogenolysis of Carbon–Halogen Bonds

It is possible with this system to obtain interesting results by observing the effect on the rate of varying in turn the nature of the alkyl group and of the halogen atom. Methyl, ethyl and vinyl chlorides have been reduced over palladium–charcoal at 248°, the first being the most difficult to reduce.[12] Isopropyl chloride is reduced slowly over platinum–pumice at 100°, but four times more rapidly than n-propyl chloride:[13] activation energies, measured between 130 and 170°, are respectively 24 and 14 kcal. mole^{-1}.[14] Similarly, isopropyl fluoride is quantitatively reduced over palladium–charcoal at 155°, while n-propyl fluoride requires temperatures greater than 190°.[12] The observed[12] heats of hydrogenolysis are recorded in Table III. These results

Table III. *Heats of Hydrogenolysis of Alkyl Halides*[12]

Reaction	$-\Delta H$*(kcal. mole*$^{-1}$*)*	*Temp. (°C)*
$CH_3Cl + H_2 \rightarrow CH_4 + HCl$	19.32	25
$C_2H_5Cl + H_2 \rightarrow C_2H_6 + HCl$	16.56	25
$C_2H_3Cl + 2H_2 \rightarrow C_2H_6 + HCl$	51.19	25
iso-$C_3H_7F + H_2 \rightarrow C_3H_8 + HF$	22.88	248
n-$C_3H_7F + H_2 \rightarrow C_3H_8 + HF$	21.11	248

Whence taking the heat of hydrogenation of ethylene at 25° to be −32.80 kcal. mole^{-1},

$$C_2H_3Cl + H_2 \rightarrow C_2H_4 + HCl + 8.39 \text{ kcal. mole}^{-1}.$$

are in qualitative agreement with the known reactivity of alkyl halides in other reactions, such as hydrolysis; they may be summarized as a reactivity sequence:

$$\text{iso–}C_3H_7X > \text{n–}C_3H_7X > C_2H_5X > CH_3X \quad (X = F \text{ or } Cl).$$

Methyl and ethyl fluorides are not quantitatively reduced over palladium–charcoal at 240°.[12] Ethyl chloride and ethyl bromide react with hydrogen over platinum and palladium films at 100° at about the same rate, although over nickel films at 250° the latter reacts much more slowly[15] (see Table IV). This establishes the halogen reactivity order as

$$Cl \geqslant Br > F;$$

no work appears to have been done on the hydrogenolysis of alkyl iodides. It might be expected that reactivities would be determined by the strengths of the carbon–halogen bonds, but information on their dissociation energies is not very extensive. However, it appears that D_{C-Cl} is about the same in both methyl and ethyl chlorides ($\sim$80 kcal. mole^{-1}),[16] although D_{C-F} in methyl fluoride is $\sim$108 kcal. mole^{-1}, which adequately explains the lower reactivity of the alkyl fluorides.

Arrhenius parameters for the hydrogenolysis of ethyl chloride and bromide over some metal films have been measured (Table IV). Nickel is less active than either palladium or platinum, and the activation energies for the reaction with ethyl bromide are particularly widely scattered. The reaction

TABLE IV. *Arrhenius Parameters for the Hydrogenolysis of Ethyl Chloride and Ethyl Bromide over Metal Films*[15] (log r calculated for 100°)

Metal	*Ethyl chloride*				*Ethyl bromide*			
	Temp. range (°C)	*E**	*log A†*	*log r†*	*Temp. range (°C)*	*E**	*log A†*	*log r†*
Ni	184–343	13	20.8	13.2	227–300	26	24.2	8.9
Pd	99–179	16	24.3	14.9	99–195	7	18.8	14.7
Pt	100–206	12	22.9	15.9	105–190	6	19.0	15.5

* E in kcal. mole^{-1}; † A and r in mol. cm.$^{-2}$ sec.$^{-1}$.

with ethyl chloride over palladium is first order in ethyl chloride at 120° and about −0.3 in hydrogen at 145°. Hydrogen chloride inhibits the reaction in proportion to its concentration. Rhodium and tungsten films were found to be so strongly poisoned by hydrogen halides that accurate rate measurements were impossible.

The deuterated ethanes resulting from the reactions of ethyl chloride and of ethyl bromide with deuterium over metal films have been analysed,[15] with results which are shown in Table V. A number of generalizations emerge. (i) There are several cases in which ethane-d_2 is the predominant product (EtCl over Rh and Pd; EtBr over Rh and Pt). (ii) A certain amount of multiple exchange often occurs, and with ethyl chloride even with those metals which do not normally encourage it (Fe and Ni), but the amount occurring with ethyl bromide is often markedly less than that occurring with ethyl chloride (compare EtCl and EtBr over Fe, Ni, Pd, Pt). (iii) Only in the case of rhodium is the ethane distribution very similar with the two halides. (iv) Tungsten shows its familiar reluctance to catalyse multiple exchange. (v) There is often a subsidiary maximum in the distribution of ethane-d_4. There is no indication that ethyl halides undergo exchange under these conditions.

TABLE V. *Analysis of Deuterated Ethanes formed in the Reaction of Ethyl Halides with Deuterium over Metal Films*[15]

Metal	*T* (°C)	Percentage composition						*M*
		d_1	d_2	d_3	d_4	d_5	d_6	
				Ethyl chloride				
W	195	45	41	4	6	3	1	1.8
Fe	181	60	10	1	3	4	22	2.5
Ni	179	57	19	7	3	3	11	2.1
Rh	226	0	61	1	9	7	22	3.3
Pd	146	1	60	3	8	6	22	3.2
Pt	142	35	33	7	5	5	15	2.6
				Ethyl bromide				
W	214	60	22	7	6	3	2	1.8
Fe	241	94	6	0	0	0	0	1.06
Ni	268	89	11	0	0	0	0	1.1
Rh	225	0	58	4	14	7	17	3.2
Pd	170	29	42	9	9	4	7	2.4
Pt	170	21	61	6	10	1	1	2.1

The reaction of the isomeric propyl chlorides with deuterium over palladium–pumice has been used to demonstrate the rapid interconversion of n- and isopropyl radicals on the catalyst surface.[13] The distributions of deuteropropanes so obtained are compared with those which result from the reaction of deuterium with propane and with cyclopropane in Table VI. The two propyl chlorides gave closely similar distributions, and the parameters of best fit (defined in Chapter 10 and 11) also agree closely. Comparison with propane and cyclopropane shows a rather closer agreement with the latter, although the value of δ_A is almost identical for all four molecules. These

TABLE VI. *Initial Distributions of Deuteropropanes from the Reactions of Deuterium with Propyl Chlorides, Propane and Cyclopropane over Palladium–Pumice*[13]

Molecule	*Temp.* (°C)	Percentage composition									ΣA	δ_A	ΣB	ΣC
		d_0	d_1	d_2	d_3	d_4	d_5	d_6	d_7	d_8				
Isopropyl chloride	100	0.7	4.8	5.8	3.8	3.7	3.1	4.8	18.3	55.0	76	96.0	15	9
n-Propyl chloride	100	4.2	4.2	3.2	3.2	5.3	2.6	4.2	15.2	57.9	74	96.9	17	9
Propane	100	—	6.3	9.6	6.4	7.4	5.3	7.9	12.7	44.4	58	96.8	25	17
Cyclo-propane	125	—	0.6	4.1	3.0	4.0	2.9	3.6	17.1	64.7	83.5	96.8	14	—

results are taken to mean that n- and isopropyl chlorides probably form n- and isopropyl radicals in the first instance: for example

$$CH_3—CH_2—CH_2—Cl + \underset{*}{D} \longrightarrow CH_3—CH_2—\underset{*}{CH_2} + DCl. \quad (g)$$

These are then rapidly interconverted, and hence give rise to deuteropropane distributions which are similar to each other and to those given by the propyl radicals formed from propane and cyclopropane (see Chapters 10 and 11). These distributions are much different from those shown in Table V.

Interesting results have been obtained from a thermochemical study of the reaction of hydrogen with fluoro-olefins.[12] These are hydrogenated readily over palladium–charcoal at about 100°. C_2F_3Cl is simultaneously hydrogenolysed to $C_2F_3H_3$ and HCl, while $F_2C = CCl_2$ suffers hydrogenolysis more readily than hydrogenation. Thus at 120° with an insufficiency of hydrogen the products are $F_2C = CHCl$ (82 per cent) and $F_2C = CH_2$ (18 per cent), no $C_2F_2H_4$ being detected. Carbon–chlorine bonds are, therefore, more readily broken than carbon–fluorine bonds, in agreement with the work described above, but furthermore the presence of the double bond greatly activates carbon–chlorine bonds. A thorough kinetic study of the reaction of hydrogen with a variety of alkyl and alkenyl halides would be of great interest. Heats of hydrogenation of fluoro-olefins are given in Table VII.

TABLE VII. *Heats of Hydrogenation of Fluoro-olefins*[12]

Reaction	$-\Delta H$*(kcal. mole*$^{-1}$*)*	*Temp. (°C)*
$F_2C{=}CCl_2 + 3H_2 \longrightarrow C_2F_2H_4 + 2HCl$	83.33	128
$F_2C{=}CFCl + 2H_2 \longrightarrow C_2F_3H_3 + HCl$	64.91	128
$F_2C{=}CHCl + 2H_2 \longrightarrow C_2F_2H_4 + HCl$	61.77	128

It is sometimes very useful in preparative organic chemistry to be able to reduce an acid halide to an aldehyde:

$$RCOX + H_2 \longrightarrow RCHO + HX \quad (h)$$

This is the Rosenmund reaction, and is effected by a supported palladium catalyst partially poisoned by a sulphur compound. This poisoning is necessary to prevent the reduction of the keto-group. No study has apparently been made of the kinetics and mechanism of this reduction, which represents a further example of a system where selective behaviour can be induced by partial poisoning.

17.5 OTHER HYDROGENOLYSES

The catalytic hydrogenolysis of carbon–oxygen bonds occurs only with difficulty over metallic catalysts. Alcohols generally decompose, even in the presence of excess hydrogen, by loss of hydrogen: thus over evaporated films of several metals methanol decomposes to carbon monoxide at about 170°, although over rhodium some C_3 and C_4 hydrocarbons are formed, and some methane over iron.[17] 2-Propanol is, however, slowly reduced to propane over platinized platinum foil between 0 and 80°.[18] Some reference has already been made to carbon–oxygen bond fission in discussing the hydrogenation of phenols and aromatic ethers (see Chapter 13), and the hydrogenation of ketones (see Chapter 14).

Halogen–halogen bonds undergo hydrogenolysis in the presence of palladium–charcoal or palladium–asbestos catalysts.[12] This has enabled the heat of formation of hydrogen chloride and of hydrogen bromide to be determined calorimetrically, and the results are:

$$-\Delta H_f\ (\text{HCl}, 248°) = 22.3\ \text{kcal. mole}^{-1};$$

$$-\Delta H_f\ (\text{HBr}, 103°) = 12.5\ \text{kcal. mole}^{-1}$$

Bromine is apparently hydrogenolysed more easily than chlorine, but no kinetic measurements appear to have been made.

References

1. A. K. Galwey and C. Kemball, *Trans. Faraday Soc.* **55** (1959); Proc. 2nd International Congress on Catalysis (Editions Technip, Paris, 1961), **1**, 1063.
2. A. Cimino, M. Boudart and H. S. Taylor, *J. Phys. Chem.* **58**, 796 (1954).
3. E. H. Taylor and H. S. Taylor, *J. Amer. Chem. Soc.* **61**, 503 (1939).
4. K. Morikawa, W. S. Benedict and H. S. Taylor, *J. Amer. Chem. Soc.* **58**, 1795 (1936).
5. C. Kemball and H. S. Taylor, *J. Amer. Chem. Soc.* **70**, 345 (1948).
6. J. R. Anderson and B. G. Baker, *Nature* **187**, 937 (1960).
7. K. Morikawa, N. R. Trenner and H. S. Taylor, *J. Amer. Chem. Soc.* **59**, 1103 (1937).
8. C. Kemball and R. L. Moss, *Proc. Roy. Soc.* **A238**, 107 (1956).
9. C Kemball and R L. Moss, *Proc. Roy. Soc.* **A244**, 398 (1958).
10. C. Kemball and R. L. Moss, *Trans. Faraday Soc.* **56**, 154 (1960).
11. G. Debus and J. C. Jungers, *Bull. Soc. chim. belges* **62**, 172 (1953).
12. J. R. Lacher, A. Kianpour, F. Oetting and J. D. Park, *Trans. Faraday Soc.* **52**, 1500 (1956).
13. J. Addy and G. C. Bond, *Trans. Faraday Soc.* **53**, 377 (1957).
14. G. C. Bond and J. F. Rowbottom, unpublished work.
15. J. S. Campbell and C. Kemball, *Trans. Faraday Soc.* **57**, 809 (1961).
16. T. L. Cottrell, *The Strengths of Chemical Bonds* (Butterworths, London, 1954).
17. J. R. Anderson and C. Kemball, *Trans. Faraday Soc.* **51**, 966 (1955).
18. A. Farkas and L. Farkas, *J. Amer. Chem. Soc.* **61**, 1336 (1939).

Chapter 18

Catalytic Dehydrogenation

18.1 The Catalytic Dehydrogenation of Hydrocarbons

The dehydrogenation of hydrocarbons is a matter of considerable industrial importance.[1] Quantities of low molecular weight paraffins are produced in the cracking of natural oil, and their conversion to the potentially more useful olefins or diolefins is obviously attractive. The dehydrogenation of six-membered alicyclic compounds, either occurring naturally or formed by isomerization or dehydrocyclization, to the corresponding benzene derivatives will result in a product of higher octane rating. Much attention has also been given to the conversion of ethyl benzene to styrene.

Some discussion of the thermodynamics of these processes has already been given (see Chapters 11 and 13), and the situation may be summarized as follows. Elevated temperatures are required for the conversion of paraffins to mono-olefins: temperatures for 50 per cent conversion at a total pressure of 1 atm. are, for ethane, 725°; for propane, n-butane and higher unbranched paraffins, 600°; and for isobutane, 540°.[1] The corresponding temperature for the conversion of 1-butene to butadiene is 660°, and for ethylbenzene to styrene, 620°. Because the reaction is accompanied by an increase in the number of molecules present higher yields are obtained at reduced pressures, and the above temperatures required to give 50 per cent conversion are lowered by about 100° if the total pressure is 0.1 atm. rather than atmospheric. Even so, the temperatures are such that, if a metallic catalyst is employed, very considerable cracking to carbon, with consequent loss of activity, will rapidly occur. Commercial dehydrogenation processes without exception, therefore, use oxide catalysts instead, particularly those containing chromia; cracking is less marked on oxides than on metals, and they are readily regenerated by oxidation.

The position with regard to the formation of aromatic compounds by dehydrogenation is, however, substantially different. As we saw in Chapter 13, significant yields of aromatic compounds can be attained at temperatures of about 250°, under which conditions metal catalysts operate efficiently and undesirable side reactions are minimal. The face-centred cubic and the close-packed hexagonal metals of Group VIII are all satisfactorily active for these processes, but the activity of copper is low.[2]

Few kinetic measurements on the dehydrogenation of cyclohexane and its derivatives have been reported. Cyclohexane and its methyl- and 1,3-dimethyl-derivatives are all dehydrogenated over nickel–alumina at the same rate and with the same activation energy (15.6 kcal. $mole^{-1}$).[3] Cyclohexane dehydrogenation over platinum on silica–alumina shows an activation energy of 18.4 kcal. $mole^{-1}$ (156 to 280°),[4] and the reaction with methylcyclohexane shows zero-order kinetics and activation energies of respectively 18.2 and 33 kcal. $mole^{-1}$ over platinized asbestos[3] and platinum–alumina.[5] The dehydrogenation of cyclohexane and some of its derivatives has also recently been studied using charcoal-supported rhenium.[6] The activation energies (in kcal. $mole^{-1}$, measured between about 250 and 350°) and pre-exponential factors [in $cm.^3$ H_2 ($cm.^3$ catalyst)$^{-1}$ $min.^{-1}$] reported are as follows: cyclohexane, E, 7.8; A, 1.7×10^4: methylcyclohexane; E, 10.3; A, 8.7×10^3: ethylcyclohexane; E, 12.6; A, 3.5×10^5. Reactivity decreases with increasing molecular weight.

As with the hydrogenation of aromatic compounds, there has been much discussion of the applicability of the "sextet" aspect of Balandin's Multiplet Hypothesis.[7] Since according to the Principle of Microscopic Reversibility both the hydrogenation of benzene and the dehydrogenation of cyclohexane must proceed through the same elementary steps, the "sextet" theory must be equally applicable or inapplicable to both. Balandin has himself recently reviewed the situation,[3, 8] and now admits the relevance of electronic as well as geometric factors. He adduces the following pieces of evidence in support of his views. (i) Over carbon-supported rhenium, the disproportionation of cyclohexene is sometimes slower than the dehydrogenation of cyclohexane;[8] this does not, however, necessarily mean that the latter process must occur by *simultaneous* loss of six hydrogen atoms, since *adsorbed* cyclohexene might be an intermediate and yet not be detected in the vapour phase. (ii) With a series of platinum–carbon catalysts of varying degrees of dispersion, the activity for cyclohexane dehydrogenation parallels the intensity of X-ray reflexions from the (111) faces, but not those from other faces.[9] (iii) The exposed (111) planes of nickel films have been shown by electron diffraction to be active in benzene dehydrogenation, but not the (110) planes.[10]

Some caution is, however, necessary in interpreting these last observations. Although it may well be true that lattice planes containing atoms in hexagonal arrays show superior activity in benzene hydrogenation and in cyclohexane dehydrogenation, this does not establish the details of the mechanism; it is perfectly possible for such planes, by reason of their favourable geometry, or related electronic properties, to show a high activity in a mechanism involving the stepwise destruction or formation of the aromatic system. The ability of palladium to dehydrogenate decahydroazulene (bicyclo[5,3,0]octane)[11] speaks strongly against the "sextet" theory.

Our assessment of the situation must be (as stated in Chapter 13) that the "sextet" postulate of the Multiplet Hypothesis may be a necessary condition, but it is not a sufficient one. Furthermore, the detailed mechanism does not automatically follow the establishment of the most active crystal face.

Over copper supported on magnesia or alumina, cyclohexene is dehydrogenated much more rapidly than cyclohexane.[2] This has been attributed to the activation of the α-methylene groups by the double bond, although it is also possible that cyclohexene is more rapidly adsorbed and that the adsorption of cyclohexane is the slow step in its dehydrogenation over copper. Cyclohexene also disproportionates over these catalysts, but above 280° this is slower than dehydrogenation.

Mention must finally be made of the use to which hydrogen transfer has been put in preparative organic chemistry.[12] The substance to be reduced is dissolved in cyclohexane, and the catalyst (preferably palladium black or palladium-on-charcoal) added: on treatment at the appropriate temperature and pressure, hydrogen transfer from the solvent occurs, with its consequent oxidation to benzene. A variety of organic substances may be readily (and sometimes selectively) reduced in this manner, and the method is particularly suited to the reduction of nitro-compounds. No molecular hydrogen is, of course required, and so agitation of the system is not essential. Hydrazine has also been used as a source of hydrogen in similar reductions.

18.2 The Catalytic Dehydrogenation of Alcohols

As noted in Chapter 1, the predominant process occurring when alcohols decompose on metallic catalysts is usually dehydrogenation. Primary alcohols thus yield aldehydes, although methanol commonly decomposes to carbon monoxide and hydrogen: secondary alcohols of course yield ketones. The only exceptions to these generalizations are the decomposition of ethanol and higher alcohols on metals which are efficient for the Fischer–Tropsch synthesis. As seen in Chapter 15, they may initiate, or be incorporated in, the synthesis, and may also decompose to give products resembling those formed in the synthesis.[13] The dehydrogenation of alcohols is an endothermic process, and hence the position of equilibrium is progressively shifted to the aldehyde or ketone side as the temperature is raised.

These reactions have been quite widely used as a yardstick for estimating the importance of the electronic factor in catalysis.[14–17] Although activation energies are usually quoted, it is unfortunate that measurements of rates and of pre-exponential factors are often ignored, and hence the results are not as meaningful as they might be. Orders of reaction are reported only infrequently. The dehydrogenation of ethanol and 1-butanol[18] on copper supported on silica–alumina is zero order at 230°, while methanol decomposition[19] over a cobalt Fischer–Tropsch catalyst at 180° conforms to the rate expression:

$$r = \frac{kP_{\mathrm{MeOH}}}{1 + bP_{\mathrm{CO}}}. \tag{1}$$

Classical studies of the dehydrogenation of alcohols were carried out by Palmer and Constable[18, 20] using copper supported on fireclay (largely silica–alumina). The activation energy for ethanol decomposition was shown to be a function of the temperature at which the oxide was reduced to the metal, and the first example of a compensation effect was thereby discovered. Reference has been made in Chapter 7 to Constable's interpretation of this, and his treatment remains acceptable after almost 35 years. Activation energies E_i for the decomposition of several alcohols were determined within the limits of 200 and 280°, and the corresponding value for ethanol E_E was also determined for each sample of catalyst used. Values of E_E lay between 18.6 and 23.0 kcal. mole^{-1}. Table I gives the observed values of E_i, $E_i - E_E$ and log (A_i/A_E), the A's being the corresponding pre-exponential factors. These results show that 1-propanol, 1- and 2-butanol, and allyl alcohol all react at the same rate over the temperature range studied: with the others, there is compensation between $E_i - E_E$ and log (A_i/A_E).

TABLE I. *Arrhenius Parameters for the Dehydrogenation of Alcohols over Copper supported on Silica–Alumina: Temperature Range, 200 to 280°* [18, 20]

For ethanol: $k_E = A_E \exp(-E_E/RT)$.
For any other alcohol: $k_i = A_i \exp(-E_i/RT)$.

Alcohol	E_i*(kcal. mole*$^{-1}$*)*	$E_i - E_E$*(kcal. mole*$^{-1}$*)*	*log*(A_i/A_E)
1-Propanol	22.5	0	0
2-Propanol	26.7	3.9	2.4
1-Butanol	23.0	0	0
2-Butanol	21.2	0	0
2-Pentanol	19.7	0.8	0.4
Cyclohexanol	27.3	6.0	2.4
Allyl alcohol	18.6	0	0

With Raney nickel as catalyst, a number of secondary alcohols decompose in the liquid phase with the same activation energy ($\sim$17.6 kcal. mole^{-1}), the reactivity sequence being: 2-propanol > 2-butanol > 2-pentanol > 4-methyl-2-pentanol > 2-hexanol > 2-octanol.[21] Both on this catalyst and on Raney copper, each ketone is some ten to twenty times more strongly adsorbed than the alcohol from which it derives, and from the dependence on temperature of the ratio of the adsorption coefficients, the difference between their heats of adsorption was estimated to be 8.5 kcal. mole^{-1}.

Activation energies for the dehydrogenation of several alcohols over alumina-supported metals have been reported,[14, 16] and the results are shown in Table II. With the primary alcohols the activation energy shown by each metal decreases with increasing molecular weight; 2-butanol always shows

TABLE II. *Activation Energies (in kcal mole⁻¹) for the Dehydrogenation of Alcohols over Alumina-supported Metals*[14, 16]

	Fe	*Co*	*Ni*	*Cu*	*Ag*	*Au*
Methanol	22.1	17.6	21.2	14.1	30.8	—
Ethanol	17.0	13.4	15.3	9.8	22.8	20.6
2-Propanol	15.8	9.9	12.2	6.4	13.7	—
1-Butanol	16.1	12.0	13.7	8.7	17.1	—
2-Butanol	14.8	9.7	12.6	7.2	14.7	—

slightly lower values than 1-butanol, but the values for 2-propanol and 2-butanol are closely similar. For each alcohol, copper always shows the lowest activation energy and either iron or silver the highest. The sequence of activation energies is the same for each alcohol; thus, for example, the value shown by silver is always about twice the value given by copper. Only in the case of ethanol decomposition on copper, silver and gold are rate measurements available: here the activity sequence at 230° is Cu > Au > Ag, and a compensation effect operates. In the absence of more comprehensive rate measurements, further discussion of these results is scarcely profitable.

Activation energies for ethanol decomposition over alumina-supported nickel–copper, nickel–silver and copper–silver alloys (?) have also been reported,[14, 16] and are shown graphically in Fig. 1: each system is characterized

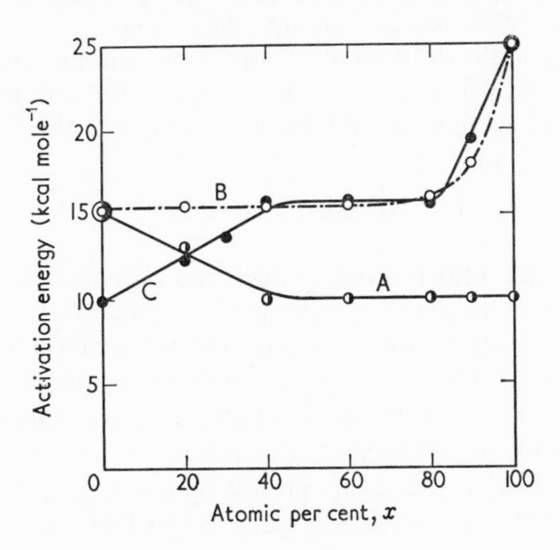

FIG. 1. Activation energies for ethanol dehydrogenation over alumina-supported alloys
A. Nickel–copper alloys (—◑—) : x = Cu.[16]
B. Nickel–silver alloys (-·-○-·-) : x = Ag.[16]
C. Copper-silver alloys (—●—) : x = Ag.[14]

by a range of composition where the activation energy is invariant. The activity of nickel–copper foils for methanol decomposition at 250° has been shown to decrease somewhat irregularly with increasing copper content.[15]

Little useful can be said about the reaction mechanisms. By analogy with the supposed mechanism for formic acid decomposition (q.v.), it has been stated[16] that the two hydrogen atoms are removed simultaneously from the alcohol to the catalyst, viz.

$$R\text{—}CH_2OH + 2* \rightarrow RCHO + 2\underset{*}{H} \rightarrow RCHO + H_2 + 2*, \qquad \text{(a)}$$

and the observed activation energies have been discussed in terms of the presumed transition state. However, in view of our knowledge concerning the exchange of alcohols with deuterium (Chapter 10), it is equally if not more likely that structures such as $R\text{—}\underset{*}{C}HOH$ and $R\text{—}CH_2\underset{*}{O}$ are intermediates in dehydrogenation.

18.3 The Decomposition of Formic Acid

18.31 Introduction, and the Nature of the Adsorbed State

The metal-catalysed decomposition of formic acid has been the subject of very many experimental investigations. In most of these, the purpose has not been directly to establish the mechanism, but rather to study the activity and kinetic parameters of the catalyst. However, as has recently become clear, it is potentially dangerous to use a reaction for this purpose until at least the principle features of its mechanism are understood.

As a test reaction the decomposition of formic acid has much to commend it. It can be examined with quite simple apparatus and the products are simple and easily analysed; with metallic catalysts, the decomposition is predominantly:

$$HCOOH \rightarrow H_2 + CO_2. \qquad \text{(b)}$$

Furthermore formic acid is strongly adsorbed on many metals, so that the observed activation energy does not require correction for the unknown heat of adsorption. We may summarize the information which studies of this reaction should yield by posing the following questions.

(i) *Stoichiometry*: what are the products of the decomposition, and what in particular are the *primary* products?

(ii) *Mechanism*: what species are present on the surface during the decomposition, and what are the mechanisms by which the observed products are formed?

(iii) *Electronic effects*: how do the rates and kinetic parameters for the decomposition depend on the electronic structure of the metal or alloy employed, and are the observed variations compatible with the proposed mechanisms?

Until recently it was widely believed that the decomposition proceeded according to the following simple mechanism:

$$HCOOH + 2* \rightarrow CO_2 + 2\underset{*}{H} \rightarrow CO_2 + H_2 + 2*. \qquad (c)$$

The slow step was presumed to be the simultaneous abstraction of the two hydrogen atoms from a physically adsorbed, or weakly chemisorbed, formic acid molecule, and the transition state

```
O=C····O
  :    :
  H    H
  :    :
  *    *
```

was invoked.[16, 22] However, it is now abundantly clear that the mechanism is more complex than this, and that adsorbed species other than hydrogen atoms are present on the surface during the decomposition. We may now, therefore, turn to an examination of the evidence which bears on this problem.

Three experimental methods have been applied: of these, the study of chemisorbed formic acid by infra-red spectroscopy is clearly the most important and is discussed fully below, but useful supplementary information comes from volumetric measurements[23] and from measurements of the changes of resistance of evaporated films following the adsorption.[24–27]

Infra-red studies have been made of formic acid chemisorbed on silica-supported nickel, palladium, platinum, rhodium, copper, silver, gold and zinc.[28–34] The various groups of workers are unanimous that it is possible to observe on nickel a strong adsorption band at 1570–1600 $cm.^{-1}$ and a weaker band at 1350–1380 $cm.^{-1}$. The species giving rise to these bands is generally described as the formate ion, $HCOO^-$, since bands at similar wavelengths are found in the infra-red spectra of metal formates.[28] The existence of the formate ion was first proposed[24–26] on the basis of measurements of the change in the resistance of hydrogen-covered nickel films following the adsorption of formic acid at 200°. The ion is presumably thought to be held by electrostatic attraction to a Ni^+ ion in the surface, so that chemisorption of formic acid according to this mechanism should be written:

$$HCOOH + 2* \rightarrow \underset{*+}{HCOO^-} + \underset{*}{H}. \qquad (d)$$

However, the concept of electron transfer *from* the catalyst *to* the adsorbate is so much at variance with the conclusions drawn from much of the earlier work that the arguments must be closely questioned. This may be done under two headings. (i) The main feature of the "free" formate ion is the equivalence of the two oxygen atoms, each of which bears on average one-half an electronic charge. Now the bare minimum of information which can be inferred from the similarity of the spectra of the adsorbed species and the "free" ion is that the former also has a symmetrical structure, but at least one group of workers[28] hesitates to specifiy the degree of ionicity in the oxygen–metal bonds. There is certainly no direct evidence to show that each adsorbed species carries a full electronic charge. (ii) Secondly, we may justly question whether the formation of adsorbed formate ion is the rate-controlling step in the decomposition, and indeed whether it is truly an intermediate.[35]

Eischens and Pliskin[34] have expressed themselves strongly on these last points. They have obtained a spectrum of formic acid on nickel–silica at $-60°$ which shows marked dissimilarities from those reported by other workers, and in particular they have detected a *strong* band at 1360 $cm.^{-1}$ and *weak* bands at 1540 and 2940 $cm.^{-1}$. While admitting that part of the 1360 $cm.^{-1}$ band could be attributed to the ionic species, the authors believe that the spectrum is essentially that of covalently chemisorbed formic acid. However, other workers[35] have also observed a band near 2940 $cm.^{-1}$ but have attributed it to gaseous or physically adsorbed formic acid. Eischens and Pliskin demonstrate[34] that the spectrum observed by other workers is shown by formic acid adsorbed on a slightly *oxidized* nickel surface, and in addition note a further band at 1700 $cm.^{-1}$: this band has also been detected by others,[29] but there is disagreement as to its assignment. They believe that in the region of room temperature, when more than a monolayer of formic acid is present, the decomposition products are capable of oxidizing the nickel surface, and in this way account for the generally observed "ionic" spectrum.

On warming from $-60°$ to $25°$, the bands attributed to covalently chemisorbed formic acid weaken and are replaced by strong bands characteristic of the linear and bridged structures of carbon monoxide.[34] This, however, does not establish that carbon monoxide is a primary product of the decomposition, since a mixture of carbon dioxide and hydrogen also leads to carbon monoxide bands. Measurements of the change of resistance of nickel films at $-193°$ following the adsorption of formic acid do seem to show that carbon monoxide is a primary decomposition product under these conditions,[36] which are, of course, far removed from those usually employed: the results may, however, be otherwise interpreted.[23] There is good evidence[34, 37, 38] that at temperatures of about 200° and above the decomposition products keep the nickel surface in a reduced rather than oxidized state. Under these conditions the formate layer is unstable, and during the decomposition the surface is substantially covered by adsorbed carbon monoxide, with only traces of formate ion and covalently adsorbed formic acid.

There are a few other facts concerning the adsorption of formic acid on nickel–silica which are worth noting. When formic acid is admitted to a hydrogen-covered nickel surface, hydrogen is released into the gas phase:[32, 33, 38]

$$\underset{*}{H} + HCOOH \rightarrow \underset{*+}{HCOO^-} + H_2. \qquad \text{(e)}$$

When formic acid is progressively added to a bare nickel surface, it is first adsorbed dissociatively, and subsequently the hydrogen atoms recombine and molecular hydrogen appears:

$$\underset{*+}{HCOO^-} + H + HCOOH \rightarrow 2\left(\underset{*+}{HCOO^-}\right) + H_2 \qquad \text{(f)}$$

Much more acid must be added before carbon dioxide appears in the gas phase, and between 20 and 100° a state is reached where there are two formate ions per surface nickel atom (or ion):[23, 32, 33]

$$2\left(\underset{*+}{HCOO^-}\right) + 2HCOOH \rightarrow 2\underset{*2+}{(HCOO^-)_2} + H_2 \qquad \text{(g)}$$

This state of affairs is only permissible if the surface nickel ions are substantially displaced from their normal lattice sites. The initial heat of adsorption of formic acid on a bare nickel surface[33] is 44 kcal. mole^{-1}.

We may now fruitfully try to discuss possible structures for the adsorbed state of formic acid on nickel. Valuable help comes from studying the infra-red spectra of deuterated formic acids.[34] The dideutero-acid on nickel–silica at −60° shows strong bands at 1325 cm.$^{-1}$ and 2190 cm.$^{-1}$, and a weak band at 1540 cm.$^{-1}$. However, perhaps the most striking facts are that HCOOD shows the same spectrum as HCOOH, and DCOOH the same as DCOOD. This points to the loss of the acidic hydrogen in the formation of the chemisorbed state, which is thus formulated as a resonance hydrid (a) of the two canonical forms (b) and (c):

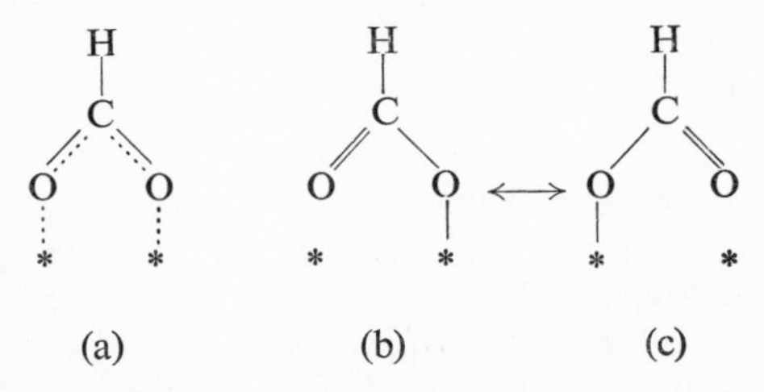

No *precise* formulation of the adsorbed ionic species has been given. It appears to be associated with adsorbed oxygen atoms or ions,[34] and to have a symmetrical structure, perhaps similar to that of structure (a) above. It is worth remembering that the covalent nickel–oxygen bond will of necessity be highly polarized, and hence the oxygen atoms in (a) will carry fractional negative charges. Indeed the distinction between (*a*) and the fully-ionized species may be quite a subtle one, only detectable by infra-red spectroscopy.

It is evident that there remains substantial disagreement concerning the normal adsorbed state of formic acid, and because this must necessarily mean disagreement concerning the mechanism of the decomposition, it is preferable to leave a critical summary until all other relevant material has been presented. At this point we may simply say that there is a *prima facie* case for believing that the structures and species present on nickel (and indeed the state of reduction of the surface) are not the same at all temperatures, and hence we must be prepared to concede the existence of different mechanisms proceeding in different ranges of temperature.

The state of formic acid adsorbed on metals other than nickel has been far less thoroughly investigated. Hirota and his associates[30] have reported that formic acid adsorbed on palladium, rhodium, platinum, copper, silver and zinc supported on silica shows the absorption bands characteristic of the ionic species. Silica-supported gold shows a weak absorption at 1530 cm.$^{-1}$.[33] The decomposition on platinum–silica takes place so rapidly at $-60°$ that no bands other than those attributable to the linear carbon monoxide structure are detectable.[34] Volumetric studies[23] indicate that the adsorbed complex existing on silver and copper powders has the composition of formic acid. It is well known that the adsorption of formic acid is much weaker on *s*-metals than on *d*-metals, and hence we must be prepared to find that the mechanism of the decomposition is different with the two classes. It is also worth noting that the noble *s*- and *d*-metals are unlikely to be oxidized by the decomposition products, so that infra-red measurements with such metals (where obtainable) should be capable of unambiguous interpretation.

18.32 The Stoichiometry of Formic Acid Decomposition

In this Section we shall discuss results of measurements on the composition of the products of the steady-state decomposition of formic acid. Although it was stated earlier that the products over metallic catalysts are predominantly hydrogen and carbon dioxide, nevertheless water and carbon monoxide, formed by the process

$$HCOOH \rightarrow H_2O + CO \quad \text{(h)}$$

are often detected in amounts which vary from traces to substantial fractions. Now this mode of decomposition is that usually favoured by oxide catalysts, and it is natural to suspect that these products may stem from a reaction proceeding on glass walls or (where appropriate) on the exposed oxide support. This is no doubt sometimes the case, but in the absence of blank measurements in the absence of the metal no firm decision is possible. Even then the possibility of the metal inducing a reaction on the support cannot be ruled out.

In some cases, however, it is beyond doubt that carbon monoxide is a true product of the decomposition on a metal surface, and in such cases it is important to know whether it is formed directly from formic acid, or whether it derives from carbon dioxide and hydrogen by the water gas shift:

$$H_2 + CO_2 \rightleftharpoons H_2O + CO. \quad \text{(i)}$$

This point is more readily discussed after the experimental results have been summarized.

Reported yields of carbon monoxide vary widely, and even for the same metal some quite discrepant values are given. The carbon monoxide yield is 0.1 per cent over silver powder at 134°, and less than 0.005 per cent over copper powder at 100°;[23] the equilibrium yield is about 6 per cent at these temperatures. Platinum–silica at −60° gives some 30 per cent carbon monoxide as a primary product,[34] and this, of course, is far more than the equilibrium yield. It is, however, for nickel that most results are available, and the following selection scans the whole spectrum. The reactions over nickel foil and single crystals between 225 and 480° yields no carbon monoxide not ascribable to a wall reaction,[37] and nickel powder at 100° gives only 0.13 per cent.[23] Much higher values are given by supported nickel and by nickel films. The latter between 150 and 190° give approximately 30 per cent of carbon monoxide, this yield being within error independent of temperature and conversion.[39] Since this figure is in excess of the equilibirum value, it is certain in this case if in no other that the water gas shift cannot have been responsible. Nickel–titania gives about 10 per cent carbon monoxide between 200 and 250°,[40] while nickel-silica between 15 and 200° gives 18 to 33 per cent carbon monoxide, the maximum yield being shown at 78°.[32] These results may be tentatively taken as indicating an induced activity of the support, but this possibility is, of course, absent in the case of nickel films.

It seems reasonable to suppose that minor genuine yields of carbon monoxide are in fact caused by the reaction between carbon dioxide and hydrogen, the primary products. The detection of substantial coverage of nickel[34, 36] and platinum[34] by carbon monoxide tends support to this view, but it must be remembered that the position of equilibrium at the surface may be considerably different from that in the gas phase, and hence that primary carbon dioxide may temporarily dissociate to carbon monoxide and an oxygen atom (or ion) at the surface, only to recombine when desorbing. The water gas equilibrium could be approached through these intermediates. The high carbon monoxide yields on nickel films, however, remain a major puzzle (see, however, Ref. 27).

18.33 The Decomposition of Deuterated Formic Acids

The greater the scope and variety of information, the nearer may the absolute truth concerning a reaction mechanism be approached. The isotopic tracer method, so fruitful in other systems, has recently been applied to the problems of formic acid decomposition, with results which though unspectacular are nevertheless helpful.[30, 32, 33, 41, 42] The results obtained are principally of two kinds: (i) measurements of the relative rates of decomposition of the three deuterated formic acids, and of "light" formic acid, and (ii) measurements of the isotopic composition of the "hydrogen" formed when deuterated formic acids decompose. The most significant results have been obtained with gold and silver catalysts, the results with nickel films[30] being less readily interpretable because of the rapid equilibration of the hydrogen isotopes.

There is no exchange of either formic acid or hydrogen with deuterium over silica-supported gold. However, when mixtures of HCOOH and HCOOD are allowed to decompose, the three molecular isotopes are formed in their equilibrium proportions.[33] This shows that the "hydrogen" atoms are lost separately, and that the decomposition is not intramolecular. The existence of adsorbed hydrogen atoms is demonstrated by their ability to reaction with oxygen and with ethylene.[32, 33, 43]

Similar results have been found with silver films[30, 42] and powders.[44] The decomposition of HCOOD on silver films between 160 and 245° leads to hydrogen deuteride yields (54 to 69 per cent) which are, however, in excess of the equilibrium proportion. This seems to indicate some intramolecular decomposition over this catalyst. The hydrogen : deuterium molecular ratio is about two at 160° and unity at 245°; the atomic percentage of deuterium is always greater than 50 per cent. Some further implications of these results will be discussed in subsection 18.36.

Several values are available for the ratio of the rates of decomposition of HCOOH and of HCOOD; these are summarized in Table III. Comparative

TABLE III. *Relative Rates of Decomposition of HCOOH and HCOOD*

Metal	*Form*	*Temp.* (°C)	r (HCOOD) / r (HCOOH)	*Ref.*
Ag	powder	190–230°	0.74	41
Ag	powder	100°	0.8	44
Ag	film	205°	0.9	30
Au	on SiO_2	?	0.6	33

measurements of the rates of decomposition of the three deuterated formic acids and of "light" formic acid over silver powder[41] show the reactivity sequence to be:

$$\text{HCOOH} > \text{HCOOD} \doteqdot \text{DCOOH} > \text{DCOOD}$$

The activation energies are respectively 19.8, 21.1, 21.7 and 22.2 kcal. mole^{-1} between 190 and 250°. These results indicate that a species containing two "hydrogen" atoms is involved in the slow step.

Reference has already been made to measurements of the infra-red spectra of deuterated formic acids.[34]

18.34 *The Kinetics of the Decomposition for Formic Acid*

Following the usual practice, this Section is devoted to summarizing the orders of reaction and the Arrhenius parameters which have been reported for formic acid decomposition on pure metals. Consideration of the relative activity of metals in the same physical state, and of the Arrhenius parameters shown by alloys, will be given in the next sub-section.

As noted earlier, this reaction has chiefly been used as a means of assessing the activities and activation energies of a wide variety of metallic catalysts, but it is nevertheless very surprising to find that thorough kinetic studies have only rarely been carried out. The reaction on various kinds of nickel catalysts is widely reported to be zero order, but this statement only applies to the order derived from the variation of initial rate with initial reactant pressure, since studies in static systems show[32, 33, 38, 39] that the products of the decomposition inhibit the rate. However, it seems not to be known which products are responsible: the sequence of inhibiting power over nickel films at 190° is[39] somewhat surprisingly:

$$CO_2 > H_2O > H_2 > CO,$$

the last apparently having no power of inhibition. A thorough study of the "course" kinetics over nickel has yet to be made.

Discordant results for the order of reactions over other Transition metals are reported. The order is said to be first over platinum foil at 206°, and over rhodium foil at an unspecified temperature.[45, 46] Orders of zero are also given for platinum and palladium foils at about 150°.[47, 48] It is possible that the difference is due to the different temperatures used.

The situation with metals of Group IB is perhaps simpler, since here the indications are that the products do not inhibit. In general, the order is found to be unity at low pressures and/or high temperatures, and zero at high pressures and/or low temperatures. The order is zero for copper powder (65 to 100°)[23] and for copper foil (120 to 240°),[48] but first at pressures of 10^{-2} to 10^{-3} mm. over copper single crystals above 230°.[49] Both zero and first orders have been detected with silver powder, depending in the expected manner on the prevailing conditions.[23] The order is reported to be first for a chemically formed silver mirror at 140 and 185°[45], but to be zero for single crystals of silver at about 170°.[50] Silica-supported gold shows an order of 0.75 at 200°.[32, 33]

It appears at first sight that the rate is determined by the fractional coverage of the surface by adsorbed formic acid, in accordance with the simple Langmuir picture, but this view has been put in doubt by the elegant work of Tamaru.[23] He has shown that for copper powder the volume adsorbed continues to rise with pressure in the range where the rate of decomposition is independent of pressure: this implies the existence of a limited number of active sites. Silver powder, however, shows the expected behaviour, viz. the rate proportional to the volume adsorbed.

Tables IV to VIII summarize most of the available measurements of activation energies and pre-exponential factors for formic acid decomposition on pure metals. The compilation makes no claim to be complete, and intentionally omits measurements on metal foils and powders which have received various mechanical or thermal treatments.[51–54] Some difficulty has arisen due to the varying units which different authors have employed to express their rates and hence pre-exponential factors. Wherever possible, these latter have been recalculated and are quoted in terms of molecules site^{-1} sec.$^{-1}$; it has been assumed where rates were quoted in cm.^{3} of hydrogen formed per unit time that the volume was corrected to S.T.P., and that apparent *and* specific areas contain 10^{15} sites per cm.^{2}. In a number of cases it has not been possible to calculate pre-exponential factors in standard units, usually because of the lack of information on surface areas, and in such cases the entries in the tables are said to be in "arbitary units." Where activation energies for the two possible reaction paths have been shown to differ, the value quoted is that for dehydrogenation.

The activation energies found with nickel catalysts (Table IV) show the usual alarming spread (from 5.6 to 30 kcal. mole^{-1}), but are on the whole more consistent than for some reactions in as much as ten of the thirteen values quoted lie within the limits of 20 ± 5 kcal. mole^{-1}. Several of the values found with copper (Table V) are within the range 23 ± 4 kcal. mole^{-1},

TABLE IV. *Arrhenius Parameters for the Decomposition of Formic Acid on Nickel Catalysts*

Form	*E(kcal. mole^{-1})*	*log A*	*Temp. range*	*Ref.*
Film	15.8	7.7*	125–189°	39
Foil	20	8.3*	225–480°	37
Foil (quenched)	20.0	—	?	55
Foil (annealed)	16.5, 19.0	—	?	55
Foil	11.6	7.2†	120–220°	56
Foil	30	12.3*	250–300°	57
Powder	24.6	—	220–270°	40
Powder	22.8	11.1†	?	55
On SiO_2	23.0	10.0*	80–200°	33
On Al_2O_3	5.6	—	?	16
On TiO_2[a]	~16.5	—	~220–270°	40
On TiO_2[b]	~22.0	—	~210–260°	40

a, Reduced at 400°; b, reduced at 500°.
*, In molecules site^{-1} sec.$^{-1}$; †, in arbitrary units.

TABLE V. *Arrhenius Parameters for the Decomposition of Formic Acid on Copper Catalysts*

Form	*E(kcal. mole^{-1})*	*log A*	*Temp. range*	*Ref.*
Foil	24	10.0*	?	54
Foil	23.4	—	?	58
Foil	22.8	11.0†	120–240°	48
Foil	36	14.6*	250–300°	57
Mono-crystal (100) face	8.5	−2.3†	230–420°	49
Mono-crystal (110) face	16.0	0.7†	230–420°	49
Mono-crystal (111) face	19.0	2.1†	230–420°	49
Powder	27.0	13.0*	65–100°	23
On Al_2O_3	19.3	11.5†	130–180°	16

*, In molecules site^{-1} sec.$^{-1}$; †, in arbitrary units.

TABLE VI. *Arrhenius Parameters for the Decomposition of Formic Acid on Silver Catalysts*

Form		*E*(*kcal. mole*$^{-1}$)	*log A*	*Temp. range*	*Ref.*
Foil		21.3	—	?	59
Foil		26.0	—	?	60
Foil		17.6	8.5*	?	61
Film (chemically-formed)		31.3	—	?	45
Mono-crystal	(100) face	26.2	10.8*	155–200°	50
	(110) face	30.4	12.8*		
	(111) face	16.0	5.9*		
Powder		30.7	12.0*	134–160°	23
Powder		19.8	—	190–250°	41
On Al_2O_3		16.7	9.8†	130–180°	16

*, In molecules site^{-1} sec.$^{-1}$; †, in arbitrary units.

TABLE VII. *Arrhenius Parameters for the Decomposition of Formic Acid on Gold Catalysts*

Form	*E*(*kcal. mole*$^{-1}$)	*log A*	*Temp. range*	*Ref.*
Foil	12.5	6.5*	?	61
Wire	14.3	5.4*	110–190°	22
Powder	23.5	—	140–185°	46
On SiO_2	14.3	5.2*	100–250°	33
On Al_2O_3	16.3	11.5†	130–180°	16

*, In molecules site^{-1} sec.$^{-1}$; †, in arbitrary units.

TABLE VIII. *Arrhenius Parameters for the Decomposition of Formic Acid on Other Metals*

Metal	*Form*	*E*(*kcal. mole*$^{-1}$)	*log A*	*Temp. range*	*Ref.*
W	film	25	9.5*	~250°	43
Fe	powder	~50	—	~230°	55
Fe	foil (quenched)	26.3, 27.0	—	?	55
Fe	foil (annealed)	25.5	—	?	55
Rh	foil	25.0	—	155–186°	46
Pd	foil	11.5	—	?	59
Pd	foil	15.3	9.2*	?	61
Pd	foil	8.0	5.4†	120–220°	47
Pd	wire	8.0	4.3*	25–60°	22
Pt	foil	22.2	—	140–234°	45
Pt	foil	6.5	3.1†	120–240°	48
Pt	foil	14.7	8.2*	?	54

*, In molecules site^{-1} sec.$^{-1}$; †, in arbitrary units.

and for gold (Table VII) between 12 and 16 kcal. mole^{-1}. No further generalizations based purely on activation energies are possible, but the compensation effect relationship (Fig. 2), using pre-exponential factors in standard units, is obeyed with moderate success. Also included in Fig. 2 are the results for

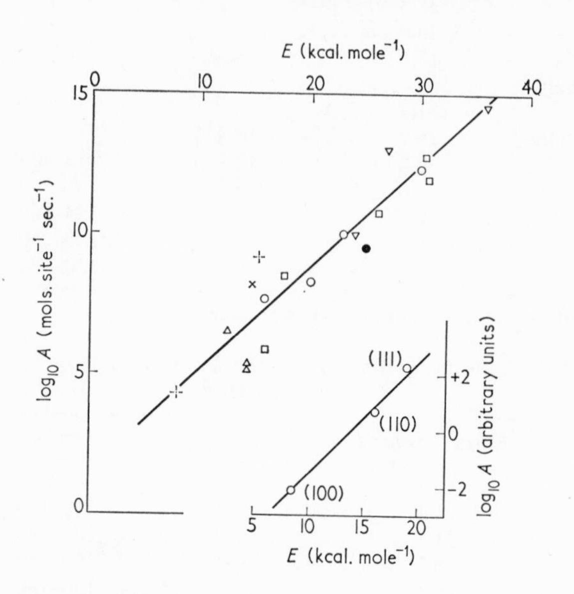

FIG. 2. Compensation effect for formic acid decomposition on pure metals (see Tables IV to VIII).
○, Nickel; ▽, copper; □, silver; △, gold; –|–, palladium; ×, platinum; ●, tungsten. Inset: compensation effect for various faces of a copper monocrystal.[49]

the various faces of a copper monocrystal: the line through the three points is almost parallel to that drawn through the main sequence of points, suggesting that use of the appropriate factor would lead to coincidence.

A short comment is necessary on the three sets of results concerning the activation energies for the reaction on different crystallographic planes of Group IB metals.[49, 50] Unfortunately the results are not particularly helpful: not only are the sequences of the activation energies quite different, but also with each metal the rates for the faces examined are much the same. The results do not therefore add significantly to our understanding the role of the geometric factor in catalysis.

18.35 The Electronic Factor in the Decomposition of Formic Acid

In this sub-section are reported values of the Arrhenius parameters for formic acid decomposition on alloys. A very large amount of work has been done on these systems, with Rienäcker, Schwab and their associates having been most active. For convenience, we may recognize three classes of alloy: (i) alloys formed between two *d*-metals; (ii) alloys of an *s*- and a *d*-metal; and (iii) alloys of two *s*-metals. As discussed in Chapter 2, the last group may be further subdivided according as the system shows a complete range of solid solutions or a number of intermetallic (Hume–Rothery) phases. The results, taken together with some concerning the relative activities of pure metals, should enable us to assess the role of the electronic factor in this reaction. We may proceed to consider the three classes of alloy in the sequence listed above.

The only investigated system falling into the first category is the iron–nickel system.[55] The logarithm of the activity of quenched and annealed foils, and of powders, is shown in Fig. 3 as a function of composition: the activities

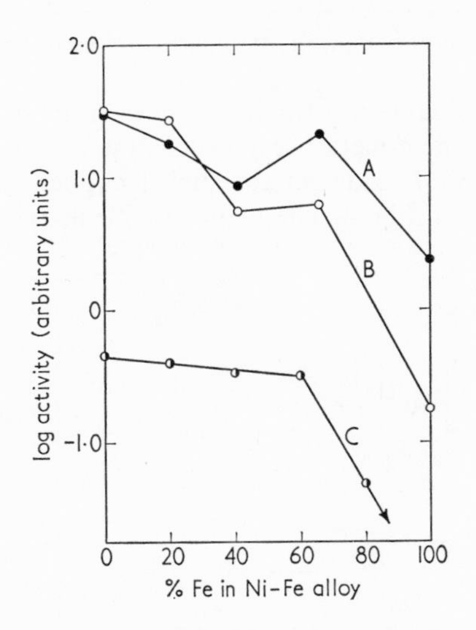

FIG. 3. The dependence of activity for formic acid decomposition on composition of nickel–iron alloys.[55]
A. Relative activities per cm.^{2} apparent area for annealed foils at 180°.
B. Relative activities per cm.^{2} apparent area for quenched foils at 200°.
C. Relative activities per m.^{2} for powders at 126°.

are corrected to unit surface area (1 cm.^{2} apparent area for foils and 1 m.^{2} true area for powders). Activation energies and pre-exponential factors are given in Table IX. There is no satisfactory compensation effect for the powders, and the sharp decrease in activity above 60 per cent iron is due to the failure of the pre-exponential factor adequately to compensate for the high activation energies. The same holds good for the iron foils. The pre-exponential factors for the foils are remarkably constant ($\log A = 11.35 \pm 0.25$ for quenched foils, and 9.58 ± 0.11 for annealed foils, excluding iron).

TABLE IX. *Arrhenius Parameters for the Decomposition of Formic Acid over Nickel–Iron Alloys*[55]

Powders			*Foils*				
				Annealed		*Quenched*	
Atomic %Fe	E^a	$\log A^b$	*Atomic %Fe*	E^a	$\log A^c$	E^a	$\log A^c$
0	22.8	11.1	0	17.7	9.69	20.0	11.15
20	13.3	5.9	20	17.7	9.47	20.8	11.48
40	13.2	5.8	40.5	18.6	9.53	21.7	11.24
60	12.8	5.0	62.7	17.8	9.56	22.5	11.64
80	16.3	6.6	100	25.5	12.18	26.6	11.11
100	50	19.6					

a, kcal. mole^{-1}; b, arbitrary units m.$^{-2}$; c, arbitrary units cm.$^{-2}$.

As usual, more valuable information comes from studies on alloys composed of one *s*- and one *d*-metal: seven such systems have received attention. Four studies have been made on the nickel–copper system,[16, 54, 56, 57] and the results are shown in Fig. 4. The two available activity patterns are shown

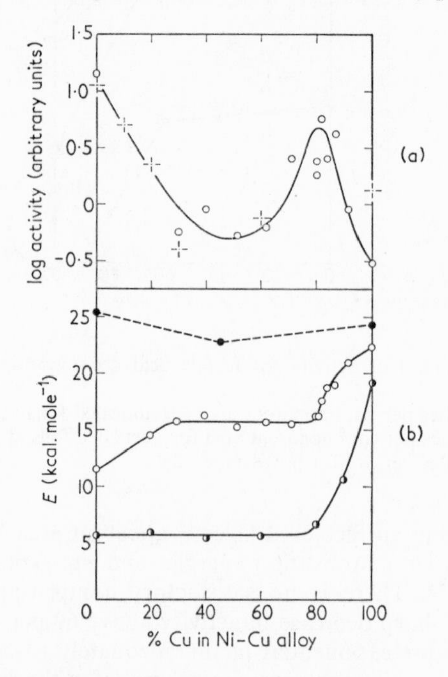

FIG. 4. Formic acid decomposition on nickel–copper alloys.
(a) Log activity as a function of composition: ○, foils at 150°:[56]; –¦–, foils at 253°:[57]
(b) Activation energy as a function of composition: ○, foils[56]; ●, foils[54]; ◑, alumina supported alloys.[16]

in Fig. 4(a): the activity clearly decreases with increasing copper content, although a second and ill-defined maximum is shown at about 80 per cent copper.[56] Three sets of activation energies are to hand, but unfortunately they show little consistency (Fig. 4(b)). One set[16] shows a constant activation energy up to about 75 per cent copper, and another[56] shows constant values between 30 and 80 per cent copper, and in both sets there is a steep rise between 80 and 100 per cent copper. From only one of the studies[56] can relative pre-exponential factors be derived: here a fair compensation effect is shown between 80 and 100 per cent copper, but in the range where the activation energy is approximately constant, so also is the pre-exponential factor ($\log A = 8.3 \pm 0.6$ arbitrary units). The change in activation energy at 80 per cent copper, and the rather doubtful activity maximum at this composition, are the only signs of an electronic effect of the expected kind. The occurrence of the break at 80 per cent (rather than 60 per cent) may be associated with the effect of temperature on the number of *d*-band vacancies in nickel.

Activation energies for formic acid decomposition on alumina-supported nickel–silver alloys have also been recorded;[16] the results are essentially equivalent to those for alumina-supported nickel–copper alloys (Fig. 4(b)) and require no further discussion.

We now consider alloys of palladium with copper,[47] silver[59, 61] and gold,[22] and of platinum with copper.[48] The activity patterns are shown in Figs. 5 and 8(a): they are not very sensitive to temperature. The palladium–copper and palladium–gold systems show analogous behaviour at the palladium-rich

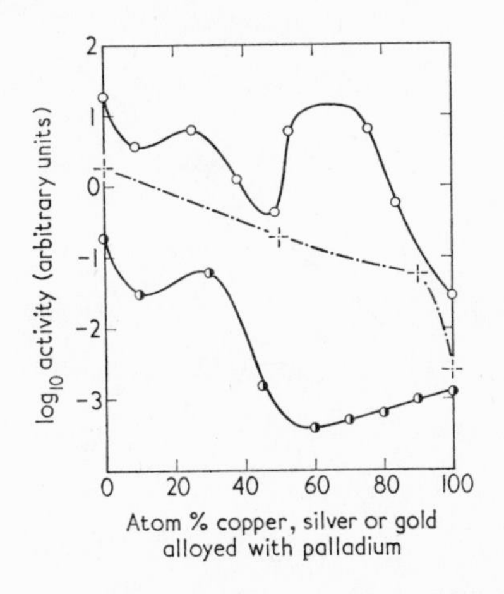

FIG. 5. Relative activities of alloys of copper, silver and gold with palladium for formic acid decomposition:

—○—, disordered palladium–copper foils at 150°:[47]

–·–¦–·–, palladium–silver foils at 150°:[14]

—◑—, palladium–gold wires at 100°.[22]

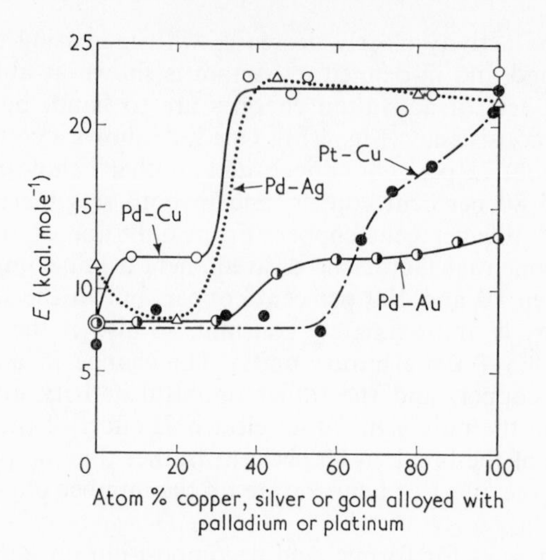

FIG. 6. The dependence of the activation energy for formic acid decomposition on composition for palladium–copper foils[47] (—○—), palladium–silver foils[59] (....△....), palladium–gold wires[22] (—◑—), and for platinum–copper foils[48] (–·–●–·–).

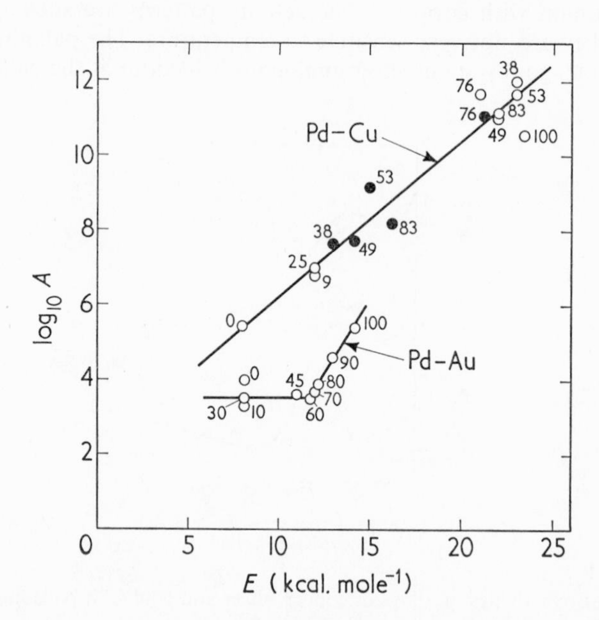

FIG. 7. Compensation effects in the decomposition of formic acid over palladium–copper foils[47] and over palladium–gold wires.[22] A is respectively in arbitrary units and in molecules (double site)$^{-1}$ sec.$^{-1}$: filled points represent ordered alloys. The percentage of copper or gold to which each point corresponds is indicated.

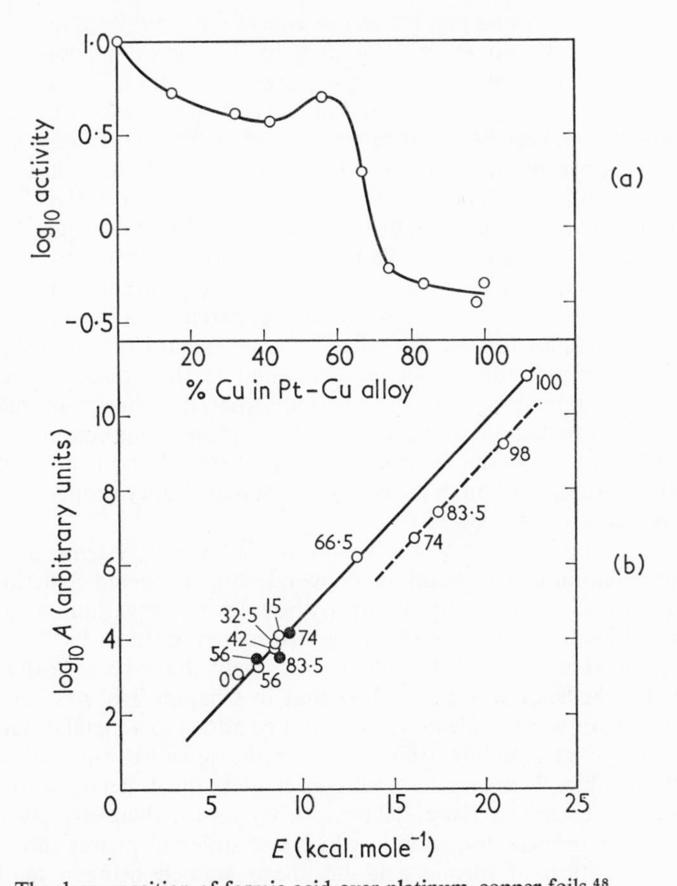

FIG. 8. The decomposition of formic acid over platinum–copper foils.[48]
(a) log activity at 160° as a function of composition.
(b) compensation effect, with the percentage copper to which each point corresponds indicated. Points for ordered alloys are filled.

end, but the former system shows a broad maximum between about 55 and 75 per cent copper which is absent in the latter. This may not be surprising if one recalls that copper is more active than gold for this, as for most other, reactions.[33] What may be a corresponding activity maximum is evident in the platinum–copper system at about 55 per cent copper. The few results[61] available for the palladium–silver system tend to suggest that it is more analogous to the palladium–copper than to the palladium–gold system. Direct evidence for the importance of unfilled *d*-bands in determining the activity is thus meagre, but perhaps is shown in the platinum–copper system. It is worth stressing that the information obtained when studying a reaction for which both metals of the alloy show comparable activity is less readily interpreted than when their activities are very substantially different.

Activation energies and compensation effects for these systems are shown in Figs. 6, 7 and 8(b). For the palladium–gold and platinum–copper systems, the activation energies are at first approximately constant, but subsequently start to rise at about 30 per cent gold and 55 per cent copper. The palladium–copper system also gives a sharp change of activation energy at about 30 per cent copper, but this is followed by a plateau at about 22 kcal. $mole^{-1}$. Discordant results are reported for the palladium–silver system.[59, 61] The variation of activation energy with composition is said to be slight[61] or as in Fig. 6,[59] where there is a large change (~15 kcal. $mole^{-1}$) between 20 and 45 per cent silver, similar to that shown by the palladium–copper system. No reason for this divergence of behaviour is apparent. Once again, therefore, unequivocal evidence for the role of the *d*-band is hard to establish, except perhaps for the platinum–copper system, and further work is needed to resolve the discrepancies. The observation[22] that the change in activation energy between palladium and gold (~6 kcal. $mole^{-1}$) approximates to the distance between the Fermi level and the top of the *d*-band is not confirmed by the other systems, although the change from palladium to copper (~8 kcal. $mole^{-1}$) is not too much larger.

The foregoing observations apply only to disordered systems, and where (as in the palladium– and platinum–copper systems) ordered structures may be formed, these are generally found to show lower activation energies and higher activities than the corresponding disordered material.[47, 48]

We come next to our third class of alloys, namely, those where both partners have filled *d*-shells. It will be recalled that in Chapter 3 it was stated that small amounts of higher-valent metals could be added to a metal of Group IB without change of structure: this results in the so-called α-phase, which is face-centred cubic. With larger amounts of higher-valent metal, various other phases occur at characteristic electron: atom ratios, there usually being a fairly narrow intermediate region in which two different phases can co-exist. The decomposition of formic acid has been studied using a number of α-phases, and other phases or mixtures of phases, as catalysts. In the interpretation of this work, emphasis has been placed on the activation energy, and correlations between it and the electron concentration of the alloy have been sought and indeed established.

Silver, and to a smaller extent gold, have been used as "solvent" metals;[61, 62] on addition of elements of Groups IIB to VB in the second long period (Cd, In, Sn, Sb), the α-phase is formed below the limiting electron : atom ratio of 1.33, while for the corresponding elements of the third long period (Hg, Tl, Pb, Bi) the limiting value is 1.1. The Arrhenius parameters for formic acid decomposition on alloys of these eight elements with silver have been measured: the activation energies are always higher than for silver, and although there is a sympathetic increase in the pre-exponential factors the net effect is a smaller activity than for silver. Some approximate values of the activation energies, interpolated from the original measurements,[61] are shown in Table X. A selection of the original results is plotted in the form of a compensation effect in Fig. 9. At *low* solute concentrations, the activation energy E_i shown by any alloy is related to that shown by pure silver (E_{Ag}) by the approximate relation:

$$E_i = E_{Ag} + Jx(n - 1)^2, \tag{2}$$

where n is the Group number and x the atomic fraction of the "solute" metal and J is a constant whose value depends on the number of the long period in question. Similar results are shown by some alloys of gold. The

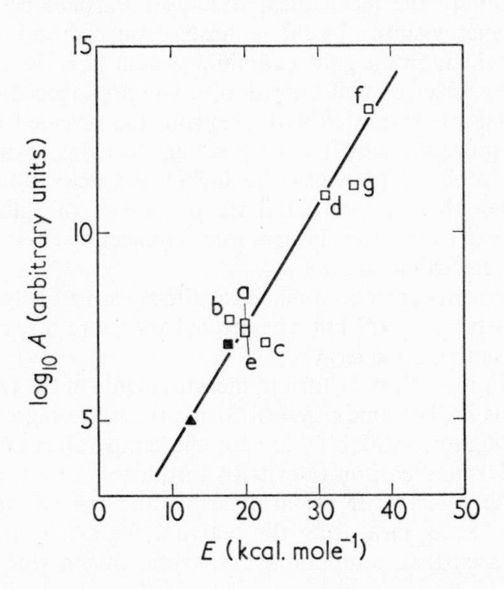

FIG. 9. Silver, gold and some alloys of silver as catalysts for formic acid decomposition: compensation effect.[61]

■, Silver; ▲, gold. Open squares represent: a, 38.4% Cd; b, 5.0% In; c, 7.5% Sn; d, 5.5% Sb; e, 4.5% Tl; f, 1.43% Pb; g, 2.0% Bi.

TABLE X. *Approximate Activation Energies for Formic Acid Decomposition over the α-phases of Alloys of Silver with Higher-valent Metals*[61] (E_{Ag} = *17.6 kcal. mole*$^{-1}$)

Metal	*Concentration (atom %)*	*E(kcal. mole^{-1})*
Cd	5	~20
In	5	~18
Sn	5	~21
Sb	5	~31
Hg	1	~21
Tl	1	~20
Pb	1	~33
Bi	1	~30

activation energy thus increases approximately as the square of the electron concentration, as does also the electrical resistance.

Further evidence supporting the view that electron transfer *to* the solid is involved in the slow step of formic acid decomposition in these systems comes from measurements of the activation energy using other intermetallic phases or mixtures of phases.[61, 62] In the copper–tin system, the activation energy changes in a manner closely similar to that of the electrical resistance, and also incidentally the mechanical hardness. Particularly notable is the high activation energy shown by the γ-phase (deformed body-centred cubic), and this is also evident in the gold–cadmium system. It is therefore concluded that the higher the electron concentration in any homogeneous phase, or the more a given phase is saturated with electrons (as revealed by its electrical resistance), the more difficult it is to transfer electrons to it from reacting formic acid molecules, and hence the higher the activation energy. Consideration of the physical and catalytic properties of intermetallic alloy phases again underlines the inseparable connection between structural (geometric) and electronic factors.

Some measurements have been made on alloys formed between the Group IB metals themselves,[60, 61, 63] but as expected there are no startling changes in activity or in activation energy.

Finally in this sub-section we turn to measurements of the relative activities of various metals in the same physical form: these are regrettably few, and indeed the only figures available[33] are for the temperatures at which metals supported on activated carbon (Norit-R4) produce a rate of decomposition of 0.16 mol. site^{-1} sec.$^{-1}$. If we arbitrarily take the reciprocals of these temperatures in °K as measuring the activity, we arrive at the figures in Table XI. It is seen that comparable activity is shown within each Group

TABLE XI. *The Relative Activities of Metals for Formic Acid Decomposition*[33]

Fe	2.00	Ru	2.57		
Co	2.05	Rh	2.43	Ir	2.82
Ni	2.14	Pd	2.51	Pt	2.88
		Ag	2.09	Au	1.91

The figures are $10^3/T_r$(°K), where T_r is the temperature which gives a log rate of −0.8 mol. site^{-1} sec.$^{-1}$.

VIII triad, the platinum triad being most active and the nickel triad least. There is a sharp drop in activity on passing to Group IB, although the change is probably least between nickel and copper (see Fig. 4). The significance of these results will be further discussed below.

18.36 The Mechanism of the Decomposition of Formic Acid

We may now attempt to summarize the present status of the problem in the light of the experimental results presented above. While it is evident that there is no unanimity concerning reaction mechanisms, and that further work is necessary before the situation may be fully clarified, a provisional assessment is called for.

The central question concerns the nature of the adsorbed species present on the surface *during the reaction*. It would appear that the formate ion is formed on nickel catalysts, at least between about 20 and 100°, perhaps as a result of the adventitious oxidation of the surface. Above and below this temperature range, the ion may have a lesser importance. It seems agreed that the slow step over nickel, and perhaps also over the other Group VIII metals, is the decomposition of the adsorbed species, be it ion or adsorbed radical; the processes may be formulated as

$$\mathrm{O{=}\overset{\displaystyle H}{\overset{|}{C}}{-}\underset{*}{O}} + 2* \rightarrow \mathrm{O{=}\underset{*}{C}{-}\underset{*}{O}} + \underset{*}{\mathrm{H}} \qquad \text{(j)}$$

or

$$\mathrm{O{=}\overset{\displaystyle H}{\overset{|}{C}}{-}\underset{*+}{O^-}} + 2* \rightarrow \mathrm{O{=}\underset{*}{C}{-}\underset{*}{O}} + \underset{*}{\mathrm{H}}. \qquad \text{(k)}$$

slow fast

The hydrogen atoms will, of course, recombine rapidly, and the adsorbed carbon dioxide may desorb, or decompose (perhaps with the assistance of hydrogen) to adsorbed carbon monoxide, which may also desorb. This picture conforms with that developed by Tamaru[23] on the basis of his volumetric work. After the initial stages of a static experiment, the rate is limited by the fraction of surface free of strongly held products, and it is here that the need for a thorough classical kinetic study is keenly felt.

The situation with the Group IB and the electron-rich alloys studied by Schwab[61, 62] is even more confused, if that were possible. Although it has been claimed that the formate ion has been recognized in some of these systems, the evidence seems slender and to require confirmation. The two key features here are (i) that the "hydrogen" atoms are lost consecutively and not by an intramolecular change, and (ii) that a species containing two hydrogen atoms is involved in the slow step. The process may then be formulated either as:

$$\mathrm{HCOOH} + 2* \xrightarrow{\text{slow}} \mathrm{HCO\underset{*}{O}} + \underset{*}{\mathrm{H}} \xrightarrow{\text{fast}} \mathrm{CO_2} + 2\underset{*}{\mathrm{H}} \qquad \text{(l)}$$

or

$$\mathrm{HCOOH} + 2* \xrightarrow{\text{fast}} \mathrm{H{-}\underset{*}{C}{-}\underset{*}{O}}\ (\text{OH on C}) \xrightarrow[+2*]{\text{slow}} \mathrm{\underset{*}{O}{-}\overset{\displaystyle H}{\overset{|}{\underset{*}{C}}}{-}\underset{*}{O}} + \underset{*}{\mathrm{H}}$$

$$\xrightarrow{\text{fast}} \mathrm{\underset{*}{O}{-}\underset{*}{C}{=}O} + 2\underset{*}{\mathrm{H}} \qquad \text{(m)}$$

followed by the usual desorption steps. Each of these mechanisms appears to accord equally well with most of the observations.

The whole concept of the role of the electronic factor in this system has been strongly criticized.[27, 33] The view has instead been advanced that the activity of a metal is determined by the heat of formation of the bulk metal formate, and that where this is high, as with iron, cobalt and nickel, the activity will be low because of the stability of the adsorbed formate ion. Furthermore, where the heat of formation is low, as with silver and gold, the activity will again be low because of the difficulty of forming the adsorbed ion. The maximum activity (at platinum and iridium) is thus attributed to the optimum cancellation of the opposing factors. It is accepted by all, but on the basis of different precepts, the low activity is associated either with high coverage or very low coverage, but it seems preferable to say that the coverage by formic acid achieved by a given metal is determined by the same fundamental properties which determine the stability of the bulk formate or indeed any other compound. Peripheral correlations of the kind discussed above seem unhelpful.

All the slow steps proposed above involve electron transfer to the solid, and are thus consistent with Schwab's work on electron-rich alloys and with the relative activities of pure metals. Indeed the sequence shown in Table XI differs from that customary in hydrogenation or dehydrogenation systems only in the relatively high activity of the Group IB metals. However, in other systems such as the hydrogenation of ketones and the exchange of alcohols, where interaction between oxygen atoms in organic molecules and the surface probably occurs, these metals are also somewhat active, and hence their activity in formic acid decomposition is not entirely inexplicable in terms of the usual model.

18.4 The Dehydrogenation of Amines

Some values of the Arrhenius parameters for the dehydrogenation of amines according to the equation

$$R\text{—}CH_2\text{—}NH_2 \rightarrow R\text{—}CH{=}NH + H_2 \qquad \text{(n)}$$

have been reported:[3] nickel–alumina and palladium–asbestos were employed between 270 and 330°. The results are shown in the form of a compensation effect in Fig. 10.

18.5 The Decomposition of Hydrogen Peroxide

This is yet another reaction which has received surprisingly little attention, particularly in recent years. Following the early work of Bredig, some sixty years ago, most of the studies of this reaction have been made in the liquid phase, often from an electrochemical standpoint.[64, 65] It seems agreed that, if the decomposition is studied using charged electrodes as catalysts, the reaction at the cathode is initiated by the acceptance of an electron by a

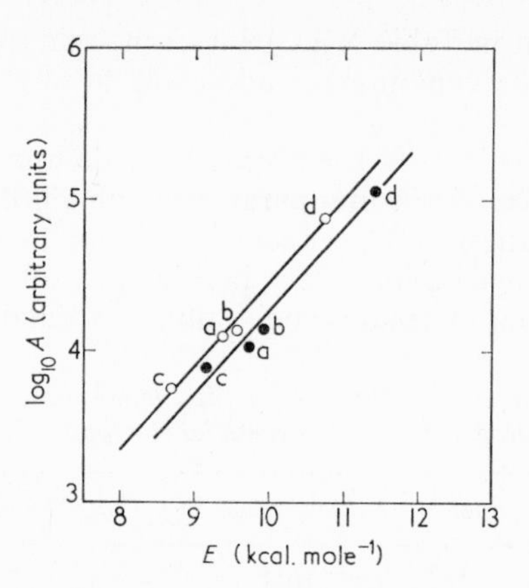

FIG. 10. Compensation effect for the dehydrogenation of amines.[3]
○, Ni–Al_2O_3; ●, Pd–asbestos.
a, 2-Aminopentane; b, 2-methyl-4-aminopentane; c, 2,4-dimethyl-4-aminopentane; d, 1-diethylamino-4-aminopentane.

hydrogen peroxide molecule. Now if the reaction proceeds according to the Haber–Weiss formulation for the homogeneous decomposition, viz.

$$H_2O_2 + \varepsilon^- \rightarrow HO\cdot + OH^-, \quad \text{(o)}$$

we should perhaps write for the surface reaction

$$H_2O_2 + \varepsilon^- + * \rightarrow \underset{*}{HO} + OH^-. \quad \text{(p)}$$

In acidic solutions the hydroxyl ion would rapidly be converted to water, and the adsorbed hydroxyl radicals could decompose either as

$$2\underset{*}{HO} \rightarrow H_2O + \tfrac{1}{2}O_2 + 2* \quad \text{(q)}$$

or as

$$2\underset{*}{HO} \rightarrow H_2 + O_2 + 2*. \quad \text{(r)}$$

There is, however, evidence for the initiation at the cathode of a homogenous chain reaction involving hydroxyl and hydroperoxyl radicals, suggesting the occurrence of the reaction

$$H_2O_2 + \varepsilon^- + H^+ \rightarrow HO_2\cdot + H_2. \quad \text{(s)}$$

The order of reaction with respect to hydrogen peroxide is generally found to be first, but a number of reaction schemes are compatible with this.[66]

If the Haber–Weiss mechanism is correct, the activity of *d*-metals should, in the absence of electrochemical assistance, be less than that of *s*-metals, and a study of hydrogen peroxide decomposition on nickel–copper foils between 60 and 80° has indeed confirmed this.[57] The observed Arrhenius parameters are given in Table XII. Alloys containing less than 60 per cent copper (that is, those containing a nominally filled *d*-band) were inactive at 60 and 70°.

A study of the reaction has been recently made using alloys of elemental semiconductors.[66] The Arrhenius parameters obtained with bismuth and some alloys of bismuth with 0.1 per cent of a Group IV or Group VI element are shown as a compensation effect in Fig. 11: values for various near-stoichiometric indium arsenide and gallium arsenide samples are also

TABLE XII. *Arrhenius Parameters for the Liquid-phase Decomposition of Hydrogen Peroxide over Nickel–Copper Foils*[57]

Atomic % copper	*E(kcal. mole⁻¹)*	*logA (mol. cm.⁻² sec.⁻¹)*
100	10.3	23.00
90	10.9	23.32
80	11.0	23.38
70	23.7	31.11

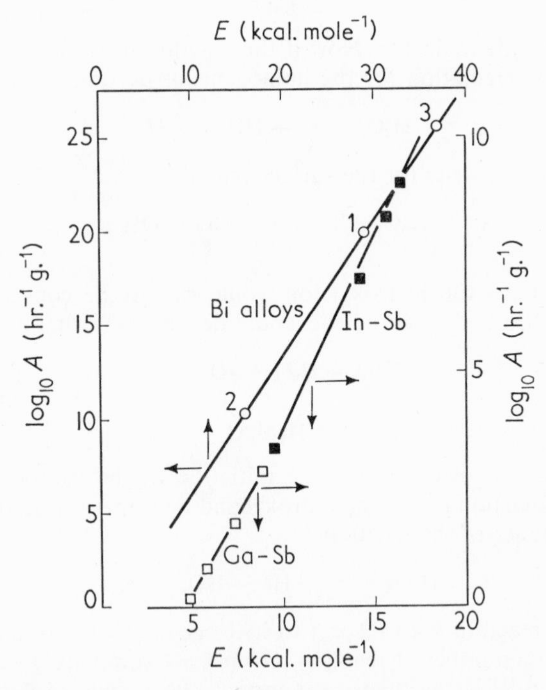

FIG. 11. The catalysis of hydrogen peroxide decomposition: compensation effects.[66] Numbered points: 1, Bi; 2, Bi + 0.1% Sn, Ge or Pb; 3, Bi + 0.1% Cr, Se or Te.
■ : various indium arsenide samples
□ : various gallium arsenide samples.

included. Rates were measured in the neighbourhood of room temperature. These alloys and compounds are p-type semiconductors, but some of the arsenides were made n-type conductors by the addition of 1 per cent tellurium: such materials showed the highest activation energy of each group, but the type of conductivity does not appear to be of primary importance. Bismuth and its alloys all show identical activity at 20°, the alloys of the Group VI elements being the most active above this temperature.

The results for bismuth and its alloys are reminiscent of those obtained by Schwab for the decomposition of formic acid over electron-rich materials, in that increasing the electron concentration raises the activation energy. This would suggest, contrary to the conclusion derived from the study of the nickel–copper alloys, that electron transfer *to* the solid is involved in the slow step. This conclusion also holds for the arsenides, where measurements of the electrical conductivity, the Hall coefficient and hence the carrier mobility for the various samples has permitted a calculation of the energy of their Fermi surface to be made. With the indium arsenside samples, some have their Fermi surface above, and some below, the top of the valence band, and the activation energy increases smoothly as the Fermi surface moves through it. With all the gallium arsenside samples, the Fermi surface is at or above the top of the valence band, and for those samples having the Fermi surface between zero and 0.1 eV. above the top, the activation energy is roughly 5–7 kcal. mole^{-1}: thereafter it rises as the Fermi surface rises, in the manner of the gallium arsenides.

References

1. K. K. Kearby, In "Catalysis", edited by P. H. Emmett (Reinhold, New York, 1954), **3,** 453.
2. B. V. Erofeyev and N. V. Nikiforova, Proc. 2nd International Congress on Catalysis (Editions Technip, Paris, 1961), **2,** 1573.
3. A. A. Balandin, *Adv. Catalysis* **10,** 96 (1958).
4. J. M. Bridges and G. Houghton, *J. Amer. Chem. Soc.* **81,** 1335 (1959).
5. J. H. Sinfelt, H. Hurwitz and R. A. Shulman, *J. Phys. Chem.* **64,** 1559 (1960).
6. A. A. Balandin, E. I. Karpeiskaya and A. A. Tolstopyatova, *Zhur. fiz. Khim.* **33,** 2471 (1959).
7. B. M. W. Trapnell, *Adv. Catalysis* **3,** 1 (1951).
8. A. A. Balandin, Proc. 2nd International Congress on Catalysis (Editions Technip, Paris, 1961), **1,** 1135.
9. A. M. Rubinstein, N. I. Shuikin and K. M. Minachev, *Doklady Akad. Nauk S.S.S.R.* **67,** 287 (1948).
10. W. M. H. Sachtler, G. J. H. Dorgelo and W. van der Knapp, *J. Chim. phys.* **51,** 491 (1954).
11. E. Kovats, P. A. Plattner and H. H. Gunthard, *Helv. Chim. Acta* **37,** 983 (1954).
12. E. A. Braude, R. P. Linstead, P. W. D. Mitchell and K. R. H. Wooldridge, *J. Chem. Soc.* 3578, 3586, 3595 (1954).
13. P. W. Darby and C. Kemball, *Trans. Faraday Soc.* **55,** 733 (1958).
14. I. Brihta and P. Luetić, *Croat. Chim. Acta* **29,** 419 (1957).
15. D. A. Dowden and P. W. Reynolds, *Discuss. Faraday Soc.* **8,** 184 (1950).
16. P. Fuderer-Leutić and I. Brihta, *Croat. Chim. Acta,* **31,** 75 (1959).
17. G.-M. Schwab and E. Schwab-Agallidis, *Ber.* **76,** 1228 (1943).
18. F. H. Constable, *Proc. Roy. Soc.* **A107,** 270, 279 (1925); **A113,** 254 (1927).
19. P. W. Darby and C. Kemball, *Trans. Faraday Soc.* **53,** 822 (1957).

20. W. G. Palmer and F. H. Constable, *Proc. Roy. Soc.* **A107,** 255 (1925).
21. C. Thonon and J. C. Jungers, *Bull. Soc. chim. belges* **59,** 604 (1950).
22. D. D. Eley and P. Luetić, *Trans. Faraday Soc.* **53,** 1476 (1957).
23. K. Tamaru, *Trans. Faraday Soc.* **55,** 824, 1191 (1959).
24. G. Rienäcker and N. Hansen, *Angew. Chem.* **68,** 41 (1956).
25. G. Rienäcker and N. Hansen, *Z. anorg. Chem.* **284,** 162 (1956).
26. G. Rienäcker and N. Hansen, *Z. Elektrochem.* **60,** 887 (1956).
27. W. J. M. Rootsaert and W. M. H. Sachtler, *Z. phys. Chem.* (*Frankfurt*) **26,** 16 (1960).
28. K. Hirota, K. Kuwata and Y. Nakai, *Bull. Chem. Soc. Japan* **31,** 861 (1958).
29. K. Hirota, T. Otaki and S. Asai, *Z. phys. Chem.* (*Frankfurt*) **21,** 438 (1959).
30. K. Hirota, K. Kuwata, T. Otaki and S. Asai, Proc. 2nd International Congress on Catalysis (Editions Technip, Paris, 1961), **1,** 809.
31. J. Fahrenfort and H. F. Hazebroek, *Z. phys. Chem.* (*Frankfurt*) **20,** 105 (1959).
32. J. Fahrenfort, L. L. van Reijen and W. M. H. Sachtler, *Z. Elektrochem.* **64,** 216 (1960).
33. W. M. H. Sachtler and J. Fahrenfort, Proc. 2nd International Congress on Catalysis (Editions Technip, Paris, 1961), **1,** 831: (also G. C. A. Schuit, personal letter.)
34. R. P. Eischens and W. A. Pliskin, Proc. 2nd International Congress on Catalysis (Editions Technip, Paris, 1961), **1,** 789.
35. J. K. A. Clarke and A. D. E. Pullin, *Trans. Faraday Soc.* **56,** 534 (1960).
36. R. Suhrmann and G. Wedler, *Z. Elektrochem.* **60,** 892 (1956); *Adv. Catalysis* **9,** 223 (1957).
37. R. J. Ruka, L. O. Brockway and J. E. Boggs, *J. Amer. Chem. Soc.* **81,** 2930 (1959).
38. G. Rienäcker and N. Hansen, *Z. anorg. Chem.* **285,** 283 (1956).
39. D. K. Walton and F. H. Verhoek, *Adv. Catalysis* **9,** 682 (1957).
40. Z. G. Szabó and F. Solymosi, Proc. 2nd International Congress on Catalysis (Editions Technip, Paris, 1961), **2,** 1627.
41. J. Block and H. Kral, *Z. Elektrochem.* **63,** 182 (1959).
42. T. Otaki, *J. Chem. Soc. Japan* **81,** 1387 (1960).
43. W. M. H. Sachtler and N. H. de Boer, *J. Phys. Chem.* **64,** 1579 (1960).
44. T. Otaki, *J. Chem. Soc. Japan* **80,** 225 (1959).
45. H. C. Tingey and C. N. Hinshelwood, *J. Chem. Soc.* **121,** 1668 (1922).
46. C. N. Hinshelwood and B. Topley, *J. Chem. Soc.* **123,** 1014 (1923).
47. G. Rienäcker, G. Wessing and G. Trautman, *Z. anorg. Chem.* **236,** 252 (1936).
48. G. Rienäcker and H. Hildebrandt, *Z. anorg. Chem.* **248,** 52 (1941).
49. A. J. Crocker and A. J. B. Robertson, *Trans. Faraday Soc.* **54,** 931 (1958).
50. H. M. C. Sosnovsky, **23,** 1486 (1955); G. Rienäcker and J. Völter, *Z. anorg. Chem.* **302,** 292, 299 (1960).
51. G. Rienäcker and H. Bremer, *Z. anorg. Chem.* **272,** 126 (1953).
52. G. Rienäcker and S. Unger, *Naturwiss.* **39,** 259 (1952).
53. G. Rienäcker. *Z. Elektrochem.* **46,** 369 (1940).
54. G.-M. Schwab and E. Schwab-Agallidis, *Ber.* **76,** 1228 (1943).
55. G. Rienäcker and J. Völter, *Z. anorg. Chem.* **296,** 210 (1958).
56. G. Rienäcker and H. Bade, *Z. anorg. Chem.* **248,** 45 (1941).
57. D. A. Dowden and P. W. Reynolds, *Discuss. Faraday Soc.* **8,** 184 (1950).
58. G.-M. Schwab and E. Schwab-Agallidis, *Naturwiss.* **31,** 322 (1943).
59. G. Rienäcker and G. Müller, unpublished; see G. Reinäcker, *Abhand. Deutsch. Akad. Wiss., Berlin* (*Kl. Chem., Geol. u. Biol.*), Nr. 3 (1955).
60. G. Rienäcker, *Z. anorg. Chem.* **227,** 353 (1936).
61. G.-M. Schwab, *Trans. Faraday Soc.* **42,** 689 (1946); G.-M. Schwab and G. Holz, *Z. anorg. Chem.* **252,** 205 (1944).
62. G.-M. Schwab, *Discuss. Faraday Soc.* **8,** 166 (1950); G. Rienäcker and G. Techel, *Z. anorg. Chem.* **304,** 58 (1960).
63. G. Rienäcker and W. Dietz, *Z. anorg. Chem.* **228,** 56 (1936).
64. J. Weiss, *Trans. Faraday Soc.* **31,** 1547 (1935).
65. R. Gerischer and H. Gerischer, *Z. phys. Chem.* (*Frankfurt*) **6,** 178 (1956).
66. P. P. Clopp and G. Parravano, *J. Phys. Chem.* **62,** 1055 (1958).

Chapter 19

Catalytic Reforming

19.1 General Principles

We come finally to consider the last aspect of the interaction of hydrocarbons and hydrogen on metallic catalysts. The process in question, known as *catalytic reforming*, is of immense industrial significance, and has achieved its present prominence only within the last decade.

The problem facing the petroleum industry is briefly the conversion of natural mineral oil into marketable fuels for motor and aircraft propulsion: this requires first the cracking of high molecular-weight hydrocarbons to products containing five to eleven carbon atoms, and boiling below 200°. Thermal cracking was originally employed for this purpose, but it is inefficient since much material of very low molecular weight is formed at the temperatures where cracking occurs at a significant rate. This was largely superseded in the mid-1930's by catalytic cracking, using natural acidic clays of the aluminosilicate type as the catalytic material. This phase of the story is well described, with full technical details, in Ref. 1.

However, the molecular-weight range of the product is not the sole criterion in determining its efficiency in internal combustion engines: its combustion characteristics, such as tendency towards pre-ignition and calorific value are also important. As is well known, the tendency to pre-ignite, which gives rise to the phenomenon of "knocking", can be overcome by the addition of tetra-ethyl lead or other suitable "anti-knock" agents: tetra-ethyl lead becomes oxidized to lead dioxide, which inhibits the growth of radical chains in the pre-ignition phase. The combustion characteristics of a petroleum product are assessed in an empirical fashion by assigning to the product an "octane rating". This was originally defined as the percentage of tetra-ethyl lead which it was found necessary to add in order just to prevent pre-ignition under standard conditions of test-engine operation. It is, however, now more generally defined as the percentage of iso-octane in an iso-octane + n-heptane mixture to which the material in question is equivalent in terms of its combustion behaviour, with the octane ratings of iso-octane and n-heptane being taken as respectively 100 and zero.

Aromatic and highly branched aliphatic hydrocarbons have particularly high octane ratings, and so the conversion of the primary products of cracking to these structures is particularly desirable. This was impossible before the advent of catalytic cracking, and the octane rating of the products of thermal cracking was only between 70 and 80.[1] Fortunately, however, the cracking catalysts not only degrade the high molecular weight hydrocarbons of natural oil but also cause the isomerization of the products to more highly branched structures, so that their octane rating is between 90 and 95. Cracking catalysts have the disadvantage that they are rapidly poisoned by carbon deposits which are formed through severe cracking at the operating temperature, and therefore require constant regeneration. Furthermore, they are unable to catalyse the cyclodehydrogenation of straight-chain paraffins, and hence do no lead to aromatic or olefinic products.

Both of these disadvantages have been in large measure overcome by the introduction of "dual-function" or reforming catalysts. They consist of a metal having high hydrogenation–dehydrogenation activity in combination with a cracking catalyst; in this way alicylic compounds are readily converted to aromatic compounds, and octane ratings of 100 are easily obtained. The introduction of the metallic component also permits the isomerization reactions to proceed at lower temperatures than would otherwise be necessary, and hence the tendency to coke formation is reduced.

The following Sections are devoted to a more detailed consideration of the structure of cracking and reforming catalysts, and of the mechanisms of the reactions which they effect.

19.2 The Structure and Operation of Cracking Catalysts[2–7]

It was recognized at an early stage in the use of natural clays as cracking catalysts that these materials have acidic properties. They catalyse not only the cracking and isomerization of hydrocarbons, but also alkylation reactions and the polymerization of olefins, all of which are also catalysed by acidic substances such as sulphuric and phosphoric acids, and Friedel–Crafts catalysts (halides of boron and aluminium). The work of Whitmore established that reactions with these latter materials proceed by carbonium ion mechanisms, and hence it was natural to suppose that hydrocarbon reactions on aluminosilicate clays also involved carbonium ions. While all the evidence points in this direction, unequivocal proof has only recently been obtained.[8]

Naturally occurring aluminosilicate clays have, however, in large measure been replaced by synthetic silica–alumina of high purity. This material is readily made by the hydrolysis of a mixture of alkoxy-compounds of silicon and aluminium either in the liquid or preferably in the vapour phase: the product is highly porous if not heated to temperatures much in excess of 500°, and is very hard. It may be used either as a fixed bed, or as a "fluidized" bed, in which the gas stream agitates the finely divided solid until it resembles a boiling liquid. Maximum acidity is shown by the material containing equiatomic parts of silicon and aluminium, although that containing about 10 per cent alumina is more suited for catalytic use. Other oxides may replace alumina, and compounds of silica with magnesia, boria and zirconia (as well as three-component mixtures) have been tried, but none is superior to the combination of silica with alumina.[1, 9]

The structure of the active material and the nature of the active sites are hard to establish, and have been the subject of some controversy. The cause of the activity and questions of mechanism are inextricably connected, and some statement of the latter must now be made. The rearrangements which carbonium ions undergo are quite well understood, and uncertainty has centred on the mechanism of their formation and destruction on the catalyst. Hydrocarbons are only very weakly chemisorbed under reaction conditions; reversible chemisorption of isobutane to the extent of 10^{-3} cm.^{3} g.$^{-1}$ has, however, been detected.[10] The low concentration of the reactive species renders their investigation difficult, although recent spectroscopic studies[8, 11] have confirmed the formation of carbonium ions from olefins and from saturated hydrocarbons (see also Ref. 12).

The mechanism of carbonium ion formation from olefins is at first sight straightforward; it would appear that the existence of available protons is required:

$$R{-}CH{=}CH_2 + H^+ \rightarrow R{-}\overset{+}{C}H{-}CH_3. \qquad (a)$$

The situation with regard to saturated hydrocarbons, which constitute the major part of the feedstock in industrial usage, is, however, more complicated. Two possibilities exist. (i) Carbonium ions may be formed according to process (a) from the small equilibrium concentration of olefin existing in the feedstock vapour at the reaction temperature: once formed initially, they may be propagated by the process:

$$R'{-}CH_2{-}CH_3 + R{-}\overset{+}{C}H{-}CH_3 \rightarrow R'{-}\overset{+}{C}H{-}CH_3 + R{-}CH_2{-}CH_3. \qquad (b)$$

(ii) The saturated hydrocarbon may lose a hydride ion (H^-) reversibly either by reaction with a catalyst proton, as

$$R{-}CH_2{-}CH_3 + H^+ \rightleftharpoons R{-}\overset{+}{C}H{-}CH_3 + H_2, \qquad (c)$$

or by reaction with a strongly electronegative catalyst site (designated as [L]) whose nature will be further discussed below:

$$R{-}CH_2{-}CH_3 + [L] \rightleftharpoons R{-}\overset{+}{C}H{-}CH_3 + H^-[L]. \qquad (d)$$

If, however, such sites exist, as recent work seems to indicate, then it is at least possible that they are capable of strongly polarizing, and even of ionizing, the π-electrons in olefins: the formulation

$$R{-}CH{=}CH_2 + [L] \rightarrow \begin{array}{c} \delta+ \\ R{-}CH\text{-----}CH_2 \\ \ddots\ \therefore \\ [L]\delta- \end{array} \qquad (e)$$

represents the polarized olefin.

Since the modes of formation of carbonium ions from hydrocarbons are uncertain, there being some evidence in favour of all the several processes described above, we must now turn our attention to the structural features of cracking catalysts which these processes imply. Unfortunately it is not even certain whether in silica–alumina the aluminium is randomly dispersed, replacing silicon isomorphously, or whether, as some workers argue,[3] activity is associated with the boundaries between microcrystalline volumes of silica and alumina. However, since the first view, or some modified form of it,[13, 14] appears the more generally accepted, we may proceed by supposing its correctness.

We may distinguish between two different kinds of acidic sites by analogy with more familiar examples drawn from general chemistry. Substances such as gaseous hydrogen chloride and the Friedel–Crafts halides are designated Lewis acids, since they can react with water or other hydroxylic compounds with the liberation of protons, which, of course, in solution are always hydrated. The electronegative sites [L], referred to above, are Lewis-acid sites, and are probably tervalent aluminium atoms or ions (see structure A below). Now substances such as the ammonium ion and the oxonium ion (H_3O^+), possessing available protons, are referred to as Brønsted acids, and the processes (a) and (c) above must therefore proceed at Brønsted-acid sites. Lewis-acid and Brønsted-acid sites may therefore be formulated respectively as in structures A and B below: these two structures are not very different

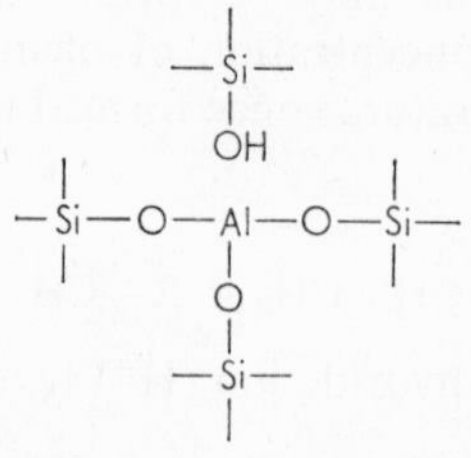

Structure A (Lewis-acid site) 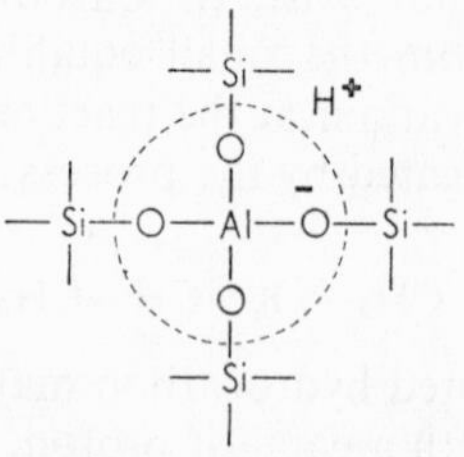 Structure B (Brønsted-acid site)

and indeed their interconversion is readily envisaged. In structure B, the negative charge is probably delocalized within the dotted circle because of the high electronegativity of the oxygen atoms. However, if steric conditions permit, a Lewis-acid site may be hydrated by a water molecule and converted to a Bronsted-acid site by the following mechanism:

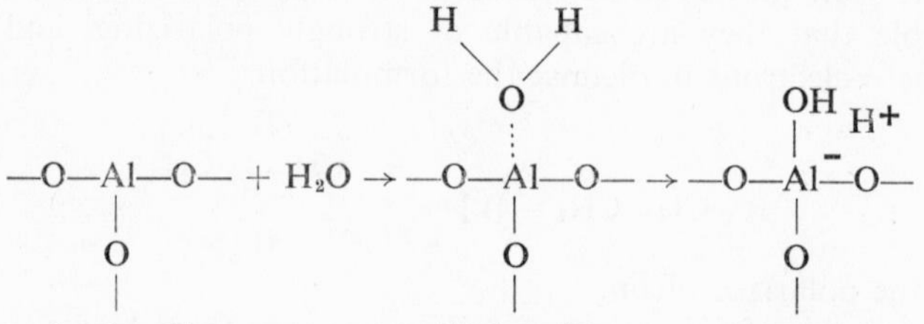

$$-O-Al(-O-)-O- + H_2O \rightarrow -O-Al(\cdots OH_2)(-O-)-O- \rightarrow -O-\overset{-}{Al}(OH)(-O-)-O-\ H^+ \quad (f).$$

Lewis-acid site — Hydrated Lewis-acid site — Brønsted-acid site

On elimination of water between the final structure of this sequence and the hydroxyl group attached to the silicon (structure A), structure B is, of course, produced. Structure B is advocated by Gray[14] on the basis of differential thermal analysis and X-ray spectroscopy of materials containing different amounts of alumina: he describes the active component as a half-inverted spinel in which some of the octahedral sites contain protons. It is thus clear that the introduction of electron-deficient aluminium atoms into the silica matrix can give rise to either kind of acid site required to initiate the formation of carbonium ions.

The constitutional water of these materials is necessary for their activity,[15] and heating above about 700° causes the collapse of their pore structure, and ultimately recrystallization into separate alumina and silica phases. Studies of these phenomena have been reported.[3, 5, 16]

The acidity of cracking catalysts may be estimated by titration with a weak base such as n-butylamine,[17] and the concentration of acidic centres is around 5×10^{13} cm.$^{-2}$: thus nearly every aluminium atom at the available surface constitutes an acidic site, although only about 0.001 of these are occupied by hydrocarbons during operation. Cracking activity increases with acidity, but in either more or less than strict proportion depending on the reactant.[3] The activation energy for formic acid decomposition decreases with increasing acidity.[18]

This brief review of the structure and operating of cracking catalysts does much less than justice to the large amount of work which has been devoted to understanding them, but it is hoped that it provides a sufficient background to the subject of reforming catalysts which the next Section considers.

19.3 Catalytic Reforming[19–21]

19.31 The Nature of Reforming Catalysts

As noted in the introductory Section, the addition of a metallic component to a cracking catalyst results in a petroleum product of much superior quality. Most of the Group VIII metals have been tried,[22] but none is more satisfactory than platinum, which is now used exclusively. Indeed in recent years more than one half of the platinum sold each year has been for the preparation of reforming catalysts. Because of the pre-eminence of platinum, the term "platinum reforming catalyst" has been abbreviated to "platforming catalyst," and the term platforming (as well as other trivial names like houdriforming and catforming) is in common use.

As the acidic phase in reforming catalysts, alumina acidified with a halogen acid (usually hydrofluoric acid) is now widely used in place of silica–alumina. The acid is introduced by impregnating the alumina with a dilute solution of the acid, and the protons so transferred to the catalyst presumably initiate the formation of carbonium ions. Three closely parallel studies of the dispersion of platinum on acidified alumina have recently been published.[23–25] Measurements of the high-temperature chemisorption of hydrogen and of carbon monoxide, and of X-ray line broadening, have enabled the size of the metallic crystallites to be measured after various treatments to the catalyst. The concentration of platinum in the catalysts studied was always less than 1 per cent, for in industrial practice concentrations of only 0.1–0.05 per cent are commonly used. The results of these three studies may be summarized as follows. Chemisorption and line-broadening measurements lead to generally consistent values of crystallite size, although the line-broadening method is not responsive to crystallites of less than 50 Å diameter. Chemisorption measurements on freshly reduced and evacuated catalysts show that a very high proportion (75 to 100 per cent) of the platinum atoms are exposed, and hence the crystallites must be very small or perhaps even in the form of "islands" of only one atom thickness. Heat treatments carried out for various times between 480 and 750° showed that loss of activity by sintering was accompanied by a growth in the mean crystallite size to 250–300 Å.

A somewhat revolutionary idea has recently been advanced to account for the specific ability of certain reforming catalysts to effect direct dehydrocyclization, for example, of n-heptane to toluene.[26] Hexachloroplatinic acid and the acidic phase are claimed to form an irreducible complex which is the active entity; the corresponding complex formed by palladium salts is easily reducible, and the resulting catalyst has a much inferior dehydrocyclization activity. This view is not altogether inconsistent with the findings recorded in the last paragraph, namely that nearly all the platinum atoms are freely available. It has also long been known that silica–alumina when impregnated with nickel salts forms a hydrous nickel aluminosilicate,[27] and that after reduction the resulting metal is so finely dispersed that it does not show the propensity to cause extreme cracking which is typical of bulk nickel.[22]

Reforming catalysts normally operate under a substantial pressure of hydrogen: model experiments[22, 28, 29] have employed hydrogen: hydrocarbon ratios of about five and total pressures of about 20 atm. This pressure of hydrogen is insufficient to affect substantially the equilibrium yield of aromatic compounds formed by dehydrogenation at the temperatures employed (roughly 300–400°). It also has the beneficial effect of inhibiting the deposition of carbon on the metal areas, a process which results in the rapid loss of activity. For this reason, reforming catalysts commonly have a life of over two years, after which they are processed to recover the platinum, which is then re-used.

Few studies have been made of the relative activities of different metals in reforming reactions, but a recent study[30] using fluorided eta-alumina, boria–alumina, gallia–alumina and chromia–alumina as the acidic phases has established the following sequence, which pertains both to isomerization and to cracking:

$$Pt > Pd > Ir > Rh.$$

Ruthenium and rhenium catalysts, while efficient in cracking, showed little isomerization activity. The alumina-supported catalysts gave faster rates than the others, the chromia–alumina-supported materials in particular showing extensive side reactions. This investigation was supplemented by the examination of combinations of metals supported on the alumina. In the binary combinations Pt–Ru, Pt–Rh, Pt–Ir, Pt–Os and Pt–Re, a maximum in isomerization activity was shown at about the composition where a homogeneous alloy would have one *d*-band hole. However, only in the systems Pt–Rh and Pt–Ir are complete ranges of solid solution possible, and in the other cases, where the component metals have different structures, the solubility of each in the other is quite limited. Over most of the composition range for these other systems, therefore, the metallic phase must have been heterogeneous.

19.32 The Kinetics and Mechanism of Reforming Reactions

Reforming catalysts effect in the presence of hydrogen the reactions of hydrogenolysis (cracking), isomerization and dehydrocyclization,[26] as well as hydrogenation and dehydrogenation. Because they operate at lower temperatures than cracking catalysts, cracking to low molecular-weight hydrocarbons is often insignificant. Isomerization involves not only an enhanced degree of chain-branching in saturated hydrocarbons, but also their cyclization to a cyclohexane through the intermediary of a substituted cyclopentane.[28, 29] Direct dehydrocyclization has been only a little studied,[26] and the specific catalyst requirements for this process were referred to in the last sub-section. Nickel–silica–alumina catalysts somewhat mysteriously fail to dehydrogenate cyclohexanes to aromatic hydrocarbons;[22] this may be because the nickel is too finely dispersed to provide the necessary array of sites. Platinum reforming catalysts, of course, do this most efficiently, a fact which probably accounts for their popularity in spite of their high cost.

Now there is little doubt that the principal function of the metal is to catalyse the dehydrogenation of saturated hydrocarbons to olefins.[22, 29] The olefins then migrate to acidic sites where they are converted to carbonium ions and suffer isomerization, the isomerized olefin returning to the metal either to be re-hydrogenated or further dehydrogenated as determined by the thermodynamics of the system. That this is so is well demonstrated by the fact that olefins are isomerized much more rapidly than the corresponding saturated molecules.[22] Thus if we consider the fate of n-hexane over a reforming catalyst incapable of effecting direct dehydrocyclization,[28, 29] 1-hexene formed by dehydrogenation may isomerize to methylcyclopentane, and the resulting methylcyclopentane may isomerize to cyclohexene, which may finally appear as benzene. The full possibilities are illustrated by the scheme on page 444. The structures shown for the olefins are only representative. Under conditions where the reforming catalyst converts about 50 per cent of either methylcyclopentane or methylcyclopentene to benzene, catalysts possessing only either the metallic or the acidic function yield only between 3 and 16 per cent benzene from these reactants.[29]

While it is possible that some reaction occurs at the junction of metallic and acidic areas,[21] the two kinds of function do not in fact have to be in close

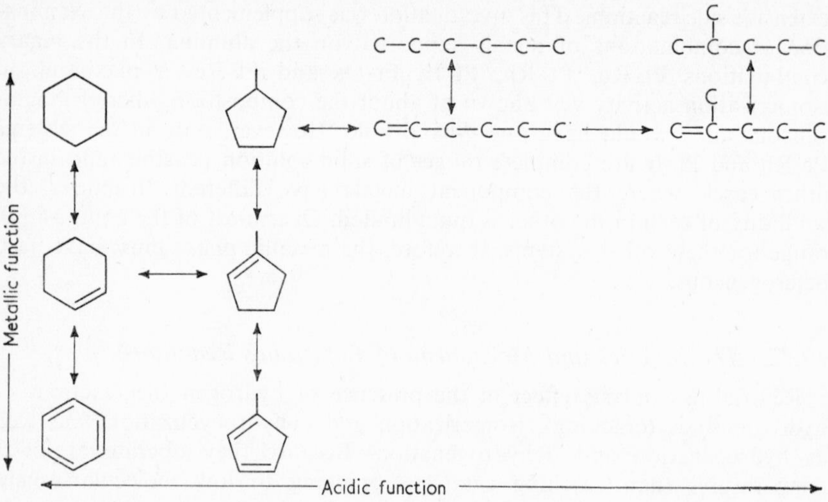

C—C—C—C—C—C

C=C—C—C—C—C

C—C(C)—C—C—C

C=C(C)—C—C—C

Metallic function

Acidic function

proximity. This has been clearly established by experiments in which platinum on non-acidic silica and silica–alumina have been mechanically mixed: the mixture shows reforming properties not much inferior to those of a normal dual-function catalyst.[31, 32] The picture is, therefore, that the olefin formed by dehydrogenation at the metal is transported through the gas phase to the acidic site and after isomerization is re-transported to the metal for hydrogenation, or if a cyclohexane, for further dehydrogenation. This model is supported by the detection of small amounts of methylcyclopentene during the reforming of methylcyclopentane.[31]

The formal kinetics of such a multi-stage system have been described:[32, 33] the system is as follows.

$$\underset{m}{A \rightleftharpoons A'} \xrightarrow[t]{\sim\sim} \underset{i}{B \rightarrow C} \xrightarrow[t]{\sim\sim} \underset{m}{D' \rightleftharpoons D}$$

The equilibria between A and D (saturated hydrocarbons) and their conjugate olefins A′ and D′ are set up at the metallic function, m: A′ is transported ($\xrightarrow{\sim\sim}$) to the acidic function where it is adsorbed as the carbonium ion B, isomerized to the ion C and transported back to the metallic function as the olefin D′. In principle either the hydrogenation–dehydrogenation or the transport or the isomerization may limit the overall rate. Which does in practice is determined by the distance between the two functions, by their activities and by the equilibrium partial pressures of the olefins. It is intuitively likely, and experiment confirms,[34] that hydrogenation–dehydrogenation steps are not rate limiting. In a normal dual-function catalyst, where both functions are in close proximity, the equilibrium partial pressure of olefins is usually sufficient for the transport process not to be rate limiting, and hence isomerization must be.[34, 35] However, in a mechanically mixed reforming catalyst, where the two functions may be many microns apart, transport of the olefin may limit the rate if the partial pressure of olefin does not exceed a critical value. Calculations show[32] that to maintain a reasonable overall rate (10^{-6} moles cm.$^{-2}$ sec.$^{-1}$) this pressure must be 10^{-2} atm. if the two functions are 0.05 mm. apart, but only 10^{-8} atm. if they are 100 Å apart.

The kinetics of the isomerization of n-pentane over a platinum reforming catalyst have been studied[34] at 372°; the rate is independent of total pressure between 8 and 28 atm., and variation of the hydrogen : n-pentane ratio (with hydrogen always in excess) leads to the rate expression:

$$r = k\left(\frac{P_{nC_5}}{P_{H_2}}\right)^{0.5}.$$

References

1. R. V. Shankland, *Adv. Catalysis* **6,** 272 (1954).
2. V. Haensel, *Adv. Catalysis* **3,** 179 (1951).
3. A. G. Oblad, T. H. Milliken and G. A. Mills, *Adv. Catalysis* **3,** 199 (1951).
4. R. C. Hansford, *Adv. Catalysis* **4,** 1 (1952).
5. H. E. Ries, *Adv. Catalysis* **4,** 88 (1952).
6. H. H. Voge, In "Catalysis", edited by P. H. Emmett (Reinhold, New York, 1958), **6,** 407.
7. L. B. Ryland, M. W. Tamele and J. N. Wilson, In "Catalysis", edited by P. H. Emmett (Reinhold, New York, 1960), **7,** 1.
8. H. P. Leftin and W. K. Hall, Proc. 2nd International Congress on Catalysis (Editions Technip. Paris, 1961), **1,** 1353.
9. E. M. Gladrow, R. W. Krebs and C. N. Kimberlin, *Ind. Eng. Chem.* **45,** 137 (1953).
10. D. S. MacIver, P. H. Emmett and H. S. Frank, *J. Phys. Chem.* **62,** 935 (1958).
11. A. N. Webb, Proc. 2nd International Congress on Catalysis (Editions Technip, Paris, 1961), **1,** 1289.
12. J. J. Rooney and R. C. Pink, *Proc. Chem. Soc.* 70 (1961).
13. J. D. Danforth, *Adv. Catalysis* **9,** 558 (1957).
14. T. J. Gray, *J. Phys. Chem.* **61,** 1341 (1957).
15. R. C. Hansford, P. G. Waldo, L. C. Drake and R. E. Honig, *Ind. Eng. Chem.* **44,** 1108 (1952).
16. Y. J. Trambouze, M. Perrin and L. de Mourgues, *Adv. Catalysis* **9,** 544 (1957).
17. H. A. Benesi, *J. Phys. Chem.* **61,** 970 (1957).
18. J. B. Fisher and F. Sebba, Proc. 2nd International Congress on Catalysis (Editions Technip, Paris, 1961), **1,** 711.
19. F. G. Ciapetta, R. M. Dobres and R. W. Baker, In "Catalysis", edited by P. H. Emmett (Reinhold, New York, 1958), **6,** 495.
20. H. Connor, *Chem. and Ind.* 1454 (1960).
21. A. I. M. Keulemans and G. C. A. Schuit, In "The Mechanism of Heterogeneous Catalysis" (Elsevier, Amsterdam, 1960), p. 159.
22. F. G. Ciapetta and J. B. Hunter, *Ind. Eng. Chem.* **45,** 147, 155, 159, 162 (1953).
23. L. Spenadel and M. J. Boudart, *J. Phys. Chem.* **64,** 204 (1960).
24. S. F. Adler and J. J. Keavney, *J. Phys. Chem.* **64,** 208 (1960).
25. G. A. Mills, S. Weller and E. B. Cornelius, Proc. 2nd International Congress on Catalysis (Editions Technip, Paris, 1961), **2,** 2221.
26. K. W. McHenry, R. J. Bertolacini, H. M. Brennan, J. L. Wilson and H. S. Seelig, Proc. 2nd International Congress on Catalysis (Editions Technip, Paris, 1961), **2,** 2295.

27. J. J. de Lange and G. H. Visser, *Ingenieur* (*Utrecht*) **58,** 24 (1946).
28. H. Heinemann, G. A. Mills, J. B. Hattman and F. W. Kirsch, *Ind. Eng. Chem.* **45,** 130 (1953).
29. G. A. Mills, H. Heinemann, T. H. Milliken and A. G. Oblad, *Ind. Eng. Chem.* **45,** 134 (1953).
30. T. J. Gray, N. G. Masse and H. G. Oswin, Proc. 2nd International Congress on Catalysis (Editions Technip, Paris, 1961), **2,** 1697.
31. S. G. Hindin, S. W. Weller and G. A. Mills, *J. Phys. Chem.* **62,** 244 (1958).
32. P. B. Weisz, Proc. 2nd International Congress on Catalysis (Editions Technip, Paris, 1961), **1,** 937.
33. P. B. Weisz and C. D. Prater, *Adv. Catalysis* **9,** 575 (1957).
34. J. H. Sinfelt, H. Hurwitz and J. A. Rohrer, *J. Phys. Chem.* **64,** 893 (1960).
35. A. I. M. Keulemans and H. H. Voge, *J. Phys. Chem.* **63,** 476 (1959).

Chapter 20

Catalytic Oxidation

20.1 Introduction

Only a very few metals can be used as heterogeneous catalysts for oxidation reactions. The reason is, of course, that most metals are unstable in oxygen, particularly at the high temperatures which it is necessary to use, and the formation of thick oxide layers (if not gross oxidation) occurs. The metals which pre-eminently resist oxidation are platinum, silver and gold, although gold is inactive when it is unable to chemisorb oxygen (see Chapter 5). The familiar picture of catalytic activity being inversely related to the strength of reactant adsorption again emerges.

Consideration will be almost entirely restricted to oxidations effected by molecular oxygen, and such reactions normally occur within a significantly higher region of temperature than do, for example, hydrogenations. This region is typically between 200 and 1000°, although significantly the oxidation of hydrogen takes place quite readily at room temperature over active metals (see Section 20.2). Above about 1000°, adsorbed species are liable to desorb, and initiate homogeneous reactions.

A particular feature of oxidation catalysis is the rearrangements which metal surfaces suffer during reaction: these changes occur at quite moderate temperatures (sometimes as low as 250°), far below the melting point of the metal. The phenomenon is further discussed in Sections 20.3 and 20.4.

The remainder of this chapter is devoted to a consideration of the catalytic oxidation of hydrogen, hydrocarbons, ammonia, carbon monoxide and sulphur dioxide. Some of these processes have (or have had) immense industrial significance, and have therefore been thoroughly studied. In each system there is, however, ample room for further progress.

20.2 The Catalytic Oxidation of Hydrogen

The noble metals of Groups VIII and IB are very efficient catalysts for this reaction: thus highly dispersed platinum and palladium will catalyse the reaction at room temperature, and the action of silver and gold may be conveniently studied in the region of 100°. Catalytic preparations are commercially available which at room temperature remove traces of either oxygen or hydrogen from gas streams containing an excess of the other.

In spite of its simplicity and technical interest, there have been surprisingly few fundamental studies of the oxidation of hydrogen, and the kinetics are not well established even for the metals which are most active. Over silver powder[1] between 60 and 130°, the order in oxygen is zero and in hydrogen is 0.63 at 100° and 0.52 at 110°: the activation energy is about 12.5 kcal. mole^{-1}, and the reaction is retarded by water vapour. Adsorption experiments showed that oxygen was strongly adsorbed, the volume taken up being independent of temperature and pressure, and that hydrogen was not adsorbed, notwithstanding the observed orders in hydrogen. The mechanism proposed involved the collision of a gaseous hydrogen molecule with a vacant site adjacent to a chemisorbed oxygen molecule, but the results are also consistent with a fairly weak adsorption of hydrogen at low temperature (perhaps by interaction with adsorbed oxygen), becoming stronger with rising temperature: this would agree with the fact that the adsorption of hydrogen on silver is activated (see Chapters 5 and 8). Further in line with this is the observation that when the reaction is carried out in a silver vessel between 650 and 700°, it is zero order in hydrogen but now first order in oxygen:[2] thus at this higher temperature there is more *ds*-promotion and hence stronger adsorption of hydrogen, while the adsorption of oxygen has weakened for the normal reason.

Over gold powder at 130°, the rate expression is:[3]

$$r \propto P_{H_2}^{2} P_{O_2} P_{H_2O}^{-1}, \tag{1}$$

and the activation energy is 20.8 kcal. mole^{-1} between 130 and 150°. Water retards the reaction over gold less strongly than the reaction over silver. Hydrogen was found not to be adsorbed, but in contradistinction to the behaviour of clean and macroscopic gold surfaces, the powder was found to adsorb oxygen strongly. No mechanism was advanced to interpret the observed kinetics. It has been shown that hydrogen atoms chemisorbed on a gold surface during the decomposition of formic acid are readily oxidized to water by molecular oxygen under conditions where the oxidation of molecular hydrogen does not take place.[4]

Early experiments[5–7] showed that the rate of the reaction over various platinum catalysts was proportional to hydrogen pressure and either independent of or inhibited by oxygen pressure, but over platinum wire between 100 and 150° it has been reported[8] to be independent of hydrogen pressure and a complex function of oxygen pressure. From the results of this last investigation, two kinds of adsorption site were postulated for oxygen. The specific activities of platinum wire and foil, and of silica-supported platinum, for the oxidation of hydrogen have been shown to be similar.[9] Over palladium films, hydrogen reacts rapidly with adsorbed oxygen and vice versa,[10] and over this metal activation energies of 1.8 and 2.8 kcal. mole^{-1} have been reported for the oxidation of hydrogen and of deuterium respectively.[11] The effects of various poisons on the activity of a palladium catalyst for this reaction have been studied.[12]

The action of copper and some copper–gold alloys has also been investigated,[13] but all are to some extent oxidized during the reaction, and it seems likely that the activity shown is due in all cases to cuprous oxide. However, at fairly low temperatures (170–330°) metallic nickel in the form of a wire appears not to be oxidized provided the hydrogen: oxygen ratio is not too low:[14] the rate is proportional to hydrogen pressure and to a fractional positive power of the oxygen pressure, and the activation energy is 5.2 kcal. mole^{-1}.

Two studies only are reported on the variation of the rate of hydrogen oxidation with composition of alloys between metals of Groups VIII and IB.[15, 16] In what is probably the earliest investigation of the activity of alloys, Tammann[15] measured the threshold temperature T_t for the oxidation over alloy wires with both rising and falling temperatures. For pure palladium, T_t (rising) was about 150° and T_t (falling) about 40°. There was a slow increase in both values with increasing silver content, until a sudden increase occurred at the 80 per cent silver alloy, for which T_t (rising) was 375° and T_t (falling) was 275°. Palladium–gold alloys showed a similar behaviour: there was little change in the threshold temperatures between pure palladium and the 70 per cent gold alloy, but for alloys containing more than 70 per cent gold, T_t rose rapidly with increasing gold content.

A more detailed study of the palladium–silver system has recently been reported by Kowaka:[16] he used a stoichiometric reactant mixture at 160 mm. pressure and alloys in the form of ribbons. Their areas were not measured but were all assumed to be the same as the geometric area of 21 cm.^{2}. At 100°, pure palladium gave an induction period which was reduced by pretreatment with hydrogen and removed altogether by pretreatment with oxygen. Silver showed a similar behaviour at 400°. The values of the activation energies and of the pre-exponential factors are given in Table I; there is no satisfactory

TABLE I. *Arrhenius Parameters for the Oxidation of Hydrogen Catalysed by Palladium–Silver Alloys*[16]

Atom % silver	*E(kcal. mole^{-1})*	*logA (A in min^{-1})*
10	9.0	5.77
20	8.5	4.77
30	9.2	4.97
40	9.0	4.85
50	8.0	4.80
60	10.4	5.06
70	11.4	4.66
80	13.0	4.20
100	19.5	5.67

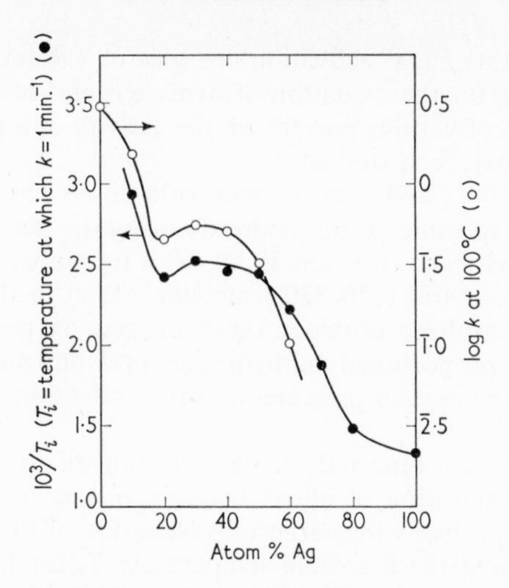

FIG. 1. The activity of palladium–silver alloys for the hydrogen–oxygen reaction.[16]
● The variation with composition of $10^3/T_i$ (T_i being the temperature at which the rate constant is 1 min.$^{-1}$).
○ The variation of log*k* at 100° with composition.

compensation effect. In Fig. 1 are shown values of log*k* (*k* in min.$^{-1}$) at 100° and also values of $10^3/T_i$ (T_i being the temperature at which the rate constant is 1 min.$^{-1}$), since the latter are available right up to 100 per cent silver. With increasing silver content the activity at first declines rapidly; a subsidiary maximum is then shown at 30 per cent silver, and above 50 per cent silver the activity again decreases rapidly. These variations are in very qualitative agreement with Tammann's results.[15] The activation energy is essentially constant for alloys containing between 10 and 50 per cent silver.

There has been no satisfactory discussion of the mechanism of this reaction, and indeed in view of the scarcity of measurements of reaction orders, this is hardly surprising. Some generalizations may, however, be made on the basis of the foregoing results. Since it is known that oxygen is readily chemisorbed by all metals except gold, the lower activity of silver as compared with platinum and palladium is probably due to its inability to activate hydrogen. The notion that the activation of the hydrogen is a relevant consideration finds support in the observation (Table I) that the activation energy is constant up to the point at which the *d*-band is presumably filled, a result which is also found for other hydrogenation reactions (see Chapters 8 and 11). However, the adsorption of hydrogen is unlikely to be rate determining in the case of *d*-metals, but the activation energy over palladium shows an isotope effect,[11] so that the fission of some bond in which hydrogen is a partner occurs in the slow step. A possible mechanism for *d*-metals is therefore as follows.

$$H_2 + 2* \rightarrow 2\underset{*}{H}\ ;\quad O_2 + 2* \rightarrow \underset{*}{O}—\underset{*}{O} \qquad (a, a')$$

$$\underset{*}{2H} + \underset{*}{O}\text{—}\underset{*}{O} \rightarrow 2\,\underset{*}{OH} + 2* \tag{b}$$

$$\underset{*}{2OH} + \underset{*}{2H} \rightarrow 2\,H_2O + 4* \tag{c}$$

There is no means at the moment of establishing which of (b) and (c) is the slowest step.

The difference in activity between palladium and silver has also been ascribed to the difference between the heats of adsorption of oxygen on the two metals.[16] This is more than twice as great for silver as for palladium,[17] but most of the change occurs between pure palladium and the 1 per cent silver alloy. This may correlate with the rapid decrease in activity found between 0 and 20 per cent silver,[16] but the later decrease (after the *d*-band is filled) cannot be wholly connected with the heat of adsorption of oxygen, and here the activation of hydrogen may be the slow step. There is indeed some kinetic evidence,[1] noted earlier, that this may be so over silver.

20.3 The Catalytic Oxidation of Hydrocarbons

20.31 The Oxidation of Saturated Hydrocarbons[18]

The catalytic oxidation of saturated hydrocarbons has been relatively little studied. Although the formation of oxygenated intermediates (such as formaldehyde or methanol from methane) is economically attractive, high yields are hard to obtain, and emphasis has been placed on homogeneous oxidation and on oxidation catalysed by metal oxides. However, respectable conversions (about 60 per cent) of methane to formaldehyde have been achieved by passing methane in admixture with air and steam over copper or silver at 500°, and supported metals have also been tried.[18] Methane may also be oxidized to carbon monoxide and hydrogen, the raw material for the Fischer–Tropsch synthesis, by passing it with a deficiency of oxygen over supported nickel between 700 and 900°:[19] the low yields (less than 5 per cent) of carbon dioxide and water suggest that the reaction proceeds through the stages

$$CH_4 + 2O_2 \rightarrow CO_2 + 2H_2O \tag{d}$$
$$CH_4 + H_2O \rightarrow CO + 3H_2 \tag{e}$$
$$CH_4 + CO_2 \rightarrow 2CO + 2H_2. \tag{f}$$

Another field of application of hydrocarbon oxidation is the removal of small quantities of hydrocarbon from air, and considerable work has been done[20, 21] using mixtures of 3 per cent methane in air. Platinum ribbon at 1000° takes some two hours to acquire a constant maximum activity, during which time the roughness factor rises from 1.5 to 2.5. Alloys of platinum with small quantities (between 2 and 25 per cent) of palladium, rhodium or iridium are less active than pure platinum, roughly in proportion to the concentration of the solute metal and independent of its chemical nature. The final activity of platinum rises only slightly with increasing temperature between 1000 and 1150°. There is evidence that above 1150° the reaction proceeds at least in part homogeneously, initiated by radicals vacating the surface, and CH and OH radicals have been detected spectroscopically in the gas phase. At these high temperatures some platinum evaporates from the surface, and an aerosol is formed: but the rate of evaporation, which has been followed by using neutron-irradiated platinum, is much faster during the reaction than when the metal is simply heated in air. This is, perhaps, not surprising in view of the considerable body of evidence to show that very substantial surface rearrangements occur during catalysis at temperatures far below the melting point of the metal, and below the temperature at which such changes would occur by purely thermal effects.[22, 23] It is uncertain whether these rearrangements take place because (i) with exothermic reactions the temperature of the surface is higher than the mean, or (ii) more probably because the adsorbed species weaken the binding of surface metal atoms to those below, and hence facilitate the migration of the former.

20.32 The Oxidation of Ethylene[18]

The catalytic oxidation of ethylene to ethylene oxide is a unique reaction in the area of oxidation catalysis, and metallic silver is the sole catalyst known to effect the reaction. The value of the product as an organic intermediate is such as to make the reaction of great commercial interest: it is now widely carried out on an industrial scale, and much technical information concerning catalyst preparation is available, especially in the patent literature.

With the use of a ten- to twenty-fold excess of air (invariably used instead of pure oxygen in commercial operation), ethylene may be converted to ethylene oxide with a selectivity of between 0.4 and 0.5 between about 240 and 280°; the remainder of the ethylene is converted to carbon dioxide. The rate and selectivity both decrease as the excess of air over ethylene is decreased. Catalysts deactivate and become less selective with use, and so the temperature is increased slowly to compensate for these changes. The addition of small amounts of chlorinated hydrocarbons have been empirically found to produce spectacular increases in selectivity. Thus the addition of 8 per cent of ethylene dichloride (based on the ethylene) increases the yield of ethylene oxide over a somewhat used catalyst at 280° by a factor of no less than four. Larger amounts, however, have harmful effects both on the selectivity and on the activity, although both recover when the supply of the dichloride is stopped. An explanation for this effect will be offered below.

All technical catalysts have metallic silver as the major component: it has been used in the form of powder, foil or supported on a carrier. For this purpose, a wide variety of inert substances have been used, but none is superior to α–Al_2O_3. Supported silver has been used in both fixed and fluidized beds. Many other metals have been studied for promotional effects, but only gold, copper, iron and manganese have the desired properties. Barium peroxide is an excellent promoter for these silver oxidation catalysts.

A number of careful studies of the kinetics of the oxidation of ethylene have been carried out, but unfortunately no agreed conclusions regarding its mechanism have been arrived at. Part of the trouble no doubt arises through the use of different kinds of catalyst, not always sufficiently characterized. The essential features of the reaction schemes which have been discussed as shown below: no attempt is made to portray the stoichiometry. It seems

$$C_2H_4 \underset{g'}{\overset{g}{\rightleftharpoons}} (C_2H_4O)_a \underset{i'}{\overset{i}{\rightleftharpoons}} C_2H_4O$$

$$(C_2H_4O)_a \xrightarrow{j} (CH_3CHO)_a \underset{m'}{\overset{m}{\rightleftharpoons}} CH_3CHO$$

$$C_2H_4 \xrightarrow{h} CO_2 + H_2O; \quad (C_2H_4O)_a \xrightarrow{k} CO_2 + H_2O; \quad (CH_3CHO)_a \xrightarrow{l} CO_2 + H_2O$$

generally agreed that ethylene is not chemisorbed by silver surfaces, and that oxygen is quite strongly adsorbed as atoms. Oxygen adsorption is activated,[24, 25] and its rate of adsorption is about the same as the rate of ethylene oxidation,[26] so that it may be the slowest step in the overall process. Adsorbed oxygen has a negative surface potential of about 0.2 V.,[26] although this is much dependent on the purity of the silver surface. The conductivity of very thin silver films, which is therefore decreased by the presence of adsorbed oxygen, increases again when the reaction is proceeding to a value approximately the same as that for a *reduced* silver surface;[27] this supports the contention that the stationary concentration of adsorbed oxygen atoms is low, and that oxygen adsorption may sometimes be the slowest step. Indeed the reaction has been on occasion[28] declared to be first order in oxygen, but the simultaneous observation that its rate is independent of ethylene concentration when this is greater than 5 mole per cent suggests limitation by mass transfer.

It is evident in a system as complex as that set down above that the straightforward expression of the kinetics of the reaction in terms of exponents of the reactant pressures[29] is by no means sufficient for the full elucidation of the mechanism. The numerous products are all capable of being adsorbed, and investigation of the effect of initially added products has been somewhat neglected. However, the reaction has been said to be inhibited by ethylene oxide,[30] by carbon dioxide[28, 30] and by water. There has been, and continues to be, much controversy over the path through which the completely oxidized products are formed, and many of the kinetic studies mentioned below have tried to establish (1) whether the direct path (h) is available, and (2) whether ethylene oxide may be directly oxidized through step (k) or whether it first isomerizes (step j) to some intermediate which may or may not be acetaldehyde. If adsorbed acetaldehyde is so formed, it must be very quickly oxidized (step l) since it is only observed at most in trace quantities in the products. These questions have more than academic significance, since the answers may affect conditions of technical operation. Thus if the selectivity is low because the desired product is oxidized, the remedy lies in its rapid removal from the catalyst zone. If, however, the direct path (h) is responsible, this will have no effect and the remedy lies in improving the catalyst.

According to Twigg,[24] to whom the first detailed study of the kinetics is due, the processes (g) and (h) occur simultaneously over silver supported on glass wool, the former using one adsorbed oxygen atom and the latter two. The fraction of the surface covered by oxygen atoms was estimated by measuring the conductivity of the silver. On a clean surface, ethylene oxide isomerizes to acetaldehyde (steps i′, j and m) and decomposes to ethylene and adsorbed oxygen (steps i′ and g′): both ethylene oxide and acetaldehyde are adsorbed as a complex of unknown composition. Kinetics were measured in a flow system, with the following results:

$$r_{g,i} \propto P_{C_2H_4} \ \theta_O, \tag{2}$$

$$r_h \propto P_{C_2H_4} \ \theta^2_O, \tag{3}$$

$$r_{j,e} \propto P_{C_2H_4O} \ \theta^0_O. \tag{4}$$

Twigg believed that during the oxidation of ethylene, some of the ethylene oxide isomerized to acetaldehyde and that this was rapidly oxidized to carbon dioxide and water. Application of the integrated forms of the differential rate equations describing the proposed steps appear to confirm his mechanism.

Orzechowski and MacCormack have also made a detailed study of the kinetics.[31] They found the activity and selectivity to be a function of the pretreatment to which their catalyst was exposed, and after changing the operating conditions (temperature or reactant ratio) a period of up to 150 hr. was required before stable behaviour resulted. They also found, in agreement with Twigg, that both ethylene oxide and carbon dioxide are initial products, but unlike him they found that conversion to carbon dioxide was not a linear function of time. The selectivity was 0.62 ± 0.02 at 234° and 0.51 ± 0.01 at 274°, independent of reactant ratio. Their empirical rate expression for ethylene oxidation is:

$$r = k\left(1 + \frac{a}{P_{C_2H_4}} + \frac{b}{P_{O_2}}\right)^{-1} \tag{5}$$

(a and b being constants), a form of expression which does not admit of a ready interpretation.

A similar rate expression was found best to represent their results for the oxidation of ethylene oxide:

$$r = k\left(1 + \frac{c}{P_{C_2H_4O}} + \frac{d}{P_{O_2}}\right)^{-1}, \tag{6}$$

c and d also being constants. By studying the decomposition of ethylene oxide in the presence of nitrogen, they concluded that isomerization to acetaldehyde was *not* the rate-determining step in its oxidation. They therefore took the view that carbon dioxide was formed via steps (g) and (k), and via steps (g), (j) and (l).

Hayes has recently shown[32] that added carbon dioxide slightly decreases the yield of ethylene oxide without affecting that of carbon dioxide: added water vapour is without affect on either. His kinetic analysis indicates that oxidation of ethylene to carbon monoxide involves adsorbed O_2^- ions, while oxidation of ethylene to ethylene oxide, and of ethylene oxide to carbon dioxide, involves adsorbed O^- ions. Added carbon dioxide lowers the rate of ethylene oxide formation because it interacts with O^- forming adsorbed carbonate ion. He believes the surface to show *a priori* heterogeneity, with the two ionic species adsorbed simultaneously on regions of differing energy. This view of the mechanism has notable similarities to that adopted by Twigg, with adsorbed ions having replaced adsorbed atoms.

Doubt has arisen as to whether adsorbed acetaldehyde is actually formed. The simultaneous oxidation of ethylene and acetaldehyde or formaldehyde leads to the formation of *more* ethylene oxide and *less* carbon dioxide than the oxidation of ethylene alone, and so aldehydes cannot be the chief intermediates.[33, 34] It has been suggested that the adsorbed intermediate isomeric with ethylene oxide is $(H_2C{=}CHOH)_a$.

The origin of the initially formed carbon dioxide has been investigated using a mixture of ^{14}C-labelled ethylene and unlabelled ethylene oxide.[33, 34] 80 per cent of the carbon dioxide comes directly from the ethylene (step h) and the remainder from ethylene oxide (either step k or steps j and l).

The oxidation of ethylene has been studied using the (211), (111) and (110) faces of a silver single crystal as catalysts, and the rates and selectivity are the same in each case.[26] Random and (110)-oriented silver films likewise show the same activity and selectivity,[23] but here the reason is that between 250 and 280° the oriented films rapidly recrystallize and so expose all low-index planes randomly.

The reason for the promotional effects shown by chlorinated hydrocarbons has been recently examined.[26] Methyl chloride was used as the test substance, and it was concluded that this decomposed to yield adsorbed chlorine atoms or ions: these reduce the activity of the catalyst in as much as they decrease the available surface, but simultaneously raise the selectivity because they increase the concentration of *isolated* oxygen atoms (or perhaps O^- ions) necessary for the formation of ethylene oxide.

Apparent activation energies have been measured, but show the usual disconcerting spread of values. Twigg[24] derived the values shown in Table II on the basis of his mechanism. Other values reported are: for oxygen removal over polycrystalline silver foil between 185 and 210°, $E = 23 \pm 0.6$ kcal.

TABLE II. *Activation Energies for Processes Occurring during the Oxidation of Ethylene over Silver*[24]

Process	*Step(s)*	*E(kcal. mole^{-1})*	*Temp. range (°C)*
Production of C_2H_4O	(g) and (i)	26 ± 2	193–235
Production of CO_2	(h)	10 ± 3	263–302
Isomerization to CH_3CHO	(j)	20 ± 5	263–302
Adsorption of O_2	—	>25	263–302

mole^{-1};[26] for ethylene oxide production, $E = 13.0$ and 19.3 kcal. mole^{-1};[29, 35] and for ethylene oxide oxidation, $E = 21$ kcal. mole^{-1}.[35]

This unusual oxidation reaction is unique to ethylene: propylene and higher olefins under the same conditions yield only the fully oxidized products, presumably because the intermediates are less stable than in the case of ethylene.

20.4 The Catalytic Oxidation of Ammonia[36–38]

The industrial demand for nitric acid is tremendous and progressively increasing, and for some forty years the only economic method of manufacture has been through the oxidation of ammonia. Industry requires both "weak" nitric acid (40 to 60 per cent) and "concentrated" nitric acid (greater than 95 per cent), the former largely for the production of inorganic nitrates as fertilizers and the latter largely for organic nitrations in the explosives and dyestuffs industries. Although the proportion required in high concentration has diminished over the years, particular efforts have been made to produce 98 per cent nitric acid directly from ammonia oxidation.[38]

The reaction is carried out with a bed of fine-mesh gauzes (usually 80 mesh) woven from thin (0.003 in.) platinum or platinum-rich alloy wire. The principal initial product is nitric oxide, and the process is highly efficient. Very short contact times ($\sim 10^{-4}$ sec.) only are required, and quite high linear gas velocities (~ 20 m. min.$^{-1}$) are used; almost every ammonia molecule striking the catalyst undergoes reaction. Operating temperatures are between 750 and 950°, optimally about 860°, and with ammonia concentrations by volume of between 8 and 9 per cent, the remainder being air, from 90 to 100 per cent (usually 94 and 98 per cent) of the ammonia is oxidized to nitric oxide, and little ammonia remains unoxidized. The ammonia not converted to nitric oxide appears as nitrogen, and much effort has been devoted to suppressing this side reaction. At much lower temperatures than those normally used nitrous oxide also is formed.[37]

The problems to be discussed below are of two kinds. The first, a largely academic problem, is the unravelling of the elementary steps which lead to the observed products. The second, an important practical problem, is the understanding of the factors affecting the useful life of the catalyst. This last problem will be dealt with first.

The oxidation of ammonia is highly exothermic (see below), and with the conditions usually employed the heat liberated is sufficient to raise the temperature of the catalyst by some 600–700°. As this is below the optimum temperature, the incoming gas must be preheated by some 200°: this is partly achieved by heat transfer from the reacted gases. The catalyst bed normally consists of a layer of about twenty gauzes, and if none of these has been used before, a noticeable induction period occurs before the catalyst ignites and the reaction commences. This can be a considerable nuisance, but the induction period disappears if one or two previously used gauzes are included with the new ones. The cause of the induction period and its removal by this method will be discussed further below.

Although about twenty layers of gauze are used, the reaction occurs predominantly on the first one or two. The reason for using the others is partly to provide a system of sufficient mechanical rigidity, although this difficulty may be overcome either by driving the gas stream *upwards* through the catalyst bed, or by supporting it on suitable supports. However, a more important reason for using so many gauzes is the fact that a gauze on which the reaction chiefly occurs quickly disintegrates. The cause of this disintegration is undoubtedly the rearrangement which the surface undergoes during reaction, a process which has been briefly discussed earlier in this chapter. In the initial stages of use, dendritic growths appear on the surface, and it is believed that these are necessary to ensure full activity, and that the induction period experienced with virgin gauzes coincides with this initial increase in surface area. However, the re-organization of the catalyst continues with use: grain sizes increase, and attrition of the gauze occurs as the dendrites are stripped out by the quickly flowing gas, but as one gauze deteriorates the adjacent one comes into operation, and the reaction is permitted to continue until all the gauzes have reached the end of their useful lives. The rate of deterioration increases rapidly with operating temperature and pressure. The spent gauzes may, of course, be reworked, and in some plants filters are incorporated to collect the metal dust blown off the catalyst; but these greatly increase the resistance to gas flow, and are not universally adopted.

This is almost the only practical problem in the catalytic process, for at the high temperatures used poisons are not troublesome, although iron-containing dust does have harmful effects. Over the years much effort has been given to finding alloys of platinum which will not deteriorate with use as rapidly as pure platinum. Ideally one wants a material which will rapidly acquire the initial surface roughening or recrystallization necessary for rapid ignition, but which will maintain its structure for more prolonged periods. The improvement sought is, therefore, mechanical rather than chemical in nature.

The material which is now very widely used is a platinum–rhodium alloy containing 10 per cent of the latter. This has long been known to lose weight less rapidly than pure platinum, and to give a slightly higher yield of nitric oxide: however, new gauzes made with it ignite less easily than pure platinum, again emphasizing the correlation between the induction period and structural changes. Moreover materials (such as platinum–rhodium–ruthenium alloys) which do not recrystallize give much smaller nitric oxide yields. A great many other alloys of platinum have been studied or are covered by patents, although none is superior to platinum–rhodium. Alloys of platinum with silver or cobalt are less satisfactory than platinum itself.[39, 40] Platinum containing 3 per cent of tungsten is more active than platinum:[41] platinum containing 3 per cent tungsten and 5 per cent rhodium is very active at 900°, even giving 97 to 98 per cent conversion to nitric oxide at 750°, and is more stable than platinum–rhodium; but a platinum–tungsten–silver alloy while very active is less stable.[42, 43] Thus tungsten appears to exert a stabilizing influence, while the reverse is true of silver. Alloys of platinum with almost all the other Transition elements in turn have been tried, and even *s*-metals and metalloids (Ba, Ce, Al, Ge, Sn, Sb) have not been overlooked.[36]

The reason for the better performance of the platinum–rhodium alloy is not well understood. The rate of weight loss is a minimum at 10 per cent rhodium, but the problem is a metallurigcal rather than a chemical one.

We come finally to a short examination of the nature of the elementary steps which participate in the overall oxidation reaction. This is a far from simple matter, because the conditions used in industrial operation are not well suited to fundamental studies of the reaction mechanism, the understanding of which is necessarily forced to rely on results obtained in model systems which differ significantly from large-scale converters. Furthermore it is necessary carefully to distinguish between those reactions which occur at the catalyst surface and those which occur homogeneously. There is also evidence that the reaction is generally transport controlled, and that the concentration of adsorbed species may be low: this of course renders a formal kinetic analysis impossible.[36]

The final products of the oxidation in the region of 850° are nitric oxide, nitrogen and water only. At temperatures above 1000°, hydroxylamine and nitrous acid are also detected, while below 500° nitrous oxide is formed to a considerable extent. The three alternative stoichiometric equations are:

$$4NH_3 + 5O_2 \rightarrow 4NO + 6H_2O \quad \text{(n)}$$

$$4NH_3 + 4O_2 \rightarrow 2N_2O + 6H_2O \quad \text{(o)}$$

$$4NH_3 + 3O_2 \rightarrow 2N_2 + 6H_2O \quad \text{(p)}$$

and all are highly exothermic ($-\Delta H_{(n)}$, 217, and $-\Delta H_{(p)}$, 303 kcal. mole^{-1}). The principal mechanistic questions concern (i) the nature of the *initial* product of the oxidation of ammonia, (ii) the origin of the nitrogen, and (iii) the mechanisms whereby the less important products are formed.

Two opposing schools of thought have existed concerning the nature of the primary product: the opposing theories are known by the names of the products believed to be formed. The "imide" theory was first proposed by Raschig in 1927, and has been recently revived by Zawadzki.[37] Zawadzki argues that the initial step must be exothermic because of the high efficiency of the reaction, and suggests this to be

$$NH_3 + \underset{**}{O} \rightarrow \underset{**}{NH} + H_2O. \quad \text{(q)}$$

This process is exothermic provided the imide radical is chemisorbed with a heat of more than about 8 kcal. mole^{-1}. He also suggests a transition state capable also of giving hydroxylamine: alternatively we may postulate the following mechanism.

$$NH_3 + \underset{**}{O} \rightarrow \underset{*}{NH_2} + \underset{*}{OH} \begin{cases} \nearrow NH_2OH \\ \searrow \underset{**}{NH} + H_2O \end{cases}$$

Nitrous acid could be formed by

$$\underset{**}{NH} + O_2 \rightarrow HNO_2 \tag{r}$$

and this may then decompose either catalytically or homogeneously according to the stoichiometric equation

$$2HNO_2 \rightarrow NO + NO_2 + H_2O. \tag{s}$$

Nitrous oxide may be formed at lower temperatures because the adsorbed species are present in a higher concentration, and so

$$\underset{**}{NH} + \underset{**}{O} \rightarrow HNO \tag{t}$$

$$2HNO \rightarrow N_2O + H_2O. \tag{u}$$

According to the "imide" theory, nitrogen could be formed (i) by the interaction of two imide radicals to form nitrogen and hydrogen (this is essentially the catalytic decomposition of ammonia), (ii) by the reaction of an imide radical with ammonia, yielding hydrazine which subsequently decomposes, (iii) by the decomposition of nitrous oxide and nitric oxide, (iv) by the gas phase reaction between nitrogen dioxide and ammonia, and (v) by the following surface processes:

$$\underset{**}{NH} + HNO \rightarrow N_2 + H_2O \tag{v}$$

$$NH_3 + HNO_2 \rightarrow N_2 + 2H_2O. \tag{w}$$

The decomposition of nitric oxide seems unlikely to be the source of nitrogen, since after formation it has to pass through many gauzes, and nevertheless high yields are still obtained.

The competing theory is known as the "nitroxyl" or "hydroxylamine" theory, since in it the initial step is postulated to be either

$$NH_3 + \underset{**}{O} \rightarrow NH_2OH \tag{x}$$

or

$$NH_3 + O_2 \rightarrow HNO + H_2O. \tag{y}$$

A more detailed formulation of process (x) has been given above; process (t) is an alternative method of forming nitroxyl. Nitric oxide may arise by

$$NH_2OH + O_2 \rightarrow HNO_2 + H_2O \tag{z}$$

followed by reaction (s), and nitrous oxide either through (y) or

$$NH_2OH + \underset{**}{O} \rightarrow HNO + H_2O \tag{aa}$$

followed by (u). An additional route to nitrogen, according to this theory, is:

$$HNO + NH_2OH \rightarrow N_2 + 2H_2O. \tag{ab}$$

Both of these theories have been substantially criticized,[36, 37] although none of the objections are compelling. While the central problem is to reveal the mechanism which obtains during industrial conditions, the theories have been constructed (or criticized) on the basis of information obtained under totally different conditions, sometimes using temperatures some 300 to 400° higher or lower than those employed in practice. It seems unreasonable to expect that the various component steps will have equal importance in such widely differing conditions. It can only be said that it is possible for a selection from the elementary steps listed above to account for the several observed products which are formed under different conditions. The reader may care to amuse himself by trying to devise the critical experiment to distinguish between the rival theories.

20.5 The Synthesis of Hydrogen Cyanide[36]

Hydrogen cyanide may be synthesized by the partial oxidation of methane–ammonia mixtures under much the same conditions as those required for the oxidation of ammonia alone. The stoichiometric equation is

$$CH_4 + NH_3 + 1.5\,O_2 \rightarrow HCN + 3H_2O + 115\text{ kcal.} \qquad \text{(ac)}$$

The process, which was discovered by Andrussow and bears his name, is operated on a commercial scale. The optimum yield, which is about 60 per cent, is obtained with a methane : ammonia ratio of about unity, and an oxygen : ammonia ratio of about 1.5. Unchanged reactants, nitrogen, and carbon monoxide account for the remaining 40 per cent. The process appears to work best at a temperature slightly higher than that used in ammonia oxidation, namely about 1000°; platinum–iridium and platinum–rhodium gauzes have been found superior to pure platinum gauzes. Supported platinum and platinum–rhodium catalysts are also in use. Like ammonia oxidation, this reaction also occurs extremely rapidly, and very short contact times are used.

The reaction can also be caused to proceed in two stages. If nitric oxide is first produced by the oxidation of ammonia, and then allowed to react with methane over supported platinum at 1100°, hydrogen cyanide is formed in 60 to 70 per cent yield.

The mechanism of the one-stage synthesis has been interpreted in terms of the "nitroxyl" theory as follows.

$$HNO + CH_4 \rightarrow H_2C{=}NH + H_2O \qquad \text{(ad)}$$

$$H_2C{=}NH \rightarrow HCN + H_2 \qquad \text{(ae)}$$

Alkyl cyanides have been produced by the partial oxidation of ammonia and hydrocarbons; thus benzonitrile results when toluene is used and acrylonitrile when propylene is used.

20.6 The Catalytic Oxidation of Carbon Monoxide

The kinetics of this reaction have been investigated on various forms of nickel, palladium, platinum, silver and gold: the results are summarized in

Table III. Carbon monoxide is more strongly chemisorbed than oxygen on the Transition metals, probably because the former involves *d*-band vacancies

TABLE III. *Kinetics of the Oxidation of Carbon Monoxide over Metals*
$r \propto P_{CO}^{x} P_{O_2}^{y}$

Metal	*Form*	*x*	*y*	*Temp.* (°*C*)	*E*(*kcal. mole*$^{-1}$)	*Temp. range* (°*C*)	*Ref.*
Pd	wire	−2	1	~100	28.3	90–130	44
Pd	foil	−1	1	300	22.2	250–320	45
Pt	wire	−1	1	—	—	225–475	46
Ag	powder	1	0	~100	13.3	80–140	47
Ag	foil	1	1	~450	13.9	400–530	45
Au	wire	0	0	~300	~0	200–400	44

which are plentiful while the latter requires *s*-electrons which are scarce[45] (see Chapter 5). The fact that the reaction is first order in oxygen, and that carbon monoxide inhibits, is thus reasonably interpreted. If the rate-determining step is the adsorption of oxygen on *x* adjacent vacant sites in an almost saturated layer of carbon monoxide, then[44]

$$r \propto P_{O_2} (1 - \theta_{CO})^{x} \propto P_{O_2} P_{CO}^{-x}. \tag{7}$$

Carbon monoxide is also more strongly adsorbed than oxygen on gold, but the observation[44] that the reaction is zero order in oxygen is unexpected. It is postulated that the oxygen is only adsorbed on special sites which constitute a very small fraction of the available surface (perhaps on dislocations or impurity centres), and which are fully covered at all oxygen pressures.

On the other hand, oxygen is more strongly adsorbed than carbon monoxide on silver, and at about 100° the reaction is zero order in oxygen, and first order in carbon monoxide:[47] but at higher temperatures, where presumably both are only weakly adsorbed, the reaction is first order in both.[45]

The reaction over supported platinum has been studied by means of infra-red spectroscopy.[48] At 35°, the removal of adsorbed carbon monoxide by gaseous oxygen is slow, and some appears to resist oxidation altogether. On the addition of gaseous carbon monoxide to an oxygen-covered surface, transient bands due to carbon monoxide appear but disappear as it is oxidized. These bands, of course, remain when the adsorbed oxygen has all reacted, but the final stages are slow, and the process has many of the features of a slow chemisorption which is inhibited by adsorbed oxygen.

It has recently been shown possible to remove carbon monoxide present in low concentration (<2.5 per cent) in hydrogen to be used for ammonia synthesis by selective oxidation:[49] supported ruthenium, rhodium and platinum are all satisfactory, but platinum is outstanding for this reaction.

During the oxidation of carbon monoxide over the (100) and (111) faces of a nickel single crystal,[50] there is no evidence for the adsorption of carbon monoxide except as a transitory species $Ni\cdots O\overset{-}{\cdots}C\overset{=}{\cdots}O$. Evidence for this intermediate has also come from infra-red spectroscopy, using supported nickel at 35°:[48] a new band at 4.56μ is observed during the reaction, and it does not appear when carbon monoxide is adsorbed on bulk nickel oxide. It is, therefore, likely that this species is formed only when carbon monoxide reacts with oxygen chemisorbed on the metal surface.

The reaction has recently been studied using a series of palladium–gold alloy wires and catalysts:[44] a stoichiometric reactant mixture was used at a total pressure not exceeding 0.2 mm. For alloys containing less than 55 per cent palladium pressure–time curves were linear, the order in total pressure was between 0 and 0.15 and the orders in each reactant were close to zero. For palladium-rich alloys, the rate at any time in a run was proportional to the reciprocal of the total pressure, but from using different initial mixtures the order was found to be between −1.25 and −1.75. The variation in the log of the specific rate constant at 150° is shown as a function of composition in Fig. 2(a); Fig. 2(b) shows the compensation effect. The activation energy

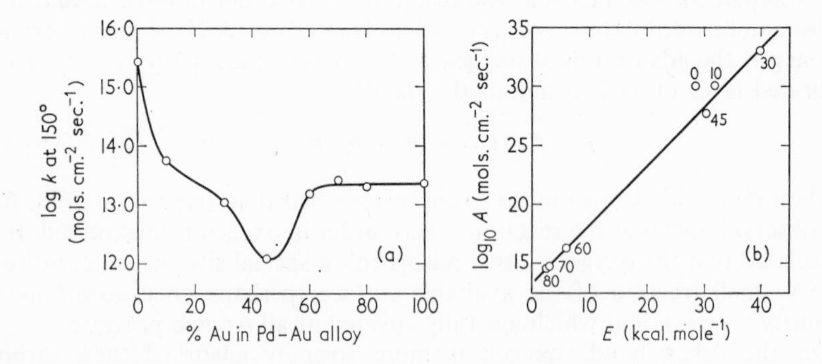

FIG. 2. The oxidation of carbon monoxide on palladium–gold wires.[44]
(a) The variation of log k at 150° with composition.
(b) Compensation effect plot (the figures against the points refer to the percentage of gold in the alloy).

is seen to decrease abruptly by some 25 kcal. mole^{-1} between alloys containing 45 and 60 per cent gold, that is, near the point at which the d-band is expected to be filled. This is, of course, a change in the opposite direction from that found in the conversion of *para*-hydrogen over the same alloys (see Chapter 8). It was suggested[44] that the low activation energy shown by the gold-rich alloys is due to the ease with which the s-electrons are available to oxygen when it prepares to adsorb: as noted earlier, the number of s-electrons is few before the d-band is filled (see also Chapter 2). This suggestion is, however, not without its shortcomings, since (i) it implies that oxygen should be readily chemisorbed by gold, which it is not, and (*ii*) the magnitude of the change in activation energy is much greater (by at least a factor of five) than the possible differences in the Fermi levels of the two metals. On the other hand, the difference between the activation energies shown by palladium and silver[45] is only about 8 kcal. mole^{-1} (see Table III), and this is much nearer the possible theoretical value of 5.5 kcal. mole^{-1}.

These studies are to be compared with that of the hydrogen–oxygen reaction described in the first Section of this Chapter: here, in the palladium–silver system, the activation energy is constant until the critical composition is attained, after which it *increases* linearly the difference between the two metals being some 10 kcal. mole^{-1}. It is evident that in this case the variation in activation energy is connected with the ability of the catalyst to activate *hydrogen* and not oxygen.

The silver-catalysed oxidation of carbon monoxide by ozone at 0° has been reported.[51] The following reactions are believed to operate:

$$O_3 + 2* \rightarrow \underset{**}{O} + O_2 \quad \text{(af)}$$

$$O_3 + \underset{**}{O} \rightarrow 2O_2 + 2* \quad \text{(ag)}$$

$$CO + \underset{**}{O} \rightarrow CO_2 + 2*, \quad \text{(ah)}$$

with $k_{(ag)}$ being approximately equal to $k_{(ah)}$.

20.7 The Catalytic Oxidation of Sulphur Dioxide[36]

The oxidation of sulphur dioxide to the trioxide is, of course, the essential step in the manufacture of sulphuric acid, and although catalysts based on vanadium pentoxide are now almost universally used, platinum catalysts were formerly widely employed, and much work has been done on the kinetics of this reaction over platinum. Platinum has undoubtedly fallen out of favour because of the ease with which it is poisoned by arsenic and the halogens, a drawback from which vanadium pentoxide does not suffer.

The reaction is exothermic, and K_p is 4180 atm.$^{-\frac{1}{2}}$ at 1200°K: K_p is related to temperature by the equation

$$\log K_p = \frac{4956}{T} - 4.678. \quad (8)$$

This means that the reaction proceeds to essential completion below about 700° K, and that catalysts must function at not much above 400°C. Several kinds of platinum catalyst have seen commercial use: these include ~10 per cent platinum on asbestos, ~0.2 per cent platinum on magnesium sulphate and 0.1 per cent platinum on silica, the latter being claimed to resist poisoning by arsenic.

The earliest kinetic study is due to Bodenstein and Fink,[52] who established the following rate expressions:

$$P_{O_2} > 0.75\, P_{SO_2} : r \propto P_{SO_2} P^0_{O_2} P^{-0.5}_{SO_3} \quad (9)$$

$$P_{O_2} < 0.75\, P_{SO_2} : r \propto P_{O_2} P^{-0.5}_{SO_3}. \quad (10)$$

According to Laidler[53] the more general forms for these expressions are respectively

$$r = \frac{kP_{SO_2}}{1 + bP_{SO_3}^{0.5}} \tag{11}$$

and

$$r = \frac{kP_{O_2}}{1 + bP_{SO_3}^{0.5}} \cdot \tag{12}$$

which are not consistent with a mechanism in which all three species are adsorbed on the same surface. The original interpretation was[52] that the slow step is the diffusion of the reactants through a multimolecular layer of sulphur trioxide whose thickness is proportional to the square root of its pressure, but this kind of explanation is not now acceptable. Alternatively the above expressions are explicable in terms of the diffusion of the reactions over the surface to reactive sites.[53]

Over platinum wire at 665°, the rate of oxidation is inversely proportional to the sulphur trioxide pressure and proportional to the distance from equilibrium:[54] the rate of the decomposition of sulphur trioxide is also proportional to the distance from equilibrium, but is uninhibited by products.

Over platinized asbestos under strictly isothermal conditions, the rate of oxidation is given by

$$r \propto P_{SO_2} P_{O_2}^0 P_{SO_3}^0 \tag{13}$$

and, when high concentrations of added sulphur trioxide are present, by

$$r \propto P_{SO_2} \left[\ln\left(\frac{P_{SO_3}}{P_{SO_2}}\right)_{eq.} - \ln\left(\frac{P_{SO_3}}{P_{SO_2}}\right) \right] \cdot \tag{14}$$

There is thus some evidence that sulphur trioxide inhibits only over macroscopic platinum, and not in the case of the supported metal.

Boreskov[55] has examined the oxidation over a variety of forms of platinum (wire, gauze, sponge and silica-supported) and concluded that the specific activities of the various forms are equal: the activation energy was 23.3 $\pm$ 0.6 kcal. mole^{-1} for the massive and supported metal. A number of other metals were also studied: tungsten, chromium, palladium, gold and platinum–gold alloys showed similar activities, all less than for platinum itself, while silver was inactive.

20.8 The Catalytic Oxidation of Methanol[18]

It has long been known that methanol may be oxidized to formaldehyde according to the equation

$$CH_3OH + \tfrac{1}{2} O_2 \rightarrow HCHO + H_2O \tag{ai}$$

in the presence of noble metal catalysts, although the mechanism is not well understood and no respectable kinetic measurements have been made. The view has been advanced that the equilibrium

$$CH_3OH \rightleftharpoons HCHO + H_2 \quad \text{(aj)}$$

is first set up: high temperatures are known to favour the forward reaction and the equilibrium yield of formaldehyde is 99 per cent at 700°. The role of the oxygen is thought to be that it maintains the necessary high temperature by oxidizing the hydrogen, also of course causing the forward reaction to proceed further. Especially over copper and gold catalysts, some carbon monoxide and dioxide is also formed. The detection of substantial amounts of hydrogen in the products is some confirmation of the above mechanism, the more so because it is sometimes much in excess of the oxides of carbon and could not, therefore, have arisen entirely through the decomposition of formaldehyde.

This oxidation is operated on a commercial scale, and yields in excess of 90 per cent are obtained using silver as catalyst at 600°.

References

1. A. F. Benton and J. C. Elgin, *J. Amer. Chem. Soc.* **48,** 3027 (1926).
2. C. N. Hinshelwood, E. A. Moelwyn-Hughes and A. C. Rolfe, *Proc. Roy. Soc.* **A139,** 521 (1933).
3. A. F. Benton and J. C. Elgin, *J. Amer. Chem. Soc.* **49,** 2426 (1927).
4. W. M. H. Sachtler and N. H. de Boer, *J. Phys. Chem.* **64,** 1579 (1960).
5. W. A. Bone and R. V. Wheeler, *Phil. Trans.* **A206,** 1 (1906).
6. I. Langmuir, *Trans. Faraday Soc.* **17,** 621 (1922).
7. H. G. Tanner and G. B. Taylor, *J. Amer. Chem. Soc.* **53,** 1289 (1931).
8. R. P. Donnelly and C. N. Hinshelwood, *J. Chem. Soc.* **132,** 1727 (1929).
9. G. K. Boreskov, M. G. Slin'ko and V. S. Chesalova, *Zhur. fiz. Khim.* **30,** 2787 (1956).
10. S. J. Stephens, *J. Phys. Chem.* **63,** 188 (1959).
11. T. Tucholski, *Z. phys. Chem. (Leipzig)* **B40,** 333 (1938).
12. G. A. Sargeant and A. F. F. Bartlett, *J. Appl. Chem.* **5,** 208 (1955).
13. A. B. van Cleave and E. K. Rideal, *Trans. Faraday Soc.* **33,** 635 (1937).
14. R. P. Donnelly, *J. Chem. Soc.* **132,** 2438 (1929).
15. G. Tammann, *Z. anorg. Chem.* **111,** 90 (1920).
16. M. Kowaka, *J. Jap. Inst. Metals* **23,** 659 (1959).
17. M. H. Bortner and G. Parravano, *Adv. Catalysis* **9,** 424 (1957).
18. J. K. Dixon and J. E. Longfield, In "Catalysis", edited by P. H. Emmett (Reinhold, New York, 1960). **7,** 183.
19. M. Prettre, C. Eichner and M. Perrin, *Trans. Faraday Soc.* **42,** 335 (1946).
20. P. Dévoré, C. Eyraud and M. Prettre, *Compt. rend.* **246,** 1200 (1958).
21. P. Bussiére, P. Dévoré, B. Domanski and M. Prettre, Proc. 2nd International Congress on Catalysis (Editions Technip, Paris, 1961), **2,** 2247.
22. R. Y. Meelheim, R. E. Cunningham, K. R. Lawless, S. Azim, R. H. Kean and A. T. Gwathmey, Proc. 2nd International Congress on Catalysis (Editions Technip, Paris, 1961), **2,** 2005; A. T. Gwathmey and R. E. Cunningham, *Adv. Catalysis* **10,** 57 (1958).
23. J. N. Wilson, H. H. Voge, D. P. Stevenson, A. E. Smith and L. T. Atkins, *J. Phys. Chem.* **63,** 460 (1959).
24. G. H. Twigg, *Proc. Roy. Soc.* **A188,** 92, 105, 123 (1946); *Trans. Faraday Soc.* **42,** 284 (1946).
25. W. W. Smeltzer, E. L. Tollefson and A. Cambron, *Canad. J. Chem.* **34,** 1046 (1956).
26. J. T. Kummer, *J. Phys. Chem.* **60,** 666 (1956).

27. G. D. Lyubarskii, *Doklady Akad. Nauk S.S.S.R.* **110,** 112 (1956).
28. D. W. Bolme, Ph.D. thesis, University of Wisconsin, 1957; see Ref. 18.
29. S. Wan, *Ind. Eng. Chem.* **45,** 234 (1946).
30. A. I. Kurilenko, N. V. Kul'kova, N. A. Rybakova and M. I. Temkin, *Zhur. fiz. Khim.* **32,** 1043 (1958).
31. A. Orzechowski and K. E. MacCormack, *Canad. J. Chem.* **32,** 388, 415, 432, 443 (1954).
32. K. E. Hayes, *Canad. J. Chem.* **38,** 2256 (1960).
33. L. Ya. Margolis and S. Z. Roginskii, *Izvest. Akad. Nauk S.S.S.R. Otdel. Khim. Nauk* 282 (1956).
34. L. Ya. Margolis and S. Z. Roginskii, In "Problems of Kinetics and Catalysis", edited by S. Z. Roginskii (U.S.S.R. Acad. Sci. Press, Moscow, 1957), **9,** 107.
35. T. I. Andrianova and O. M. Todes, *Zhur. fiz. Khim.* **30,** 522 (1956).
36. J. K. Dixon and J. E. Longfield, In "Catalysis", edited by P. H. Emmett (Reinhold, New York, 1960) **7,** 281.
37. J. Zawadzki, *Discuss. Faraday Soc.* **8,** 140 (1950).
38. A. W. Holmes, *Platinum Metals Review* **3,** 2 (1959).
39. I. E. Adadurov, Ya. M. Deich and N. A. Prozorovskii, *Zhur. priklad. Khim.* **9,** 807 (1936).
40. I. E. Adadurov, *J. Chem. Ind.* (*U.S.S.R.*), **14,** 917 (1937).
41. I. E. Adadurov and V. I. Atroshchenko, *Zhur. priklad. Khim.* **9,** 1221.
42. I. E. Adadurov and V. I. Atroshchenko, *Ukrain. Khim. Zhur.* **11,** 209 (1936).
43. I. E. Adadurov and N. I. Pevnyi, *Zhur. fiz. Khim.* **9,** 592 (1937).
44. A. G. Daglish and D. D. Eley, Proc. 2nd International Congress on Catalysis (Editions Technip, Paris, 1961).
45. G.-M. Schwab and K. Gossner, *Z. phys. Chem.* (*Frankfurt*) **16,** 39 (1958).
46. I. Langmuir, *Trans. Faraday Soc.* **17,** 621 (1922).
47. A. F. Benton and R. T. Bell, *J. Amer. Chem. Soc.* **56,** 501 (1934).
48. R. P. Eischens and W. A. Pliskin, *Adv. Catalysis* **10,** 1 (1958).
49. M. L. Brown, A. W. Green, G. Cohn and H. C. Anderson, *Ind. Eng. Chem.* **52,** 841 (1960).
50. J. A. Feighan and K. A. Krieger, Proc. 2nd International Congress on Catalysis (Editions Technip, Paris, 1961), **1,** 1027.
51. D. Garvin, *J. Amer. Chem. Soc.* **76,** 1581 (1954).
52. M. Bodenstein and C. G. Fink, *Z. phys. Chem.* (*Leipzig*) **60,** 1, 46 (1907).
53. K. J. Laidler, In "Catalysis", edited by P. H. Emmett (Reinhold, New York, 1954), **1,** 119.
54. G. B. Taylor and S. Lenher, *Z. phys. Chem.* (*Leipzig*) 30. Bondenstein Festband (1931).
55. G. K. Boreskov, *Zhur. fiz. Khim.* **19,** 535 (1945); G. K. Boreskov and V. S. Chesalova, *Zhur. fiz. Khim.* **30,** 2560 (1956).

Chapter 21

Catalysis and Chemistry

21.1 The Object of the Game

There are within the subject which it has been the object of this book to review, a great variety of kinds of problem. Some of these are solely of practical interest and are a principal concern of large-scale users of catalysts: for example, questions concerning the external and mechanical properties of catalysts fall into this category. Other problems are, for the moment at least, of more academic interest: these are, in general, questions concerning reaction mechanisms. It is natural and right that, in the attempted solution of these varied problems, a wide selection of techniques should have been employed, a large number of systems investigated, and a variety of theoretical approaches followed. This book is a witness to the wealth of information which has been accumulated; but scientific information however extensive is unsatisfying until it has acquired order and shape. We are, therefore, driven to pose this question: is there any central and fundamental theme which may in the future give to the whole phenomenon of catalysis by metals a structure and coherence which it now lacks?

We have cause to believe that there is. Although reasons were advanced in the Preface for preferring to classify the subject matter to be presented by the type of reaction rather than by the chemical nature of the catalyst, this has had the consequence which was foreseen there that questions concerning the influence of the catalytic metal on the rate and direction of reactions have emerged in almost all the last fifteen Chapters. This then must be the sought-for central theme, for no other classification would seem to have any similarly pervading issue. This theme is therefore provided by the answer to the very broad question: how does the catalytic action of a metal depend on its geometric and electronic properties? It is the object of this concluding chapter to review the experimental results which have been described earlier and which bear on this question: and this object has suggested the Chapter's title.

The notion that it is the ultimate object of the game to discover and explain correlations between the catalytic behaviour and the physico-chemical properties of metals is one which seems to be generally if not universally held. According to this view, the establishment of the mechanism which operates in a particular system is only the first move in the game, because as should by now be quite clear the mechanism for a given reaction may change significantly from one metal (or group of metals) to another. In the context of heterogeneous catalysis, a mechanism may be defined as an accurate knowledge of the nature and proportions of the adsorbed species existing during the reaction, and the modes of their interaction: but the game is only concluded when this information has been assembled for a number of metals, and the basic relations between the parameters of the reaction and its mechanism, and the physicochemical properties of the metal, are set down and interpreted. Because of the formidable complexity of many catalytic systems, this is usually a counsel of perfection, and so emphasis will be placed in this Chapter on those fairly simple systems for which the fullest information is already available and in which the most rapid further progress is to be expected.

It has long been recognized that differences between the behaviours of metal surfaces may be interpreted in terms of geometric and electronic effects. The close and inevitable connection between the two was stressed in Chapter 2, but before proceeding to a careful examination of the importance of electronic factors we may briefly survey the available information on geometric effects.

Meaningful information on the importance of surface geometry may be expected to be revealed by comparing the catalytic and chemisorptive behaviour of either (i) different crystal faces of the same metal, or (ii) metals having different crystal structures but similar radii and electronic structures, or (iii) metals showing substantially different radii but the same crystal structures. With respect to the first point, the original view that metal films could be prepared having a preferred exposed orientation is now suspect, and information under this heading can only come from work on single metal crystals, or from field-emission microscopy. There is good evidence that rates of chemisorption and of surface migration vary substantially from one face to another, and there is also evidence that rates of oxidation and of carbiding show definite preferences: but the extent and quality of measurements made to determine rates and kinetics of catalytic processes on different crystal faces are both somewhat disappointing (see for example Chapter 18) and no clear indication has been given of how surface geometry may of itself affect the issue.

With regard to the second point, there is some slight evidence (see Chapter 9) that the parameters of the ethane–deuterium exchange may depend significantly on crystal structure, but the statement (see Chapter 12) that close-packed hexagonal metals are inactive for the hydrogenation of acetylene must now be accepted with reserve. Similarly, there is no unequivocal evidence that metal radius is of itself a generally significant quantity. Providentially all those metals which on other scores are potential catalysts possess radii which satisfy the apparently elastic spatial requirements of the reactants. Only perhaps in the cases of surface polymerizations are interatomic distances of real significance, and it is easy to see why this should be so. Thus, for example, the failure of rhodium, palladium, iridium and platinum to catalyse the Fischer–Tropsch synthesis (see Chapter 15), or to catalyze the formation of substantial quantities of polymeric products from the hydrogenation of acetylene, may reasonably be ascribed to a genuine effect of metallic radius. The different behaviours of iron and ruthenium in the Fischer–Tropsch synthesis may find a similar interpretation.

We must, however, conclude that geometric effects play only at most a small role in determining the catalytic properties of metal surfaces. We may, therefore, now turn our attention to the more fruitful field of electronic effects.

21.2 The Theoretical Basis for Electronic Effects in Chemisorption

21.21 The Observations

It is clear that an understanding of the part played by electronic factors in catalysis must follow rather than precede an understanding of their role in chemisorption. The object of this Section is, therefore, to review the observations and theories on chemisorption phenomena, and to assess the present status of this problem.

We may start by recognizing that atoms in the surface of metals possess bonding capabilities which are not shown either by atoms within the metal or by isolated atoms. Thus, the Transition metals can chemisorb for example hydrogen and various hydrocarbons, with the formation of what may be regarded as new chemical species for which there are generally no analogies in the known stoichiometric compounds of these metals, either solid or gaseous. It is not difficult to see in principle why this should be so. Using the language of the Valence Bond Theory, there must be available at the surface of metals certain orbitals which are either not employed or may be readily made available: such orbitals will probably be fully engaged in the case of bulk atoms, and may not exist in isolated metal atoms.

The theoretical description of the electronic structure of surface atoms presents formidable difficulties, although qualitative approaches have been made.[1] The next best thing which can be done is to suppose that there is some *correspondence* between the electronic structures of bulk and surface atoms, and hence to try to correlate chemisorption behaviour with observed and theoretical parameters of the bulk. It must be emphasized that this is a potentially dangerous course to follow, for the correspondence may not be precise, but no other course is open to us at the moment.

The basic question is: how are adsorbed species bound to metal surfaces? There must of course be as many answers to this question as there are metals and kinds of adsorbed species, so some generalizations must be entertained. The material presented in Chapter 5 showed that chemisorption activity is largely restricted to the Transition metals. We must, however, be careful not to read too much into this observation, because failure to show chemisorption (as for example in the hydrogen–silver system) is probably due to the existence of a prohibitive activation energy rather than to any thermodynamic disability. The fact that hydrogen *atoms* can adsorb on Group IB metals is an important clue to the nature of the binding of hydrogen to metals. Chemisorption activity is of course a function also of the adsorbate as well as of the adsorbent. Thus, oxygen is almost universally adsorbed, while the ability to adsorb nitrogen is not widely shown, and even in those cases where some activity appears high coverages do not result. Molecules posessing lone pairs of electrons are especially strongly adsorbed, and constitute catalyst poisons.

The above qualitative statements on chemisorption activity are supplemented to a degree which varies substantially from one system to another by quantitative information on heats of adsorption, and we must suppose that the *initial* heat of adsorption in any system is a quantitative measure of the strength of the bond formed in the reaction. It is helpful to find that, with the partial exception of oxygen, the sequence of heats of adsorption shown by different metals is the same for all adsorbates which have been studied. This indicates that the same kind of bond is probably formed in all cases, again with the exception of oxygen. Heats of adsorption are lowest for the noble Group VIII metals, higher in the iron triad and highest in Groups VA and VIA. A successful theoretical treatment must, therefore, explain the qualitative and quantitative information available on the relative activities in chemisorption shown by different metals and by different molecules.

21.22 The Nature of Chemisorption Bonds

We see, therefore, that electronic effects in chemisorption must operate through the nature and strength of the new chemical bonds which are formed, and that the descriptive chemistry of adsorption must suggest their nature, and the quantitative information their strength. This subsection will discuss the former and the next subsection the latter.

We must decide at this stage which theory of the metallic state we will use. The Electron Band and Valence Bond Theories were described in Chapter 2 and their relative merits for our purposes discussed. We saw that the former was the more fundamental and better adapted to a discussion of the behaviour of alloys, while the latter was more empirical but better suited to a discussion of the behaviour of Transition metals. Both theories recognize the existence of two separate functions for valency electrons in these metals: one function is to bind the atoms together and the other to account for magnetic and conductive properties. These functions are assigned by the Band Theory respectively to electrons in overlapping *d*- and *s*-bands and to holes in the *d*-band, and by the Valence Bond Theory to electrons in *dsp*-hybridized orbitals and electrons in atomic *d*-orbitals. Thus, although the terminology differs, the basic ideas are not dissimilar. We shall, however, in this Section prefer to employ the Valence Bond approach, since it has enabled some discussion of possible emergent orbitals at metal surfaces,[1] and also because numbers have been attached (albeit somewhat empirically) to the percentage of *d*-character in the bonds between atoms of the Transition metals.

There have been two opposing schools of thought concerning the nature of the bonds formed in chemisorption: the case of oxygen must, however, be temporarily excluded from our discussion. The first view, to which Trapnell subscribed[2] and Beeck apparently also, was that *the chemisorption bond is a covalence between electrons from the adsorbate and unpaired electrons in atomic d-orbitals*. This concept at once interprets the high chemisorption activity of Transition metals, the decrease in magnetic susceptibility which can follow chemisorption, and quantitatively at least the increase in adsorption strength on passing from Groups VIII_3 to VIA and the inability of metals in Groups VIII_2 and VIII_3 to chemisorb nitrogen. The alternative view, which was first discussed by Eley in 1950 and has been adopted in a modified form by Dowden,[1] is that *the metal-adsorbate bond is essentially similar to the metal–metal bond*, that is to say, that an unengaged *dsp*-orbital is employed. According to this view in its latest form, the role of the unpaired *d*-electrons is relegated to the formation of an intermediate (Type C adsorbed state) without which the final "strong" state cannot be attained, unless a high activity energy is overcome or the adsorbate previously atomized. This view has the merits of accounting for the ability of Group IB metals to adsorb atoms and of enabling simple quantitative calculation of the strength of adsorbate–metal bonds. The successes and failures of such calculations are discussed in the next subsection and provide the basis for a comparative assessment of the two views presented above.

Before finishing with the more qualitative aspects of chemisorption bonds, however, a further word must be said concerning the importance of the kind of adsorbate, as this aspect of the subject will not receive much further attention. The above discussion specifically referred to substances such as hydrogen, ethylene and carbon monoxide, for which surface potential measurements indicate that their bonds to the surface are essentially covalent. With adsorbed oxygen, however, surface potential measurements show the oxygen–metal bonds to be substantially ionic, and in the case of the non-Transition metals it has been suggested[2] that electron donation to the oxygen atoms occurs from *sp*-hybridized orbitals in the metal. It is not, therefore, surprising to find that chemisorbed oxide layers bear a close energetic relation to corresponding bulk oxides: the results shown in Table IV of Chapter 5 which are plotted in Fig. 1 (with some slight modifications[3] noted in the legend), establish this firmly. Corresponding thermochemical measurements on bulk and surface nitrides are largely lacking, but a point for tantalum nitride[3] is included in Fig. 1 and fits well with the results for oxygen. There is a rough proportionality between the heats of adsorption for oxygen and hydrogen with those metals where the results are available for both, and this may either mean that oxygen–metal bonds have an important covalent contribution or that the same basic factors influence both ionic and covalent bonds. It is, however, interesting to note that the point for hydrogen on nickel and nickel hydride in Fig. 1 fits the extrapolated line through the points for adsorbed

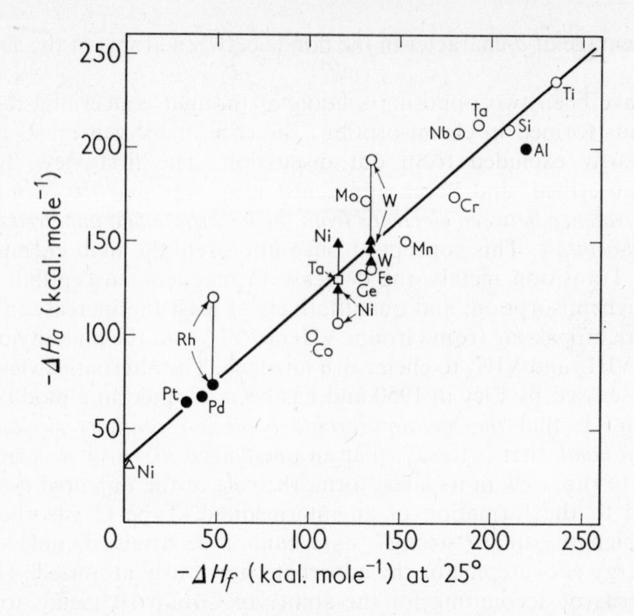

FIG. 1. The dependence of heat of adsorption on heat of formation of the most closely corresponding bulk compound.[3] Circles and filled triangles, oxygen and oxides: open circles, initial or maximum heats of adsorption (Brennan, Hayward and Trapnell: see Table IV of Chapter 5); filled circles, integral heats (*idem*); filled triangles, other workers' values for heats (see Tables IV and X of Chapter 5). Heats of formation as in Table IV of Chapter 5, except for Al, where value for AlO_2^- is used in place of that for Al_2O_3.[3]
Square, nitrogen and nitride.[3] Open triangle, hydrogen and hydride.[3]

oxygen and the oxides. In view of the satisfactory correlation between surface and bulk properties in the case of oxygen, we need not concern ourselves in the next subsection with attempts to calculate the strengths of oxygen–metal bonds.

21.23 The Strengths of Chemisorption Bonds

We saw above that the view that the chemisorption bond is a covalence involving partly filled *d*-orbitals is not susceptible to quantitative test by calculation: if one takes the percentage of *d*-character in the metallic bonds (δ) as a measure of unavailability of electrons in atomic *d*-orbitals and hence of the weakness of binding strength expected, one finds (Fig. 7 of Chapter 5) a smooth correlation between δ and heat of adsorption of hydrogen in Group VIII, but between iron and chromium the heat rises by 13 kcal. mole^{-1} for essentially no change in δ, and tungsten is incorrigible. However, if the surface bond is supposed to be akin to the metallic bonds in the bulk, the bond energy D_{MH} is readily obtained if the latent heat of sublimation of the metal and the electronegativity difference are known (see Table XII of Chapter 5 and relevant text). In the quantum mechanical calculation of

Higuchi, Ree and Eyring, the ionic and covalent contributions are estimated on the basis of surface potential results, and combined to give the total energy. The agreement obtained with the observed results is reasonable, but the best agreement is found in Stevenson's calculation (see Fig. 2) where the electronegativity difference is computed from the work functions of the metals.

These calculations are of course based on the assumption that strength of the metal–hydrogen bond is the arithmetic mean of the metal–metal and hydrogen–hydrogen bond strengths, together with the correction for electronegativity difference. Ehrlich[8] has recently questioned this assumption, since with some *gaseous* hydrides the degree of agreement with observation is much better if the geometric mean rule is used. However, when this is used to obtain the strength of metal–hydrogen bonds in adsorbed hydrogen, the results are 20 to 35 per cent too low (see also Fig. 2). It is not at the moment clear whether these findings constitute a valid objection to the Eley–Stevenson approach.

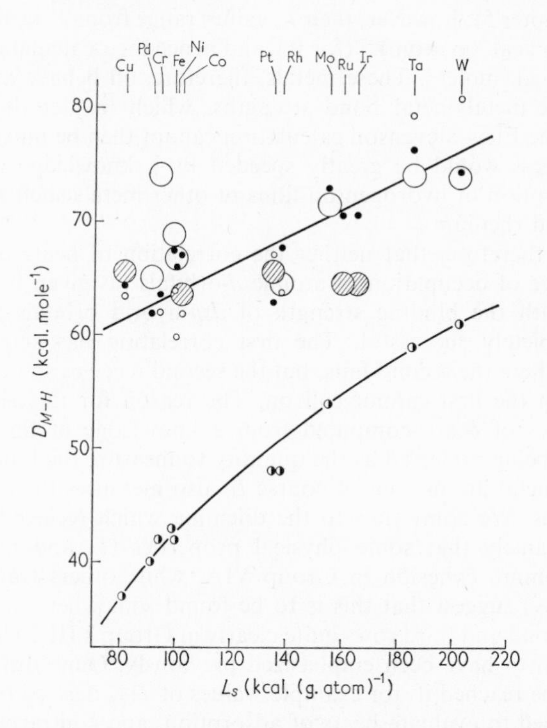

FIG. 2. The dependence of observed and calculated strengths of hydrogen–metal bonds at zero coverage on latent heat of sublimation of the metal, L_s. Calculated values: filled circles, Stevenson's calculation (Table XII of Chapter 4): small open circles, Higuchi, Ree and Eyring (*ibid.*): half-filled circles, calculated by the geometric mean rule. The straight line passes through $D_{MH} = 51.5$ kcal. mole^{-1} at $L_s = 0$.

Observed values: large open circles, films; large hatched circles, silica-supported metals. Size of circle represents $\pm$ 2 kcal. mole^{-1} on heat of adsorption.

Now although the calculations referred to above show broad agreement with observation, the agreement is in all cases quite definitely unsatisfactory for chromium (where the calculated heat is always too low) and for ruthenium, rhodium and iridium (where the calculated heats are always too high). The cause of these failures is readily traced to the chosen value of D_{MM} and hence to the value of L_s, since the electronegativity corrections are always small. Chromium has an L_s of 94 kcal. (g. atom)$^{-1}$, the values for molybdenum and tungsten being respectively 155 and 202 kcal. (g. atom)$^{-1}$, and since the observed heats are the same for chromium and tungsten, and the calculated heats for molybdenum and tungsten are about right, the calculated heat for chromium is necessarily low. The situation in Group VIA is thus anomalous, regardless of whether L_s or δ is taken as the basis for correlation.

The noble Group VIII metals, which constitute the other area of disagreement, are characterized by heats of adsorption which are found to be almost constant (24 to 28 kcal. mole^{-1}) and independent of the physical form of the metal (see Chapter 5); however, their L_s values range from 91 kcal. (g. atom)$^{-1}$ (for Pd) to 165 kcal. (g. atom)$^{-1}$ (for Ir), and hence their calculated heats from 22.5 to 38.1 kcal. mole^{-1}. These metals, therefore, all behave as if they had closely similar metal–metal bond strengths, which in fact they have not. The basis of the Eley–Stevenson calculation cannot then be universally valid. Further progress would be greatly speeded by a knowledge of the initial heats of adsorption of hydrogen on films of other metals such as vanadium, manganese and rhenium.

It appears, therefore, that neither the correlation of heats of adsorption with the degree of occupation of atomic *d*-orbitals (as given by δ) nor their correlation with the binding strength of *dsp*-hybrid orbitals (as given by $L_s/6$) is completely successful. The first correlation has some success in Group VIII where the second fails, but the second receives some quantitative support which the first cannot call on. The reason for this situation is as follows. Values of δ are computed from a knowledge of the radii of the metals, these being preferred as the quantity to measure the binding strength between the metal atoms: but of course L_s also measures the cohesive force between atoms. We come thus to the dilemma which received attention in Chapter 2, namely that some physical properties (L_s and melting point) indicate maximum cohesion in Group VIA, while others (radius, density, compressibility) suggest that this is to be found somewhere in Group VIII, and in the second and third rows quite clearly in Group VIII$_1$. This distinction does not seem to have been emphasized previously. Quite different conclusions would be reached if, for example, values of D_{MM} derived from observed radii, were used to evaluate heats of adsorption, and contrariwise Pauling's values would be other than they are had he based his treatment on, for example, melting points.

It is not evident how this dilemma, if real, is to be resolved. For the present purposes we will suppose that there are two aspects of electronic structure, one of which determines radius and density, and hence δ and the chemisorption behaviour of the noble Group VIII metals, and another of which determines L_s and melting point, and hence chemisorption behaviour elsewhere. It is perhaps not impossible that two aspects of electronic structure should co-exist. We recognized earlier that some electrons are involved in bonding while others reside in atomic *d*-orbitals, the latter determining magnetic properties; and it was indeed to estimate the ability of electrons in these atomic orbitals that the parameter δ was selected[2] (rather as a *faute de mieux* than with the conviction that this was sound). It is evident when values of δ are compared with saturation moments of magnetization in the iron triad and with magnetic susceptibilities in the noble Group VIII metals that the connection is slender. It must therefore be stressed that δ probably does not reflect the bonding capacities of atomic *d*-orbitals, but rather that it relates to that aspect of electronic structure which determines radius and density. It does, however, have the slight merit of showing monotonic trends, which broadly correspond to observed behaviour in adsorption and catalysis, while all other physical properties possess maxima and minima. However, it seems most doubtful whether the successful correlation of any observed quantity with δ should be used to infer the nature of the surface bonding which it obtains.

The various interrelations between the physical, adsorptive and catalytic

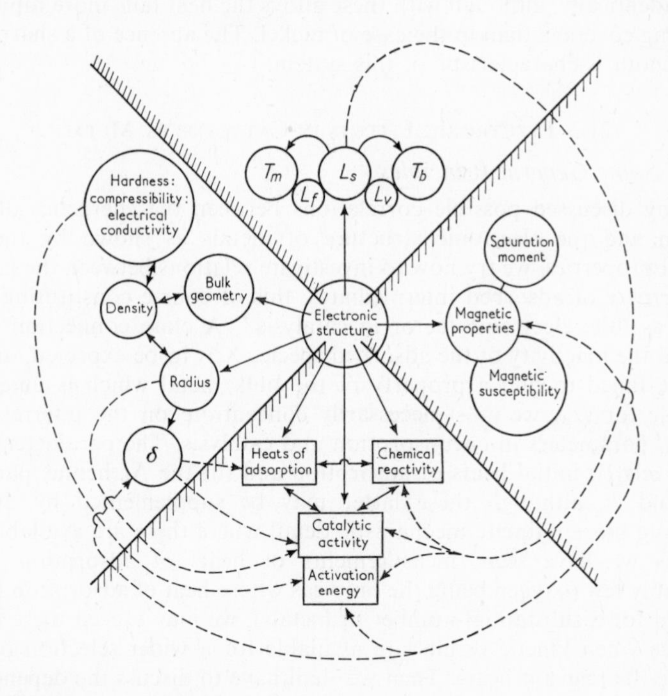

FIG. 3. Proposed and established interrelations between the physical and catalytic properties of metals.

Proposed, - - →; established, ——→.

properties of metals which have been established or proposed are shown diagrammatically in Fig. 3: some of these relations will be reverted to in the following Section.

To summarize, we may say that no single physical property of the bulk metal can be successfully correlated with all the known quantitative information on chemisorption; and since we have recognized that the correspondence between metal atoms in the bulk and on the surface may not be complete, this is not altogether surprising, nor should it be too discouraging. Further advances must await more extensive experimental work and a more complete theoretical treatment of the properties of surface metal atoms.

No important information has yet come from studies of the chemisorptive properties of alloy series in which the *d*-band becomes filled. The heat of adsorption of oxygen on some palladium–silver alloy powders has been measured,[4] but the heat drops rapidly with the first few per cent of silver added, and thereafter becomes constant: the homogeneity of the alloys was not established. The heat of adsorption of hydrogen on nickel–copper alloy powders[5] also falls rapidly with the initial addition of copper: thus, the initial heat for nickel is 24 kcal. mole^{-1} and for the 5 per cent copper alloy, 15 kcal. mole^{-1}. Alloys containing 5 per cent and 62 per cent copper behave almost identically, although with these alloys the heat falls more rapidly with increasing coverage than in the case of nickel. The absence of a sharp change in behaviour is characteristic of this system.

21.3 Electronic Effects in Catalysis by Metals

21.31 Some General Principles

Having discussed possible correlations between the energetics of chemisorption and the electronic structure of metals as shown by their bulk physical properties, we try now to investigate relations between the latter and the *reactivity* of adsorbed intermediates, this of course constituting what is known as "the electronic factor in catalysis." A close connection between D_{MX} and the reactivity of the adsorbed species X is to be expected, and since we have failed to find a property of the bulk metal which is uniquely responsible for D_{MX} we must necessarily concentrate on the interrelation of *observed* parameters in chemisorption and catalysis. The parameters will be respectively (i) initial heats of adsorption and (ii) the Arrhenius parameters k, A and E, although these latter may be supplemented by quantities describing more intimate mechanistic detail where these are available. Now, since as we have seen, measurements of heats of adsorption are still regrettably few (oxygen being the only gas whose heat of adsorption has been obtained for a substantial number of metals), we may exceed these terms of reference when kinetic results are available for a wider selection of metals than are the relevant heats. Then we shall have to discuss the dependence of the kinetic results on δ and on L_s, although with all the reservations mentioned in the last section.

The expected connection between D_{MX} and the reactivity of the species X may only be apparent for reactions of sufficient mechanistic simplicity, and for this reason we shall place emphasis in this Section on simple reactions involving adsorbed hydrogen atoms—*para*-hydrogen conversion, hydrogen–deuterium equilibration and hydrogen-atom recombination.

Attempts to establish this connection may, however, founder for one of two reasons. First, we compare heats of adsorption measured at low coverage with kinetic parameters measured at high coverage, because of the difficulty of knowing the value to which the heats fall: so that if no correlation is obtained, it may be due to a lack of correspondence between heats or bond energies at high and low coverages. Second, it is highly likely in some cases at least that during reactions types of adsorbed species may exist which have no counterpart in the normal (that is, "strong") chemisorbed state: these species may be in a weak (Type C) state of adsorption. Now in Chapter 5 the formation of species in this state was directly tied to the existence in the surface metal atoms of vacant atomic *d*-orbitals: whereas we have now on balance decided to connect the final strong state with *dsp*-bonding orbitals. Unfortunately the degree of vacancy of the atomic *d*-orbitals increases as the strength of metallic bonds increase, that is, on passing through the Transition series leftwards from Group VIII_3, at least as far as Group VIA. Thus, the strengths of binding to expect for both Type A and Type C states will tend to run parallel, and it will not be easy to disentangle the two effects until we come to compare activities in Groups VIII_3 and IB.

We must now note a recent paper[6] which criticizes the concept of electronic factors in metal catalysis, and emphasizes instead the connection (discussed

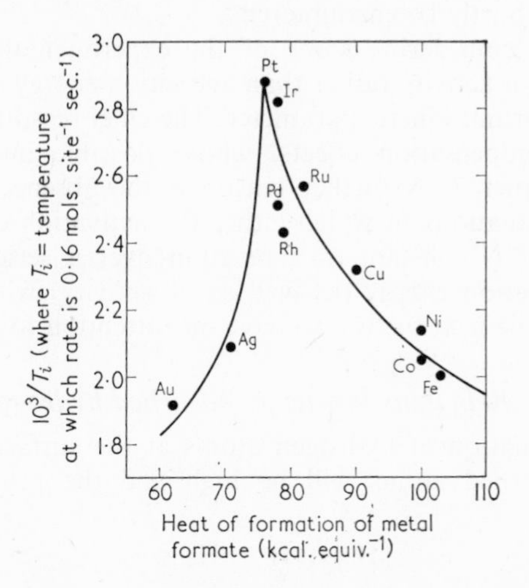

FIG. 4. The activity of metals in formic acid decomposition as a function of the calculated heats of formation of the metal formates (kcal. equiv.$^{-1}$).[6] T_i is the temperature at which the rate becomes 0.16 mols. site^{-1} sec.$^{-1}$; most of the results refer to metals supported on activated charcoal.

earlier in this Chapter) between the energetics of surface and bulk compounds. It has been found[7] that the activity of metals for the decomposition of formic acid could be related to the known or computed heats of formation of the metal formates by what was described as a "volcano-shaped" curve (see Fig. 4). The interpretation advanced was that when the heat of formation is low (as with silver and gold), the rate is low because the concentration of adsorbed species is low but when the heat of formation is high (as with tungsten), the rate is low because the adsorbed species are too strongly held. A maximum rate is, therefore, to be expected when the heat of formation is such as just to give a fully covered surface. Extension of this concept to hydrogenation and related reactions was attempted[6] on the assumption that the heats of formation of the adsorbed species (that is, their bond energies) were all proportional to the heat of formation of the relevant bulk oxide. Correlations between activity and this last parameter are not really successful, and for reasons which are not clearly stated, L_s is subsequently used instead. We have thus returned to the point reached earlier, where we recognize the likely connection between activity and L_s through D_{MX}. The above approach fails at the moment because of the lack of *directly relevant* information on the energetics of surface compounds.

This paper does, however, serve to fix our attention on two important points. (i) The expected inverse relation between activity and strength of binding will only be found when, in a one-reactant system, the coverage is constant. (ii) In a two-reactant system, the activity will be a function both of (a) the relative coverages by the two species (though the rate constant will not), and of (b) their separate strengths of adsorption. Examples illustrating these points will shortly be encountered.

Finally, before considering some of the experimental results, we must justify the choice of activity rather than activation energy or pre-exponential factor as the important kinetic parameter. The chief reason is the widespread occurrence of compensation effects, whose possible interpretations were discussed in Chapter 7. A further reason is the absence of a real understanding of the situations in which either the activation energy or the pre-exponential factor is constant in a reaction over a series of metals. The variation of activation energy (as well as of activity) will, however, be of concern when in the next section we give our attention to alloys.

21.32 "Simple" Reactions involving Adsorbed hydrogen Atoms

In the recombination of hydrogen atoms at the surface of *d*-metals, the coverage by adsorbed atoms will be high and the principal mechanism should be

$$H\cdot + \underset{*}{H} \rightarrow H_2 + *.$$

The recombination coefficient γ will be less than unity to an extent which depends on the relative chances of a collision between a gaseous atom and the hydrogen-covered surface leading to the above process or to reflexion, and this will be a function of D_{MH} *at full coverage*. On the *sp*-metals (except possibly copper) adsorbed atoms will have a much greater desire to desorb and form molecules, and hence the coverage will be kept low; the rate of recombination will be determined by the rate of surface diffusion at low temperatures, but γ will tend to unity with increasing temperature.[8]

We observed in Fig. 10 of Chapter 8 a remarkably satisfactory correlation between relative efficiency for this reaction and the *initial* heat of adsorption of hydrogen. This encourages us to trying plotting efficiency against L_s (for *d*-metals only) and the result is shown in Fig. 5: as before, some selection of

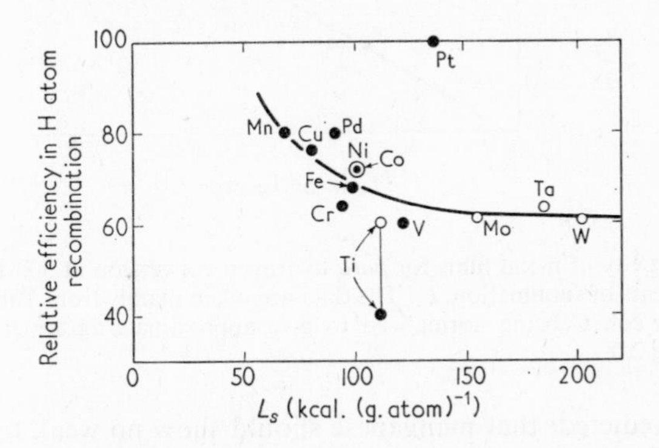

FIG. 5. The relative efficiency of metals in hydrogen atom recombination as a function of their latent heats of sublimation, L_s (see Table XII of Chapter 8).

● Results obtained by Wood and Wise.

○ Results obtained by Nakada, normalized to fit at Ni.

the results has been made, the results obtained by Wood and Wise being generally preferred to those reported by Nakada. The correlation is in the expected sense and about equally as satisfactory as that given earlier with the startling exception of platinum: it is a metal whose value of L_s would lead to too high a calculated heat by Stevenson's method if it were not for a large and questionable electronegativity correction. Measurements on other noble Group VIII metals would be of great assistance here. Correlations between efficiency and δ or metallic radius are quite unhelpful. We conclude then that in this, probably the simplest of all catalytic processes, there is evidence for a direct correlation between activity and bond strength, and for a connection between bond strength and L_s. A much more intensive study of this simple system should be rewarding.

We come now to the hydrogen equilibration reactions, where a relation between activity and L_s has already been reported.[9] Unfortunately it is in the wrong sense, for tungsten (L_s = 202 kcal. (g. atom^{-1}) is the most active metal and manganese (L_s = 68 kcal. (g. atom)$^{-1}$) the least (see Fig. 6). We may be witnessing the onset of confusion caused by mechanistic complexity.

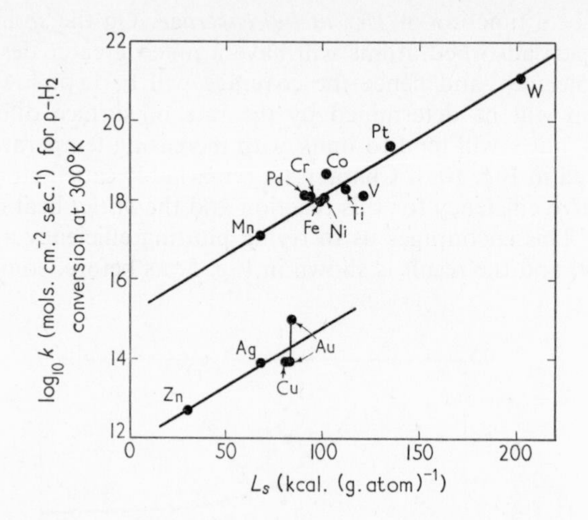

FIG. 6. The activity of metal films for *para*-hydrogen conversion at 300°K as a function of their latent heats of sublimation, L_s. The data are taken mainly from Table V of Chapter 8, the values in col. C being normalized to give approximate agreement with those in col. B by adding 2.0.

It has been predicted[1] that manganese should show no weak form of chemisorption, while its occurrence is well recognized with tungsten. A possible explanation of this activity pattern is that the rate is governed by the stationary concentration of Type C adsorbed hydrogen and that since this is a weak state its concentration increases with the degree of vacancy of the *d*-orbitals, and hence also with L_s. For metals to the left of Group VIA of course the connection between degree of *d*-orbital occupation and L_s no longer holds.

There are insufficient data for a plot of activity against heat of hydrogen adsorption to be useful, and it is potentially unpromising because tungsten and chromium show the same heats but activities which differ by about a thousand-fold. No correlation between activity and either δ or metallic radius is apparent.

21.33 Complex Reactions involving Adsorbed Hydrogen Atoms

In this subsection we consider the exchange of saturated hydrocarbons with deuterium, the hydrogenation of olefins and the exchange and decomposition of ammonia. Broad activity patterns from related systems are also briefly introduced.

In the exchange of saturated hydrocarbons with deuterium, we encounter our first example of where the activity is likely to be determined not only by the strengths of adsorption of the reactive species, but also by the ratio of their concentrations. The activity of metals for ethane exchange (Table IV of Chapter 9) shows a tendency to increase with L_s (see Fig. 7 and Ref. 6): this is of course the reverse of what we expect if activity decreases with increasing bond strength, and bond strength increases with L_s. Thus, the high activity of tungsten must be due to a favourable concentration ratio (that is, a fairly high concentration of ethyl radicals) and the low activity of nickel to a very low concentration of ethyl radicals. In this system, therefore, it seems that activity depends on the ethyl radical concentration, and activity increases with L_s because of the influence of L_s on the strength of adsorption of the *hydrocarbon*. This view finds some support in the kinetics of methane exchange (Table III of Chapter 9), and in more qualitative information on the capacities of various metals to interact with saturated hydrocarbons. Tungsten is relatively less active than other metals in methane exchange, and palladium in propane exchange.

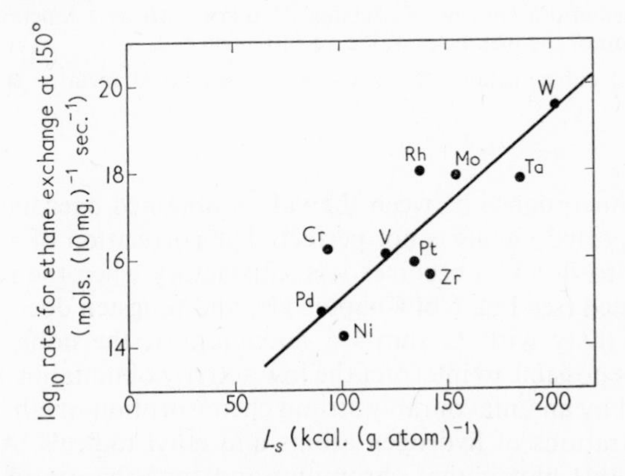

FIG. 7. The activity of metals for ethane exchange at 150° as a function of their latent heats of sublimation, L_s (see Table IV of Chapter 9, and ref. 6).

When seeking to establish correlations between the catalytic behaviour of metals and their other properties it is important that we use all the available information and in the case of hydrocarbon exchange a useful additional parameter is the tendency to multiple exchange, given by the mean deuterium number M. We confine our attention to the results for ethane exchange, which are the most extensive. Of the correlations which were essayed in Figs. 4 and 5 of Chapter 10, perhaps the most meaningful is that between M and heats of hydrogen adsorption. It is, therefore, not surprising to find a reasonable correlation between M and L_s (Fig. 8), although ruthenium, rhodium and platinum as usual fail to conform. It is quite generally found in the exchange of hydrocarbons that the noble Group VIII metals have the highest propensity to cause multiple exchange. This would seem to tie up with their low heats of hydrogen adsorption and their high values of δ, although it is not very clear why. None of the body-centred cubic metals show much tendency to give multiple exchange, and some of them show quite low activation energies.

A considerable body of information is available on the relative activities of metals for the hydrogenation of ethylene (see Table VII of Chapter 11),

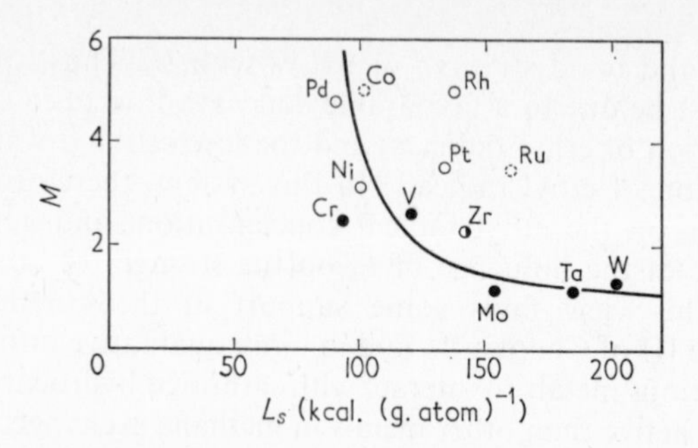

FIG. 8. Mean deuterium content of exchanged ethanes, *M*, as a function of the latent heat of sublimation of the metal (see Table VI of Chapter 9).

○, face-centred cubic metals: ◑, close-packed hexagonal metal: ●, body-centred cubic metals.

although the concordance between the values obtained over metal films and over silica-supported metals is not perfect. The correlation of activity with δ (originally due to Beeck[10]) becomes less satisfactory when the results for the latter are included (see Fig. 6 of Chapter 11), and tungsten does not conform. The plot of activity with L_s shows a maximum at the noble Group VIII metals[6] and it is possible to interpret the low activity of tantalum and tungsten as being caused by an unfavourably strong chemisorption of ethylene, leading to low concentrations of hydrogen atoms and ethyl radicals. An important implication of this plot is that chromium and tungsten are of low activity *for different reasons*, a suggestion which kinetic studies should quickly confirm or deny.

Direct correlations between activity and the heats of adsorption of both the reactants are possible, and both are equally acceptable.[10] In Fig. 9, the correlation with hydrogen heats is brought up to date by showing the activities found for supported metals (Table VII, Chapter 11) as a function of the hydrogen heats for the same catalysts (Table VIII of Chapter 5). The results for cobalt and nickel fall out of line probably because the heats are low, and iridium probably because the activity is low. In other systems, iridium seems to be at least as active as rhodium. We are not surprised to find copper falling out of line.

The general success of heat–activity correlations suggests that activity variation in this system is satisfactorily accounted for by variation in the strength of adsorption of the reactive species, with part of the variation being due to variation in the *relative* strengths of adsorption of the reactants, for which there is some evidence from the observed orders of reaction (see Chapter 11). A correlation between activity and L_s should, therefore, hold to the extent which the heat–L_s correlation holds.

In the olefin–hydrogen system, we are blessed (or perhaps cursed) with a superfluity of additional parameters. These include (i) the relative tendencies

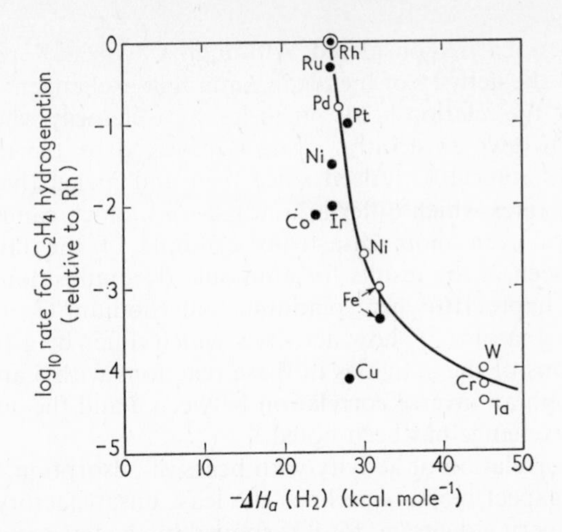

FIG. 9. The relative activity of metals for ethylene hydrogenation as a function of their initial heats of adsorption of hydrogen (see Tables III to V of Chapter 11).
○, Films; ●, silica-supported metals.

of metals to effect double-bond migration or olefin exchange rather than hydrogenation, and (ii) the relative facilities of metals to effect redistribution reactions during the interaction between olefins and deuterium. With regard to the first point, iron, nickel, rhodium and palladium show marked tendencies to effect isomerization and olefin exchange:[11] cobalt has not been studied in this connection, and the information for iron is scanty. Iridium and platinum show a distinct preference for hydrogenation,[11] while osmium and ruthenium are intermediate in behaviour.[12]

With respect to the second point, a correlation has been shown to exist between σ (the parameter describing the distribution of saturated deuterocarbons) and M, the mean deuterium number in ethane exchange. Thus, for tungsten σ is 0.2 and M is 1.3, while for palladium and platinum σ is between 0.5 and 0.6 and M is between 3.5 and 5. A close connection exists between the behaviour of a metal in hydrocarbon exchange and in olefin hydrogenation, although the connection has not been precisely worked out.

The activity patterns shown in the hydrogenation of other unsaturated hydrocarbons are broadly similar to that shown by ethylene. The only notable feature of the pattern shown by acetylene (Chapter 12) is the high activity of palladium, while in benzene hydrogenation (Chapter 13) it has a low activity. Possible reasons for this have been mentioned earlier. The similarity between the activity patterns shown by different systems encourages the belief that there are certain features which are common to all hydrogenations.

The general principles which have emerged from our discussion of the interactions of hydrogen with hydrocarbons seem to break down when other families of reactions are considered. Although a "volcano" relation has been claimed[6] when the activity of metals in ammonia exchange is plotted against their L_s values, the relation holds much less satisfactorily when the temperature required to give an arbitrary rate is replaced by the rates at 77° (see Table IV of Chapter 10). Indeed since iron and nickel (having about the same L_s) show rates which differ a hundred-fold, much cannot come of this correlation. An even more disastrous example of the failure of the L_s correlation is seen in the results for ammonia decomposition on metal films (Table II of Chapter 16): here platinum and rhodium (L_s respectively 135 and 138 kcal. (g. atom)$^{-1}$) show activities which differ by a factor of almost 10^4! Correlations of the activities in these reactions with δ are quite unsatisfactory, although an inverse correlation between δ and the activation energy for ammonia exchange has been noted.[13]

The direct correlation of activity with heats of adsorption, from which we have come to expect most, is perhaps the least unsatisfactory of all: it does not, however, merit a diagram, for it is spoiled by the low activity of platinum in the decomposition and by the low activity of iron in the exchange.

No correlations are apparent between the bulk properties of metals and their activities for reactions of oxygen-containing compounds (hydrogenation of ketones, dehydrogenation of alcohols, etc.). As a result of the ability of the oxygen atom to form a bond with the surface of *sp*-metals, copper, silver and gold show a relatively greater activity in these reactions (and also in formic acid decomposition) than in the hydrogenation of unsaturated hydrocarbons. Ruthenium shows an especially high activity in the hydrogenation of the keto-group: this is, however, an inevitable consequence of the Multiplet Hypothesis.[14] Osmium appears not yet to have been studied in this connection. A "volcano" relation between L_s and the activity of metals in acetone hydrogenation has been indicated.[6] The rationalization of the results in these systems is rendered difficult by the absence of directly relevant information, such as heats of adsorption; the heats of hydrogen adsorption do not seem to be the determining factor.

21.4 The Catalytic Properties of Alloys

The last section has shown that for a number of reactions involving hydrogen either alone or with hydrocarbons, the activity sequence of metals may be broadly assessed as

$$\text{Ru, Rh, Pd, Os, Ir Pt} > \text{Fe. Co, Ni} > \text{Ta, W, Cr} \doteqdot \text{Cu.}$$

Tungsten is on occasion very active, and palladium relatively inactive. This sequence correlates well with the observed heats of adsorption of hydrogen, and hence with values of D_{MH}, which (except in the case of the noble Group VIII metals) reflects the strength of the metal–metal bond and hence L_s. When some partial reversal of this order is observed, it may indicate either that the stability of the Type C state is important or (in a two-reactant system) that the relative concentrations of the two reactant species is the determining factor. We now look to the results found with alloy systems for clarification of this situation.

A word of caution is necessary first. Although much work has been done on the catalytic properties of alloys, some of it is only of limited use for a variety of reasons, some of which are the following. (i) Not all the Arrhenius parameters are always quoted, and k and A often appear in non-specific units. (ii) The alloys are not always sufficiently characterized with respect to their homogeneity. Supported alloys are naturally suspect, and indeed on one occasion alloy formation has been claimed between metals which possess an extensive miscibility gap. (iii) The low area of foils sometimes necessitates their use at temperatures *much* in excess of those at which the reaction in question is normally studied, and the mechanisms may be quite different at the different temperatures.

Discrepancies are observed between the results for identical systems obtained by different workers, for one or more of the above reasons. The discrepancies are particularly acute for activation energies, but are also observed with relative activities (see Figs. 4 and 6 of Chapter 18). Measurements are furthermore of only very limited value unless the composition intervals are sufficiently small ($\sim$10 per cent). Particular regard needs to be paid to the reproducibility of activation energy measurements, since these may have some fundamental significance in alloy systems, and because of the existence of compensation effects, reproducibility of rates is not sufficient.

It must be now clear that electronic factors should manifest themselves differently in different reaction systems, although some correspondence should be evident between, for example, the activity patterns shown by hydrogen equilibrations and those shown by other hydrogenations. Where activation energies change significantly with alloy composition, the activity pattern (that is, the variation of rate at a given temperature with composition) will be temperature-dependent, sometimes quite markedly so (see Figs. 6 and 7 of Chapter 12). Alloys between metals of Groups VIII_3 and IB are clearly the most interesting, but even here substantial differences in behaviour are observed between, for example, the Ni–Cu and the Pd–Ag systems. The differences between the physical properties of these two systems were discussed in Chapter 2, and it is now generally agreed that the Ni–Cu system is not the best for catalytic studies. A contributing factor is the relatively high activity of chemically prepared copper. The Pd–Ag and Pd–Au systems should behave similarly and indeed sometimes do, and these would be ideal for catalytic work were it not for the fact that they have a large and variable ability to absorb hydrogen. The Pt–Ag and Pt–Au systems which would be free from this objection show large miscibility gaps. In the Pd–Cu and Pt–Cu systems, the change in radius is substantial, but (more important) ordered superlattices are formed at certain compositions, and these do not always have the same catalytic properties as the corresponding disordered alloy. In other words, the ideal system for our purposes does not exist.

We may note here one last objection to the "volcano" theory[6] in as much as it involves relating activity to L_s. It is simply that palladium and gold have values of L_s (respectively 91 and 84 kcal. (g. atom)$^{-1}$) which differ by less than 10 per cent, while their catalytic activities are as different as chalk and cheese. It is significant that this paper[6] makes no reference to alloys.

We must now quickly review the experimental results, with a view to establishing the areas of agreement between the various systems studied. Attention will be restricted to results for alloys between metals of Groups VIII_3, and IB where no miscibility gap is shown. The following generalizations can first be made. (i) In all reactions in which hydrogen is a reactant, the Group VIII_3 metal is more active than the Group IB metal, and shows the lower activation energy. (ii) Where the reactant molecule contains oxygen (decomposition of formic acid and ethanol) and in the oxidation of carbon monoxide, the Group IB is *relatively* more active than in hydrogenations. (iii) A normal (Type I) compensation effect is usually shown. It is sometimes found that *two* compensation-effect lines are shown, with points corresponding to alloys having greater than about 70 to 80 per cent of the Group IB metal lying on one line, and the remainder on the other. The Pd–Cu and Pt–Cu systems often show this behaviour (see Figs. 9 and 10 in Chapters 8 and 11) and the Ni–Cu system occasionally (Fig. 9 of Chapter 8). No particular significance can at the moment be attributed to this phenomenon, which has, however, not been specifically remarked on before.

Particular interest attaches to changes in activity and activation energy E at or near the point at which the d-band becomes filled; we have seen in Chapter 2 that this probably occurs with alloys containing about 60 per cent of the Group IB metal. It has been suggested that changes in E may be especially significant, because they may arise through a change in rate at which the Fermi level rises with the progressive introduction of electrons into the alloy. However, in view of the adventitious factors which may affect the observed value of E, and the occurrence of compensation effects, activity changes also merit consideration.

Let us first look at changes in E. There are a number of cases in which E remains constant as the concentration of the Group IB metal is increased, until the critical composition is reached: reactions involving molecular hydrogen over Pd–Ag and Pd–Au alloys provide the clearest examples. The Pd–Cu and Pt–Cu systems behave similarly, but the change in E sometimes occurs very late (see Fig. 7 in Chapter 8 for an example). In all these cases E subsequently rises, usually progressively. In the Ni–Cu system, a sharp change in E is not observed at the critical composition, although it sometimes occurs later. Changes in E with composition for formic acid decomposition provide a less clear picture, perhaps because of mechanistic complications, although here again values of E are often constant over some range of composition. We may conclude that there is an *a priori* case for associating changes in E with changes in the level of the Fermi surface, but some systems do not conform at all closely to the expected pattern, and numerical values of the changes in E are sometimes unreasonably large.

The suggestion is then that in hydrogenation reactions, the activation energy is constant until the point where the Type C state is unable to form:

in this range the bond energies D_{MX} are not expected to vary greatly, and hence E is reasonably associated with D_{MX}. When the *d*-band has been filled, and the Type C state cannot be formed, the increasing value of E is a measure of the progressively greater difficulty which the reactants (or one of them) experience in becoming adsorbed. This interpretation has clear kinetic implications, and it is a great pity that more orders of reaction are not available for reactions on alloys.

Turning now to measurements of activity changes, we first note that there are a number of cases in which the activity at first *rises* with increase in the concentration of the Group IB metal. This occurs in almost all types of alloy and with most kinds of reaction: it sometimes occurs only at either high or low temperatures. It leads to a maximum rate when the concentration of the Group IB metal is between 10 and 40 per cent, usually between 30 and 35 per cent. The phenomenon has not received great emphasis in the past. It would seem to imply that the rate is in these cases, a function of the strength of binding in the weak state of adsorption, while as noted in the last paragraph, the activation energy is a function of the strength of binding in the strong state. We have already said that a possible interpretation of the relative activities of metals for hydrogen equilibrations is in terms of the varying stabilities of the Type C state, and this thesis may, therefore, have quite wide validity.

The above behaviour is not of course universal, and examples have been quoted where the rate is either independent of the concentration of *d*-band holes, or declines linearly with it. The former case will obtain if a weak state is not importantly involved in the reaction, and the latter when the rate is controlled by the concentration of species in the weak state.

This Section does not claim to be a wholly adequate discussion of the manner in which the electronic properties of alloys can influence catalytic behaviour. The situation is complicated theoretically and confused experimentally. The literature shows some marked disagreements and some notable gaps, and much more work on well-defined and simple systems will be necessary before all the connections can be evaluated.

21.5 Conclusion

It will by now be evident that much progress remains to be made in the correlation of catalytic behaviour with the electronic properties of metals and alloys. That some correlation exists cannot reasonably be denied, but advance is limited by (i) inadequate and discordant results, and (ii) inadequate or unusable theory. Views on the nature of the bonds formed at metal surfaces are not yet perfectly clarified, nor is it firmly established for any reaction what intermediates may intervene nor how they are attached to the surface. While only indirect correlations are possible, it is inevitable that they should be imperfect.

It would, however, be wrong to end on a note of pessimism. The chemical basis of catalysis becomes yearly more clear, and it seems likely that further progress will most rapidly stem from the collection of a mass of broadly based information on systems of relative simplicity. In this connection, the plea must be reiterated for the determination of heats of adsorption and of the kinetics (*including orders of reaction*) of simple processes on metals and alloys of impeccable quality. The main features of the structure of catalysis by metals can only thus be established, but within this basic framework many smaller patterns of behaviour, concerning for example specificity and selectivity, must be assembled. The accumulation and rationalization of all these patterns is a lengthy but exhilarating process: the worker in this field may fear neither unemployment nor boredom.

References

1. D. A. Dowden, In "Chemisorption", edited by W. E. Garner. (Butterworths, London, 1957); *Bull. Soc. chim. belges* **67,** 439 (1958); D. A. Dowden and D. Wells, Proc. 2nd International Congress on Catalysis (Editions Technip, Paris, 1961), **2,** 1499.
2. B. M. W. Trapnell, In "Chemisorption", (Butterworths, London, 1955).
3. M. W. Roberts, *Nature* **188,** 1020 (1960).
4. M. H. Bortner and G. Parravano, *Adv. Catalysis* **9,** 424 (1957).
5. L. S. Shield and W. W. Russell, *J. Phys. Chem.* **64,** 1592 (1960).
6. G. C. A. Schuit, L. L. van Reijen and W. M. H. Sachtler, Proc. 2nd International Congress on Catalysis (Editions Technip, Paris, 1961), **1,** 893.
7. W. M. H. Sachtler and J. Fahrenfort, Proc. 2nd International Congress on Catalysis (Editions Technip, Paris, 1961) **1,** 831.
8. G. Ehrlich, *J. Chem. Phys.* **31,** 1111 (1959).
9. D. D. Eley and D. Shooter, *Proc. Chem. Soc.* 315 (1959).
10. O. Beeck, *Discuss. Faraday Soc.* **8,** 118 (1950).
11. G. C. Bond and J. M. Winterbottom, unpublished work.
12. G. C. Bond and G. Webb, unpublished work.
13. M. McD. Baker and G. I. Jenkins, *Adv. Catalysis* **7,** 1 (1955).
14. A. A. Balandin, Proc. 2nd International Congress on Catalysis (Editions Technip, Paris, 1961), **1,** 1135.

Appendix I

Some Physical Properties of Metals in the Three Long Series

(The significance of the symbols in the column headings and the units employed are given below)

Metals of the First Long Series

M	l	r	T_m	T_b	L_s	φ	d	ρ	E	χ
K	b.c.c.	2.31	63	760	21.5	2.15	0.86	6.6	−2.92	+0.52
Ca	f.c.c.	1.96	850	1440	46	2.76	1.55	4.24	−2.84	+1.10
Sc	c.p.h.	1.66	1400	3900	93	3.3	—	—	—	—
Ti	c.p.h.	1.46	1660	3535	112	3.95	4.51	47.8	−1.75	+1.25
V	b.c.c.	1.31	1900	3000	121	4.12	6.11	24.8	−1.5	+1.4
Cr	b.c.c.	1.25	1550	2482	94	4.58	7.14	13.0	−0.71	+3.08
Mn	A 6	1.29	1245	2097	68	3.83	7.44	—	−1.05	+11.8
Fe	b.c.c.	1.24	1540	2735	99	4.48	7.87	10	−0.44	—
Co	f.c.c.	1.25	1493	3550	102	4.41	8.90	5.67	−0.27	—
Ni	f.c.c.	1.24	1455	2732	101	4.50	8.90	7.8	−0.23	—
Cu	f.c.c.	1.27	1083	2595	81	4.46	8.96	1.72	+0.34	−0.09
Zn	c.p.h.	1.33	419	906	30.0	3.66	7.14	5.8	−0.76	−0.16
Ga	A 11	1.33	29.7	1983	66	3.80	5.97	56.8	−0.52	−0.24

Metals of the Second Long Series

M	l	r	T_m	T_b	L_s	φ	d	ρ	E	χ
Rb	b.c.c.	2.43	39	679	20.5	2.13	1.53	12.0	−2.98	+0.21
Sr	f.c.c.	2.15	770	1380	39.2	2.35	2.6	23	−2.89	−0.20
Y	c.p.h.	1.80	1452	4100	103	3.3	4.34	—	—	+5.3
Zr	c.p.h.	1.58	1852	5000	142	3.60	6.55	45	—	+1.28
Nb	b.c.c.	1.43	2468	3300	185	3.99	8.57	13.2	—	+1.5
Mo	b.c.c.	1.36	2622	4800	155	4.48	10.2	5.78	−0.2	+0.04
Tc	c.p.h.	1.36	2140	—	140	4.4	11.50	—	—	+6.3
Ru	c.p.h.	1.32	2400	4900	160	4.52	11.90	7.4	—	+0.50
Rh	f.c.c.	1.34	1966	4500	138	4.65	12.44	4.51	+0.6	+1.11
Pd	f.c.c.	1.37	1554	3980	91	4.49	12.02	10.8	+0.83	+5.4
Ag	f.c.c.	1.44	960	2212	68	4.44	10.49	1.59	+0.80	−0.20
Cd	c.p.h.	1.48	321	767	26.5	4.00	8.65	6.83	−0.40	−0.18
In	A 6	1.62	156	2000	58	—	7.31	9	−0.34	−0.11
Sn	A 5	1.50	232	2337	70	4.09	7.3	11.5	−0.14	−0.25

Metals of the Third Long Series

M	l	r	T_m	T_b	L_s	φ	d	ρ	E	χ
Cs	b.c.c.	2.62	30	690	18.8	1.89	1.90	19.0	−2.92	−0.22
Ba	b.c.c.	2.27	710	1500	42	2.28	3.5	60	−2.92	+0.9
La	c.p.h.	1.86	835	4242	93	3.3	6.2	—	−2.4	—
Hf	c.p.h.	1.57	2130	5400	170	3.53	13.36	32.4	—	—
Ta	b.c.c.	1.43	2996	5300	185	3.96	16.6	12.4	—	+0.87
W	b.c.c.	1.37	3410	5900	202	4.56	19.3	5.48	—	+0.28
Re	c.p.h.	1.37	3167	5900	189	4.74	21.4	21	—	+0.37
Os	c.p.h.	1.33	3045	5500	174	4.55	22.48	9.5	—	+0.05
Ir	f.c.c.	1.35	2454	5300	165	4.57	22.5	4.9	+1.0	+0.15
Pt	f.c.c.	1.38	1773	4530	135	4.52	21.45	10.6	+1.2	+1.10
Au	f.c.c.	1.44	1063	2966	84	4.46	19.3	2.44	+1.42	−0.15
Hg	A 10	1.50	−39	357	14.5	4.52	13.55	96	+0.80	−0.17
Tl	c.p.h.	1.70	303	1457	43	3.84	11.85	18	−0.33	−0.24
Pb	f.c.c.	1.75	327	1750	46.3	3.94	11.3	22	−0.13	−0.12

Notes on the Above Tables

Column 1 gives the symbol of the metal, which is underlined in those cases where the existence of allotropic modifications is well established.

Column 2 gives the normal lattice structure of the metal, that is, that commonly shown at room temperature and pressure (Ref. a). The abbreviations f.c.c. (face-centred cubic; A 1; α), c.p.h. (close-packed hexagonal; A 2; β) and b.c.c. (body-centred cubic; A 3; γ) are used, but when the structure is other than these, the Strukturbericht symbol is employed.

Column 3 gives the metallic radius in Å corresponding to the lattice structure quoted in column 2 (Refs. a, b and c).

Columns 4 and 5 give the melting-points T_m and boiling-points T_b in °C (Ref. d). Temperatures especially above 2000°C are to some extent uncertain, and the values quoted are not of equal reliability. The degree of "roundness" of the figure is some indication of its accuracy.

Column 6 gives the latent heat of sublimation L_s in kcal. (g. atom)$^{-1}$. The quoted values are considered the "best" on the basis of the available literature (Refs. d, e, f, g, h, i and j).

Column 7 gives the work function of the metal (φ) in eV. Assessment of the literature in this area is very difficult, and some highly divergent results have been given: an attempt has therefore been made to present *consistent* series of values. The values recorded for the metals Ti . . . . Ni are those given in Ref. k, and were obtained by the thermionic method. Wherever else possible, values found by the contact-potential method have been quoted, since this appears to be the most reliable; the majority come from Ref. 1. Elsewhere, Michaelson's (Ref. m) "best" values are given. Other recent measurements are presented in Refs. i, n and o.

Columns 8 and 9 respectively give the density d (g. cm.$^{-3}$) and the specific resistance ρ ($\mu\Omega$–cm.) at room temperature (Ref. a).

Column 10 gives the standard electrode potential E (V.) between the metal and its most highly charged, uncomplexed ions (for example Mo^{3+}, Mn^{3+}, Au^{3+}); some of the values are somewhat ill established (Ref. a).

Column 11 gives mass magnetic susceptibilities of the metals (χ) in c.g.s. units, all multiplied by 10^6; these call for no comment (Ref. p).

The quoted physical properties of technetium were taken from Ref. i.

References

a. C. A. Hampel (editor), "Rare Metals Handbook" (Reinhold Publishing Corp., New York, 1954).

b. L. Pauling, "The Nature of the Chemical Bond" (Cornell University Press, Ithaca, N.Y., 1948 and 1960).

c. M. C. Neuburger, *Z. Krist.* **93,** 1 (1936).

d. National Bureau of Standards circular 500, "Selected Values of Chemical Thermodynamic Properties" (1952).

e. E. C. Baughan, *Trans. Faraday Soc.* **50,** 322 (1954).

f. L. H. Long, *Quart. Rev.* **7,** 134 (1953).

g. T. L. Cottrell, "The Strengths of Chemical Bonds" (Butterworths, London, 1954).

h. J. F. Haefling and A. H. Daane, *Trans. Met. Soc. Amer.* 115 (1958).

i. G. E. Boyd, *J. Chem. Educ.* **36,** 3 (1959); E. Anderson, R. A. Buckley, A. Hellawell and W. Hume-Rothery, *Nature* **188,** 48 (1960); D. A. Robins, *Less-Common Metals* **1,** 396 (1959).

j. K. H. Mann and A. W. Tickner, *J. Phys. Chem.* **64,** 251 (1960); L. H. Drager and J. L. Margrave, *J. Phys. Chem.* **64,** 1323 (1960).

k. S. C. Jain and K. S. Krishnan, *Proc. Roy. Soc.* **A215,** 431 (1952).

l. O. Klein and E. Lange, *Z. Elektrochem.* **44,** 542 (1938).

m. H. B. Michaelson, *J. Appl. Phys.* **21,** 536 (1950).

n. J. Giner and E. Lange, *Naturwiss.* **19,** 506 (1953).

o. J. C. Rivière, *Proc. Phys. Soc.* **70B,** 676 (1957).

p. W. Hume-Rothery, "Atomic Theory for Students of Metallurgy" (Institute of Metals, London, 1947, 1952).

Appendix II

Literature References to some Physical Properties of Alloy Systems

This Appendix is intended to supplement the list of references given at the end of Chapter 2. It was seen that when binary alloys are prepared in a finely divided state by chemical methods, it is desirable to check if possible that homogeneous alloys have indeed been formed. In such cases, their electrical conductivity cannot be satisfactorily measured, and recourse must be made to measurements of (i) the lattice spacing, and (ii) their magnetic properties. The following references may be found helpful when such problems arise.

Lattice Spacings in Alloys

Pearson's book (Ref. a) surveys most (but not quite all) the available literature, and the following original references are therefore given.

Nickel–copper: Refs. a, b, c, d, e and f.
Palladium–silver: Refs. a and c.
Iron–cobalt and cobalt–nickel: Refs. a and f.
Iron–nickel: Refs. a and g.

Magnetic Properties of Alloys

Nickel–copper: Refs. c, h, i, j, k, l and m.
Palladium–silver: Refs. c, i and m.
Cobalt–nickel: Ref. n.

References

a. W. B. Pearson, "Latice Spacings and Structures of Metals and Alloys" (Pergamon Press, London, 1958).
b. E. A. Owen and B. Pickup, *Z. Krist.* **88,** 116 (1934).
c. B. R. Coles, *J. Inst. Metals* **84,** 346 (1956).
d. L. E. Cratty and W. W. Russell, *J. Amer. Chem. Soc.* **80,** 767 (1958).
e. W. K. Hall and L. Alexander, *J. Phys. Chem.* **61,** 242 (1957).
f. J. H. Long, J. C. W. Frazer and E. Ott, *J. Amer. Chem. Soc.* **56,** 1101 (1934).
g. F. Hund, *Z. Elektrochem.* **56,** 609 (1952).
h. A. J. P. Meyer and C. Wolff, *Compt. rend.* **246,** 576 (1958).
i. E. W. Pugh and F. M. Ryan, *Phys. Rev.* **111,** 1038 (1958).
j. S. A. Ahern, M. J. C. Martin and W. Sucksmith, *Proc. Roy. Soc.* **A248,** 145 (1958).
k. J. A. Sabatka and P. W. Selwood, *J. Phys. Chem.* **61,** 1564 (1957).
l. A. D. Kaufmann and C. Starr, *Phys. Rev.* **63,** 445 (1943).
m. W. H. Keesom and B. Kurrelmeyer, *Physica* **7,** 1003 (1940).
n. S. Foner and E. M. Pugh, *Phys. Rev.* **91,** 20 (1953).

Appendix III

Terminology and Symbolism for Surface Sites

No one really knows what constitutes a site. It has long been assumed each metal atom on the surface is equivalent to one site, and information on the ratio of the hydrogen monolayer volume to the number of surface atoms as indicated by BET area measurements has tended to confirm this view: but whether the hydrogen atoms are located on top of the metal atoms, or in interstices between them, is not yet decided and is anyhow irrelevant to all but the most refined discussions of mechanism. The meaning of the term "site" may differ from one reactant to another on the same surface. Thus, for example, ethylene may require two adjacent metal atoms for its adsorption, and this pair of atoms may be regarded as one site for ethylene: but this site, by reason of its geometry, may be unsuited to, say, acetylene, and so a given surface may display a variety of kinds of site. No attempt has been made to allow for these varied possibilities in the symbolism used in this book.

The asterisk was introduced by Eley to represent a covalent bond between the adsorbed species of the surface, and its significance has been extended to represent also a surface site. These two meanings are almost indistinguishable (except in rare instances to be discussed below) and the asterisk has been employed in this book where these meanings are interchangeable. It is preferred to the symbol *S* because of its possible if unlikely confusion with either sulphur or entropy, and to the symbol *M* which carries implications as to the nature of the site. The asterisk may, therefore, be regarded for the purpose of balancing equations as a univalent chemical entity; thus in the process

$$H_2 + 2* \rightarrow 2\,\underset{*}{H},$$

the asterisk is a reactant and the species $\underset{*}{H}$ is one in which valency requirements are fulfilled. The asterisk, therefore, represents a free valence at the metal surface.

Where it is desired to indicate which atom in a complex species is attached to the catalyst, the asterisk is set below that atom (e.g. $\underset{*}{C}H_2{-}CH_3$): where this is irrelevant or unknown, the asterisk is set under the formulae for the species (e.g. $\underset{*}{C_2H_5}$).

This symbolism is further extended in Chapter 18 to describe a proposed step involving electron transfer from the metal to the adsorbate:

$$A + * \rightarrow \underset{*^+}{A^-}.$$

Here, of course, the bonding suggested is purely ionic, and $*^+$ only represents a surface site which has lost an electron.

The limitation of this system becomes apparent when considering species which may be multiply bonded to the surface from the same atom. Thus in the species $\underset{***}{\mathrm{N}}$, the nitrogen atom may make three covalent bonds either to the same metal atom (if the metal atom is willing) or to three different metal atoms. Very often these two situations are experimentally indistinguishable, but in the case of carbon monoxide the structures in which the carbon atom forms two bonds with the same and with different metal atoms are both recognized by infra-red spectroscopy, and these are readily represented with the aid of the symbol *M* (see Chapter 5).

On occasions when it is merely necessary to show whether a given species is adsorbed or not, the adsorbed state is denoted by a subscript *a* in brackets. The subscript *a* is reserved for quantities describing the adsorbed state or the act of adsorption.

AUTHOR INDEX

Numbers in brackets are reference numbers and are included to assist in locating references in which the authors' names are not mentioned in the text. Numbers in italics indicate the page on which the reference is listed.

C

G

L

R

S

T

U

V

W

Y

Z

SUBJECT INDEX

N

O

P

R

DATE	ISSUED TO